TABLES OF
PROBABILITY FUNCTIONS
Volume II

$$\frac{1}{\sqrt{2\pi}}\, e^{-\frac{x^2}{2}} \text{ and } \frac{1}{\sqrt{2\pi}} \int_{-x}^{x} e^{-\frac{\alpha^2}{2}}\, d\alpha$$

Prepared by the
FEDERAL WORKS AGENCY
WORK PROJECTS ADMINISTRATION
for the City of New York
AS A REPORT OF OFFICIAL PROJECT NO. 165-2-97-22
MATHEMATICAL TABLES PROJECT

ARNOLD N. LOWAN, Ph. D.
Technical Director

Conducted under the sponsorship of the
NATIONAL BUREAU OF STANDARDS

LYMAN J. BRIGGS, Director   IRVING V. A. HUIE, Administrator
National Bureau of Standards   Work Projects Administration
Official Sponsor   for the City of New York

1942

ACKNOWLEDGMENT

This volume has been reproduced by a photo-offset process, by the W.P.A. New Reading Materials Project (665-97-3-88 W.P. 4) a project operated under the sponsorship of the Board of Education of the City of New York.

Grateful acknowledgments are due to the Work Projects Committee of the Board of Education and the Public Activities Programs Section for their assistance in reproducing this volume.

MURRAY PFEFERMAN

Administrative Supervisor

TECHNICAL STAFF

ARNOLD N. LOWAN, Ph.D., Technical Director

MILTON ABRAMOWITZ,	M. A.	JACK LADERMAN,	M. A.
GERTRUDE BLANCH,	Ph.D.	JACOB L. MILLER,	B. A.
WILLIAM HORENSTEIN,	B. S.	MATILDA PERSILY,	B. A.
WILLIAM KAUFMAN		IDA RHODES,	M. A.
FREDERICK G. KING,	B. A.	HERBERT E. SALZER,	M. A.

PREFACE

The following table is one in a series of mathematical tables prepared by the *Project for the Computation of Mathematical Tables* conducted by the Work Projects Administration for the City of New York, under the sponsorship of the National Bureau of Standards, Washington, D. C. This project has been in operation since January 3, 1938 and has been engaged in the preparation and computation of tables according to procedures developed by the project itself and approved by the Work Projects Administration and the sponsoring agency.

Mr. Malcolm Morrow of the Work Projects Administration was instrumental in the preliminary planning of the project. A broad outline of work for the first few months was laid out at a conference called by Dr. Lyman J. Briggs, Director of the National Bureau of Standards. This conference, held in Washington, D. C. during January 1938, was attended by representatives of the Bureau of Standards, the Committee on Mathematical Tables and Aids to Computation of the National Research Council, the United States Geological Survey, and the Work Projects Administration.

It has been the policy of the project to select for tabulation mathematical functions of fundamental importance in

PREFACE

pure and applied mathematics.   In the selection of the functions to be tabulated and in the choice of the most useful range and interval of the argument, the project has had the advantage of a continual exchange of views with outstanding mathematicians, physicists and engineers, both here and abroad.

FOREWORD

The principal practical uses of these tables in statistics will be in testing the significance of a deviation in a normally distributed variate and in fitting normal distributions to observations. For the former use the entries in the table need only to be subtracted from unity. For the second use they may be divided by two. The table of probabilities associated with very large deviations will be particularly useful in tests of significance in which large deviations are considered necessary for demonstrative value because the particular test has been chosen from among a large though perhaps uncertain number of alternative tests that might have applied. In cases where the uncertainty or vagueness regarding the process of selection makes it impossible to correct exactly for the bias introduced through the selection of the test giving greatest significance, it is particularly important that a more stringent level of probability be insisted upon than is customary where only a single predetermined test is applied to observations.

Extraordinary methods were used in the effort to make these tables entirely free from error. For this reason the present volume should serve as an adequate source for condensed textbook tables of the normal distribution. The high accuracy of these tables with their fifteen decimal places will also make them par-

ticularly suitable to serve as a basis for the computation of further
tables of functions related to the normal distribution.

      Statisticians everywhere owe a debt of gratitude to Dr.
Lyman J. Briggs, Director of the National Bureau of Standards, for
sponsoring an undertaking of outstanding value.

HAROLD HOTELLING

Columbia University

New York City.

March 18, 1941

CONTENTS

Note. The figures in square brackets denote the range, the interval between successive arguments, and the number of decimal places or significant figures in the
tabulated entries. The letters "D" and "S" indicate decimal places and significant
figures respectively. In Table II, for instance, the entries are given to 7 significant figures, over the range from 6 to 10, at intervals of 0.01.

INTRODUCTION

The probability functions $\frac{1}{\sqrt{2\pi}} e^{-\frac{1}{2}x^2}$ and $\frac{1}{\sqrt{2\pi}} \int_{-x}^{x} e^{-\frac{1}{2}t^2} dt$ are of fundamental importance in statistics. Many short tables of these functions have been computed at various times, and as might be expected, under many different designations. They have been frequently called the ordinate and area respectively of the normal frequency curve; and the symbols z_x and α_x (for the ordinate and area respectively) are encountered frequently in the literature. In the present work, it will be more convenient to designate the functions as follows:

$$Q(x) = \frac{1}{\sqrt{2\pi}} e^{-\frac{1}{2}x^2}$$

$$P(x) = \frac{1}{\sqrt{2\pi}} \int_{-x}^{x} e^{-\frac{1}{2}t^2} dt.$$

In format and contents, this is a companion volume to the previously published tables of the probability functions $\frac{2}{\sqrt{\pi}} \int_{0}^{x} e^{-t^2} dt$ and $\frac{2}{\sqrt{\pi}} e^{-x^2}$. Specifically, the functions $Q(x)$ and $P(x)$ are tabulated here to 15 decimal places, at intervals of 0.0001 in the range of x between 0 and 1, and at intervals of 0.001 for x ranging between 1 and 7.8. For larger values of x, the functions converge rapidly to 0 and 1 respectively, and their values to fifteen decimals may be read by inspection from the last page of the table.

A supplementary table (Table II) is included, with values of $Q(x)$ and of $[1-P(x)]$ to seven significant figures in the range of x between 6 and 10 at intervals of 0.01. For smaller values of x, these functions may be obtained from the main table to at least seven significant figures.

DIRECT INTERPOLATION

Let $f(x)$ represent either of the functions tabulated,

and let h denote the interval between two consecutive arguments. By Taylor's theorem

(1) $f(x \pm ph) = f(x) \pm phf'(x) + \dfrac{(ph)^2}{2!} f''(x) \pm \dfrac{(ph)^3}{3!} f'''(x)$

$$+ \dfrac{(ph)^4}{4!} f^{(4)}(x) \pm \dfrac{(ph)^5}{5!} f^{(5)}(x \pm th)$$

where $|t| < p$.

When $f(x)$ is the tabulated integral $P(x)$, its derivative is $2Q(x)$; and since $Q(x)$ is also tabulated, interpolation in both functions may be readily obtained with the aid of the successive derivatives of $P(x)$, namely:

$$P''(x) = 2Q'(x) = -2xQ(x); \quad P'''(x) = 2Q(x)(x^2 - 1);$$

$$P^{(4)}(x) = 2Q(x)(-x^3 + 3x); \qquad P^{(5)}(x) = 2Q(x)(x^4 - 6x^2 + 3).$$

The corresponding derivatives of $Q(x)$ may be obtained from the relation

$$Q^{(r-1)}(x) = \tfrac{1}{2}P^{(r)}(x).$$

Let it be required to find the values of $P(x)$ and $Q(x)$ corresponding to an argument x lying between two tabulated arguments. Let x_0 be the nearest tabulated argument, and let $x = x_0 + ph$, where p is either positive or negative, and no greater than one-half numerically. For brevity, $P(x_0)$ and $Q(x_0)$ will be denoted by P_0 and Q_0 respectively. If the derivatives of the second and higher orders are neglected, the interpolation formula for $P(x)$ reduces to:

(2) $P(x_0 + ph) = P_0 + 2phQ_0$.

The error in the evaluation of $P(x)$ by the above formula will be approximately $p^2h^2xQ_0$. Since $xQ(x)$ is always less than $\tfrac{1}{4}$, $P(x)$

may be obtained to 7 decimals or better everywhere by means of formula (2). This accuracy is probably sufficient for most practical purposes. Accuracy to within about a unit in the fifteenth decimal place may be obtained by means of the following formula:

$$(3) \quad P(x) = P_0 + 2phQ_0 - p^2h^2Q_0[x_0 - \frac{ph}{3}(x_0^2 - 1) + \frac{p^2h^2}{12} x_0(x_0^2 - 3)]$$

The term involving h^4 may be dropped when x is less than one or greater than 2.9; when x is greater than 5.3, the term involving h^3 may also be dropped.

For interpolation in $Q(x)$ the following formula may be used:

$$(4) \qquad\qquad Q(x_0 + ph) = Q_0[1 - phx_0]$$

The calculated value will be in error by less than 1×10^{-9} when x is less than one, and by less than 3×10^{-8} when x is greater than one. The maximum attainable accuracy may be obtained from the following formula:

$$(5) \quad Q(x_0 + ph) = Q_0(1 - phx_0)$$

$$+ \frac{p^2h^2}{2} Q_0\{(x^2 - 1) - \frac{ph}{3} x_0(x_0^2 - 3) + \frac{p^2h^2}{12} [(x_0^2 - 3)^2 - 6]\}$$

The term in h^4 may be dropped when x is less than 1 or greater than 2.1. When x is greater than 5.5, the term involving h^3 may also be dropped. Formulae (3) and (5) may also be used for interpolation in Table II.

Example.

Let it be required to find $P(x)$ and $Q(x)$ corresponding to $x = 2.23542$.

Solution.

$x_0 = 2.235$; ph = 0.00042.

$P_0 = 0.97458\ 26512\ 55308$;

$Q_0 = 0.03282\ 54538\ 28083$.

Let

$$A = x_0 - \frac{ph}{3}(x_0^2 - 1) + \frac{p^2 h^2}{12} x_0 (x_0^2 - 3) = 2.23444074$$

$$B = (x_0^2 - 1) - \frac{ph}{3} x_0 (x_0^2 - 3) + \frac{p^2 h^2}{12} \{(x_0^2 - 3)^2 - 6\} = 3.99494564$$

$$C = p^2 h^2 A = 0.00000\ 03941\ 55347$$

$$D = \frac{p^2 h^2}{2} B = 0.00000\ 03523\ 54205.$$

The required terms in the formulae may now be conveniently calculated as follows:

$P_0 = 0.97458\ 26512\ 55308$	$Q_0 = 0.03282\ 54538\ 28083$
$2phQ_0 = 0.00002\ 75733\ 81215\ 6$	$-phx_0Q_0 = -0.00003\ 08132\ 53508\ 4$
$-CQ_0 = \underline{-0.00000\ 00129\ 38328\ 1}$	$DQ_0 = \underline{0.00000\ 00115\ 66186\ 7}$
$P(x) = 0.97461\ 02116\ 98195$	$Q(x) = 0.03279\ 46521\ 40761$

THE PROBLEM OF APPROXIMATE ARGUMENTS

In the construction of a table, the function is tabulated to a convenient number of decimal places or significant figures, corresponding to exact arguments. In practical applications, however, it frequently happens that the arguments are known only approximately -- to a certain number of decimals, say. The question arises: How many decimal places (or significant figures) may be retained in the computed value of the function on the basis of a given uncertainty in the argument? If Δy denotes the uncertainty in a function $f(x)$ corresponding to an uncertainty Δx in the argument, then for Δx sufficiently small, we have the relation

$$(6) \qquad\qquad \Delta y \cong f'(x)\Delta x^*.$$

*The symbol $\cong$ will be used to denote approximate equality. The relation (6) holds generally for functions having a continuous derivative different from zero.

For instance, in the illustrative example of the preceding section, it was tacitly assumed that the argument 2.23542 was exact. If, now, we regard the argument as known only to five decimal places, with a possible error of one unit in the last place, the uncertainty in the computed value of $P(x)$ will be as great as $10^{-5}P'(x) = 2Q(x)10^{-5}$ or approximately 6×10^{-7}, even if the most elaborate interpolation formula is employed. The very simple formula (2) would yield the required accuracy in this case.

The error in an interpolated value may be ascribed to two distinct causes:

(a) The limitations imposed by the extent of the uncertainty in the argument and by the rounding errors in the tabulated entries between which interpolation is performed.

(b) The limitations inherent in the particular interpolation formula employed. Whenever the error due to cause (a) is large, it would obviously be pointless to use an elaborate formula, capable of yielding an arithmetically high accuracy.

INVERSE INTERPOLATION

The problem of approximate arguments is of particular importance in inverse interpolation. For inverse interpolation, it is convenient to regard the entries $f(x)$ as exact, in which case the arguments must be regarded as approximate. The counterpart of (6) now becomes:

(7) $\Delta x \cong \Delta y / f'(x)$.

Replacing Δy by the upper bound of error in the tabulated entries, namely, $\tfrac{1}{2}10^{-15}$, we obtain an approximation to the uncertainty in

the argument x, when the corresponding entries $f(x)$ are regarded
as exact. Since an interpolated value is in general no more accu-
rate than the entries between which interpolation is made, formula
(7) furnishes a measure of the maximum accuracy which can be obtained from the main table in an interpolated value of x.

A glance at the table will show that for x less than
one, $P'(x)[= 2Q(x)]$ ranges approximately between 0.80 and 0.49 so
that according to (7), inverse interpolation in x may be made to
yield accuracy to 15 decimal places, with an error less than two
units in the last place, after taking account of rounding errors.
As x increases, $Q(x)$ decreases very rapidly, and the accuracy with
which x may be obtained from this table decreases correspondingly.

Let it be required to find x, corresponding to a given
value of $X = P(x)$, lying between the tabulated entries X_0 and X_1,
corresponding to two consecutive arguments x_0 and $x_0 + h$ respectively.
Let X_0 be the nearest tabulated entry to X and let $X-X_0 = a$. A
simple approximation to the corresponding value of x is given by

$$(8) \qquad\qquad\qquad x = x_0 + \frac{a}{2Q_0}$$

This formula is easier to apply than the usual formula for inverse
linear interpolation, and it gives somewhat better accuracy as
well. The error in the value obtained by means of this formula
is usually not greater than $\frac{x}{8}h^2$, and the true value of x is *larger*
than the value given by (8). In the region where the interval h
is 0.0001, interpolation by (8) will yield accuracy to 9 decimal
places or better. For x greater than one, six decimals may be
obtained by means of the above formula. This accuracy may be ample
for practical requirements — for large values of x, it is more
than sufficient for obtaining the highest accuracy attainable on

the basis of (7).

When greater accuracy than that obtainable by means of (8) is required, one may use the following formula:

$$(9) \quad x = x_0 + \frac{a}{2Q_0} + \frac{x_0}{2}\left[\frac{a}{2Q_0}\right]^2 + \frac{(2x_0^2 + 1)}{6}\left[\frac{a}{2Q_0}\right]^3 + \frac{(6x_0^3 + 7x_0)}{24}\left[\frac{P}{2Q_0}\right]^4 .$$

Example.

Let it be required to find x corresponding to $P(x) = .97461\ 02116\ 98$, the value being assumed to be correct to within a half unit in the twelfth decimal place.

Solution.

The nearest tabulated entry is $P(2.235) = .97458\ 26512\ 55308$; $a = P(x) - P(2.235) = .00002\ 7560443$; $Q_0 = .08282\ 54538\ 28083$.

By formula (7), $\Delta y / f'(x) \approxeq \Delta y / 2Q_0 = \frac{1}{2}10^{-12}/.06 = 8 \times 10^{-12}$. Hence 11 decimals may be retained in the computed value of x. The calculations follow:

$$
\begin{aligned}
x_0 &= 2.235 \\
a/2Q_0 = t &= .00041\ 98029\ 24 \\
x_0 t^2 /2 &= 1969\ 42 \\
(2x_0^2 + 1) t^3 /6 &= \underline{1\ 35} \\
x &= 2.23542\ 00000\ 0
\end{aligned}
$$

THE ASYMPTOTIC EXPANSION OF $P(x)$

For large values of x, $P(x)$ may be computed advantageously from the asymptotic expansion given below:

$$1 - P(x) = \frac{2}{\sqrt{2\pi}}\ \frac{e^{-\frac{1}{2}x^2}}{x}\left[1 - \frac{1}{x^2} + \frac{1\cdot3}{x^4} - \frac{1\cdot3\cdot5}{x^6} + \frac{1\cdot3\cdot5\cdot7}{x^8} - \cdots\right]$$

If S_n and S_{n+1} denote the partial sums of the above series, including n and n+1 terms respectively, the true value of $[1 - P(x)]$ lies between S_n and S_{n+1}; hence the difference between $[1 - P(x)]$ and S_n is less than the first term in the series which is neglected.

METHOD OF COMPUTATION

The main table was computed and checked by the method outlined in Volume I for the corresponding functions $H(x)$ and $H'(x)$. In constructing Table II, the function $Q(x)$ was computed with the aid of the tables of e^{-x} computed by this organization.[1] The values of $F(x) = \frac{1}{2}[1 - P(x)]/Q(x)$ given in the tables of the British Association for the Advancement of Science[2] were then multiplied by $2Q(x)$. Every tenth value was checked by computing $[1 - P(x)]$ directly from the asymptotic expansion, and all the values were differenced.

[1] Federal Works Agency, Work Projects Administration for the City of New York, *Tables of the Exponential Function e^x*.   1939.
[2] See Bibliography.

The tables listed below are original computations, or systematic compilations of other tables with considerable added material. They supersede older tables of their type. For an account of earlier tables, the reader is referred to the introduction in the table of Burgess. No attempt has been made to list the numerous abridged tables which may be found in various reference texts.

NOTATION. For the sake of conciseness, the following notation will be adopted:

$$I = I(t) = \frac{2}{\sqrt{\pi}} e^{-t^2}; \quad H = H(x) = \int_0^x I(t)\, dt$$

$$z = z_t = \frac{1}{\sqrt{2\pi}} e^{-t^2/2}; \quad \alpha = \alpha_x = \int_{-x}^x z_t\, dt$$

$$F = F(x) = \tfrac{1}{2}(1 - \alpha_x)/z_x = e^{x^2/2} \int_x^\infty e^{-t^2/2}\, dt$$

L: Defined from $H = 1 - \dfrac{I(t)L}{2t}$

   (Laplace's continued fraction used in tables of Burgess.)

$$G = \int_x^\infty e^{-t^2}\, dt$$

ρ: Defined from $H(\rho) = \tfrac{1}{2}$

   (used in the tables of Burgess.)

$$L(x) = -\log_e \tfrac{1}{2}(1 - \alpha_x); \quad l(x) = \log_{10} \tfrac{1}{2}(1 - \alpha_x)$$

$$p = \tfrac{1}{2}(1 + \alpha_x) = \frac{1}{\sqrt{2\pi}} \int_{-\infty}^x e^{-t^2/2}\, dt; \quad q = \tfrac{1}{2}(1 - \alpha_x) = \frac{1}{\sqrt{2\pi}} \int_x^\infty e^{-t^2/2}\, dt$$

These symbols do not always coincide with the ones used by the authors.

JAMES BURGESS. *On the Definite Integral* $\frac{2}{\sqrt{\pi}} \int_0^t e^{-t^2} dt$. *with Extended Tables of Values.* Roy. Soc. Edinburgh, Vol. XXXIX, Part II, 1898 pp. 257-321. H, I, [0(.001)1.25; 9D] with first and second differences for H. I, [1.25(.01)1.50(.02)2.20(.05)3(.1)6; 15 to 27D], H and $\log_{10}$ I, [1(.001)1.5(.002)3; 15D] with required differences for interpolation in H; H, L, [3(.1)5; 15D]; e^{-t^2} [3(.1)5(.5)6; 15 to 27D]. H, L, G for t = 5.5 and 6;15 to 24D. Values of ρ, $1/\rho$ and 29 other constants, with their common logarithms to 23 decimals. Historical account of earlier tables with extensive notes on methods of computation.

BRITISH ASSN. ADV. SCI. Mathematical Tables Vol. VII, *The Probability Integral* by **W. F. SHEPPARD**, Univ. Press, Cambridge, Eng. 1939. Table I: F(x), [0(.01)10; 12D]. Table II: F(x), [0(.1)10; 24D]; both tables with all required "reduced derivatives" for interpolating to the full power of the tables. Table III: L(x), [0(1)10; 24D]; Table IV: L(x), [0(.1)10; 16D] with reduced derivatives. Table V: l(x), [0(.1)10; 12D] with reduced derivatives; Table VI: l(x), [0(.01)10; 8D] with second central differences. Introductory chapter with an account of other tables, particularly Sheppard's.

KARL PEARSON, editor. *Tables for Statisticians and Biometricians,* Part I Biometric Lab., Cambridge Univ. Press, Third Edition, 1930. Sheppard's Tables:- Table I: Deviates of the Normal Curve for Each Permille of Frequency; x tabulated for $\frac{1}{2}(1+\alpha_x)$ = [0(.001)1; 4D]. Published previously in Biometrica Vol. V, p. 405. Table II: $\frac{1}{2}(1+\alpha_x)$ and z [0(.01)4; 7D]; [4(.01)6; 5D]; with first and second differences. Table III: Abscissa and Ordinate in Terms of difference of Areas [0(01).8; 7D] with 3 differences. Previously published in Biometrica, Vol. II pp. 174-190. Table IV (computed by Julia Bell): Extension of Table of the Probability Integral $\frac{1}{2}(1-\alpha)$. 1(x) tabulated for x = [5(1)50(10)100(50)500; 5D]. Previously published in Draper's Research Memoirs, Biometric Series, VIII, p. 27. Extensive introductory material on statistics.

_____ *Tables for Statisticians and Biometricians.* Part II. Table II: (Table by T. KONDO and E. M. ELDERTON) Table of Normal Curve Functions to Each Permille of Frequency. x, z, $\frac{1}{2}(1+\alpha_x)/z$; $\frac{1}{2}(1-\alpha_x)/z$, $z/\frac{1}{2}(1+\alpha_x)$, $z/\frac{1}{2}(1-\alpha_x)$, for $\frac{1}{2}(1+\alpha_x)$ = [.500(.001).999; 10D]. Previously published in Biometrica, Vol. XXII, parts III and IV, May, 1931, pp. 368–376. [Tables of F(x), etc., later superseded by B. A. tables, may also be found in this volume.] Extensive introductory notes for statisticians.

R. A. FISHER. *Statistical Methods for Research Workers*, Oliver & Boyd, Edinburgh and London, Seventh Edition, 1938. Table I: The Deviation in the Normal Distribution in Terms of the Standard Deviation. x tabulated for P = $(1-\alpha_x)$ = [0(.01) 1; 6D]. Table II: Five decimal place values of x for P = .001, .0001, .00001, .000001, .0000001, .00000001, .000000001.

TRUMAN L. KELLEY. *The Kelley Statistical Tables*, New York, MacMillan Co., 1938. x, z, q, $.\sqrt{pq}$, $\sqrt{1-p^2}$, $\sqrt{1-q^2}$ for p = [.5(.0001).9999; 8D] and x, z, q for p = .9999; .99995; .999995 ... , to .999999995; 6 to 9 significant figures. Table of Lagrangian coefficients to 10 decimal places.

TABLE I

$$\frac{1}{\sqrt{2\pi}}\, e^{-\frac{x^2}{2}} \text{ and } \frac{1}{\sqrt{2\pi}} \int_{-x}^{x} e^{-\frac{\alpha^2}{2}}\, d\alpha$$

x	$\dfrac{1}{\sqrt{2\pi}}\,e^{-\frac{x^2}{2}}$	$\dfrac{1}{\sqrt{2\pi}}\displaystyle\int_{-x}^{x} e^{-\frac{\alpha^2}{2}}\,d\alpha$
0.0000	0.39894 22804 01433	0.00000 00000 00000
01	.39894 22784 06721	.00007 97884 55947
02	.39894 22724 22587	.00015 95769 11097
03	.39894 22624 49030	.00023 93653 64650
04	.39894 22484 86052	.00031 91538 15810
0.0005	0.39894 22305 33651	0.00039 89422 63779
06	.39894 22085 91829	.00047 87307 07758
07	.39894 21826 60586	.00055 85191 46950
08	.39894 21527 39923	.00063 83075 80556
09	.39894 21188 29842	.00071 80960 07780
0.0010	0.39894 20809 30342	0.00079 78844 27822
11	.39894 20390 41426	.00087 76728 39886
12	.39894 19931 63094	.00095 74612 43173
13	.39894 19432 95348	.00103 72496 36885
14	.39894 18894 38189	.00111 70380 20225
0.0015	0.39894 18315 91620	0.00119 68263 92394
16	.39894 17697 55641	.00127 66147 52596
17	.39894 17039 30254	.00135 64031 00031
18	.39894 16341 15462	.00143 61914 33902
19	.39894 15603 11266	.00151 59797 53411
0.0020	0.39894 14825 17670	0.00159 57680 57760
21	.39894 14007 34674	.00167 55563 46152
22	.39894 13149 62282	.00175 53446 17788
23	.39894 12252 00497	.00183 51328 71871
24	.39894 11314 49320	.00191 49211 07602
0.0025	0.39894 10337 08754	0.00199 47093 24185
26	.39894 09319 78804	.00207 44975 20820
27	.39894 08262 59471	.00215 42856 96710
28	.39894 07165 50759	.00223 40738 51058
29	.39894 06028 52671	.00231 38619 83065
0.0030	0.39894 04851 65210	0.00239 36500 91933
31	.39894 03634 88381	.00247 34381 76865
32	.39894 02378 22186	.00255 32262 37062
33	.39894 01081 66630	.00263 30142 71728
34	.39893 99745 21716	.00271 28022 80063
0.0035	0.39893 98368 87448	0.00279 25902 61270
36	.39893 96952 63832	.00287 23782 14552
37	.39893 95496 50869	.00295 21661 39110
38	.39893 94000 48566	.00303 19540 34146
39	.39893 92464 56927	.00311 17418 98863
0.0040	0.39893 90888 75956	0.00319 15297 32463
41	.39893 89273 05657	.00327 13175 34148
42	.39893 87617 46037	.00335 11053 03120
43	.39893 85921 97099	.00343 08930 38580
44	.39893 84186 58849	.00351 06807 39732
0.0045	0.39893 82411 31292	0.00359 04684 05778
46	.39893 80596 14434	.00367 02560 35919
47	.39893 78741 08279	.00375 00436 29358
48	.39893 76846 12834	.00382 98311 85296
49	.39893 74911 28104	.00390 96187 02937
0.0050	0.39893 72936 54095	0.00398 94061 81482

x	$\dfrac{1}{\sqrt{2\pi}}\, e^{-\frac{x^2}{2}}$	$\dfrac{1}{\sqrt{2\pi}}\displaystyle\int_{-x}^{x} e^{-\frac{\alpha^2}{2}}\, d\alpha$
0.0050	0.39893 72936 54095	0.00398 94061 81482
51	.39893 70921 90812	.00406 91936 20133
52	.39893 68867 38263	.00414 89810 18092
53	.39893 66772 96452	.00422 87683 74562
54	.39893 64638 65387	.00430 85556 88745
0.0055	0.39893 62464 45074	0.00438 83429 59842
56	.39893 60250 35518	.00446 81301 87057
57	.39893 57996 36728	.00454 79173 69590
58	.39893 55702 48709	.00462 77045 06645
59	.39893 53368 71469	.00470 74915 97424
0.0060	0.39893 50995 05014	0.00478 72786 41128
61	.39893 48581 49352	.00486 70656 36960
62	.39893 46128 04489	.00494 68525 84122
63	.39893 43634 70434	.00502 66394 81816
64	.39893 41101 47194	.00510 64263 29244
0.0065	0.39893 38528 34776	0.00518 62131 25609
66	.39893 35915 33188	.00526 59998 70112
67	.39893 33262 42437	.00534 57865 61956
68	.39893 30569 62533	.00542 55732 00343
69	.39893 27836 93483	.00550 53597 84475
0.0070	0.39893 25064 35294	0.00558 51463 13555
71	.39893 22251 87977	.00566 49327 86783
72	.39893 19399 51537	.00574 47192 03364
73	.39893 16507 25986	.00582 45055 62498
74	.39893 13575 11330	.00590 42918 63388
0.0075	0.39893 10603 07580	0.00598 40781 05237
76	.39893 07591 14743	.00606 38642 87245
77	.39893 04539 32829	.00614 36504 08617
78	.39893 01447 61847	.00622 34364 68553
79	.39892 98316 01806	.00630 32224 66255
0.0080	0.39892 95144 52716	0.00638 30084 00927
81	.39892 91933 14586	.00646 27942 71771
82	.39892 88681 87426	.00654 25800 77987
83	.39892 85390 71246	.00662 23658 18780
84	.39892 82059 66055	.00670 21514 93350
0.0085	0.39892 78688 71863	0.00678 19371 00900
86	.39892 75277 88681	.00686 17226 40633
87	.39892 71827 16519	.00694 15081 11750
88	.39892 68336 55386	.00702 12935 13453
89	.39892 64806 05295	.00710 10788 44946
0.0090	0.39892 61235 66255	0.00718 08641 05429
91	.39892 57625 38276	.00726 06492 94106
92	.39892 53975 21370	.00734 04344 10179
93	.39892 50285 15548	.00742 02194 52849
94	.39892 46555 20821	.00750 00044 21319
0.0095	0.39892 42785 37200	0.00757 97893 14791
96	.39892 38975 64696	.00765 95741 32468
97	.39892 35126 03320	.00773 93588 73551
98	.39892 31236 53085	.00781 91435 37244
99	.39892 27307 14002	.00789 89281 22747
0.0100	0.39892 23337 86082	0.00797 87126 29263

x	$\dfrac{1}{\sqrt{2\pi}}\,e^{-\frac{x^2}{2}}$	$\dfrac{1}{\sqrt{2\pi}}\displaystyle\int_{-x}^{x} e^{-\frac{\alpha^2}{2}}\,d\alpha$
0.0100	0.39892 23337 86082	0.00797 87126 29263
01	.39892 19328 69338	.00805 84970 55995
02	.39892 15279 63782	.00813 82814 02145
03	.39892 11190 69425	.00821 80656 66915
04	.39892 07061 86281	.00829 78498 49507
0.0105	0.39892 02893 14360	0.00837 76339 49123
06	.39891 98684 53677	.00845 74179 64967
07	.39891 94436 04244	.00853 72018 96239
08	.39891 90147 66072	.00861 69857 42142
09	.39891 85819 39176	.00869 67695 01879
0.0110	0.39891 81451 23568	0.00877 65531 74652
11	.39891 77043 19261	.00885 63367 59663
12	.39891 72595 26269	.00893 61202 56114
13	.39891 68107 44604	.00901 59036 63208
14	.39891 63579 74281	.00909 56869 80146
0.0115	0.39891 59012 15313	0.00917 54702 06131
16	.39891 54404 67713	.00925 52533 40366
17	.39891 49757 31495	.00933 50363 82053
18	.39891 45070 06674	.00941 48193 30393
19	.39891 40342 93263	.00949 46021 84589
0.0120	0.39891 35575 91277	0.00957 43849 43844
21	.39891 30769 00730	.00965 41676 07360
22	.39891 25922 21636	.00973 39501 74339
23	.39891 21035 54010	.00981 37326 43983
24	.39891 16108 97866	.00989 35150 15494
0.0125	0.39891 11142 53220	0.00997 32972 88076
26	.39891 06136 20086	.01005 30794 60930
27	.39891 01089 98479	.01013 28615 33258
28	.39890 96003 88414	.01021 26435 04263
29	.39890 90877 89907	.01029 24253 73148
0.0130	0.39890 85712 02972	0.01037 22071 39113
31	.39890 80506 27627	.01045 19888 01363
32	.39890 75260 63885	.01053 17703 59098
33	.39890 69975 11763	.01061 15518 11523
34	.39890 64649 71277	.01069 13331 57837
0.0135	0.39890 59284 42442	0.01077 11143 97245
36	.39890 53879 25276	.01085 08955 28948
37	.39890 48434 19793	.01093 06765 52149
38	.39890 42949 26010	.01101 04574 66050
39	.39890 37424 43944	.01109 02382 69854
0.0140	0.39890 31859 73612	0.01117 00189 62762
41	.39890 26255 15029	.01124 97995 43977
42	.39890 20610 68213	.01132 95800 12702
43	.39890 14926 33181	.01140 93603 68139
44	.39890 09202 09950	.01148 91406 09490
0.0145	0.39890 03437 98537	0.01156 89207 35957
46	.39889 97633 98959	.01164 87007 46743
47	.39889 91790 11233	.01172 84806 41051
48	.39889 85906 35378	.01180 82604 18082
49	.39889 79982 71411	.01188 80400 77039
0.0150	0.39889 74019 19349	0.01196 78196 17124

x	$\dfrac{1}{\sqrt{2\pi}}\,e^{-\frac{x^2}{2}}$	$\dfrac{1}{\sqrt{2\pi}}\displaystyle\int_{-x}^{x} e^{-\frac{\alpha^2}{2}}\,d\alpha$
0.0150	0.39889 74019 19349	0.01196 78196 17124
51	.39889 68015 79211	.01204 75990 37541
52	.39889 61972 51015	.01212 73783 37490
53	.39889 55889 34778	.01220 71575 16175
54	.39889 49766 30519	.01228 69365 72798
0.0155	0.39889 43603 38256	0.01236 67155 06562
56	.39889 37400 58008	.01244 64943 16668
57	.39889 31157 89793	.01252 62730 02319
58	.39889 24875 33630	.01260 60515 62718
59	.39889 18552 89539	.01268 58299 97067
0.0160	0.39889 12190 57537	0.01276 56083 04568
61	.39889 05788 37644	.01284 53864 84424
62	.39888 99346 29880	.01292 51645 35837
63	.39888 92864 34262	.01300 49424 58010
64	.39888 86342 50812	.01308 47202 50145
0.0165	0.39888 79780 79549	0.01316 44979 11444
66	.39888 73179 20491	.01324 42754 41111
67	.39888 66537 73660	.01332 40528 38347
68	.39888 59856 39074	.01340 38301 02354
69	.39888 53135 16755	.01348 36072 32336
0.0170	0.39888 46374 06721	0.01356 33842 27495
71	.39888 39573 08994	.01364 31610 87033
72	.39888 32732 23594	.01372 29378 10153
73	.39888 25851 50541	.01380 27143 96057
74	.39888 18930 89856	.01388 24908 43947
0.0175	0.39888 11970 41560	0.01396 22671 53027
76	.39888 04970 05674	.01404 20433 22498
77	.39887 97929 82218	.01412 18193 51563
78	.39887 90849 71214	.01420 15952 39425
79	.39887 83729 72682	.01428 13709 85286
0.0180	0.39887 76569 86646	0.01436 11465 88348
81	.39887 69370 13124	.01444 09220 47815
82	.39887 62130 52141	.01452 06973 62888
83	.39887 54851 03716	.01460 04725 32770
84	.39887 47531 67873	.01468 02475 56664
0.0185	0.39887 40172 44632	0.01476 00224 33771
86	.39887 32773 34016	.01483 97971 63296
87	.39887 25334 36048	.01491 95717 44439
88	.39887 17855 50749	.01499 93461 76404
89	.39887 10336 78141	.01507 91204 58393
0.0190	0.39887 02778 18249	0.01515 88945 89610
91	.39886 95179 71093	.01523 86685 69255
92	.39886 87541 36698	.01531 84423 96532
93	.39886 79863 15085	.01539 82160 70644
94	.39886 72145 06278	.01547 79895 90792
0.0195	0.39886 64387 10301	0.01555 77629 56181
96	.39886 56589 27175	.01563 75361 66011
97	.39886 48751 56925	.01571 73092 19486
98	.39886 40873 99575	.01579 70821 15808
99	.39886 32956 55147	.01587 68548 54180
0.0200	0.39886 24999 23666	0.01595 66274 33804

x	$\dfrac{1}{\sqrt{2\pi}}\,e^{-\frac{x^2}{2}}$	$\dfrac{1}{\sqrt{2\pi}}\displaystyle\int_{-x}^{x} e^{-\frac{\alpha^2}{2}}\,d\alpha$
0.0200	0.39886 24999 23666	0.01595 66274 33804
01	.39886 17002 05155	.01603 63998 53883
02	.39886 08964 99639	.01611 61721 13620
03	.39886 00888 07142	.01619 59442 12217
04	.39885 92771 27687	.01627 57161 48877
0.0205	0.39885 84614 61299	0.01635 54879 22803
06	.39885 76418 08003	.01643 52595 33196
07	.39885 68181 67823	.01651 50309 79260
08	.39885 59905 40784	.01659 48022 60197
09	.39885 51589 26911	.01667 45733 75211
0.0210	0.39885 43233 26228	0.01675 43443 23502
11	.39885 34837 38761	.01683 41151 04275
12	.39885 26401 64535	.01691 38857 16732
13	.39885 17926 03575	.01699 36561 60075
14	.39885 09410 55907	.01707 34264 33508
0.0215	0.39885 00855 21556	0.01715 31965 36232
16	.39884 92260 00548	.01723 29664 67451
17	.39884 83624 92908	.01731 27362 26366
18	.39884 74949 98663	.01739 25058 12182
19	.39884 66235 17839	.01747 22752 24100
0.0220	0.39884 57480 50461	0.01755 20444 61323
21	.39884 48685 96556	.01763 18135 23054
22	.39884 39851 56151	.01771 15824 08496
23	.39884 30977 29271	.01779 13511 16851
24	.39884 22063 15944	.01787 11196 47322
0.0225	0.39884 13109 16196	0.01795 08879 99112
26	.39884 04115 30054	.01803 06561 71423
27	.39883 95081 57545	.01811 04241 63458
28	.39883 86007 98696	.01819 01919 74420
29	.39883 76894 53534	.01826 99596 03512
0.0230	0.39883 67741 22087	0.01834 97270 49936
31	.39883 58548 04382	.01842 94943 12895
32	.39883 49315 00447	.01850 92613 91592
33	.39883 40042 10309	.01858 90282 85229
34	.39883 30729 33997	.01866 87949 93010
0.0235	0.39883 21376 71537	0.01874 85615 14137
36	.39883 11984 22959	.01882 83278 47813
37	.39883 02551 88290	.01890 80939 93241
38	.39882 93079 67559	.01898 78599 49623
39	.39882 83567 60794	.01906 76257 16162
0.0240	0.39882 74015 68023	0.01914 73912 92061
41	.39882 64423 89276	.01922 71566 76523
42	.39882 54792 24580	.01930 69218 68751
43	.39882 45120 73966	.01938 66868 67947
44	.39882 35409 37461	.01946 64516 73315
0.0245	0.39882 25658 15096	0.01954 62162 84057
46	.39882 15867 06899	.01962 59806 99375
47	.39882 06036 12899	.01970 57449 18474
48	.39881 96165 33127	.01978 55089 40555
49	.39881 86254 67611	.01986 52727 64821
0.0250	0.39881 76304 16382	0.01994 50363 90476

x	$\dfrac{1}{\sqrt{2\pi}}\,e^{-\frac{x^2}{2}}$	$\dfrac{1}{\sqrt{2\pi}}\displaystyle\int_{-x}^{x} e^{-\frac{\alpha^2}{2}}\,d\alpha$
0.0250	0.39881 76304 16382	0.01994 50363 90476
51	.39881 66313 79469	.02002 47998 16722
52	.39881 56283 56902	.02010 45630 42762
53	.39881 46213 48712	.02018 43260 67799
54	.39881 36103 54928	.02026 40888 91036
0.0255	0.39881 25953 75582	0.02034 38515 11675
56	.39881 15764 10702	.02042 36139 28920
57	.39881 05534 60321	.02050 33761 41974
58	.39880 95265 24468	.02058 31381 50039
59	.39880 84956 03174	.02066 28999 52318
0.0260	0.39880 74606 96471	0.02074 26615 48014
61	.39880 64218 04389	.02082 24229 36331
62	.39880 53789 26959	.02090 21841 16471
63	.39880 43320 64214	.02098 19450 87636
64	.39880 32812 16183	.02106 17058 49031
0.0265	0.39880 22263 82899	0.02114 14663 99857
66	.39880 11675 64394	.02122 12267 39318
67	.39880 01047 60698	.02130 09868 66617
68	.39879 90379 71845	.02138 07467 80957
69	.39879 79671 97866	.02146 05064 81540
0.0270	.39879 68924 38792	0.02154 02659 67570
71	.39879 58136 94657	.02162 00252 38250
72	.39879 47309 65493	.02169 97842 92782
73	.39879 36442 51332	.02177 95431 30370
74	.39879 25535 52206	.02185 93017 50217
0.0275	0.39879 14588 68149	0.02193 90601 51526
76	.39879 03601 99193	.02201 88183 33499
77	.39878 92575 45372	.02209 85762 95340
78	.39878 81509 06718	.02217 83340 36251
79	.39878 70402 83264	.02225 80915 55437
0.0280	0.39878 59256 75044	0.02233 78488 52099
81	.39878 48070 82091	.02241 76059 25441
82	.39878 36845 04439	.02249 73627 74666
83	.39878 25579 42122	.02257 71193 98977
84	.39878 14273 95173	.02265 68757 97577
0.0285	0.39878 02928 63626	0.02273 66319 69670
86	.39877 91543 47515	.02281 63879 14457
87	.39877 80118 46874	.02289 61436 31143
88	.39877 68653 61738	.02297 58991 18930
89	.39877 57148 92141	.02305 56543 77022
0.0290	0.39877 45604 38118	0.02313 54094 04621
91	.39877 34019 99702	.02321 51642 00932
92	.39877 22395 76929	.02329 49187 65156
93	.39877 10731 69835	.02337 46730 96497
94	.39876 99027 78452	.02345 44271 94158
0.0295	0.39876 87284 02818	0.02353 41810 57343
96	.39876 75500 42967	.02361 39346 85254
97	.39876 63676 98934	.02369 36880 77094
98	.39876 51813 70754	.02377 34412 32068
99	.39876 39910 58464	.02385 31941 49377
0.0300	0.39876 27967 62100	0.02393 29468 28225

x	$\dfrac{1}{\sqrt{2\pi}}e^{-\frac{x^2}{2}}$	$\dfrac{1}{\sqrt{2\pi}}\displaystyle\int_{-x}^{x} e^{-\frac{\alpha^2}{2}}\, d\alpha$
0.0300	0.39876 27967 62100	0.02393 29468 28225
01	.39876 15984 81696	.02401 26992 67816
02	.39876 03962 17289	.02409 24514 67352
03	.39875 91899 68915	.02417 22034 26037
04	.39875 79797 36610	.02425 19551 43074
0.0305	0.39875 67655 20410	0.02433 17066 17666
06	.39875 55473 20352	.02441 14578 49017
07	.39875 43251 36473	.02449 12088 36329
08	.39875 30989 68808	.02457 09595 78806
09	.39875 18688 17395	.02465 07100 75651
0.0310	0.39875 06346 82271	0.02473 04603 26067
11	.39874 93965 63473	.02481 02103 29258
12	.39874 81544 61037	.02488 99600 84427
13	.39874 69083 75001	.02496 97095 90777
14	.39874 56583 05403	.02504 94588 47512
0.0315	0.39874 44042 52280	0.02512 92078 53834
16	.39874 31462 15669	.02520 89566 08947
17	.39874 18841 95608	.02528 87051 12054
18	.39874 06181 92136	.02536 84533 62360
19	.39873 93482 05289	.02544 82013 59066
0.0320	0.39873 80742 35107	0.02552 79491 01376
21	.39873 67962 81627	.02560 76965 88494
22	.39873 55143 44887	.02568 74438 19623
23	.39873 42284 24927	.02576 71907 93967
24	.39873 29385 21785	.02584 69375 10728
0.0325	0.39873 16446 35498	0.02592 66839 69110
26	.39873 03467 66107	.02600 64301 68316
27	.39872 90449 13650	.02608 61761 07551
28	.39872 77390 78167	.02616 59217 86016
29	.39872 64292 59695	.02624 56672 02916
0.0330	0.39872 51154 58275	0.02632 54123 57455
31	.39872 37976 73946	.02640 51572 48834
32	.39872 24759 06748	.02648 49018 76259
33	.39872 11501 56720	.02656 46462 38931
34	.39871 98204 23901	.02664 43903 36056
0.0335	0.39871 84867 08332	0.02672 41341 66835
36	.39871 71490 10054	.02680 38777 30474
37	.39871 58073 29104	.02688 36210 26174
38	.39871 44616 65526	.02696 33640 53140
39	.39871 31120 19357	.02704 31068 10575
0.0340	0.39871 17583 90640	0.02712 28492 97682
41	.39871 04007 79414	.02720 25915 13665
42	.39870 90391 85720	.02728 23334 57728
43	.39870 76736 09599	.02736 20751 29074
44	.39870 63040 51093	.02744 18165 26907
0.0345	0.39870 49305 10241	0.02752 15576 50429
46	.39870 35529 87086	.02760 12984 98845
47	.39870 21714 81668	.02768 10390 71358
48	.39870 07859 94030	.02776 07793 67172
49	.39869 93965 24212	.02784 05193 85491
0.0350	0.39869 80030 72256	0.02792 02591 25517

x	$\dfrac{1}{\sqrt{2\pi}}e^{-\frac{x^2}{2}}$	$\dfrac{1}{\sqrt{2\pi}}\displaystyle\int_{-x}^{x}e^{-\frac{\alpha^2}{2}}\,d\alpha$
0.0350	0.39869 80030 72256	0.02792 02591 25517
51	.39869 66056 38204	.02799 99985 86454
52	.39869 52042 22098	.02807 97377 67506
53	.39869 37988 23980	.02815 94766 67877
54	.39869 23894 43892	.02823 92152 86771
0.0355	0.39869 09760 81877	0.02831 89536 23389
56	.39868 95587 37976	.02839 86916 76938
57	.39868 81374 12233	.02847 84294 46619
58	.39868 67121 04690	.02855 81669 31637
59	.39868 52828 15389	.02863 79041 31196
0.0360	0.39868 38495 44373	0.02871 76410 44498
61	.39868 24122 91686	.02879 73776 70748
62	.39868 09710 57371	.02887 71140 09149
63	.39867 95258 41470	.02895 68500 58905
64	.39867 80766 44028	.02903 65858 19220
0.0365	0.39867 66234 65087	0.02911 63212 89298
66	.39867 51663 04691	.02919 60564 68341
67	.39867 37051 62884	.02927 57913 55554
68	.39867 22400 39710	.02935 55259 50141
69	.39867 07709 35212	.02943 52602 51305
0.0370	0.39866 92978 49435	0.02951 49942 58249
71	.39866 78207 82423	.02959 47279 70179
72	.39866 63397 34220	.02967 44613 86297
73	.39866 48547 04870	.02975 41945 05807
74	.39866 33656 94418	.02983 39273 27913
0.0375	0.39866 18727 02909	0.02991 36598 51820
76	.39866 03757 30388	.02999 33920 76729
77	.39865 88747 76899	.03007 31240 01846
78	.39865 73698 42487	.03015 28556 26375
79	.39865 58609 27198	.03023 25869 49518
0.0380	0.39865 43480 31076	0.03031 23179 70480
81	.39865 28311 54168	.03039 20486 88465
82	.39865 13102 96518	.03047 17791 02676
83	.39864 97854 58173	.03055 15092 12318
84	.39864 82566 39177	.03063 12390 16594
0.0385	0.39864 67238 39577	0.03071 09685 14708
86	.39864 51870 59419	.03079 06977 05865
87	.39864 36462 98748	.03087 04265 89267
88	.39864 21015 57612	.03095 01551 64119
89	.39864 05528 36056	.03102 98834 29625
0.0390	0.39863 90001 34126	0.03110 96113 84988
91	.39863 74434 51870	.03118 93390 29413
92	.39863 58827 89334	.03126 90663 62103
93	.39863 43181 46565	.03134 87933 82263
94	.39863 27495 23609	.03142 85200 89097
0.0395	0.39863 11769 20514	0.03150 82464 81807
96	.39862 96003 37327	.03158 79725 59599
97	.39862 80197 74095	.03166 76983 21677
98	.39862 64352 30866	.03174 74237 67244
99	.39862 48467 07687	.03182 71488 95504
0.0400	0.39862 32542 04605	0.03190 68737 05662

x	$\dfrac{1}{\sqrt{2\pi}} e^{-\frac{x^2}{2}}$	$\dfrac{1}{\sqrt{2\pi}} \displaystyle\int_{-x}^{x} e^{-\frac{\alpha^2}{2}}\, d\alpha$
0.0400	0.39862 32542 04605	0.03190 68737 05662
01	.39862 16577 21669	.03198 65981 96920
02	.39862 00572 58926	.03206 63223 68485
03	.39861 84528 16425	.03214 60462 19559
04	.39861 68443 94212	.03222 57697 49346
0.0405	0.39861 52319 92338	0.03230 54929 57051
06	.39861 36156 10849	.03238 52158 41878
07	.39861 19952 49795	.03246 49384 03030
08	.39861 03709 09224	.03254 46606 39712
09	.39860 87425 89185	.03262 43825 51129
0.0410	0.39860 71102 89726	0.03270 41041 36483
11	.39860 54740 10897	.03278 38253 94979
12	.39860 38337 52746	.03286 35463 25822
13	.39860 21895 15323	.03294 32669 28215
14	.39860 05412 98677	.03302 29872 01363
0.0415	0.39859 88891 02858	0.03310 27071 44469
16	.39859 72329 27914	.03318 24267 56739
17	.39859 55727 73896	.03326 21460 37375
18	.39859 39086 40854	.03334 18649 85583
19	.39859 22405 28837	.03342 15836 00566
0.0420	0.39859 05684 37895	0.03350 13018 81529
21	.39858 88923 68079	.03358 10198 27676
22	.39858 72123 19438	.03366 07374 38211
23	.39858 55282 92023	.03374 04547 12339
24	.39858 38402 85885	.03382 01716 49263
0.0425	0.39858 21483 01075	0.03389 98882 48188
26	.39858 04523 37642	.03397 96045 08318
27	.39857 87523 95638	.03405 93204 28857
28	.39857 70484 75113	.03413 90360 09011
29	.39857 53405 76120	.03421 87512 47982
0.0430	0.39857 36286 98708	0.03429 84661 44976
31	.39857 19128 42930	.03437 81806 99197
32	.39857 01930 08837	.03445 78949 09848
33	.39856 84691 96480	.03453 76087 76135
34	.39856 67414 05911	.03461 73222 97261
0.0435	0.39856 50096 37182	0.03469 70354 72432
36	.39856 32738 90344	.03477 67483 00851
37	.39856 15341 65451	.03485 64607 81723
38	.39855 97904 62553	.03493 61729 14252
39	.39855 80427 81704	.03501 58846 97643
0.0440	0.39855 62911 22955	0.03509 55961 31100
41	.39855 45354 86359	.03517 53072 13827
42	.39855 27758 71970	.03525 50179 45029
43	.39855 10122 79838	.03533 47283 23910
44	.39854 92447 10018	.03541 44383 49676
0.0445	0.39854 74731 62563	0.03549 41480 21529
46	.39854 56976 37525	.03557 38573 38675
47	.39854 39181 34958	.03565 35663 00319
48	.39854 21346 54915	.03573 32749 05664
49	.39854 03471 97449	.03581 29831 53916
0.0450	0.39853 85557 62615	0.03589 26910 44278

x	$\dfrac{1}{\sqrt{2\pi}}\,e^{-\frac{x^2}{2}}$	$\dfrac{1}{\sqrt{2\pi}}\displaystyle\int_{-x}^{x} e^{-\frac{\alpha^2}{2}}\,d\alpha$
0.0450	0.39853 85557 62615	0.03589 26910 44278
51	.39853 67603 50465	.03597 23985 75956
52	.39853 49609 61054	.03605 21057 48153
53	.39853 31575 94436	.03613 18125 60075
54	.39853 13502 50665	.03621 15190 10926
0.0455	0.39852 95389 29794	0.03629 12250 99910
56	.39852 77236 31878	.03637 09308 26233
57	.39852 59043 56973	.03645 06361 89098
58	.39852 40811 05131	.03653 03411 87710
59	.39852 22538 76408	.03661 00458 21275
0.0460	0.39852 04226 70858	0.03668 97500 88996
61	.39851 85874 88538	.03676 94539 90078
62	.39851 67483 29500	.03684 91575 23726
63	.39851 49051 93801	.03692 88606 89145
64	.39851 30580 81497	.03700 85634 85538
0.0465	0.39851 12069 92641	0.03708 82659 12112
66	.39850 93519 27290	.03716 79679 68070
67	.39850 74928 85499	.03724 76696 52618
68	.39850 56298 67325	.03732 73709 64959
69	.39850 37628 72823	.03740 70719 04300
0.0470	0.39850 18919 02048	0.03748 67724 69844
71	.39850 00169 55057	.03756 64726 60795
72	.39849 81380 31907	.03764 61724 76360
73	.39849 62551 32653	.03772 58719 15743
74	.39849 43682 57352	.03780 55709 78148
0.0475	0.39849 24774 06061	0.03788 52696 62781
76	.39849 05825 78836	.03796 49679 68846
77	.39848 86837 75734	.03804 46658 95548
78	.39848 67809 96812	.03812 43634 42091
79	.39848 48742 42126	.03820 40606 07681
0.0480	0.39848 29635 11735	0.03828 37573 91523
81	.39848 10488 05696	.03836 34537 92821
82	.39847 91301 24065	.03844 31498 10780
83	.39847 72074 66901	.03852 28454 44605
84	.39847 52808 34260	.03860 25406 93502
0.0485	0.39847 33502 26201	0.03868 22355 56674
86	.39847 14156 42782	.03876 19300 33327
87	.39846 94770 84061	.03884 16241 22666
88	.39846 75345 50095	.03892 13178 23896
89	.39846 55880 40943	.03900 10111 36221
0.0490	0.39846 36375 56663	0.03908 07040 58847
91	.39846 16830 97314	.03916 03965 90979
92	.39845 97246 62955	.03924 00887 31821
93	.39845 77622 53643	.03931 97804 80579
94	.39845 57958 69439	.03939 94718 36458
0.0495	0.39845 38255 10400	0.03947 91627 98662
96	.39845 18511 76586	.03955 88533 66397
97	.39844 98728 68056	.03963 85435 38868
98	.39844 78905 84869	.03971 82333 15279
99	.39844 59043 27086	.03979 79226 94836
0.0500	0.39844 39140 94764	0.03987 76116 76745

x	$\frac{1}{\sqrt{2\pi}} e^{-\frac{x^2}{2}}$	$\frac{1}{\sqrt{2\pi}} \int_{-x}^{x} e^{-\frac{\alpha^2}{2}} d\alpha$
0.0500	0.39844 39140 94764	0.03987 76116 76745
01	.39844 19198 87964	.03995 73002 60209
02	.39843 99217 06747	.04003 69884 44435
03	.39843 79195 51171	.04011 66762 28627
04	.39843 59134 21296	.04019 63636 11991
0.0505	0.39843 39033 17183	0.04027 60505 93731
06	.39843 18892 38893	.04035 57371 73053
07	.39842 98711 86484	.04043 54233 49161
08	.39842 78491 60019	.04051 51091 21262
09	.39842 58231 59557	.04059 47944 88560
0.0510	0.39842 37931 85159	0.04067 44794 50261
11	.39842 17592 36887	.04075 41640 05570
12	.39841 97213 14800	.04083 38481 53691
13	.39841 76794 18961	.04091 35318 93831
14	.39841 56335 49430	.04099 32152 25194
0.0515	0.39841 35837 06269	0.04107 28981 46985
16	.39841 15298 89538	.04115 25806 58411
17	.39840 94720 99301	.04123 22627 58676
18	.39840 74103 35617	.04131 19444 46986
19	.39840 53445 98550	.04139 16257 22546
0.0520	0.39840 32748 88161	0.04147 13065 84561
21	.39840 12012 04512	.04155 09870 32236
22	.39839 91235 47665	.04163 06670 64778
23	.39839 70419 17683	.04171 03466 81390
24	.39839 49563 14628	.04179 00258 81280
0.0525	0.39839 28667 38562	0.04186 97046 63651
26	.39839 07731 89548	.04194 93830 27710
27	.39838 86756 67649	.04202 90609 72662
28	.39838 65741 72927	.04210 87384 97712
29	.39838 44687 05446	.04218 84156 02067
0.0530	0.39838 23592 65269	0.04226 80922 84930
31	.39838 02458 52459	.04234 77685 45508
32	.39837 81284 67080	.04242 74443 83006
33	.39837 60071 09194	.04250 71197 96630
34	.39837 38817 78865	.04258 67947 85585
0.0535	0.39837 17524 76157	0.04266 64693 49077
36	.39836 96192 01135	.04274 61434 86310
37	.39836 74819 53861	.04282 58171 96492
38	.39836 53407 34400	.04290 54904 78827
39	.39836 31955 42816	.04298 51633 32521
0.0540	0.39836 10463 79173	0.04306 48357 56780
41	.39835 88932 43537	.04314 45077 50808
42	.39835 67361 35970	.04322 41793 13812
43	.39835 45750 56539	.04330 38504 44998
44	.39835 24100 05307	.04338 35211 43570
0.0545	0.39835 02409 82339	0.04346 31914 08735
46	.39834 80679 87702	.04354 28612 39698
47	.39834 58910 21459	.04362 25306 35665
48	.39834 37100 83676	.04370 21995 95842
49	.39834 15251 74418	.04378 18681 19434
0.0550	0.39833 93362 93751	0.04386 15362 05647

x	$\dfrac{1}{\sqrt{2\pi}}\,e^{-\frac{x^2}{2}}$	$\dfrac{1}{\sqrt{2\pi}}\displaystyle\int_{-x}^{x} e^{-\frac{\alpha^2}{2}}\,d\alpha$
0.0550	0.39833 93362 93751	0.04386 15362 05647
51	.39833 71434 41741	.04394 12038 53687
52	.39833 49466 18452	.04402 08710 62759
53	.39833 27458 23952	.04410 05378 32069
54	.39833 05410 58305	.04418 02041 60824
0.0555	0.39832 83323 21579	0.04425 98700 48228
56	.39832 61196 13839	.04433 95354 93488
57	.39832 39029 35151	.04441 92004 95809
58	.39832 16822 85582	.04449 88650 54397
59	.39831 94576 65199	.04457 85291 68458
0.0560	0.39831 72290 74068	0.04465 81928 37198
61	.39831 49965 12256	.04473 78560 59823
62	.39831 27599 79829	.04481 75188 35539
63	.39831 05194 76856	.04489 71811 63550
64	.39830 82750 03402	.04497 68430 43065
0.0565	0.39830 60265 59536	0.04505 65044 73287
66	.39830 37741 45325	.04513 61654 53424
67	.39830 15177 60835	.04521 58259 82680
68	.39829 92574 06136	.04529 54860 60263
69	.39829 69930 81294	.04537 51456 85378
0.0570	0.39829 47247 86377	0.04545 48048 57231
71	.39829 24525 21454	.04553 44635 75028
72	.39829 01762 86592	.04561 41218 37975
73	.39828 78960 81860	.04569 37796 45278
74	.39828 56119 07326	.04577 34369 96143
0.0575	0.39828 33237 63058	0.04585 30938 89776
76	.39828 10316 49125	.04593 27503 25384
77	.39827 87355 65596	.04601 24063 02171
78	.39827 64355 12540	.04609 20618 19345
79	.39827 41314 90025	.04617 17168 76112
0.0580	0.39827 18234 98120	0.04625 13714 71677
81	.39826 95115 36895	.04633 10256 05246
82	.39826 71956 06419	.04641 06792 76027
83	.39826 48757 06762	.04649 03324 83224
84	.39826 25518 37992	.04656 99852 26045
0.0585	0.39826 02240 00179	0.04664 96375 03695
86	.39825 78921 93394	.04672 92893 15380
87	.39825 55564 17706	.04680 89406 60308
88	.39825 32166 73185	.04688 85915 37683
89	.39825 08729 59902	.04696 82419 46712
0.0590	0.39824 85252 77925	0.04704 78918 86602
91	.39824 61736 27327	.04712 75413 56559
92	.39824 38180 08176	.04720 71903 55789
93	.39824 14584 20545	.04728 68388 83498
94	.39823 90948 64503	.04736 64869 38892
0.0595	0.39823 67273 40122	0.04744 61345 21179
96	.39823 43558 47472	.04752 57816 29564
97	.39823 19803 86624	.04760 54282 63253
98	.39822 96009 57649	.04768 50744 21454
99	.39822 72175 60620	.04776 47201 03372
0.0600	0.39822 48301 95607	0.04784 43653 08214

14

x	$\frac{1}{\sqrt{2\pi}} e^{-\frac{x^2}{2}}$	$\frac{1}{\sqrt{2\pi}} \int_{-x}^{x} e^{-\frac{\alpha^2}{2}} d\alpha$
0.0600	0.39822 48301 95607	0.04784 43653 08214
01	.39822 24388 62682	.04792 40100 35186
02	.39822 00435 61916	.04800 36542 83494
03	.39821 76442 93381	.04808 32980 52346
04	.39821 52410 57149	.04816 29413 40947
0.0605	0.39821 28338 53293	0.04824 25841 48504
06	.39821 04226 81884	.04832 22264 74224
07	.39820 80075 42994	.04840 18683 17313
08	.39820 55884 36696	.04848 15096 76977
09	.39820 31653 63063	.04856 11505 52423
0.0610	0.39820 07383 22167	0.04864 07909 42857
11	.39819 83073 14080	.04872 04308 47487
12	.39819 58723 38875	.04880 00702 65518
13	.39819 34333 96627	.04887 97091 96158
14	.39819 09904 87406	.04895 93476 38613
0.0615	0.39818 85436 11288	0.04903 89855 92089
16	.39818 60927 68344	.04911 86230 55793
17	.39818 36379 58650	.04919 82600 28932
18	.39818 11791 82277	.04927 78965 10712
19	.39817 87164 39299	.04935 75325 00340
0.0620	0.39817 62497 29792	0.04943 71679 97023
21	.39817 37790 53827	.04951 68029 99968
22	.39817 13044 11481	.04959 64375 08380
23	.39816 88258 02825	.04967 60715 21468
24	.39816 63432 27936	.04975 57050 38437
0.0625	0.39816 38566 86887	0.04983 53380 58494
26	.39816 13661 79752	.04991 49705 80847
27	.39815 88717 06607	.04999 46026 04702
28	.39815 63732 67526	.05007 42341 29265
29	.39815 38708 62584	.05015 38651 53745
0.0630	0.39815 13644 91855	0.05023 34956 77346
31	.39814 88541 55416	.05031 31256 99277
32	.39814 63398 53341	.05039 27552 18744
33	.39814 38215 85705	.05047 23842 34954
34	.39814 12993 52585	.05055 20127 47114
0.0635	0.39813 87731 54055	0.05063 16407 54431
36	.39813 62429 90191	.05071 12682 56111
37	.39813 37088 61069	.05079 08952 51362
38	.39813 11707 66766	.05087 05217 39391
39	.39812 86287 07356	.05095 01477 19405
0.0640	0.39812 60826 82916	0.05102 97731 90610
41	.39812 35326 93523	.05110 93981 52213
42	.39812 09787 39252	.05118 90226 03423
43	.39811 84208 20181	.05126 86465 43445
44	.39811 58589 36386	.05134 82699 71487
0.0645	0.39811 32930 87944	0.05142 78928 86755
46	.39811 07232 74931	.05150 75152 88457
47	.39810 81494 97425	.05158 71371 75801
48	.39810 55717 55502	.05166 67585 47992
49	.39810 29900 49241	.05174 63794 04239
0.0650	0.39810 04043 78717	0.05182 59997 43748

x	$\frac{1}{\sqrt{2\pi}}e^{-\frac{x^2}{2}}$	$\frac{1}{\sqrt{2\pi}}\int_{-x}^{x}e^{-\frac{\alpha^2}{2}}d\alpha$
0.0650	0.39810 04043 78717	0.05182 59997 43748
51	.39809 78147 44010	.05190 56195 65726
52	.39809 52211 45195	.05198 52388 69381
53	.39809 26235 82352	.05206 48576 53920
54	.39809 00220 55557	.05214 44759 18550
0.0655	0.39808 74165 64889	0.05222 40936 62478
56	.39808 48071 10426	.05230 37108 84911
57	.39808 21936 92246	.05238 33275 85058
58	.39807 95763 10427	.05246 29437 62124
59	.39807 69549 65048	.05254 25594 15318
0.0660	0.39807 43296 56187	0.05262 21745 43846
61	.39807 17003 83923	.05270 17891 46916
62	.39806 90671 48334	.05278 14032 23735
63	.39806 64299 49500	.05286 10167 73511
64	.39806 37887 87499	.05294 06297 95451
0.0665	0.39806 11436 62411	0.05302 02422 88762
66	.39805 84945 74315	.05309 98542 52651
67	.39805 58415 23290	.05317 94656 86327
68	.39805 31845 09416	.05325 90765 88997
69	.39805 05235 32772	.05333 86869 59867
0.0670	0.39804 78585 93437	0.05341 82967 98145
71	.39804 51896 91493	.05349 79061 03040
72	.39804 25168 27018	.05357 75148 73758
73	.39803 98400 00094	.05365 71231 09507
74	.39803 71592 10799	.05373 67308 09494
0.0675	0.39803 44744 59214	0.05381 63379 72927
76	.39803 17857 45420	.05389 59445 99013
77	.39802 90930 69498	.05397 55506 86961
78	.39802 63964 31527	.05405 51562 35977
79	.39802 36958 31589	.05413 47612 45269
0.0680	0.39802 09912 69765	0.05421 43657 14045
81	.39801 82827 46135	.05429 39696 41513
82	.39801 55702 60781	.05437 35730 26880
83	.39801 28538 13784	.05445 31758 69353
84	.39801 01334 05225	.05453 27781 68141
0.0685	0.39800 74090 35186	0.05461 23799 22451
86	.39800 46807 03748	.05469 19811 31491
87	.39800 19484 10994	.05477 15817 94469
88	.39799 92121 57004	.05485 11819 10592
89	.39799 64719 41862	.05493 07814 79067
0.0690	0.39799 37277 65648	0.05501 03804 99104
91	.39799 09796 28446	.05508 99789 69910
92	.39798 82275 30337	.05516 95768 90692
93	.39798 54714 71405	.05524 91742 60658
94	.39798 27114 51730	.05532 87710 79016
0.0695	0.39797 99474 71397	0.05540 83673 44974
96	.39797 71795 30488	.05548 79630 57741
97	.39797 44076 29086	.05556 75582 16523
98	.39797 16317 67273	.05564 71528 20528
99	.39796 88519 45134	.05572 67468 68965
0.0700	0.39796 60681 62751	0.05580 63403 61042

x	$\dfrac{1}{\sqrt{2\pi}}\,e^{-\frac{x^2}{2}}$	$\dfrac{1}{\sqrt{2\pi}}\displaystyle\int_{-x}^{x} e^{-\frac{\alpha^2}{2}}\,d\alpha$
0.0700	0.39796 60681 62751	0.05580 63403 61042
01	.39796 32804 20208	.05588 59332 95967
02	.39796 04887 17587	.05596 55256 72946
03	.39795 76930 54974	.05604 51174 91190
04	.39795 48934 32451	.05612 47087 49904
0.0705	0.39795 20898 50102	0.05620 42994 48299
06	.39794 92823 08012	.05628 38895 85580
07	.39794 64708 06264	.05636 34791 60958
08	.39794 36553 44943	.05644 30681 73639
09	.39794 08359 24133	.05652 26566 22832
0.0710	0.39793 80125 43918	0.05660 22445 07745
11	.39793 51852 04383	.05668 18318 27585
12	.39793 23539 05612	.05676 14185 81562
13	.39792 95186 47691	.05684 10047 68884
14	.39792 66794 30705	.05692 05903 88758
0.0715	0.39792 38362 54737	0.05700 01754 40392
16	.39792 09891 19875	.05707 97599 22995
17	.39791 81380 26202	.05715 93438 35776
18	.39791 52829 73804	.05723 89271 77942
19	.39791 24239 62767	.05731 85099 48702
0.0720	0.39790 95609 93176	0.05739 80921 47263
21	.39790 66940 65117	.05747 76737 72835
22	.39790 38231 78676	.05755 72548 24625
23	.39790 09483 33939	.05763 68353 01843
24	.39789 80695 30992	.05771 64152 03695
0.0725	0.39789 51867 69921	0.05779 59945 29391
26	.39789 23000 50813	.05787 55732 78139
27	.39788 94093 73753	.05795 51514 49148
28	.39788 65147 38829	.05803 47290 41625
29	.39788 36161 46127	.05811 43060 54779
0.0730	0.39788 07135 95735	0.05819 38824 87819
31	.39787 78070 87738	.05827 34583 39954
32	.39787 48966 22224	.05835 30336 10391
33	.39787 19821 99280	.05843 26082 98339
34	.39786 90638 18994	.05851 21824 03007
0.0735	0.39786 61414 81453	0.05859 17559 23603
36	.39786 32151 86744	.05867 13288 59335
37	.39786 02849 34954	.05875 09012 09413
38	.39785 73507 26173	.05883 04729 73046
39	.39785 44125 60487	.05891 00441 49440
0.0740	0.39785 14704 37985	0.05898 96147 37806
41	.39784 85243 58754	.05906 91847 37352
42	.39784 55743 22883	.05914 87541 47286
43	.39784 26203 30460	.05922 83229 66817
44	.39783 96623 81574	.05930 78911 95154
0.0745	0.39783 67004 76314	0.05938 74588 31506
46	.39783 37346 14767	.05946 70258 75081
47	.39783 07647 97023	.05954 65923 25088
48	.39782 77910 23171	.05962 61581 80736
49	.39782 48132 93299	.05970 57234 41234
0.0750	0.39782 18316 07497	0.05978 52881 05790

x	$\dfrac{1}{\sqrt{2\pi}}\,e^{-\frac{x^2}{2}}$	$\dfrac{1}{\sqrt{2\pi}}\displaystyle\int_{-x}^{x} e^{-\frac{\alpha^2}{2}}\,d\alpha$
0.0750	0.39782 18316 07497	0.05978 52881 05790
51	.39781 88459 65855	.05986 48521 73613
52	.39781 58563 68461	.05994 44156 43912
53	.39781 28628 15405	.06002 39785 15896
54	.39780 98653 06776	.06010 35407 88775
0.0755	0.39780 68638 42666	0.06018 31024 61755
56	.39780 38584 23162	.06026 26635 34048
57	.39780 08490 48356	.06034 22240 04861
58	.39779 78357 18338	.06042 17838 73404
59	.39779 48184 33197	.06050 13431 38885
0.0760	0.39779 17971 93024	0.06058 09018 00513
61	.39778 87719 97910	.06066 04598 57498
62	.39778 57428 47945	.06074 00173 09049
63	.39778 27097 43219	.06081 95741 54374
64	.39777 96726 83824	.06089 91303 92682
0.0765	0.39777 66316 69851	0.06097 86860 23184
66	.39777 35867 01390	.06105 82410 45087
67	.39777 05377 78533	.06113 77954 57601
68	.39776 74849 01371	.06121 73492 59935
69	.39776 44280 69995	.06129 69024 51298
0.0770	0.39776 13672 84498	0.06137 64550 30899
71	.39775 83025 44970	.06145 60069 97948
72	.39775 52338 51503	.06153 55583 51653
73	.39775 21612 04190	.06161 51090 91225
74	.39774 90846 03122	.06169 46592 15871
0.0775	0.39774 60040 48391	0.06177 42087 24802
76	.39774 29195 40090	.06185 37576 17227
77	.39773 98310 78310	.06193 33058 92355
78	.39773 67386 63145	.06201 28535 49395
79	.39773 36422 94688	.06209 24005 87557
0.0780	0.39773 05419 73029	0.06217 19470 06049
81	.39772 74376 98264	.06225 14928 04082
82	.39772 43294 70484	.06233 10379 80865
83	.39772 12172 89782	.06241 05825 35607
84	.39771 81011 56252	.06249 01264 67517
0.0785	0.39771 49810 69987	0.06256 96697 75806
86	.39771 18570 31080	.06264 92124 59682
87	.39770 87290 39626	.06272 87545 18355
88	.39770 55970 95716	.06280 82959 51034
89	.39770 24611 99447	.06288 78367 56930
0.0790	0.39769 93213 50910	0.06296 73769 35251
91	.39769 61775 50201	.06304 69164 85207
92	.39769 30297 97413	.06312 64554 06007
93	.39768 98780 92640	.06320 59936 96862
94	.39768 67224 35977	.06328 55313 56981
0.0795	0.39768 35628 27519	0.06336 50683 85573
96	.39768 03992 67360	.06344 46047 81848
97	.39767 72317 55595	.06352 41405 45016
98	.39767 40602 92318	.06360 36756 74287
99	.39767 08848 77624	.06368 32101 68870
0.0800	0.39766 77055 11609	0.06376 27440 27975

x	$\dfrac{1}{\sqrt{2\pi}}\,e^{-\frac{x^2}{2}}$	$\dfrac{1}{\sqrt{2\pi}}\displaystyle\int_{-x}^{x} e^{-\frac{\alpha^2}{2}}\,d\alpha$
0.0800	0.39766 77055 11609	0.06376 27440 27975
01	.39766 45221 94367	.06384 22772 50811
02	.39766 13349 25995	.06392 18098 36589
03	.39765 81437 06587	.06400 13417 84518
04	.39765 49485 36239	.06408 08730 93808
0.0805	0.39765 17494 15047	0.06416 04037 63669
06	.39764 85463 43105	.06423 99337 93311
07	.39764 53393 20511	.06431 94631 81943
08	.39764 21283 47361	.06439 89919 28776
09	.39763 89134 23749	.06447 85200 33019
0.0810	0.39763 56945 49774	0.06455 80474 93882
11	.39763 24717 25530	.06463 75743 10575
12	.39762 92449 51114	.06471 71004 82309
13	.39762 60142 26624	.06479 66260 08292
14	.39762 27795 52155	.06487 61508 87736
0.0815	0.39761 95409 27805	0.06495 56751 19850
16	.39761 62983 53671	.06503 51987 03844
17	.39761 30518 29849	.06511 47216 38928
18	.39760 98013 56436	.06519 42439 24313
19	.39760 65469 33531	.06527 37655 59207
0.0820	0.39760 32885 61230	0.06535 32865 42823
21	.39760 00262 39631	.06543 28068 74369
22	.39759 67599 68832	.06551 23265 53055
23	.39759 34897 48930	.06559 18455 78093
24	.39759 02155 80023	.06567 13639 48692
0.0825	0.39758 69374 62210	0.06575 08816 64062
26	.39758 36553 95588	.06583 03987 23413
27	.39758 03693 80255	.06590 99151 25957
28	.39757 70794 16311	.06598 94308 70902
29	.39757 37855 03853	.06606 89459 57460
0.0830	0.39757 04876 42980	0.06614 84603 84840
31	.39756 71858 33791	.06622 79741 52254
32	.39756 38800 76384	.06630 74872 58911
33	.39756 05703 70859	.06638 69997 04021
34	.39755 72567 17315	.06646 65114 86796
0.0835	0.39755 39391 15850	0.06654 60226 06445
36	.39755 06175 66565	.06662 55330 62179
37	.39754 72920 69558	.06670 50428 53208
38	.39754 39626 24929	.06678 45519 78744
39	.39754 06292 32778	.06686 40604 37995
0.0840	0.39753 72918 93204	0.06694 35682 30174
41	.39753 39506 06307	.06702 30753 54489
42	.39753 06053 72188	.06710 25818 10153
43	.39752 72561 90946	.06718 20875 96375
44	.39752 39030 62682	.06726 15927 12366
0.0845	0.39752 05459 87496	0.06734 10971 57337
46	.39751 71849 65488	.06742 06009 30498
47	.39751 38199 96760	.06750 01040 31060
48	.39751 04510 81411	.06757 96064 58234
49	.39750 70782 19543	.06765 91082 11230
0.0850	0.39750 37014 11257	0.06773 86092 89258

x	$\dfrac{1}{\sqrt{2\pi}} e^{-\frac{x^2}{2}}$	$\dfrac{1}{\sqrt{2\pi}} \displaystyle\int_{-x}^{x} e^{-\frac{\alpha^2}{2}} \, d\alpha$
0.0850	0.39750 37014 11257	0.06773 86092 89258
51	.39750 03206 56653	.06781 81096 91531
52	.39749 69359 55833	.06789 76094 17258
53	.39749 35473 08898	.06797 71084 65650
54	.39749 01547 15949	.06805 66068 35918
0.0855	0.39748 67581 77089	0.06813 61045 27274
56	.39748 33576 92419	.06821 56015 38926
57	.39747 99532 62039	.06829 50978 70087
58	.39747 65448 86054	.06837 45935 19968
59	.39747 31325 64563	.06845 40884 87779
0.0860	0.39746 97162 97670	0.06853 35827 72731
61	.39746 62960 85477	.06861 30763 74035
62	.39746 28719 28086	.06869 25692 90902
63	.39745 94438 25599	.06877 20615 22543
64	.39745 60117 78120	.06885 15530 68169
0.0865	0.39745 25757 85750	0.06893 10439 26991
66	.39744 91358 48593	.06901 05340 98221
67	.39744 56919 66751	.06909 00235 81068
68	.39744 22441 40328	.06916 95123 74744
69	.39743 87923 69427	.06924 90004 78461
0.0870	0.39743 53366 54151	0.06932 84878 91429
71	.39743 18769 94604	.06940 79746 12860
72	.39742 84133 90889	.06948 74606 41964
73	.39742 49458 43109	.06956 69459 77953
74	.39742 14743 51369	.06964 64306 20038
0.0875	0.39741 79989 15772	0.06972 59145 67431
76	.39741 45195 36423	.06980 53978 19342
77	.39741 10362 13425	.06988 48803 74982
78	.39740 75489 46882	.06996 43622 33564
79	.39740 40577 36900	.07004 38433 94298
0.0880	0.39740 05625 83582	0.07012 33238 56396
81	.39739 70634 87033	.07020 28036 19069
82	.39739 35604 47358	.07028 22826 81528
83	.39739 00534 64662	.07036 17610 42985
84	.39738 65425 39049	.07044 12387 02651
0.0885	0.39738 30276 70625	0.07052 07156 59738
86	.39737 95088 59494	.07060 01919 13456
87	.39737 59861 05763	.07067 96674 63019
88	.39737 24594 09536	.07075 91423 07636
89	.39736 89287 70919	.07083 86164 46520
0.0890	0.39736 53941 90018	0.07091 80898 78881
91	.39736 18556 66938	.07099 75626 03933
92	.39735 83132 01785	.07107 70346 20885
93	.39735 47667 94666	.07115 65059 28951
94	.39735 12164 45685	.07123 59765 27340
0.0895	0.39734 76621 54951	0.07131 54464 15266
96	.39734 41039 22568	.07139 49155 91940
97	.39734 05417 48644	.07147 43840 56572
98	.39733 69756 33285	.07155 38518 08376
99	.39733 34055 76597	.07163 33188 46563
0.0900	0.39732 98315 78688	0.07171 27851 70344

x	$\dfrac{1}{\sqrt{2\pi}}\,e^{-\frac{x^2}{2}}$	$\dfrac{1}{\sqrt{2\pi}}\displaystyle\int_{-x}^{x} e^{-\frac{\alpha^2}{2}}\,d\alpha$
0.0900	0.39732 98315 78688	0.07171 27851 70344
01	.39732 62536 39665	.07179 22507 78932
02	.39732 26717 59633	.07187 17156 71537
03	.39731 90859 38702	.07195 11798 47373
04	.39731 54961 76977	.07203 06433 05650
0.0905	0.39731 19024 74567	0.07211 01060 45581
06	.39730 83048 31578	.07218 95680 66377
07	.39730 47032 48119	.07226 90293 67251
08	.39730 10977 24297	.07234 84899 47414
09	.39729 74882 60220	.07242 79498 06078
0.0910	0.39729 38748 55997	0.07250 74089 42455
11	.39729 02575 11734	.07258 68673 55758
12	.39728 66362 27541	.07266 63250 45197
13	.39728 30110 03525	.07274 57820 09986
14	.39727 93818 39796	.07282 52382 49336
0.0915	0.39727 57487 36462	0.07290 46937 62459
16	.39727 21116 93631	.07298 41485 48568
17	.39726 84707 11412	.07306 36026 06874
18	.39726 48257 89914	.07314 30559 36590
19	.39726 11769 29247	.07322 25085 36927
0.0920	0.39725 75241 29518	0.07330 19604 07099
21	.39725 38673 90839	.07338 14115 46317
22	.39725 02067 13318	.07346 08619 53793
23	.39724 65420 97064	.07354 03116 28739
24	.39724 28735 42187	.07361 97605 70369
0.0925	0.39723 92010 48797	0.07369 92087 77894
26	.39723 55246 17004	.07377 86562 50526
27	.39723 18442 46918	.07385 81029 87478
28	.39722 81599 38649	.07393 75489 87962
29	.39722 44716 92306	.07401 69942 51191
0 0930	0.39722 07795 08001	0.07409 64387 76377
31	.39721 70833 85844	.07417 58825 62732
32	.39721 33833 25946	.07425 53256 09468
33	.39720 96793 28416	.07433 47679 15799
34	.39720 59713 93366	.07441 42094 80937
0.0935	0.39720 22595 20907	0.07449 36503 04094
36	.39719 85437 11150	.07457 30903 84483
37	.39719 48239 64206	.07465 25297 21316
38	.39719 11002 90186	.07473 19683 13806
39	.39718 73726 59202	.07481 14061 61166
0.0940	0.39718 36411 01365	0.07489 08432 62608
41	.39717 99056 06787	.07497 02796 17344
42	.39717 61661 75579	.07504 97152 24588
43	.39717 24228 07853	.07512 91500 83552
44	.39716 86755 03722	.07520 85841 93449
0.0945	0.39716 49242 63297	0.07528 80175 53491
46	.39716 11690 86691	.07536 74501 62891
47	.39715 74099 74015	.07544 68820 20863
48	.39715 36469 25383	.07552 63131 26619
49	.39714 98799 40907	.07560 57434 79371
0.0950	0.39714 61090 20700	0.07568 51730 78333

x	$\dfrac{1}{\sqrt{2\pi}} e^{-\frac{x^2}{2}}$	$\dfrac{1}{\sqrt{2\pi}} \displaystyle\int_{-x}^{x} e^{-\frac{\alpha^2}{2}} \, d\alpha$
0.0950	0.39714 61090 20700	0.07568 51730 78333
51	.39714 23341 64873	.07576 46019 22717
52	.39713 85553 73541	.07584 40300 11736
53	.39713 47726 46817	.07592 34573 44604
54	.39713 09859 84813	.07600 28839 20533
0.0955	0.39712 71953 87642	0.07608 23097 38735
56	.39712 34008 55418	.07616 17347 98425
57	.39711 96023 88256	.07624 11590 98815
58	.39711 57999 86267	.07632 05826 39118
59	.39711 19936 49566	.07640 00054 18547
0.0960	0.39710 81833 78266	0.07647 94274 36316
61	.39710 43691 72483	.07655 88486 91636
62	.39710 05510 32329	.07663 82691 83723
63	.39709 67289 57919	.07671 76889 11787
64	.39709 29029 49367	.07679 71078 75043
0.0965	0.39708 90730 06788	0.07687 65260 72705
66	.39708 52391 30297	.07695 59435 03984
67	.39708 14013 20007	.07703 53601 68094
68	.39707 75595 76033	.07711 47760 64250
69	.39707 37138 98492	.07719 41911 91663
0.0970	0.39706 98642 87496	0.07727 36055 49547
71	.39706 60107 43163	.07735 30191 37115
72	.39706 21532 65606	.07743 24319 53582
73	.39705 82918 54942	.07751 18439 98159
74	.39705 44265 11285	.07759 12552 70062
0.0975	0.39705 05572 34752	0.07767 06657 68502
76	.39704 66840 25458	.07775 00754 92693
77	.39704 28068 83518	.07782 94844 41850
78	.39703 89258 09050	.07790 88926 15185
79	.39703 50408 02168	.07798 83000 11911
0.0980	0.39703 11518 62990	0.07806 77066 31243
81	.39702 72589 91630	.07814 71124 72394
82	.39702 33621 88207	.07822 65175 34578
83	.39701 94614 52836	.07830 59218 17007
84	.39701 55567 85634	.07838 53253 18897
0.0985	0.39701 16481 86717	0.07846 47280 39460
86	.39700 77356 56203	.07854 41299 77909
87	.39700 38191 94209	.07862 35311 33460
88	.39699 98988 00852	.07870 29315 05325
89	.39699 59744 76248	.07878 23310 92718
0.0990	0.39699 20462 20516	0.07886 17298 94853
91	.39698 81140 33772	.07894 11279 10944
92	.39698 41779 16135	.07902 05251 40205
93	.39698 02378 67721	.07909 99215 81849
94	.39697 62938 88650	.07917 93172 35090
0.0995	0.39697 23459 79038	0.07925 87120 99142
96	.39696 83941 39004	.07933 81061 73219
97	.39696 44383 68666	.07941 74994 56536
98	.39696 04786 68143	.07949 68919 48305
99	.39695 65150 37552	.07957 62836 47741
0.1000	0.39695 25474 77012	0.07965 56745 54058

x	$\frac{1}{\sqrt{2\pi}} e^{-\frac{x^2}{2}}$	$\frac{1}{\sqrt{2\pi}} \int_{-x}^{x} e^{-\frac{\alpha^2}{2}} d\alpha$
0.1000	0.39695 25474 77012	0.07965 56745 54058
01	.39694 85759 86642	.07973 50646 66470
02	.39694 46005 66560	.07981 44539 84191
03	.39694 06212 16886	.07989 38425 06434
04	.39693 66379 37738	.07997 32302 32415
0.1005	0.39693 26507 29236	0.08005 26171 61348
06	.39692 86595 91498	.08013 20032 92445
07	.39692 46645 24645	.08021 13886 24922
08	.39692 06655 28795	.08029 07731 57993
09	.39691 66626 04068	.08037 01568 90872
0.1010	0.39691 26557 50583	0.08044 95398 22773
11	.39690 86449 68461	.08052 89219 52910
12	.39690 46302 57822	.08060 83032 80498
13	.39690 06116 18785	.08068 76838 04751
14	.39689 65890 51471	.08076 70635 24884
0.1015	0.39689 25625 55999	0.08084 64424 40110
16	.39688 85321 32491	.08092 58205 49644
17	.39688 44977 81066	.08100 51978 52701
18	.39688 04595 01846	.08108 45743 48495
19	.39687 64172 94951	.08116 39500 36240
0.1020	0.39687 23711 60502	0.08124 33249 15151
21	.39686 83210 98620	.08132 26989 84443
22	.39686 42671 09426	.08140 20722 43329
23	.39686 02091 93040	.08148 14446 91024
24	.39685 61473 49586	.08156 08163 26744
0.1025	0.39685 20815 79183	0.08164 01871 49703
26	.39684 80118 81954	.08171 95571 59114
27	.39684 39382 58020	.08179 89263 54194
28	.39683 98607 07503	.08187 82947 34156
29	.39683 57792 30525	.08195 76622 98215
0.1030	0.39683 16938 27207	0.08203 70290 45586
31	.39682 76044 97672	.08211 63949 75484
32	.39682 35112 42043	.08219 57600 87123
33	.39681 94140 60441	.08227 51243 79719
34	.39681 53129 52989	.08235 44878 52486
0.1035	0.39681 12079 19810	0.08243 38505 04638
36	.39680 70989 61026	.08251 32123 35392
37	.39680 29860 76761	.08259 25733 43961
38	.39679 88692 67136	.08267 19335 29561
39	.39679 47485 32276	.08275 12928 91406
0.1040	0.39679 06238 72303	0.08283 06514 28712
41	.39678 64952 87340	.08291 00091 40694
42	.39678 23627 77512	.08298 93660 26566
43	.39677 82263 42941	.08306 87220 85543
44	.39677 40859 83752	.08314 80773 16841
0.1045	0.39676 99417 00067	0.08322 74317 19675
46	.39676 57934 92011	.08330 67852 93259
47	.39676 16413 59709	.08338 61380 36810
48	.39675 74853 03283	.08346 54899 49542
49	.39675 33253 22858	.08354 48410 30670
0.1050	0.39674 91614 18559	0.08362 41912 79409

x	$\dfrac{1}{\sqrt{2\pi}} e^{-\frac{x^2}{2}}$	$\dfrac{1}{\sqrt{2\pi}} \displaystyle\int_{-x}^{x} e^{-\frac{\alpha^2}{2}} d\alpha$
0.1050	0.39674 91614 18559	0.08362 41912 79409
51	.39674 49935 90510	.08370 35406 94976
52	.39674 08218 38835	.08378 28892 76584
53	.39673 66461 63660	.08386 22370 23450
54	.39673 24665 65109	.08394 15839 34788
0.1055	0.39672 82830 43306	0.08402 09300 09814
56	.39672 40955 98378	.08410 02752 47744
57	.39671 99042 30449	.08417 96196 47792
58	.39671 57089 39645	.08425 89632 09174
59	.39671 15097 26090	.08433 83059 31106
0.1060	0.39670 73065 89910	0.08441 76478 12803
61	.39670 30995 31232	.08449 69888 53481
62	.39669 88885 50180	.08457 63290 52354
63	.39669 46736 46881	.08465 56684 08639
64	.39669 04548 21461	.08473 50069 21551
0.1065	0.39668 62320 74045	0.08481 43445 90306
66	.39668 20054 04759	.08489 36814 14120
67	.39667 77748 13731	.08497 30173 92207
68	.39667 35403 01087	.08505 23525 23784
69	.39666 93018 66953	.08513 16868 08066
0.1070	0.39666 50595 11455	0.08521 10202 44269
71	.39666 08132 34722	.08529 03528 31609
72	.39665 65630 36878	.08536 96845 69301
73	.39665 23089 18052	.08544 90154 56562
74	.39664 80508 78371	.08552 83454 92607
0.1075	0.39664 37889 17962	0.08560 76746 76652
76	.39663 95230 36952	.08568 70030 07913
77	.39663 52532 35469	.08576 63304 85606
78	.39663 09795 13640	.08584 56571 08946
79	.39662 67018 71593	.08592 49828 77150
0.1080	0.39662 24203 09456	0.08600 43077 89433
81	.39661 81348 27357	.08608 36318 45012
82	.39661 38454 25424	.08616 29550 43103
83	.39660 95521 03785	.08624 22773 82921
84	.39660 52548 62568	.08632 15988 63683
0.1085	0.39660 09537 01902	0.08640 09194 84605
86	.39659 66486 21916	.08648 02392 44903
87	.39659 23396 22737	.08655 95581 43792
88	.39658 80267 04495	.08663 88761 80490
89	.39658 37098 67319	.08671 81933 54213
0.1090	0.39657 93891 11337	0.08679 75096 64176
91	.39657 50644 36679	.08687 68251 09596
92	.39657 07358 43474	.08695 61396 89690
93	.39656 64033 31852	.08703 54534 03672
94	.39656 20669 01941	.08711 47662 50761
0.1095	0.39655 77265 53871	0.08719 40782 30172
96	.39655 33822 87772	.08727 33893 41121
97	.39654 90341 03775	.08735 26995 82826
98	.39654 46820 02007	.08743 20089 54502
99	.39654 03259 82601	.08751 13174 55365
0.1100	0.39653 59660 45686	0.08759 06250 84634

x	$\dfrac{1}{\sqrt{2\pi}}\, e^{-\frac{x^2}{2}}$	$\dfrac{1}{\sqrt{2\pi}} \displaystyle\int_{-x}^{x} e^{-\frac{\alpha^2}{2}}\, d\alpha$
0.1100	0.39653 59660 45686	0.08759 06250 84634
01	.39653 16021 91392	.08766 99318 41523
02	.39652 72344 19849	.08774 92377 25249
03	.39652 28627 31188	.08782 85427 35029
04	.39651 84871 25541	.08790 78468 70080
0.1105	0.39651 41076 03036	0.08798 71501 29618
06	.39650 97241 63806	.08806 64525 12860
07	.39650 53368 07982	.08814 57540 19023
08	.39650 09455 35693	.08822 50546 47323
09	.39649 65503 47072	.08830 43543 96976
0.1110	0.39649 21512 42250	0.08838 36532 67200
11	.39648 77482 21358	.08846 29512 57212
12	.39648 33412 84529	.08854 22483 66228
13	.39647 89304 31892	.08862 15445 93465
14	.39647 45156 63581	.08870 08399 38139
0.1115	0.39647 00969 79727	0.08878 01343 99469
16	.39646 56743 80462	.08885 94279 76670
17	.39646 12478 65919	.08893 87206 68960
18	.39645 68174 36229	.08901 80124 75556
19	.39645 23830 91525	.08909 73033 95674
0.1120	0.39644 79448 31940	0.08917 65934 28531
21	.39644 35026 57605	.08925 58825 73345
22	.39643 90565 68655	.08933 51708 29333
23	.39643 46065 65220	.08941 44581 95712
24	.39643 01526 47435	.08949 37446 71698
0.1125	0.39642 56948 15433	0.08957 30302 56510
26	.39642 12330 69346	.08965 23149 49364
27	.39641 67674 09309	.08973 15987 49477
28	.39641 22978 35454	.08981 08816 56067
29	.39640 78243 47914	.08989 01636 68350
0.1130	0.39640 33469 46824	0.08996 94447 85545
31	.39639 88656 32318	.09004 87250 06868
32	.39639 43804 04528	.09012 80043 31537
33	.39638 98912 63590	.09020 72827 58769
34	.39638 53982 09637	.09028 65602 87781
0.1135	0.39638 09012 42803	0.09036 58369 17792
36	.39637 64003 63224	.09044 51126 48018
37	.39637 18955 71032	.09052 43874 77676
38	.39636 73868 66363	.09060 36614 05985
39	.39636 28742 49352	.09068 29344 32162
0.1140	0.39635 83577 20133	0.09076 22065 55424
41	.39635 38372 78841	.09084 14777 74989
42	.39634 93129 25611	.09092 07480 90075
43	.39634 47846 60579	.09100 00174 99899
44	.39634 02524 83879	.09107 92860 03678
0.1145	0.39633 57163 95647	0.09115 85536 00632
46	.39633 11763 96019	.09123 78202 89976
47	.39632 66324 85129	.09131 70860 70929
48	.39632 20846 63115	.09139 63509 42709
49	.39631 75329 30111	.09147 56149 04534
0.1150	0.39631 29772 86253	0.09155 48779 55621

X	$\frac{1}{\sqrt{2\pi}}e^{-\frac{x^2}{2}}$	$\frac{1}{\sqrt{2\pi}}\int_{-x}^{x}e^{-\frac{\alpha^2}{2}}d\alpha$
0.1150	0.39631 29772 86253	0.09155 48779 55621
51	.39630 84177 31678	.09163 41400 95187
52	.39630 38542 66522	.09171 34013 22452
53	.39629 92868 90922	.09179 26616 36633
54	.39629 47156 05012	.09187 19210 36948
0.1155	0.39629 01404 08931	0.09195 11795 22615
56	.39628 55613 02814	.09203 04370 92851
57	.39628 09782 86799	.09210 96937 46875
58	.39627 63913 61022	.09218 89494 83905
59	.39627 18005 25621	.09226 82043 03159
0.1160	0.39626 72057 80732	0.09234 74582 03855
61	.39626 26071 26493	.09242 67111 85211
62	.39625 80045 63040	.09250 59632 46445
63	.39625 33980 90512	.09258 52143 86775
64	.39624 87877 09047	.09266 44646 05420
0.1165	0.39624 41734 18781	0.09274 37139 01598
66	.39623 95552 19852	.09282 29622 74527
67	.39623 49331 12399	.09290 22097 23426
68	.39623 03070 96559	.09298 14562 47512
69	.39622 56771 72471	.09306 07018 46004
0.1170	0.39622 10433 40273	0.09313 99465 18120
71	.39621 64056 00103	.09321 91902 63079
72	.39621 17639 52100	.09329 84330 80100
73	.39620 71183 96402	.09337 76749 68400
74	.39620 24689 33149	.09345 69159 27198
0.1175	0.39619 78155 62478	0.09353 61559 55712
76	.39619 31582 84529	.09361 53950 53162
77	.39618 84970 99442	.09369 46332 18766
78	.39618 38320 07354	.09377 38704 51742
79	.39617 91630 08406	.09385 31067 51308
0.1180	0.39617 44901 02737	0.09393 23421 16684
81	.39616 98132 90486	.09401 15765 47089
82	.39616 51325 71793	.09409 08100 41740
83	.39616 04479 46799	.09417 00425 99857
84	.39615 57594 15642	.09424 92742 20658
0.1185	0.39615 10669 78462	0.09432 85049 03363
86	.39614 63706 35401	.09440 77346 47189
87	.39614 16703 86598	.09448 69634 51357
88	.39613 69662 32193	.09456 61913 15084
89	.39613 22581 72327	.09464 54182 37589
0.1190	0.39612 75462 07140	0.09472 46442 18092
91	.39612 28303 36774	.09480 38692 55812
92	.39611 81105 61369	.09488 30933 49967
93	.39611 33868 81065	.09496 23164 99776
94	.39610 86592 96005	.09504 15387 04459
0.1195	0.39610 39278 06328	0.09512 07599 63234
96	.39609 91924 12177	.09519 99802 75321
97	.39609 44531 13693	.09527 91996 39939
98	.39608 97099 11017	.09535 84180 56306
99	.39608 49628 04291	.09543 76355 23643
0.1200	0.39608 02117 93656	0.09551 68520 41168

x	$\frac{1}{\sqrt{2\pi}} e^{-\frac{x^2}{2}}$	$\frac{1}{\sqrt{2\pi}} \int_{-x}^{x} e^{-\frac{\alpha^2}{2}} d\alpha$
0.1200	0.39608 02117 93656	0.09551 68520 41168
01	.39607 54568 79255	.09559 60676 08100
02	.39607 06980 61229	.09567 52822 23659
03	.39606 59353 39721	.09575 44958 87064
04	.39606 11687 14872	.09583 37085 97535
0.1205	0.39605 63981 86826	0.09591 29203 54290
06	.39605 16237 55723	.09599 21311 56549
07	.39604 68454 21708	.09607 13410 03532
08	.39604 20631 84923	.09615 05498 94458
09	.39603 72770 45509	.09622 97578 28546
0.1210	0.39603 24870 03611	0.09630 89648 05016
11	.39602 76930 59372	.09638 81708 23087
12	.39602 28952 12933	.09646 73758 81979
13	.39601 80934 64439	.09654 65799 80912
14	.39601 32878 14033	.09662 57831 19105
0.1215	0.39600 84782 61859	0.09670 49852 95778
16	.39600 36648 08060	.09678 41865 10150
17	.39599 88474 52779	.09686 33867 61441
18	.39599 40261 96161	.09694 25860 48871
19	.39598 92010 38349	.09702 17843 71659
0.1220	0.39598 43719 79487	0.09710 09817 29026
21	.39597 95390 19720	.09718 01781 20191
22	.39597 47021 59192	.09725 93735 44374
23	.39596 98613 98048	.09733 85680 00795
24	.39596 50167 36431	.09741 77614 88673
0.1225	0.39596 01681 74486	0.09749 69540 07229
26	.39595 53157 12359	.09757 61455 55683
27	.39595 04593 50193	.09765 53361 33254
28	.39594 55990 88135	.09773 45257 39163
29	.39594 07349 26328	.09781 37143 72629
0.1230	0.39593 58668 64919	0.09789 29020 32874
31	.39593 09949 04052	.09797 20887 19115
32	.39592 61190 43873	.09805 12744 30575
33	.39592 12392 84527	.09813 04591 66473
34	.39591 63556 26160	.09820 96429 26029
0.1235	0.39591 14680 68919	0.09828 88257 08464
36	.39590 65766 12948	.09836 80075 12997
37	.39590 16812 58394	.09844 71883 38849
38	.39589 67820 05402	.09852 63681 85240
39	.39589 18788 54120	.09860 55470 51391
0.1240	0.39588 69718 04693	0.09868 47249 36522
41	.39588 20608 57268	.09876 39018 39853
42	.39587 71460 11991	.09884 30777 60605
43	.39587 22272 69010	.09892 22526 97998
44	.39586 73046 28470	.09900 14266 51253
0.1245	0.39586 23780 90520	0.09908 05996 19590
46	.39585 74476 55305	.09915 97716 02229
47	.39585 25133 22973	.09923 89425 98392
48	.39584 75750 93672	.09931 81126 07299
49	.39584 26329 67548	.09939 72816 28170
0.1250	0.39583 76869 44749	0.09947 64496 60226

x	$\frac{1}{\sqrt{2\pi}} e^{-\frac{x^2}{2}}$	$\frac{1}{\sqrt{2\pi}} \int_{-x}^{x} e^{-\frac{\alpha^2}{2}} d\alpha$
0.1250	0.39583 76869 44749	0.09947 64496 60226
51	.39583 27370 25424	.09955 56167 02688
52	.39582 77832 09718	.09963 47827 54776
53	.39582 28254 97781	.09971 39478 15712
54	.39581 78638 89761	.09979 31118 84716
0.1255	0.39581 28983 85804	0.09987 22749 61008
56	.39580 79289 86061	.09995 14370 43810
57	.39580 29556 90678	.10003 05981 32343
58	.39579 79784 99804	.10010 97582 25827
59	.39579 29974 13588	.10018 89173 23483
0.1260	0.39578 80124 32179	0.10026 80754 24533
61	.39578 30235 55725	.10034 72325 28196
62	.39577 80307 84374	.10042 63886 33695
63	.39577 30341 18277	.10050 55437 40250
64	.39576 80335 57582	.10058 46978 47083
0.1265	0.39576 30291 02439	0.10066 38509 53414
66	.39575 80207 52996	.10074 30030 58464
67	.39575 30085 09403	.10082 21541 61455
68	.39574 79923 71810	.10090 13042 61608
69	.39574 29723 40366	.10098 04533 58144
0.1270	0.39573 79484 15222	0.10105 96014 50285
71	.39573 29205 96527	.10113 87485 37251
72	.39572 78888 84430	.10121 78946 18264
73	.39572 28532 79083	.10129 70396 92545
74	.39571 78137 80636	.10137 61837 59316
0.1275	0.39571 27703 89238	0.10145 53268 17798
76	.39570 77231 05041	.10153 44688 67212
77	.39570 26719 28195	.10161 36099 06780
78	.39569 76168 58850	.10169 27499 35724
79	.39569 25578 97158	.10177 18889 53264
0.1280	0.39568 74950 43270	0.10185 10269 58623
81	.39568 24282 97336	.10193 01639 51022
82	.39567 73576 59507	.10200 92999 29683
83	.39567 22831 29936	.10208 84348 93827
84	.39566 72047 08773	.10216 75688 42675
0.1285	0.39566 21223 96169	0.10224 67017 75451
86	.39565 70361 92278	.10232 58336 91374
87	.39565 19460 97249	.10240 49645 89668
88	.39564 68521 11236	.10248 40944 69554
89	.39564 17542 34389	.10256 32233 30253
0.1290	0.39563 66524 66862	0.10264 23511 70988
91	.39563 15468 08806	.10272 14779 90981
92	.39562 64372 60374	.10280 06037 89452
93	.39562 13238 21719	.10287 97285 65626
94	.39561 62064 92991	.10295 88523 18722
0.1295	0.39561 10852 74345	0.10303 79750 47963
96	.39560 59601 65934	.10311 70967 52572
97	.39560 08311 67909	.10319 62174 31770
98	.39559 56982 80424	.10327 53370 84780
99	.39559 05615 03633	.10335 44557 10823
0.1300	0.39558 54208 37687	0.10343 35733 09122

x	$\dfrac{1}{\sqrt{2\pi}}\,e^{-\frac{x^2}{2}}$	$\dfrac{1}{\sqrt{2\pi}}\displaystyle\int_{-x}^{x} e^{-\frac{\alpha^2}{2}}\,d\alpha$
0.1300	0.39558 54208 37687	0.10343 35733 09122
01	.39558 02762 82742	.10351 26898 78899
02	.39557 51278 38950	.10359 18054 19376
03	.39556 99755 06464	.10367 09199 29775
04	.39556 48192 85439	.10375 00334 09319
0.1305	0.39555 96591 76029	0.10382 91458 57230
06	.39555 44951 78386	.10390 82572 72731
07	.39554 93272 92666	.10398 73676 55043
08	.39554 41555 19022	.10406 64770 03389
09	.39553 89798 57609	.10414 55853 16991
0.1310	0.39553 38003 08581	0.10422 46925 95072
11	.39552 86168 72092	.10430 37988 36855
12	.39552 34295 48298	.10438 29040 41562
13	.39551 82383 37353	.10446 20082 08415
14	.39551 30432 39411	.10454 11113 36638
0.1315	0.39550 78442 54628	0.10462 02134 25452
16	.39550 26413 83159	.10469 93144 74081
17	.39549 74346 25158	.10477 84144 81746
18	.39549 22239 80782	.10485 75134 47672
19	.39548 70094 50186	.10493 66113 71079
0.1320	0.39548 17910 33525	0.10501 57082 51193
21	.39547 65687 30955	.10509 48040 87234
22	.39547 13425 42631	.10517 38988 78426
23	.39546 61124 68710	.10525 29926 23992
24	.39546 08785 09347	.10533 20853 23154
0.1325	0.39545 56406 64699	0.10541 11769 75137
26	.39545 03989 34922	.10549 02675 79161
27	.39544 51533 20171	.10556 93571 34452
28	.39543 99038 20605	.10564 84456 40230
29	.39543 46504 36378	.10572 75330 95721
0.1330	0.39542 93931 67648	0.10580 66195 00146
31	.39542 41320 14572	.10588 57048 52729
32	.39541 88669 77306	.10596 47891 52693
33	.39541 35980 56008	.10604 38723 99261
34	.39540 83252 50835	.10612 29545 91656
0.1335	0.39540 30485 61943	0.10620 20357 29102
36	.39539 77679 89491	.10628 11158 10822
37	.39539 24835 33635	.10636 01948 36039
38	.39538 71951 94533	.10643 92728 03977
39	.39538 19029 72344	.10651 83497 13858
0.1340	0.39537 66068 67224	0.10659 74255 64907
41	.39537 13068 79333	.10667 65003 56346
42	.39536 60030 08827	.10675 55740 87400
43	.39536 06952 55865	.10683 46467 57291
44	.39535 53836 20605	.10691 37183 65243
0.1345	0.39535 00681 03206	0.10699 27889 10480
46	.39534 47487 03826	.10707 18583 92226
47	.39533 94254 22624	.10715 09268 09703
48	.39533 40982 59758	.10722 99941 62136
49	.39532 87672 15387	.10730 90604 48748
0.1350	0.39532 34322 89671	0.10738 81256 68763

x	$\dfrac{1}{\sqrt{2\pi}}e^{-\frac{x^2}{2}}$	$\dfrac{1}{\sqrt{2\pi}}\displaystyle\int_{-x}^{x}e^{-\frac{\alpha^2}{2}}\,d\alpha$
0.1350	0.39532 34322 89671	0.10738 81256 68763
51	.39531 80934 82769	.10746 71898 21405
52	.39531 27507 94838	.10754 62529 05898
53	.39530 74042 26040	.10762 53149 21465
54	.39530 20537 76533	.10770 43758 67329
0.1355	0.39529 66994 46477	0.10778 34357 42716
56	.39529 13412 36032	.10786 24945 46849
57	.39528 59791 45356	.10794 15522 78952
58	.39528 06131 74611	.10802 06089 38249
59	.39527 52433 23956	.10809 96645 23963
0.1360	0.39526 98695 93551	0.10817 87190 35320
61	.39526 44919 83556	.10825 77724 71542
62	.39525 91104 94132	.10833 68248 31855
63	.39525 37251 25440	.10841 58761 15481
64	.39524 83358 77639	.10849 49263 21646
0.1365	0.39524 29427 50891	0.10857 39754 49574
66	.39523 75457 45355	.10865 30234 98488
67	.39523 21448 61194	.10873 20704 67613
68	.39522 67400 98569	.10881 11163 56174
69	.39522 13314 57639	.10889 01611 63394
0.1370	0.39521 59189 38567	0.10896 92048 88498
71	.39521 05025 41514	.10904 82475 30711
72	.39520 50822 66641	.10912 72890 89256
73	.39519 96581 14110	.10920 63295 63359
74	.39519 42300 84083	.10928 53689 52244
0.1375	0.39518 87981 76722	0.10936 44072 55134
76	.39518 33623 92188	.10944 34444 71256
77	.39517 79227 30643	.10952 24805 99833
78	.39517 24791 92250	.10960 15156 40090
79	.39516 70317 77170	.10968 05495 91251
0.1380	0.39516 15804 85567	0.10975 95824 52542
81	.39515 61253 17603	.10983 86142 23187
82	.39515 06662 73440	.10991 76449 02411
83	.39514 52033 53242	.10999 66744 89438
84	.39513 97365 57170	.11007 57029 83494
0.1385	0.39513 42658 85388	0.11015 47303 83802
86	.39512 87913 38059	.11023 37566 89589
87	.39512 33129 15347	.11031 27819 00079
88	.39511 78306 17413	.11039 18060 14497
89	.39511 23444 44423	.11047 08290 32068
0.1390	0.39510 68543 96539	0.11054 98509 52017
91	.39510 13604 73925	.11062 88717 73568
92	.39509 58626 76745	.11070 78914 95948
93	.39509 03610 05163	.11078 69101 18381
94	.39508 48554 59343	.11086 59276 40092
0.1395	0.39507 93460 39448	0.11094 49440 60306
96	.39507 38327 45643	.11102 39593 78249
97	.39506 83155 78092	.11110 29735 93146
98	.39506 27945 36960	.11118 19867 04222
99	.39505 72696 22412	.11126 09987 10703
0.1400	0.39505 17408 34611	0.11134 00096 11813

x	$\frac{1}{\sqrt{2\pi}} e^{-\frac{x^2}{2}}$	$\frac{1}{\sqrt{2\pi}} \int_{-x}^{x} e^{-\frac{\alpha^2}{2}} d\alpha$
0.1400	0.39505 17408 34611	0.11134 00096 11813
01	.39504 62081 73723	.11141 90194 06778
02	.39504 06716 39913	.11149 80280 94824
03	.39503 51312 33346	.11157 70356 75176
04	.39502 95869 54186	.11165 60421 47059
0.1405	0.39502 40388 02599	0.11173 50475 09700
06	.39501 84867 78751	.11181 40517 62322
07	.39501 29308 82806	.11189 30549 04153
08	.39500 73711 14931	.11197 20569 34417
09	.39500 18074 75291	.11205 10578 52341
0.1410	0.39499 62399 64051	0.11213 00576 57149
11	.39499 06685 81379	.11220 90563 48068
12	.39498 50933 27439	.11228 80539 24324
13	.39497 95142 02399	.11236 70503 85141
14	.39497 39312 06423	.11244 60457 29747
0.1415	0.39496 83443 39680	0.11252 50399 57366
16	.39496 27536 02334	.11260 40330 67224
17	.39495 71589 94553	.11268 30250 58549
18	.39495 15605 16504	.11276 20159 30564
19	.39494 59581 68353	.11284 10056 82497
0.1420	0.39494 03519 50267	0.11291 99943 13574
21	.39493 47418 62413	.11299 89818 23019
22	.39492 91279 04959	.11307 79682 10061
23	.39492 35100 78071	.11315 69534 73923
24	.39491 78883 81918	.11323 59376 13834
0.1425	0.39491 22628 16666	0.11331 49206 29018
26	.39490 66333 82483	.11339 39025 18703
27	.39490 10000 79538	.11347 28832 82113
28	.39489 53629 07997	.11355 18629 18476
29	.39488 97218 68029	.11363 08414 27019
0.1430	0.39488 40769 59802	0.11370 98188 06966
31	.39487 84281 83484	.11378 87950 57545
32	.39487 27755 39244	.11386 77701 77981
33	.39486 71190 27249	.11394 67441 67502
34	.39486 14586 47669	.11402 57170 25334
0.1435	0.39485 57944 00671	0.11410 46887 50704
36	.39485 01262 86425	.11418 36593 42837
37	.39484 44543 05100	.11426 26288 00960
38	.39483 87784 56865	.11434 15971 24301
39	.39483 30987 41888	.11442 05643 12085
0.1440	0.39482 74151 60340	0.11449 95303 63540
41	.39482 17277 12388	.11457 84952 77892
42	.39481 60363 98204	.11465 74590 54367
43	.39481 03412 17955	.11473 64216 92193
44	.39480 46421 71813	.11481 53831 90597
0.1445	0.39479 89392 59946	0.11489 43435 48804
46	.39479 32324 82525	.11497 33027 66043
47	.39478 75218 39719	.11505 22608 41540
48	.39478 18073 31699	.11513 12177 74521
49	.39477 60889 58636	.11521 01735 64215
0.1450	0.39477 03667 20698	0.11528 91282 09847

x	$\dfrac{1}{\sqrt{2\pi}}e^{-\frac{x^2}{2}}$	$\dfrac{1}{\sqrt{2\pi}}\displaystyle\int_{-x}^{x}e^{-\frac{\alpha^2}{2}}\,d\alpha$
0.1450	0.39477 03667 20698	0.11528 91282 09847
51	.39476 46406 18057	.11536 80817 10645
52	.39475 89106 50884	.11544 70340 65837
53	.39475 31768 19349	.11552 59852 74648
54	.39474 74391 23623	.11560 49353 36307
0.1455	0.39474 16975 63876	0.11568 38842 50040
56	.39473 59521 40281	.11576 28320 15075
57	.39473 02028 53007	.11584 17786 30638
58	.39472 44497 02227	.11592 07240 95958
59	.39471 86926 88111	.11599 96684 10262
0.1460	0.39471 29318 10831	0.11607 86115 72776
61	.39470 71670 70559	.11615 75535 82729
62	.39470 13984 67467	.11623 64944 39347
63	.39469 56260 01725	.11631 54341 41858
64	.39468 98496 73507	.11639 43726 89490
0.1465	0.39468 40694 82984	0.11647 33100 81470
66	.39467 82854 30329	.11655 22463 17026
67	.39467 24975 15713	.11663 11813 95385
68	.39466 67057 39309	.11671 01153 15774
69	.39466 09101 01290	.11678 90480 77423
0.1470	0.39465 51106 01828	0.11686 79796 79558
71	.39464 93072 41096	.11694 69101 21406
72	.39464 35000 19267	.11702 58394 02197
73	.39463 76889 36513	.11710 47675 21157
74	.39463 18739 93008	.11718 36944 77514
0.1475	0.39462 60551 88925	0.11726 26202 70496
76	.39462 02325 24438	.11734 15448 99332
77	.39461 44059 99719	.11742 04683 63249
78	.39460 85756 14943	.11749 93906 61475
79	.39460 27413 70282	.11757 83117 93237
0.1480	0.39459 69032 65911	0.11765 72317 57765
81	.39459 10613 02003	.11773 61505 54286
82	.39458 52154 78733	.11781 50681 82029
83	.39457 93657 96274	.11789 39846 40221
84	.39457 35122 54802	.11797 28999 28090
0.1485	0.39456 76548 54489	0.11805 18140 44865
86	.39456 17935 95511	.11813 07269 89775
87	.39455 59284 78041	.11820 96387 62046
88	.39455 00595 02256	.11828 85493 60909
89	.39454 41866 68329	.11836 74587 85590
0.1490	0.39453 83099 76435	0.11844 63670 35319
91	.39453 24294 26750	.11852 52741 09323
92	.39452 65450 19448	.11860 41800 06832
93	.39452 06567 54705	.11868 30847 27074
94	.39451 47646 32696	.11876 19882 69277
0.1495	0.39450 88686 53596	0.11884 08906 32670
96	.39450 29688 17582	.11891 97918 16481
97	.39449 70651 24828	.11899 86918 19940
98	.39449 11575 75510	.11907 75906 42274
99	.39448 52461 69805	.11915 64882 82713
0.1500	0.39447 93309 07889	0.11923 53847 40485

x	$\dfrac{1}{\sqrt{2\pi}} e^{-\frac{x^2}{2}}$	$\dfrac{1}{\sqrt{2\pi}} \displaystyle\int_{-x}^{x} e^{-\frac{\alpha^2}{2}} d\alpha$
0.1500	0.39447 93309 07889	0.11923 53847 40485
01	.39447 34117 89937	.11931 42800 14819
02	.39446 74888 16126	.11939 31741 04944
03	.39446 15619 86632	.11947 20670 10088
04	.39445 56313 01631	.11955 09587 29482
0.1505	0.39444 96967 61301	0.11962 98492 62352
06	.39444 37583 65818	.11970 87386 07929
07	.39443 78161 15358	.11978 76267 65441
08	.39443 18700 10099	.11986 65137 34118
09	.39442 59200 50218	.11994 53995 13189
0.1510	0.39441 99662 35891	0.12002 42841 01881
11	.39441 40085 67296	.12010 31674 99426
12	.39440 80470 44611	.12018 20497 05051
13	.39440 20816 68013	.12026 09307 17987
14	.39439 61124 37679	.12033 98105 37462
0.1515	0.39439 01393 53787	0.12041 86891 62705
16	.39438 41624 16516	.12049 75665 92946
17	.39437 81816 26042	.12057 64428 27415
18	.39437 21969 82545	.12065 53178 65340
19	.39436 62084 86201	.12073 41917 05951
0.1520	0.39436 02161 37190	0.12081 30643 48477
21	.39435 42199 35690	.12089 19357 92149
22	.39434 82198 81879	.12097 08060 36195
23	.39434 22159 75937	.12104 96750 79845
24	.39433 62082 18040	.12112 85429 22328
0.1525	0.39433 01966 08370	0.12120 74095 62875
26	.39432 41811 47104	.12128 62750 00715
27	.39431 81618 34421	.12136 51392 35077
28	.39431 21386 70501	.12144 40022 65192
29	.39430 61116 55523	.12152 28640 90289
0.1530	0.39430 00807 89666	0.12160 17247 09598
31	.39429 40460 73111	.12168 05841 22348
32	.39428 80075 06035	.12175 94423 27770
33	.39428 19650 88621	.12183 82993 25094
34	.39427 59188 21046	.12191 71551 13549
0.1535	0.39426 98687 03491	0.12199 60096 92365
36	.39426 38147 36137	.12207 48630 60774
37	.39425 77569 19162	.12215 37152 18003
38	.39425 16952 52749	.12223 25661 63285
39	.39424 56297 37077	.12231 14158 95848
0.1540	0.39423 95603 72326	0.12239 02644 14923
41	.39423 34871 58677	.12246 91117 19740
42	.39422 74100 96312	.12254 79578 09530
43	.39422 13291 85410	.12262 68026 83522
44	.39421 52444 26154	.12270 56463 40947
0.1545	0.39420 91558 18723	0.12278 44887 81036
46	.39420 30633 63299	.12286 33300 03018
47	.39419 69670 60064	.12294 21700 06125
48	.39419 08669 09199	.12302 10087 89586
49	.39418 47629 10885	.12309 98463 52632
0.1550	0.39417 86550 65305	0.12317 86826 94494

x	$\dfrac{1}{\sqrt{2\pi}}e^{-\frac{x^2}{2}}$	$\dfrac{1}{\sqrt{2\pi}}\int_{-x}^{x}e^{-\frac{\alpha^2}{2}}\,d\alpha$
0.1550	0.39417 86550 65305	0.12317 86826 94494
51	.39417 25433 72639	.12325 75178 14402
52	.39416 64278 33070	.12333 63517 11586
53	.39416 03084 46779	.12341 51843 85278
54	.39415 41852 13950	.12349 40158 34709
0.1555	0.39414 80581 34764	0.12357 28460 59108
56	.39414 19272 09403	.12365 16750 57706
57	.39413 57924 38050	.12373 05028 29735
58	.39412 96538 20887	.12380 93293 74425
59	.39412 35113 58098	.12388 81546 91007
0.1560	0.39411 73650 49864	0.12396 69787 78712
61	.39411 12148 96369	.12404 58016 36770
62	.39410 50608 97796	.12412 46232 64414
63	.39409 89030 54328	.12420 34436 60873
64	.39409 27413 66148	.12428 22628 25379
0.1565	0.39408 65758 33439	0.12436 10807 57163
66	.39408 04064 56385	.12443 98974 55456
67	.39407 42332 35170	.12451 87129 19490
68	.39406 80561 69977	.12459 75271 48494
69	.39406 18752 60990	.12467 63401 41701
0.1570	0.39405 56905 08393	0.12475 51518 98342
71	.39404 95019 12369	.12483 39624 17649
72	.39404 33094 73104	.12491 27716 98851
73	.39403 71131 90781	.12499 15797 41182
74	.39403 09130 65584	.12507 03865 43871
0.1575	0.39402 47090 97699	0.12514 91921 06152
76	.39401 85012 87309	.12522 79964 27254
77	.39401 22896 34600	.12530 67995 06410
78	.39400 60741 39756	.12538 56013 42852
79	.39399 98548 02962	.12546 44019 35810
0.1580	0.39399 36316 24403	0.12554 32012 84517
81	.39398 74046 04264	.12562 19993 88204
82	.39398 11737 42731	.12570 07962 46103
83	.39397 49390 39989	.12577 95918 57445
84	.39396 87004 96223	.12585 83862 21463
0.1585	0.39396 24581 11619	0.12593 71793 37387
86	.39395 62118 86363	.12601 59712 04451
87	.39394 99618 20640	.12609 47618 21886
88	.39394 37079 14636	.12617 35511 88923
89	.39393 74501 68539	.12625 23393 04796
0.1590	0.39393 11885 82532	0.12633 11261 68735
91	.39392 49231 56804	.12640 99117 79973
92	.39391 86538 91539	.12648 86961 37742
93	.39391 23807 86926	.12656 74792 41273
94	.39390 61038 43150	.12664 62610 89800
0.1595	0.39389 98230 60398	0.12672 50416 82555
96	.39389 35384 38856	.12680 38210 18769
97	.39388 72499 78713	.12688 25990 97674
98	.39388 09576 80155	.12696 13759 18504
99	.39387 46615 43368	.12704 01514 80491
0.1600	0.39386 83615 68541	0.12711 89257 82866

x	$\frac{1}{\sqrt{2\pi}} e^{-\frac{x^2}{2}}$	$\frac{1}{\sqrt{2\pi}} \int_{-x}^{x} e^{-\frac{\alpha^2}{2}} d\alpha$
0.1600	0.39386 83615 68541	0.12711 89257 82866
01	.39386 20577 55860	.12719 76988 24862
02	.39385 57501 05514	.12727 64706 05712
03	.39384 94386 17689	.12735 52411 24648
04	.39384 31232 92574	.12743 40103 80903
0.1605	0.39383 68041 30357	0.12751 27783 73710
06	.39383 04811 31225	.12759 15451 02300
07	.39382 41542 95366	.12767 03105 65906
08	.39381 78236 22968	.12774 90747 63762
09	.39381 14891 14221	.12782 78376 95100
0.1610	0.39380 51507 69311	0.12790 65993 59152
11	.39379 88085 88429	.12798 53597 55152
12	.39379 24625 71762	.12806 41188 82332
13	.39378 61127 19498	.12814 28767 39925
14	.39377 97590 31828	.12822 16333 27164
0.1615	0.39377 34015 08940	0.12830 03886 43282
16	.39376 70401 51023	.12837 91426 87512
17	.39376 06749 58265	.12845 78954 59087
18	.39375 43059 30857	.12853 66469 57239
19	.39374 79330 68989	.12861 53971 81203
0.1620	0.39374 15563 72848	0.12869 41461 30211
21	.39373 51758 42625	.12877 28938 03497
22	.39372 87914 78510	.12885 16402 00293
23	.39372 24032 80693	.12893 03853 19833
24	.39371 60112 49363	.12900 91291 61350
0.1625	0.39370 96153 84711	0.12908 78717 24077
26	.39370 32156 86927	.12916 66130 07248
27	.39369 68121 56200	.12924 53530 10096
28	.39369 04047 92723	.12932 40917 31855
29	.39368 39935 96684	.12940 28291 71758
0.1630	0.39367 75785 68275	0.12948 15653 29038
31	.39367 11597 07686	.12956 03002 02930
32	.39366 47370 15109	.12963 90337 92666
33	.39365 83104 90734	.12971 77660 97480
34	.39365 18801 34752	.12979 64971 16607
0.1635	0.39364 54459 47355	0.12987 52268 49279
36	.39363 90079 28733	.12995 39552 94730
37	.39363 25660 79079	.13003 26824 52195
38	.39362 61203 98584	.13011 14083 20906
39	.39361 96708 87439	.13019 01329 00099
0.1640	0.39361 32175 45836	0.13026 88561 89006
41	.39360 67603 73967	.13034 75781 86862
42	.39360 02993 72024	.13042 62988 92900
43	.39359 38345 40200	.13050 50183 06355
44	.39358 73658 78685	.13058 37364 26461
0.1645	0.39358 08933 87674	0.13066 24532 52451
46	.39357 44170 67357	.13074 11687 83561
47	.39356 79369 17928	.13081 98830 19023
48	.39356 14529 39579	.13089 85959 58073
49	.39355 49651 32503	.13097 73075 99944
0.1650	0.39354 84734 96893	0.13105 60179 43870

x	$\frac{1}{\sqrt{2\pi}}e^{-\frac{x^2}{2}}$	$\frac{1}{\sqrt{2\pi}}\int_{-x}^{x}e^{-\frac{\alpha^2}{2}}\,d\alpha$
0.1650	0.39354 84734 96893	0.13105 60179 43870
51	.39354 19780 32942	.13113 47269 89087
52	.39353 54787 40843	.13121 34347 34828
53	.39352 89756 20789	.13129 21411 80328
54	.39352 24686 72974	.13137 08463 24821
0.1655	0.39351 59578 97590	0.13144 95501 67542
56	.39350 94432 94832	.13152 82527 07725
57	.39350 29248 64893	.13160 69539 44605
58	.39349 64026 07966	.13168 56538 77416
59	.39348 98765 24247	.13176 43525 05393
0.1660	0.39348 33466 13928	0.13184 30498 27771
61	.39347 68128 77204	.13192 17458 43784
62	.39347 02753 14269	.13200 04405 52667
63	.39346 37339 25317	.13207 91339 53654
64	.39345 71887 10543	.13215 78260 45982
0.1665	0.39345 06396 70142	0.13223 65168 28883
66	.39344 40868 04307	.13231 52063 01595
67	.39343 75301 13234	.13239 38944 63350
68	.39343 09695 97118	.13247 25813 13385
69	.39342 44052 56154	.13255 12668 50934
0.1670	0.39341 78370 90536	0.13262 99510 75232
71	.39341 12651 00460	.13270 86339 85515
72	.39340 46892 86121	.13278 73155 81018
73	.39339 81096 47715	.13286 59958 60975
74	.39339 15261 85438	.13294 46748 24622
0.1675	0.39338 49388 99484	0.13302 33524 71194
76	.39337 83477 90050	.13310 20287 99927
77	.39337 17528 57331	.13318 07038 10055
78	.39336 51541 01524	.13325 93775 00815
79	.39335 85515 22825	.13333 80498 71441
0.1680	0.39335 19451 21430	0.13341 67209 21169
81	.39334 53348 97535	.13349 53906 49235
82	.39333 87208 51336	.13357 40590 54873
83	.39333 21029 83031	.13365 27261 37320
84	.39332 54812 92815	.13373 13918 95812
0.1685	0.39331 88557 80886	0.13381 00563 29583
86	.39331 22264 47441	.13388 87194 37869
87	.39330 55932 92676	.13396 73812 19907
88	.39329 89563 16789	.13404 60416 74932
89	.39329 23155 19977	.13412 47008 02179
0.1690	0.39328 56709 02437	0.13420 33586 00885
91	.39327 90224 64366	.13428 20150 70285
92	.39327 23702 05963	.13436 06702 09616
93	.39326 57141 27424	.13443 93240 18113
94	.39325 90542 28948	.13451 79764 95012
0.1695	0.39325 23905 10733	0.13459 66276 39550
96	.39324 57229 72976	.13467 52774 50962
97	.39323 90516 15876	.13475 39259 28484
98	.39323 23764 39630	.13483 25730 71354
99	.39322 56974 44438	.13491 12188 78806
0.1700	0.39321 90146 30497	0.13498 98633 50077

x	$\frac{1}{\sqrt{2\pi}} e^{-\frac{x^2}{2}}$	$\frac{1}{\sqrt{2\pi}} \int_{-x}^{x} e^{-\frac{\alpha^2}{2}} d\alpha$
0.1700	0.39321 90146 30497	0.13498 98633 50077
01	.39321 23279 98007	.13506 85064 84403
02	.39320 56375 47165	.13514 71482 81021
03	.39319 89432 78171	.13522 57887 39168
04	.39319 22451 91223	.13530 44278 58078
0.1705	0.39318 55432 86521	0.13538 30656 36990
06	.39317 88375 64264	.13546 17020 75138
07	.39317 21280 24650	.13554 03371 71761
08	.39316 54146 67879	.13561 39709 26094
09	.39315 86974 94151	.13569 76033 37374
0.1710	0.39315 19765 03665	0.13577 62344 04837
11	.39314 52516 96621	.13585 48641 27721
12	.39313 85230 73219	.13593 34925 05261
13	.39313 17906 33658	.13601 21195 36695
14	.39312 50543 78139	.13609 07452 21260
0.1715	0.39311 83143 06861	0.13616 93695 58192
16	.39311 15704 20025	.13624 79925 46729
17	.39310 48227 17831	.13632 66141 86106
18	.39309 80712 00479	.13640 52344 75561
19	.39309 13158 68171	.13648 38534 14332
0.1720	0.39308 45567 21107	0.13656 24710 01654
21	.39307 77937 59487	.13664 10872 36766
22	.39307 10269 83512	.13671 97021 18904
23	.39306 42563 93384	.13679 83156 47305
24	.39305 74819 89304	.13687 69278 21207
0.1725	0.39305 07037 71473	0.13695 55386 39847
26	.39304 39217 40091	.13703 41481 02461
27	.39303 71358 95361	.13711 27562 08288
28	.39303 03462 37485	.13719 13629 56565
29	.39302 35527 66663	.13726 99683 46529
0.1730	0.39301 67554 83097	0.13734 85723 77418
31	.39300 99543 86990	.13742 71750 48468
32	.39300 31494 78544	.13750 57763 58918
33	.39299 63407 57960	.13758 43763 08006
34	.39298 95282 25440	.13766 29748 94967
0.1735	0.39298 27118 81188	0.13774 15721 19042
36	.39297 58917 25406	.13782 01679 79466
37	.39296 90677 58295	.13789 87624 75478
38	.39296 22399 80059	.13797 73556 06315
39	.39295 54083 90901	.13805 59473 71216
0.1740	0.39294 85729 91023	0.13813 45377 69417
41	.39294 17337 80629	.13821 31268 00158
42	.39293 48907 59921	.13829 17144 62676
43	.39292 80439 29102	.13837 03007 56208
44	.39292 11932 88377	.13844 88856 79993
0.1745	0.39291 43388 37948	0.13852 74692 33269
46	.39290 74805 78019	.13860 60514 15274
47	.39290 06185 08794	.13868 46322 25247
48	.39289 37526 30477	.13876 32116 62424
49	.39288 68829 43270	.13884 17897 26045
0.1750	0.39288 00094 47379	0.13892 03664 15347

x	$\frac{1}{\sqrt{2\pi}} e^{-\frac{x^2}{2}}$	$\frac{1}{\sqrt{2\pi}} \int_{-x}^{x} e^{-\frac{\alpha^2}{2}} d\alpha$
0.1750	0.39288 00094 47379	0.13892 03664 15347
51	.39287 31321 43008	.13899 89417 29570
52	.39286 62510 30360	.13907 75156 67951
53	.39285 93661 09640	.13915 60882 29728
54	.39285 24773 81052	.13923 46594 14141
0.1755	0.39284 55848 44801	0.13931 32292 20427
56	.39283 86885 01092	.13939 17976 47825
57	.39283 17883 50129	.13947 03646 95573
58	.39282 48843 92118	.13954 89303 62911
59	.39281 79766 27263	.13962 74946 49076
0.1760	0.39281 10650 55769	0.13970 60575 53308
61	.39280 41496 77841	.13978 46190 74845
62	.39279 72304 93685	.13986 31792 12926
63	.39279 03075 03507	.13994 17379 66789
64	.39278 33807 07511	.14002 02953 35673
0.1765	0.39277 64501 05904	0.14009 88513 18818
66	.39276 95156 98891	.14017 74059 15462
67	.39276 25774 86678	.14025 59591 24844
68	.39275 56354 69472	.14033 45109 46203
69	.39274 86896 47477	.14041 30613 78778
0.1770	0.39274 17400 20901	0.14049 16104 21808
71	.39273 47865 89949	.14057 01580 74533
72	.39272 78293 54828	.14064 87043 36191
73	.39272 08683 15745	.14072 72492 06021
74	.39271 39034 72907	.14080 57926 83263
0.1775	0.39270 69348 26519	0.14088 43347 67157
76	.39269 99623 76789	.14096 28754 56940
77	.39269 29861 23925	.14104 14147 51854
78	.39268 60060 68132	.14111 99526 51136
79	.39267 90222 09618	.14119 84891 54028
0.1780	0.39267 20345 48591	0.14127 70242 59767
81	.39266 50430 85257	.14135 55579 67594
82	.39265 80478 19825	.14143 40902 76747
83	.39265 10487 52502	.14151 26211 86468
84	.39264 40458 83496	.14159 11506 95995
0.1785	0.39263 70392 13014	0.14166 96788 04568
86	.39263 00287 41265	.14174 82055 11427
87	.39262 30144 68457	.14182 67308 15811
88	.39261 59963 94798	.14190 52547 16961
89	.39260 89745 20495	.14198 37772 14116
0.1790	0.39260 19488 45759	0.14206 22983 06516
91	.39259 49193 70796	.14214 08179 93401
92	.39258 78860 95816	.14221 93362 74011
93	.39258 08490 21028	.14229 78531 47586
94	.39257 38081 46640	.14237 63686 13366
0.1795	0.39256 67634 72861	0.14245 48826 70591
96	.39255 97149 99901	.14253 33953 18502
97	.39255 26627 27968	.14261 19065 56338
98	.39254 56066 57272	.14269 04163 83339
99	.39253 85467 88023	.14276 89247 98747
0.1800	0.39253 14831 20429	0.14284 74318 01801

x	$\frac{1}{\sqrt{2\pi}}e^{-\frac{x^2}{2}}$	$\frac{1}{\sqrt{2\pi}}\int_{-x}^{x}e^{-\frac{\alpha^2}{2}}d\alpha$
0.1800	0.39253 14831 20429	0.14284 74318 01801
01	.39252 44156 54700	.14292 59373 91742
02	.39251 73443 91047	.14300 44415 67810
03	.39251 02693 29678	.14308 29443 29246
04	.39250 31904 70805	.14316 14456 75289
0.1805	0.39249 61078 14636	0.14323 99456 05181
06	.39248 90213 61383	.14331 84441 18162
07	.39248 19311 11255	.14339 69412 13472
08	.39247 48370 64463	.14347 54368 90353
09	.39246 77392 21217	.14355 39311 48045
0.1810	0.39246 06375 81728	0.14363 24239 85788
11	.39245 35321 46207	.14371 09154 02824
12	.39244 64229 14864	.14378 94053 98394
13	.39243 93098 87910	.14386 78939 71737
14	.39243 21930 65558	.14394 63811 22096
0.1815	0.39242 50724 48016	0.14402 48668 48711
16	.39241 79480 35498	.14410 33511 50822
17	.39241 08198 28214	.14418 18340 27672
18	.39240 36878 26376	.14426 03154 78500
19	.39239 65520 30195	.14433 87955 02549
0.1820	0.39238 94124 39884	0.14441 72740 99060
21	.39238 22690 55653	.14449 57512 67272
22	.39237 51218 77716	.14457 42270 06429
23	.39236 79709 06283	.14465 27013 15771
24	.39236 08161 41567	.14473 11741 94539
0.1825	0.39235 36575 83781	0.14480 96456 41974
26	.39234 64952 33136	.14488 81156 57319
27	.39233 93290 89846	.14496 65842 39815
28	.39233 21591 54122	.14504 50513 88702
29	.39232 49854 26178	.14512 35171 03224
0.1830	0.39231 78079 06226	0.14520 19813 82620
31	.39231 06265 94480	.14528 04442 26133
32	.39230 34414 91151	.14535 89056 33005
33	.39229 62525 96454	.14543 73656 02477
34	.39228 90599 10602	.14551 58241 33791
0.1835	0.39228 18634 33808	0.14559 42812 26188
36	.39227 46631 66285	.14567 27368 78912
37	.39226 74591 08248	.14575 11910 91202
38	.39226 02512 59909	.14582 96438 62302
39	.39225 30396 21483	.14590 80951 91454
0.1840	0.39224 58241 93183	0.14598 65450 77898
41	.39223 86049 75224	.14606 49935 20878
42	.39223 13819 67819	.14614 34405 19636
43	.39222 41551 71183	.14622 18860 73413
44	.39221 69245 85531	.14630 03301 81452
0.1845	0.39220 96902 11076	0.14637 87728 42994
46	.39220 24520 48034	.14645 72140 57283
47	.39219 52100 96618	.14653 56538 23561
48	.39218 79643 57044	.14661 40921 41069
49	.39218 07148 29527	.14669 25290 09051
0.1850	0.39217 34615 14282	0.14677 09644 26749

x	$\dfrac{1}{\sqrt{2\pi}}e^{-\frac{x^2}{2}}$	$\dfrac{1}{\sqrt{2\pi}}\displaystyle\int_{-x}^{x}e^{-\frac{\alpha^2}{2}}\,d\alpha$
0.1850	0.39217 34615 14282	0.14677 09644 26749
51	.39216 62044 11523	.14684 93983 93404
52	.39215 89435 21466	.14692 78309 08261
53	.39215 16788 44327	.14700 62619 70561
54	.39214 44103 80320	.14708 46915 79546
0.1855	0.39213 71381 29662	0.14716 31197 34460
56	.39212 98620 92567	.14724 15464 34546
57	.39212 25822 69253	.14731 99716 79045
58	.39211 52986 59934	.14739 83954 67201
59	.39210 80112 64827	.14747 68177 98256
0.1860	0.39210 07200 84147	0.14755 52386 71454
61	.39209 34251 18112	.14763 36580 86038
62	.39208 61263 66936	.14771 20760 41249
63	.39207 88238 30838	.14779 04925 36332
64	.39207 15175 10033	.14786 89075 70529
0.1865	0.39206 42074 04737	0.14794 73211 43084
66	.39205 68935 15169	.14802 57332 53239
67	.39204 95758 41544	.14810 41439 00238
68	.39204 22543 84079	.14818 25530 83323
69	.39203 49291 42992	.14826 09608 01739
0.1870	0.39202 76001 18500	0.14833 93670 54728
71	.39202 02673 10820	.14841 77718 41534
72	.39201 29307 20170	.14849 61751 61400
73	.39200 55903 46767	.14857 45770 13570
74	.39199 82461 90828	.14865 29773 97287
0.1875	.39199 08982 52572	0.14873 13763 11794
76	.39198 35465 32216	.14880 97737 56336
77	.39197 61910 29979	.14888 81697 30155
78	.39196 88317 46078	.14896 65642 32496
79	.39196 14686 80731	.14904 49572 62601
0.1880	0.39195 41018 34157	0.14912 33488 19716
81	.39194 67312 06575	.14920 17389 03083
82	.39193 93567 98202	.14928 01275 11947
83	.39193 19786 09258	.14935 85146 45550
84	.39192 45966 39961	.14943 69003 03138
0.1885	0.39191 72108 90529	0.14951 52844 83954
86	.39190 98213 61183	.14959 36671 87242
87	.39190 24280 52141	.14967 20484 12247
88	.39189 50309 63622	.14975 04281 58211
89	.39188 76300 95845	.14982 88064 24380
0.1890	0.39188 02254 49030	0.14990 71832 09998
91	.39187 28170 23396	.14998 55585 14308
92	.39186 54048 19163	.15006 39323 36555
93	.39185 79888 36551	.15014 23046 75984
94	.39185 05690 75779	.15022 06755 31838
0.1895	0.39184 31455 37068	0.15029 90449 03362
96	.39183 57182 20637	.15037 74127 89801
97	.39182 82871 26706	.15045 57791 90399
98	.39182 08522 55496	.15053 41441 04400
99	.39181 34136 07228	.15061 25075 31049
0.1900	0.39180 59711 82121	0.15069 08694 69591

x	$\dfrac{1}{\sqrt{2\pi}}e^{-\frac{x^2}{2}}$	$\dfrac{1}{\sqrt{2\pi}}\displaystyle\int_{-x}^{x}e^{-\frac{\alpha^2}{2}}\,d\alpha$
0.1900	0.39180 59711 82121	0.15069 08694 69591
01	.39179 85249 80397	.15076 92299 19270
02	.39179 10750 02275	.15084 75888 79331
03	.39178 36212 47977	.15092 59463 49019
04	.39177 61637 17724	.15100 43023 27579
0.1905	0.39176 87024 11736	15108 26568 14255
06	.39176 12373 30236	15116 10098 08292
07	.39175 37684 73443	.15123 93613 08935
08	.39174 62958 41580	.15131 77113 15429
09	.39173 88194 34868	.15139 60598 27020
0.1910	0.39173 13392 53528	0.15147 44068 42952
11	.39172 38552 97782	.15155 27523 62470
12	.39171 63675 67852	.15163 10963 84819
13	.39170 88760 63960	.15170 94389 09245
14	.39170 13807 86328	.15178 77799 34993
0.1915	0.39169 38817 35178	0.15186 61194 61308
16	.39168 63789 10732	.15194 44574 87436
17	.39167 88723 13212	.15202 27940 12621
18	.39167 13619 42841	.15210 11290 36110
19	.39166 38477 99842	.15217 94625 57147
0.1920	0.39165 63298 84437	0.15225 77945 74978
21	.39164 88081 96849	.15233 61250 88849
22	.39164 12827 37300	.15241 44540 98005
23	.39163 37535 06015	.15249 27816 01692
24	.39162 62205 03215	.15257 11075 99156
0.1925	0.39161 86837 29124	0.15264 94320 89642
26	.39161 11431 83966	.15272 77550 72396
27	.39160 35988 67963	.15280 60765 46665
28	.39159 60507 81340	.15288 43965 11692
29	.39158 84989 24320	.15296 27149 66726
0.1930	0.39158 09432 97126	0.15304 10319 11011
31	.39157 33838 99983	.15311 93473 43793
32	.39156 58207 33115	.15319 76612 64319
33	.39155 82537 96745	.15327 59736 71835
34	.39155 06830 91098	.15335 42845 65587
0.1935	0.39154 31086 16397	0.15343 25939 44820
36	.39153 55303 72869	.15351 09018 08782
37	.39152 79483 60736	.15358 92081 56718
38	.39152 03625 80224	.15366 75129 87875
39	.39151 27730 31558	.15374 58163 01499
0.1940	0.39150 51797 14961	0.15382 41180 96837
41	.39149 75826 30660	.15390 24183 73134
42	.39148 99817 78878	.15398 07171 29638
43	.39148 23771 59842	.15405 90143 65594
44	.39147 47687 73777	.15413 73100 80250
0.1945	0.39146 71566 20908	0.15421 56042 72853
46	.39145 95407 01460	.15429 38969 42648
47	.39145 19210 15659	.15437 21880 88882
48	.39144 42975 63731	.15445 04777 10803
49	.39143 66703 45901	.15452 87658 07657
0.1950	0.39142 90393 62396	0.15460 70523 78690

x	$\dfrac{1}{\sqrt{2\pi}}e^{-\frac{x^2}{2}}$	$\dfrac{1}{\sqrt{2\pi}}\displaystyle\int_{-x}^{x}e^{-\frac{\alpha^2}{2}}\,d\alpha$
0.1950	0.39142 90393 62396	0.15460 70523 78690
51	.39142 14046 13441	.15468 53374 23151
52	.39141 37660 99263	.15476 36209 40285
53	.39140 61238 20088	.15484 19029 29339
54	.39139 84777 76142	.15492 01833 89562
0.1955	0.39139 08279 67652	0.15499 84623 20199
56	.39138 31743 94844	.15507 67397 20498
57	.39137 55170 57945	.15515 50155 89706
58	.39136 78559 57182	.15523 32899 27070
59	.39136 01910 92782	.15531 15627 31838
0.1960	0.39135 25224 64971	0.15538 98340 03256
61	.39134 48500 73977	.15546 81037 40573
62	.39133 71739 20027	.15554 63719 43035
63	.39132 94940 03348	.15562 46386 09890
64	.39132 18103 24168	.15570 29037 40385
0.1965	0.39131 41228 82714	0.15578 11673 33769
66	.39130 64316 79215	.15585 94293 89288
67	.39129 87367 13897	.15593 76899 06190
68	.39129 10379 86988	.15601 59488 83723
69	.39128 33354 98718	.15609 42063 21134
0.1970	0.39127 56292 49312	0.15617 24622 17671
71	.39126 79192 39001	.15625 07165 72583
72	.39126 02054 68012	.15632 89693 85116
73	.39125 24879 36574	.15640 72206 54519
74	.39124 47666 44914	.15648 54703 80040
0.1975	0.39123 70415 93263	0.15656 37185 60927
76	.39122 93127 81848	.15664 19651 96427
77	.39122 15802 10898	.15672 02102 85789
78	.39121 38438 80642	.15679 84538 28260
79	.39120 61037 91310	.15687 66958 23090
0.1980	0.39119 83599 43131	0.15695 49362 69526
81	.39119 06123 36333	.15703 31751 66817
82	.39118 28609 71147	.15711 14125 14210
83	.39117 51058 47801	.15718 96483 10955
84	.39116 73469 66525	.15726 78825 56299
0.1985	0.39115 95843 27550	0.15734 61152 49491
86	.39115 18179 31104	.15742 43463 89780
87	.39114 40477 77418	.15750 25759 76413
88	.39113 62738 66722	.15758 08040 08640
89	.39112 84961 99246	.15765 90304 85709
0.1990	0.39112 07147 75220	0.15773 72554 06869
91	.39111 29295 94875	.15781 54787 71369
92	.39110 51406 58440	.15789 37005 78457
93	.39109 73479 66148	.15797 19208 27382
94	.39108 95515 18227	.15805 01395 17393
0.1995	0.39108 17513 14910	0.15812 83566 47739
96	.39107 39473 56427	.15820 65722 17669
97	.39106 61396 43009	.15828 47862 26431
98	.39105 83281 74887	.15836 29986 73275
99	.39105 05129 52292	.15844 12095 57451
0.2000	0.39104 26939 75456	0.15851 94188 78206

x	$\frac{1}{\sqrt{2\pi}}\,e^{-\frac{x^2}{2}}$	$\frac{1}{\sqrt{2\pi}}\int_{-x}^{x} e^{-\frac{\alpha^2}{2}}\,d\alpha$
0.2000	0.39104 26939 75456	0.15851 94188 78206
01	.39103 48712 44610	.15859 76266 34791
02	.39102 70447 59986	.15867 58328 26454
03	.39101 92145 21815	.15875 40374 52444
04	.39101 13805 30329	.15883 22405 12012
0.2005	0.39100 35427 85761	0.15891 04420 04406
06	.39099 57012 88341	.15898 86419 28876
07	.39098 78560 38302	.15906 68402 84671
08	.39098 00070 35877	.15914 50370 71041
09	.39097 21542 81297	.15922 32322 87236
0.2010	0.39096 42977 74796	0.15930 14259 32504
11	.39095 64375 16604	.15937 96180 06095
12	.39094 85735 06956	.15945 78085 07260
13	.39094 07057 46084	.15953 59974 35248
14	.39093 28342 34220	.15961 41847 89309
0.2015	0.39092 49589 71599	0.15969 23705 68692
16	.39091 70799 58452	.15977 05547 72647
17	.39090 91971 95013	.15984 87374 00425
18	.39090 13106 81515	.15992 69184 51275
19	.39089 34204 18191	.16000 50979 24448
0.2020	0.39088 55264 05276	0.16008 32758 19193
21	.39087 76286 43002	.16016 14521 34760
22	.39086 97271 31604	.16023 96268 70400
23	.39086 18218 71315	.16031 78000 25363
24	.39085 39128 62369	.16039 59715 98899
0.2025	0.39084 60001 05000	0.16047 41415 90258
26	.39083 80835 99443	.16055 23099 98691
27	.39083 01633 45931	.16063 04768 23448
28	.39082 22393 44699	.16070 86420 63779
29	.39081 43115 95981	.16078 68057 18936
0.2030	0.39080 63801 00013	0.16086 49677 88168
31	.39079 84448 57028	.16094 31282 70726
32	.39079 05058 67261	.16102 12871 65861
33	.39078 25631 30947	.16109 94444 72823
34	.39077 46166 48322	.16117 76001 90863
0.2035	0.39076 66664 19621	0.16125 57543 19233
36	.39075 87124 45078	.16133 39068 57182
37	.39075 07547 24928	.16141 20578 03961
38	.39074 27932 59409	.16149 02071 58822
39	.39073 48280 48754	.16156 83549 21015
0.2040	0.39072 68590 93199	0.16164 65010 89792
41	.39071 88863 92981	.16172 46456 64403
42	.39071 09099 48335	.16180 27886 44099
43	.39070 29297 59498	.16188 09300 28132
44	.39069 49458 26704	.16195 90698 15753
0.2045	0.39068 69581 50191	0.16203 72080 06213
46	.39067 89667 30194	.16211 53445 98764
47	.39067 09715 66951	.16219 34795 92656
48	.39066 29726 60697	.16227 16129 87141
49	.39065 49700 11670	.16234 97447 81471
0.2050	0.39064 69636 20105	0.16242 78749 74896

x	$\frac{1}{\sqrt{2\pi}}e^{-\frac{x^2}{2}}$	$\frac{1}{\sqrt{2\pi}}\int_{-x}^{x}e^{-\frac{\alpha^2}{2}}d\alpha$
0.2050	0.39064 69636 20105	0.16242 78749 74896
51	.39063 89534 86240	.16250 60035 66669
52	.39063 09396 10312	.16258 41305 56041
53	.39062 29219 92558	.16266 22559 42264
54	.39061 49006 33214	.16274 03797 24589
0.2055	0.39060 68755 32519	0.16281 85019 02268
56	.39059 88466 90709	.16289 66224 74553
57	.39059 08141 08022	.16297 47414 40695
58	.39058 27777 84696	.16305 28587 99946
59	.39057 47377 20968	.16313 09745 51559
0.2060	0.39056 66939 17076	0.16320 90886 94785
61	.39055 86463 73258	.16328 72012 28877
62	.39055 05950 89752	.16336 53121 53085
63	.39054 25400 66796	.16344 34214 66663
64	.39053 44813 04628	.16352 15291 68863
0.2065	0.39052 64188 03487	0.16359 96352 58936
66	.39051 83525 63611	.16367 77397 36135
67	.39051 02825 85238	.16375 58425 99712
68	.39050 22088 68608	.16383 39438 48920
69	.39049 41314 13959	.16391 20434 83010
0.2070	0.39048 60502 21530	0.16399 01415 01236
71	.39047 79652 91560	.16406 82379 02850
72	.39046 98766 24287	.16414 63326 87104
73	.39046 17842 19952	.16422 44258 53250
74	.39045 36880 78793	.16430 25174 00543
0.2075	0.39044 55882 01050	0.16438 06073 28233
76	.39043 74845 86963	.16445 86956 35574
77	.39042 93772 36770	.16453 67823 21819
78	.39042 12661 50712	.16461 48673 86220
79	.39041 31513 29029	.16469 29508 28030
0.2080	0.39040 50327 71960	0.16477 10326 46502
81	.39039 69104 79746	.16484 91128 40890
82	.39038 87844 52626	.16492 71914 10445
83	.39038 06546 90841	.16500 52683 54422
84	.39037 25211 94632	.16508 33436 72072
0.2085	0.39036 43839 64238	0.16516 14173 62651
86	.39035 62429 99901	.16523 94894 25409
87	.39034 80983 01860	.16531 75598 59602
88	.39033 99498 70358	.16539 56286 64481
89	.39033 17977 05634	.16547 36958 39301
0.2090	0.39032 36418 07930	0.16555 17613 83314
91	.39031 54821 77487	.16562 98252 95775
92	.39030 73188 14546	.16570 78875 75937
93	.39029 91517 19348	.16578 59482 23052
94	.39029 09808 92135	.16586 40072 36376
0.2095	0.39028 28063 33149	0.16594 20646 15160
96	.39027 46280 42631	.16602 01203 58660
97	.39026 64460 20822	.16609 81744 66129
98	.39025 82602 67965	.16617 62269 36820
99	.39025 00707 84302	.16625 42777 69987
0.2100	0.39024 18775 70074	0.16633 23269 64885

x	$\frac{1}{\sqrt{2\pi}} e^{-\frac{x^2}{2}}$	$\frac{1}{\sqrt{2\pi}} \int_{-x}^{x} e^{-\frac{\alpha^2}{2}} d\alpha$
0.2100	0.39024 18775 70074	0.16633 23269 64885
01	.39023 36806 25525	.16641 03745 20766
02	.39022 54799 50895	.16648 84204 36886
03	.39021 72755 46428	.16656 64647 12498
04	.39020 90674 12367	.16664 45073 46856
0.2105	0.39020 08555 48952	0.16672 25483 39214
06	.39019 26399 56429	.16680 05876 88827
07	.39018 44206 35038	.16687 86253 94948
08	.39017 61975 85024	.16695 66614 56833
09	.39016 79708 06629	.16703 46958 73734
0.2110	0.39015 97403 00097	0.16711 27286 44907
11	.39015 15060 65670	.16719 07597 69605
12	.39014 32681 03592	.16726 87892 47084
13	.39013 50264 14106	.16734 68170 76598
14	.39012 67809 97457	.16742 48432 57402
0.2115	0.39011 85318 53887	0.16750 28677 88749
16	.39011 02789 83641	.16758 08906 69895
17	.39010 20223 86962	.16765 89119 00094
18	.39009 37620 64094	.16773 69314 78601
19	.39008 54980 15282	.16781 49494 04671
0.2120	0.39007 72302 40770	0.16789 29656 77559
21	.39006 89587 40801	.16797 09802 96519
22	.39006 06835 15621	.16804 89932 60807
23	.39005 24045 65474	.16812 70045 69677
24	.39004 41218 90605	.16820 50142 22385
0.2125	0.39003 58354 91258	0.16828 30222 18185
26	.39002 75453 67678	.16836 10285 56333
27	.39001 92515 20111	.16843 90332 36084
28	.39001 09539 48800	.16851 70362 56693
29	.39000 26526 53992	.16859 50376 17415
0.2130	0.38999 43476 35932	0.16867 30373 17506
31	.38998 60388 94865	.16875 10353 56221
32	.38997 77264 31036	.16882 90317 32816
33	.38996 94102 44692	.16890 70264 46545
34	.38996 10903 36077	.16898 50194 96665
0.2135	0.38995 27667 05438	0.16906 30108 82432
36	.38994 44393 53021	.16914 10006 03100
37	.38993 61082 79071	.16921 89886 57925
38	.38992 77734 83835	.16929 69750 46163
39	.38991 94349 67559	.16937 49597 67070
0.2140	0.38991 10927 30489	0.16945 29428 19902
41	.38990 27467 72872	.16953 09242 03914
42	.38989 43970 94955	.16960 89039 18363
43	.38988 60436 96983	.16968 68819 62504
44	.38987 76865 79204	.16976 48583 35594
0.2145	0.38986 93257 41865	0.16984 28330 36888
46	.38986 09611 85212	.16992 08060 65643
47	.38985 25929 09493	.16999 87774 21114
48	.38984 42209 14955	.17007 67471 02559
49	.38983 58452 01845	.17015 47151 09232
0.2150	0.38982 74657 70411	0.17023 26814 40392

X	$\frac{1}{\sqrt{2\pi}} e^{-\frac{x^2}{2}}$	$\frac{1}{\sqrt{2\pi}} \int_{-x}^{x} e^{-\frac{\alpha^2}{2}} d\alpha$
0.2150	0.38982 74657 70411	0.17023 26814 40392
51	.38981 90826 20899	.17031 06460 95293
52	.38981 06957 53559	.17038 86090 73192
53	.38980 23051 68637	.17046 65703 73346
54	.38979 39108 66381	.17054 45299 95012
0.2155	0.38978 55128 47039	0.17062 24879 37445
56	.38977 71111 10860	.17070 04441 99903
57	.38976 87056 58091	.17077 83987 81642
58	.38976 02964 88981	.17085 63516 81918
59	.38975 18836 03777	.17093 43028 99989
0.2160	0.38974 34670 02729	0.17101 22524 35112
61	.38973 50466 86086	.17109 02002 86543
62	.38972 66226 54095	.17116 81464 53539
63	.38971 81949 07005	.17124 60909 35357
64	.38970 97634 45066	.17132 40337 31254
0.2165	0.38970 13282 68526	0.17140 19748 40487
66	.38969 28893 77635	.17147 99142 62314
67	.38968 44467 72641	.17155 78519 95991
68	.38967 60004 53795	.17163 57880 40775
69	.38966 75504 21345	.17171 37223 95924
0.2170	0.38965 90966 75541	0.17179 16550 60696
71	.38965 06392 16632	.17186 95860 34347
72	.38964 21780 44869	.17194 75153 16135
73	.38963 37131 60501	.17202 54429 05318
74	.38962 52445 63779	.17210 33688 01152
0.2175	0.38961 67722 54951	0.17218 12930 02896
76	.38960 82962 34269	.17225 92155 09806
77	.38959 98165 01982	.17233 71363 21142
78	.38959 13330 58342	.17241 50554 36160
79	.38958 28459 03598	.17249 29728 54118
0.2180	0.38957 43550 38001	0.17257 08885 74274
81	.38956 58604 61802	.17264 88025 95886
82	.38955 73621 75251	.17272 67149 18211
83	.38954 88601 78600	.17280 46255 40508
84	.38954 03544 72100	.17288 25344 62035
0.2185	0.38953 18450 56001	0.17296 04416 82050
86	.38952 33319 30554	.17303 83471 99810
87	.38951 48150 96012	.17311 62510 14575
88	.38950 62945 52626	.17319 41531 25602
89	.38949 77703 00647	.17327 20535 32149
0.2190	0.38948 92423 40326	0.17334 99522 33475
91	.38948 07106 71916	.17342 78492 28838
92	.38947 21752 95668	.17350 57445 17496
93	.38946 36362 11835	.17358 36380 98709
94	.38945 50934 20668	.17366 15299 71734
0.2195	0.38944 65469 22420	0.17373 94201 35830
96	.38943 79967 17342	.17381 73085 90256
97	.38942 94428 05688	.17389 51953 34270
98	.38942 08851 87710	.17397 30803 67131
99	.38941 23238 63660	.17405 09636 88098
0.2200	0.38940 37588 33790	0.17412 88452 96429

x	$\frac{1}{\sqrt{2\pi}} e^{-\frac{x^2}{2}}$	$\frac{1}{\sqrt{2\pi}} \int_{-x}^{x} e^{-\frac{\alpha^2}{2}} d\alpha$
0.2200	0.38940 37588 33790	0.17412 88452 96429
01	.38939 51900 98355	17420 67251 91384
02	.38938 66176 57607	.17428 46033 72222
03	.38937 80415 11798	.17436 24798 38200
04	.38936 94616 61182	.17444 03545 88579
0.2205	.38936 08781 06012	0.17451 82276 22618
06	.38935 22908 46542	.17459 60989 39575
07	.38934 36998 83025	.17467 39685 38709
08	.38933 51052 15714	.17475 18364 19281
09	.38932 65068 44863	.17482 97025 80549
0.2210	0.38931 79047 70726	0.17490 75670 21772
11	.38930 92989 93557	.17498 54297 42210
12	.38930 06895 13609	.17506 32907 41123
13	.38929 20763 31137	.17514 11500 17769
14	.38928 34594 46395	.17521 90075 71408
0.2215	0.38927 48388 59638	0.17529 68634 01301
16	.38926 62145 71119	.17537 47175 06705
17	.38925 75865 81093	.17545 25698 86882
18	.38924 89548 89815	.17553 04205 41091
19	.38924 03194 97539	.17560 82694 68591
0.2220	0.38923 16804 04520	0.17568 61166 68643
21	.38922 30376 11014	.17576 39621 40507
22	.38921 43911 17275	.17584 18058 83441
23	.38920 57409 23558	.17591 96478 96707
24	.38919 70870 30118	.17599 74881 79564
0.2225	0.38918 84294 37212	0.17607 53267 31272
26	.38917 97681 45093	.17615 31635 51092
27	.38917 11031 54019	.17623 09986 38284
28	.38916 24344 64244	.17630 88319 92107
29	.38915 37620 76025	.17638 66636 11823
0.2230	0.38914 50859 89616	0.17646 44934 96691
31	.38913 64062 05275	.17654 23216 45972
32	.38912 77227 23257	.17662 01480 58927
33	.38911 90355 43818	.17669 79727 34815
34	.38911 03446 67215	.17677 57956 72898
0.2335	0.38910 16500 93704	0.17685 36168 72435
36	.38909 29518 23541	.17693 14363 32689
37	.38908 42498 56984	.17700 92540 52918
38	.38907 55441 94288	.17708 70700 32385
39	.38906 68348 35711	.17716 48842 70350
0.2240	0.38905 81217 81510	0.17724 26967 66073
41	.38904 94050 31941	.17732 05075 18816
42	.38904 06845 87262	.17739 83165 27839
43	.38903 19604 47730	.17747 61237 92404
44	.38902 32326 13602	.17755 39293 11772
0.2245	0.38901 45010 85136	0.17763 17330 85204
46	.38900 57658 62589	.17770 95351 11960
47	.38899 70269 46219	.17778 73353 91302
48	.38898 82843 36284	.17786 51339 22492
49	.38897 95380 33042	.17794 29307 04791
0.2250	0.38897 07880 36749	0.17802 07257 37459

x	$\dfrac{1}{\sqrt{2\pi}}\,e^{-\frac{x^2}{2}}$	$\dfrac{1}{\sqrt{2\pi}}\displaystyle\int_{-x}^{x} e^{-\frac{\alpha^2}{2}}\,d\alpha$
0.2250	0.38897 07880 36749	0.17802 07257 37459
51	.38896 20343 47666	.17809 85190 19759
52	.38895 32769 66049	.17817 63105 50952
53	.38894 45158 92157	.17825 41003 30299
54	.38893 57511 26249	.17833 18883 57063
0.2255	0.38892 69826 68583	0.17840 96746 30504
56	.38891 82105 19417	.17848 74591 49884
57	.38890 94346 79010	.17856 52419 14466
58	.38890 06551 47622	.17864 30229 23510
59	.38889 18719 25510	.17872 08021 76279
0.2260	0.38888 30850 12935	0.17879 85796 72034
61	.38887 42944 10154	.17887 63554 10038
62	.38886 55001 17428	.17895 41293 89552
63	.38885 67021 35015	.17903 19016 09839
64	.38884 79004 63176	.17910 96720 70160
0.2265	0.38883 90951 02169	0.17918 74407 69778
66	.38883 02860 52254	.17926 52077 07955
67	.38882 14733 13692	.17934 29728 83953
68	.38881 26568 86741	.17942 07362 97035
69	.38880 38367 71662	.17949 84979 46462
0.2270	0.38879 50129 68715	0.17957 62578 31497
71	.38878 61854 78160	.17965 40159 51404
72	.38877 73543 00257	.17973 17723 05443
73	.38876 85194 35267	.17980 95268 92878
74	.38875 96808 83450	.17988 72797 12971
0.2275	0.38875 08386 45068	0.17996 50307 64985
76	.38874 19927 20379	.18004 27800 48183
77	.38873 31431 09646	.18012 05275 61828
78	.38872 42898 13129	.18019 82733 05182
79	.38871 54328 31089	.18027 60172 77507
0.2280	0.38870 65721 63787	0.18035 37594 78068
81	.38869 77078 11485	.18043 14999 06127
82	.38868 88397 74444	.18050 92385 60947
83	.38867 99680 52925	.18058 69754 41791
84	.38867 10926 47190	.18066 47105 47923
0.2285	0.38866 22135 57500	0.18074 24438 78605
86	.38865 33307 84118	.18082 01754 33100
87	.38864 44443 27304	.18089 79052 10673
88	.38863 55541 87322	.18097 56332 10586
89	.38862 66603 64432	.18105 33594 32102
0.2290	0.38861 77628 58898	0.18113 10838 74486
91	.38860 88616 70980	.18120 88065 37000
92	.38859 99568 00943	.18128 65274 18909
93	.38859 10482 49048	.18136 42465 19475
94	.38858 21360 15558	.18144 19638 37963
0.2295	0.38857 32201 00735	0.18151 96793 73636
96	.38856 43005 04843	.18159 73931 25758
97	.38855 53772 28144	.18167 51050 93592
98	.38854 64502 70901	.18175 28152 76404
99	.38853 75196 33377	.18183 05236 73455
0.2300	0.38852 85853 15836	0.18190 82302 84012

x	$\dfrac{1}{\sqrt{2\pi}}\,e^{-\frac{x^2}{2}}$	$\dfrac{1}{\sqrt{2\pi}}\displaystyle\int_{-x}^{x} e^{-\frac{\alpha^2}{2}}\,d\alpha$
0.2300	0.38852 85853 15836	0.18190 82302 84012
01	.38851 96473 18540	.18198 59351 07336
02	.38851 07056 41754	.18206 36381 42694
03	.38850 17602 85741	.18214 13393 89348
04	.38849 28112 50763	.18221 90388 46563
0.2305	0.38848 38585 37086	0.18229 67365 13603
06	.38847 49021 44973	.18237 44323 89732
07	.38846 59420 74687	.18245 21264 74216
08	.38845 69783 26493	.18252 98187 66317
09	.38844 80109 00656	.18260 75092 65301
0.2310	0.38843 90397 97438	0.18268 51979 70432
11	.38843 00650 17105	.18276 28848 80975
12	.38842 10865 59921	.18284 05699 96194
13	.38841 21044 26151	.18291 82533 15354
14	.38840 31186 16059	.18299 59348 37719
0.2315	0.38839 41291 29909	0.18307 36145 62555
16	.38838 51359 67968	.18315 12924 89126
17	.38837 61391 30500	.18322 89686 16697
18	.38836 71386 17769	.18330 66429 44533
19	.38835 81344 30042	.18338 43154 71899
0.2320	0.38834 91265 67583	0.18346 19861 98060
21	.38834 01150 30658	.18353 96551 22282
22	.38833 10998 19532	.18361 73222 43828
23	.38832 20809 34471	.18369 49875 61964
24	.38831 30583 75740	.18377 26510 75957
0.2325	0.38830 40321 43606	0.18385 03127 85070
26	.38829 50022 38334	.18392 79726 88569
27	.38828 59686 60190	.18400 56307 85720
28	.38827 69314 09441	.18408 32870 75788
29	.38826 78904 86353	.18416 09415 58039
0.2330	0.38825 88458 91191	0.18423 85942 31738
31	.38824 97976 24223	.18431 62450 96151
32	.38824 07456 85715	.18439 38941 50543
33	.38823 16900 75933	.18447 15413 94180
34	.38822 26307 95145	.18454 91868 26329
0.2335	0.38821 35678 43617	0.18462 68304 46254
36	.38820 45012 21616	.18470 44722 53222
37	.38819 54309 29409	.18478 21122 46498
38	.38818 63569 67263	.18485 97504 25349
39	.38817 72793 35446	.18493 73867 89040
0.2340	0.38816 81980 34225	0.18501 50213 36838
41	.38815 91130 63867	.18509 26540 68009
42	.38815 00244 24640	.18517 02849 81819
43	.38814 09321 16812	.18524 79140 77534
44	.38813 18361 40651	.18532 55413 54421
0.2345	0.38812 27364 96423	0.18540 31668 11746
46	.38811 36331 84398	.18548 07904 48775
47	.38810 45262 04844	.18555 84122 64775
48	.38809 54155 58028	.18563 60322 59013
49	.38808 63012 44218	.18571 36504 30754
0.2350	0.38807 71832 63685	0.18579 12667 79266

x	$\dfrac{1}{\sqrt{2\pi}}\,e^{-\frac{x^2}{2}}$	$\dfrac{1}{\sqrt{2\pi}}\displaystyle\int_{-x}^{x} e^{-\frac{\alpha^2}{2}}\,d\alpha$
0.2350	0.38807 71832 63685	0.18579 12667 79266
51	.38806 80616 16695	.18586 88813 03815
52	.38805 89363 03517	.18594 64940 03668
53	.38804 98073 24420	.18602 41048 78092
54	.38804 06746 79674	.18610 17139 26354
0.2355	0.38803 15383 69546	0.18617 93211 47720
56	.38802 23983 94306	.18625 69265 41457
57	.38801 32547 54224	.18633 45301 06833
58	.38800 41074 49567	.18641 21318 43115
59	.38799 49564 80606	.18648 97317 49569
0.2360	0.38798 58018 47610	0.18656 73298 25463
61	.38797 66435 50849	.18664 49260 70063
62	.38796 74815 90592	.18672 25204 82639
63	.38795 83159 67108	.18680 01130 62455
64	.38794 91466 80669	.18687 77038 08781
0.2365	0.38793 99737 31543	0.18695 52927 20884
66	.38793 07971 20001	.18703 28797 98030
67	.38792 16168 46314	.18711 04650 39487
68	.38791 24329 10750	.18718 80484 44524
69	.38790 32453 13581	.18726 56300 12408
0.2370	0.38789 40540 55077	0.18734 32097 42405
71	.38788 48591 35509	.18742 07876 33786
72	.38787 56605 55147	.18749 83636 85816
73	.38786 64583 14263	.18757 59378 97764
74	.38785 72524 13126	.18765 35102 68897
0.2375	0.38784 80428 52008	0.18773 10807 98485
76	.38783 88296 31181	.18780 86494 85794
77	.38782 96127 50915	.18788 62163 30093
78	.38782 03922 11481	.18796 37813 30651
79	.38781 11680 13152	.18804 13444 86734
0.2380	0.38780 19401 56198	0.18811 89057 97612
81	.38779 27086 40891	.18819 64652 62553
82	.38778 34734 67503	.18827 40228 80824
83	.38777 42346 36305	.18835 15786 51696
84	.38776 49921 47571	.18842 91325 74435
0.2385	0.38775 57460 01571	0.18850 66846 48311
86	.38774 64961 98577	.18858 42348 72592
87	.38773 72427 38863	.18866 17832 46547
88	.38772 79856 22700	.18873 93297 69444
89	.38771 87248 50360	.18881 68744 40552
0.2390	0.38770 94604 22117	0.18889 44172 59140
91	.38770 01923 38243	.18897 19582 24477
92	.38769 09205 99010	.18904 94973 35832
93	.38768 16452 04692	.18912 70345 92473
94	.38767 23661 55562	.18920 45699 93670
0.2395	0.38766 30834 51892	0.18928 21035 38692
96	.38765 37970 93956	.18935 96352 26807
97	.38764 45070 82026	.18943 71650 57286
98	.38763 52134 16377	.18951 46930 29396
99	.38762 59160 97282	.18959 22191 42409
0.2400	0.38761 66151 25014	0.18966 97433 95592

x	$\dfrac{1}{\sqrt{2\pi}}e^{-\frac{x^2}{2}}$	$\dfrac{1}{\sqrt{2\pi}}\displaystyle\int_{-x}^{x}e^{-\frac{\alpha^2}{2}}\,d\alpha$
0.2400	0.38761 66151 25014	0.18966 97433 95592
01	.38760 73104 99847	.18974 72657 88215
02	.38759 80022 22055	.18982 47863 19548
03	.38758 86902 91912	.18990 23049 88860
04	.38757 93747 09691	.18997 98217 95421
0.2405	0.38757 00554 75667	0.19005 73367 38501
06	.38756 07325 90114	.19013 48498 17368
07	.38755 14060 53306	.19021 23610 31293
08	.38754 20758 65518	.19028 98703 79546
09	.38753 27420 27024	.19036 73778 61396
0.2410	0.38752 34045 38099	0.19044 48834 76114
11	.38751 40633 99017	.19052 23872 22968
12	.38750 47186 10053	.19059 98891 01230
13	.38749 53701 71483	.19067 73891 10169
14	.38748 60180 83581	.19075 48872 49055
0.2415	0.38747 66623 46622	0.19083 23835 17159
16	.38746 73029 60881	.19090 98779 13751
17	.38745 79399 26634	.19098 73704 38100
18	.38744 85732 44157	.19106 48610 89478
19	.38743 92029 13724	.19114 23498 67155
0.2420	0.38742 98289 35612	0.19121 98367 70400
21	.38742 04513 10096	.19129 73217 98486
22	.38741 10700 37451	.19137 48049 50681
23	.38740 16851 17955	.19145 22862 26258
24	.38739 22965 51882	.19152 97656 24485
0.2425	0.38738 29043 39510	0.19160 72431 44635
26	.38737 35084 81114	.19168 47187 85978
27	.38736 41089 76971	.19176 21925 47785
28	.38735 47058 27357	.19183 96644 29326
29	.38734 52990 32548	.19191 71344 29873
0.2430	0.38733 58885 92822	0.19199 46025 48696
31	.38732 64745 08455	.19207 20687 85067
32	.38731 70567 79723	.19214 95331 38256
33	.38730 76354 06905	.19222 69956 07536
34	.38729 82103 90277	.19230 44561 92176
0.2435	0.38728 87817 30116	0.19238 19148 91449
36	.38727 93494 26699	.19245 93717 04625
37	.38726 99134 80304	.19253 68266 30977
38	.38726 04738 91209	.19261 42796 69775
39	.38725 10306 59690	.19269 17308 20290
0.2440	0.38724 15837 86026	0.19276 91800 81796
41	.38723 21332 70494	.19284 66274 53562
42	.38722 26791 13372	.19292 40729 34861
43	.38721 32213 14938	.19300 15165 24965
44	.38720 37598 75471	.19307 89582 23144
0.2445	0.38719 42947 95249	0.19315 63980 28672
46	.38718 48260 74549	.19323 38359 40820
47	.38717 53537 13650	.19331 12719 58859
48	.38716 58777 12831	.19338 87060 82062
49	.38715 63980 72370	.19346 61383 09702
0.2450	0.38714 69147 92546	0.19354 35686 41049

x	$\frac{1}{\sqrt{2\pi}} e^{-\frac{x^2}{2}}$	$\frac{1}{\sqrt{2\pi}} \int_{-x}^{x} e^{-\frac{\alpha^2}{2}} d\alpha$
0.2450	0.38714 69147 92546	0.19354 35686 41049
51	.38713 74278 73638	.19362 09970 75376
52	.38712 79373 15925	.19369 84236 11956
53	.38711 84431 19685	.19377 58482 50060
54	.38710 89452 85198	.19385 32709 88961
0.2455	0.38709 94438 12744	0.19393 06918 27931
56	.38708 99387 02600	.19400 81107 66244
57	.38708 04299 55048	.19408 55278 03170
58	.38707 09175 70365	.19416 29429 37983
59	.38706 14015 48833	.19424 03561 69956
0.2460	0.38705 18818 90730	0.19431 77674 98360
61	.38704 23585 96337	.19439 51769 22470
62	.38703 28316 65934	.19447 25844 41556
63	.38702 33010 99799	.19454 99900 54894
64	.38701 37668 98215	.19462 73937 61754
0.2465	0.38700 42290 61460	0.19470 47955 61410
66	.38699 46875 89816	.19478 21954 53136
67	.38698 51424 83562	.19485 95934 36204
68	.38697 55937 42979	.19493 69895 09887
69	.38696 60413 68348	.19501 43836 73459
0.2470	0.38695 64853 59950	0.19509 17759 26192
71	.38694 69257 18065	.19516 91662 67361
72	.38693 73624 42975	.19524 65546 96237
73	.38692 77955 34960	.19532 39412 12096
74	.38691 82249 94301	.19540 13258 14209
0.2475	0.38690 86508 21281	0.19547 87085 01851
76	.38689 90730 16179	.19555 60892 74296
77	.38688 94915 79279	.19563 34681 30816
78	.38687 99065 10860	.19571 08450 70685
79	.38687 03178 11206	.19578 82200 93178
0.2480	0.38686 07254 80597	0.19586 55931 97568
81	.38685 11295 19316	.19594 29643 83128
82	.38684 15299 27644	.19602 03336 49133
83	.38683 19267 05864	.19609 77009 94857
84	.38682 23198 54258	.19617 50664 19574
0.2485	0.38681 27093 73108	0.19625 24299 22557
86	.38680 30952 62697	.19632 97915 03081
87	.38679 34775 23306	.19640 71511 60420
88	.38678 38561 55219	.19648 45088 93848
89	.38677 42311 58718	.19656 18647 02640
0.2490	0.38676 46025 34086	0.19663 92185 86070
91	.38675 49702 81606	.19671 65705 43412
92	.38674 53344 01561	.19679 39205 73941
93	.38673 56948 94234	.19687 12686 76931
94	.38672 60517 59908	.19694 86148 51657
0.2495	0.38671 64049 98866	0.19702 59590 97393
96	.38670 67546 11393	.19710 33014 13414
97	.38669 71005 97771	.19718 06417 98996
98	.38668 74429 58284	.19725 79802 53412
99	.38667 77816 93215	.19733 53167 75937
0.2500	0.38666 81168 02849	0.19741 26513 65847

x	$\dfrac{1}{\sqrt{2\pi}}\,e^{-\frac{x^2}{2}}$	$\dfrac{1}{\sqrt{2\pi}}\displaystyle\int_{-x}^{x} e^{-\frac{\alpha^2}{2}}\,d\alpha$
0.2500	0.38666 81168 02849	0.19741 26513 65847
01	.38665 84482 87470	.19748 99840 22417
02	.38664 87761 47361	.19756 73147 44921
03	.38663 91003 82806	.19764 46435 32634
04	.38662 94209 94090	.19772 19703 84832
0.2505	0.38661 97379 81497	0.19779 92953 00790
06	.38661 00513 45312	.19787 66182 79783
07	.38660 03610 85819	.19795 39393 21087
08	.38659 06672 03302	.19803 12584 23976
09	.38658 09696 98047	.19810 85755 87727
0.2510	0.38657 12685 70338	0.19818 58908 11614
11	.38656 15638 20460	.19826 32040 94913
12	.38655 18554 48698	.19834 05154 36901
13	.38654 21434 55337	.19841 78248 36851
14	.38653 24278 40663	.19849 51322 94041
0.2515	0.38652 27086 04960	0.19857 24378 07746
16	.38651 29857 48515	.19864 97413 77242
17	.38650 32592 71613	.19872 70430 01804
18	.38649 35291 74538	.19880 43426 80709
19	.38648 37954 57579	.19888 16404 13233
0.2520	0.38647 40581 21019	0.19895 89361 98651
21	.38646 43171 65145	.19903 62300 36240
22	.38645 45725 90243	.19911 35219 25276
23	.38644 48243 96599	.19919 08118 65035
24	.38643 50725 84499	.19926 80998 54793
0.2525	0.38642 53171 54230	0.19934 53858 93827
26	.38641 55581 06078	.19942 26699 81414
27	.38640 57954 40330	.19949 99521 16829
28	.38639 60291 57272	.19957 72322 99349
29	.38638 62592 57191	.19965 45105 28250
0.2530	0.38637 64857 40375	0.19973 17868 02810
31	.38636 67086 07109	.19980 90611 22305
32	.38635 69278 57681	.19988 63334 86012
33	.38634 71434 92378	.19996 36038 93207
34	.38633 73555 11487	.20004 08723 43168
0.2535	0.38632 75639 15296	0.20011 81388 35171
36	.38631 77687 04092	.20019 54033 68493
37	.38630 79698 78163	.20027 26659 42412
38	.38629 81674 37797	.20034 99265 56203
39	.38628 83613 83280	.20042 71852 09146
0.2540	0.38627 85517 14902	0.20050 44419 00516
41	.38626 87384 32949	.20058 16966 29591
42	.38625 89215 37710	.20065 89493 95648
43	.38624 91010 29474	.20073 62001 97965
44	.38623 92769 08528	.20081 34490 35819
0.2545	0.38622 94491 75161	0.20089 06959 08488
46	.38621 96178 29661	.20096 79408 15248
47	.38620 97828 72317	.20104 51837 55379
48	.38619 99443 03418	.20112 24247 28156
49	.38619 01021 23252	.20119 96637 32859
0.2550	0.38618 02563 32108	0.20127 69007 68765

x	$\frac{1}{\sqrt{2\pi}}e^{-\frac{x^2}{2}}$	$\frac{1}{\sqrt{2\pi}}\int_{-x}^{x}e^{-\frac{\alpha^2}{2}}\,d\alpha$
0.2550	0.38618 02563 32108	0.20127 69007 68765
51	.38617 04069 30275	.20135 41358 35151
52	.38616 05539 18043	.20143 13689 31296
53	.38615 06972 95700	.20150 86000 56478
54	.38614 08370 63535	.20158 58292 09974
0.2555	0.38613 09732 21839	0.20166 30563 91063
56	.38612 11057 70900	.20174 02815 99022
57	.38611 12347 11009	.20181 75048 33131
58	.38610 13600 42454	.20189 47260 92666
59	.38609 14817 65525	.20197 19453 76907
0.2560	0.38608 15998 80514	.20204 91626 85132
61	.38607 17143 87708	.20212 63780 16619
62	.38606 18252 87399	.20220 35913 70646
63	.38605 19325 79877	.20228 08027 46493
64	.38604 20362 65432	.20235 80121 43438
0.2565	0.38603 21363 44354	0.20243 52195 60759
66	.38602 22328 16935	.20251 24249 97735
67	.38601 23256 83463	.20258 96284 53645
68	.38600 24149 44231	.20266 68299 27768
69	.38599 25005 99529	.20274 40294 19383
0.2570	0.38598 25826 49647	0.20282 12269 27768
71	.38597 26610 94877	.20289 84224 52202
72	.38596 27359 35511	.20297 56159 91965
73	.38595 28071 71838	.20305 28075 46336
74	.38594 28748 04151	.20312 99971 14594
0.2575	0.38593 29388 32740	0.20320 71846 96017
76	.38592 29992 57898	.20328 43702 89887
77	.38591 30560 79916	.20336 15538 95480
78	.38590 31092 99085	.20343 87355 12078
79	.38589 31589 15697	.20351 59151 38960
0.2580	0.38588 32049 30045	0.20359 30927 75404
81	.38587 32473 42420	.20367 02684 20692
82	.38586 32861 53115	.20374 74420 74101
83	.38585 33213 62421	.20382 46137 34913
84	.38584 33529 70631	.20390 17834 02406
0.2585	0.38583 33809 78037	0.20397 89510 75861
86	.38582 34053 84932	.20405 61167 54557
87	.38581 34261 91608	.20413 32804 37775
88	.38580 34433 98358	.20421 04421 24794
89	.38579 34570 05475	.20428 76018 14894
0.2590	0.38578 34670 13252	0.20436 47595 07356
91	.38577 34734 21982	.20444 19152 01460
92	.38576 34762 31957	.20451 90688 96485
93	.38575 34754 43471	.20459 62205 91713
94	.38574 34710 56818	.20467 33702 86423
0.2595	0.38573 34630 72291	0.20475 05179 79896
96	.38572 34514 90183	.20482 76636 71412
97	.38571 34363 10787	.20490 48073 60252
98	.38570 34175 34399	.20498 19490 45696
99	.38569 33951 61310	.20505 90887 27026
0.2600	0.38568 33691 91816	0.20513 62264 03521

x	$\dfrac{1}{\sqrt{2\pi}}\,e^{-\frac{x^2}{2}}$	$\dfrac{1}{\sqrt{2\pi}}\displaystyle\int_{-x}^{x}e^{-\frac{\alpha^2}{2}}\,d\alpha$
0.2600	0.38568 33691 91816	0.20513 62264 03521
01	.38567 33396 26210	.20521 33620 74463
02	.38566 33064 64787	.20529 04957 39132
03	.38565 32697 07840	.20536 76273 96809
04	.38564 32293 55664	.20544 47570 46775
0.2605	0.38563 31854 08553	0.20552 18846 88312
06	.38562 31378 66802	.20559 90103 20699
07	.38561 30867 30706	.20567 61339 43219
08	.38560 30320 00558	.20575 32555 55152
09	.38559 29736 76655	.20583 03751 55779
0.2610	0.38558 29117 59290	0.20590 74927 44383
11	.38557 28462 48759	.20598 46083 20243
12	.38556 27771 45358	.20606 17218 82643
13	.38555 27044 49380	.20613 88334 30862
14	.38554 26281 61121	.20621 59429 64183
0.2615	0.38553 25482 80878	0.20629 30504 81887
16	.38552 24648 08945	.20637 01559 83256
17	.38551 23777 45618	.20644 72594 67571
18	.38550 22870 91192	.20652 43609 34115
19	.38549 21928 45964	.20660 14603 82168
0.2620	0.38548 20950 10230	0.20667 85578 11014
21	.38547 19935 84284	.20675 56532 19933
22	.38546 18885 68425	.20683 27466 08208
23	.38545 17799 62947	.20690 98379 75121
24	.38544 16677 68147	.20698 69273 19954
0.2625	0.38543 15519 84321	0.20706 40146 41989
26	.38542 14326 11766	.20714 10999 40509
27	.38541 13096 50779	.20721 81832 14795
28	.38540 11831 01656	.20729 52644 64130
29	.38539 10529 64694	.20737 23436 87796
0.2630	0.38538 09192 40190	0.20744 94208 85076
31	.38537 07819 28441	.20752 64960 55253
32	.38536 06410 29744	.20760 35691 97609
33	.38535 04965 44397	.20768 06403 11426
34	.38534 03484 72695	.20775 77093 95937
0.2635	0.38533 01968 14938	0.20783 47764 50576
36	.38532 00415 71422	.20791 18414 74474
37	.38530 98827 42446	.20798 89044 66965
38	.38529 97203 28306	.20806 59654 27332
39	.38528 95543 29300	.20814 30243 54858
0.2640	0.38527 93847 45728	0.20822 00812 48825
41	.38526 92115 77885	.20829 71361 08517
42	.38525 90348 26071	.20837 41889 33217
43	.38524 88544 90584	.20845 12397 22209
44	.38523 86705 71723	.20852 82884 74774
0.2645	0.38522 84830 69784	0.20860 53351 90198
46	.38521 82919 85068	.20868 23798 67764
47	.38520 80973 17872	.20875 94225 06754
48	.38519 78990 68495	.20883 64631 06452
49	.38518 76972 37237	.20891 35016 66142
0.2650	0.38517 74918 24395	0.20899 05381 85108

x	$\frac{1}{\sqrt{2\pi}}e^{-\frac{x^2}{2}}$	$\frac{1}{\sqrt{2\pi}}\int_{-x}^{x}e^{-\frac{\alpha^2}{2}}\,d\alpha$
0.2650	0.38517 74918 24395	0.20899 05381 85108
51	.38516 72828 30270	.20906 75726 62633
52	.38515 70702 55159	.20914 46050 98001
53	.38514 68540 99363	.20922 16354 90496
54	.38513 66343 63181	.20929 86638 39402
0.2655	0.38512 64110 46911	0.20937 56901 44003
56	.38511 61841 50854	.20945 27144 03583
57	.38510 59536 75309	.20952 97366 17425
58	.38509 57196 20575	.20960 67567 84814
59	.38508 54819 86954	.20968 37749 05034
0.2660	0.38507 52407 74743	0.20976 07909 77370
61	.38506 49959 84244	.20983 78050 01106
62	.38505 47476 15757	.20991 48169 75525
63	.38504 44956 69581	.20999 18268 99914
64	.38503 42401 46018	.21006 88347 73555
0.2665	0.38502 39810 45367	0.21014 58405 95734
66	.38501 37183 67928	.21022 28443 65734
67	.38500 34521 14003	.21029 98460 82842
68	.38499 31822 83893	.21037 68457 46342
69	.38498 29088 77897	.21045 38433 55517
0.2670	0.38497 26318 96317	0.21053 08389 09654
71	.38496 23513 39454	.21060 78324 08038
72	.38495 20672 07609	.21068 48238 49952
73	.38494 17795 01083	.21076 18132 34682
74	.38493 14882 20177	.21083 88005 61514
0.2675	0.38492 11933 65193	0.21091 57858 29732
76	.38491 08949 36433	.21099 27690 38622
77	.38490 05929 34197	.21106 97501 87468
78	.38489 02873 58788	.21114 67292 75557
79	.38487 99782 10507	.21122 37063 02174
0.2680	0.38486 96654 89656	0.21130 06812 66603
81	.38485 93491 96537	.21137 76541 68131
82	.38484 90293 31453	.21145 46250 06044
83	.38483 87058 94705	.21153 15937 79626
84	.38482 83788 86595	.21160 85604 88164
0.2685	0.38481 80483 07427	0.21168 55251 30943
86	.38480 77141 57502	.21176 24877 07249
87	.38479 73764 37123	.21183 94482 16368
88	.38478 70351 46593	.21191 64066 57585
89	.38477 66902 86214	.21199 33630 30188
0.2690	0.38476 63418 56290	0.21207 03173 33462
91	.38475 59898 57124	.21214 72695 66693
92	.38474 56342 89017	.21222 42197 29167
93	.38473 52751 52275	.21230 11678 20170
94	.38472 49124 47199	.21237 81138 38990
0.2695	0.38471 45461 74093	0.21245 50577 84911
96	.38470 41763 33261	.21253 19996 57222
97	.38469 38029 25006	.21260 89394 55207
98	.38468 34259 49633	.21268 58771 78154
99	.38467 30454 07443	.21276 28128 25349
0.2700	0.38466 26612 98743	0.21283 97463 96079

x	$\frac{1}{\sqrt{2\pi}} e^{-\frac{x^2}{2}}$	$\frac{1}{\sqrt{2\pi}} \int_{-x}^{x} e^{-\frac{\alpha^2}{2}} d\alpha$
0.2700	0.38466 26612 98743	0.21283 97463 96079
01	.38465 22736 23835	.21291 66778 89631
02	.38464 18823 83023	.21299 36073 05291
03	.38463 14875 76612	.21307 05346 42346
04	.38462 10892 04906	.21314 74599 00084
0.2705	0.38461 06872 68209	0.21322 43830 77791
06	.38460 02817 66826	.21330 13041 74753
07	.38458 98727 01062	.21337 82231 90260
08	.38457 94600 71220	.21345 51401 23596
09	.38456 90438 77606	.21353 20549 74051
0.2710	0.38455 86241 20524	0.21360 89677 40910
11	.38454 82008 00280	.21368 58784 23461
12	.38453 77739 17178	.21376 27870 20992
13	.38452 73434 71525	.21383 96935 32791
14	.38451 69094 63623	.21391 65979 58143
0.2715	0.38450 64718 93781	0.21399 35002 96339
16	.38449 60307 62301	.21407 04005 46664
17	.38448 55860 69492	.21414 72987 08406
18	.38447 51378 15656	.21422 41947 80854
19	.38446 46860 01102	.21430 10887 63295
0.2720	0.38445 42306 26134	0.21437 79806 55017
21	.38444 37716 91058	.21445 48704 55308
22	.38443 33091 96180	.21453 17581 63456
23	.38442 28431 41807	.21460 86437 78749
24	.38441 23735 28245	.21468 55273 00476
0.2725	0.38440 19003 55799	0.21476 24087 27923
26	.38439 14236 24778	.21483 92880 60381
27	.38438 09433 35486	.21491 61652 97136
28	.38437 04594 88230	.21499 30404 37478
29	.38435 99720 83318	.21506 99134 80694
0.2730	0.38434 94811 21056	0.21514 67844 26074
31	.38433 89866 01751	.21522 36532 72905
32	.38432 84885 25710	.21530 05200 20477
33	.38431 79868 93241	.21537 73846 68079
34	.38430 74817 04649	.21545 42472 14998
0.2735	0.38429 69729 60243	0.21553 11076 60523
36	.38428 64606 60331	.21560 79660 03945
37	.38427 59448 05219	.21568 48222 44550
38	.38426 54253 95215	.21576 16763 81630
39	.38425 49024 30627	.21583 85284 14472
0.2740	0.38424 43759 11762	0.21591 53783 42365
41	.38423 38458 38929	.21599 22261 64599
42	.38422 33122 12436	.21606 90718 80464
43	.38421 27750 32590	.21614 59154 89247
44	.38420 22342 99700	.21622 27569 90240
0.2745	0.38419 16900 14075	0.21629 95963 82730
46	.38418 11421 76021	.21637 64336 66009
47	.38417 05907 85849	.21645 32688 39364
48	.38416 00358 43867	.21653 01019 02086
49	.38414 94773 50382	.21660 69328 53465
0.2750	0.38413 89153 05705	0.21668 37616 92790

x	$\dfrac{1}{\sqrt{2\pi}}\,e^{-\frac{x^2}{2}}$	$\dfrac{1}{\sqrt{2\pi}}\displaystyle\int_{-x}^{x} e^{-\frac{\alpha^2}{2}}\,d\alpha$
0.2750	0.38413 89153 05705	0.21668 37616 92790
51	.38412 83497 10143	.21676 05884 19350
52	.38411 77805 64007	.21683 74130 32437
53	.38410 72078 67604	.21691 42355 31339
54	.38409 66316 21245	.21699 10559 15347
0.2755	0.38408 60518 25238	0.21706 78741 83751
56	.38407 54684 79892	.21714 46903 35841
57	.38406 48815 85518	.21722 15043 70907
58	.38405 42911 42425	.21729 83162 88238
59	.38404 36971 50922	.21737 51260 87127
0.2760	0.38403 30996 11319	0.21745 19337 66862
61	.38402 24985 23927	.21752 87393 26735
62	.38401 18938 89054	.21760 55427 66035
63	.38400 12857 07012	.21768 23440 84054
64	.38399 06739 78109	.21775 91432 80082
0.2765	0.38398 00587 02657	0.21783 59403 53409
66	.38396 94398 80967	.21791 27353 03326
67	.38395 88175 13347	.21798 95281 29125
68	.38394 81916 00109	.21806 63188 30095
69	.38393 75621 41563	.21814 31074 05529
0.2770	0.38392 69291 38021	0.21821 98938 54716
71	.38391 62925 89793	.21829 66781 76947
72	.38390 56524 97189	.21837 34603 71515
73	.38389 50088 60522	.21845 02404 37710
74	.38388 43616 80102	.21852 70183 74823
0.2775	0.38387 37109 56240	0.21860 37941 82146
76	.38386 30566 89247	.21868 05678 58969
77	.38385 23988 79436	.21875 73394 04585
78	.38384 17375 27118	.21883 41088 18285
79	.38383 10726 32603	.21891 08760 99360
0.2780	0.38382 04041 96205	0.21898 76412 47102
81	.38380 97322 18234	.21906 44042 60802
82	.38379 90566 99003	.21914 11651 39753
83	.38378 83776 38823	.21921 79238 83246
84	.38377 76950 38007	.21929 46804 90573
0.2785	0.38376 70088 96867	0.21937 14349 61025
86	.38375 63192 15716	.21944 81872 93895
87	.38374 56259 94865	.21952 49374 88476
88	.38373 49292 34627	.21960 16855 44057
89	.38372 42289 35315	.21967 84314 59933
0.2790	0.38371 35250 97241	0.21975 51752 35396
91	.38370 28177 20719	.21983 19168 69736
92	.38369 21068 06060	.21990 86563 62248
93	.38368 13923 53579	.21998 53937 12223
94	.38367 06743 63588	.22006 21289 18954
0.2795	0.38365 99528 36400	0.22013 88619 81733
96	.38364 92277 72329	.22021 55928 99852
97	.38363 84991 71687	.22029 23216 72606
98	.38362 77670 34790	.22036 90482 99285
99	.38361 70313 61949	.22044 57727 79184
0.2800	0.38360 62921 53479	0.22052 24951 11594

x	$\dfrac{1}{\sqrt{2\pi}} e^{-\frac{x^2}{2}}$	$\dfrac{1}{\sqrt{2\pi}} \displaystyle\int_{-x}^{x} e^{-\frac{\alpha^2}{2}} \, d\alpha$
0.2800	0.38360 62921 53479	0.22052 24951 11594
01	.38359 55494 09693	.22059 92152 95810
02	.38358 48031 30905	.22067 59333 31123
03	.38357 40533 17430	.22075 26492 16826
04	.38356 32999 69581	.22082 93629 52214
0.2805	0.38355 25430 87672	0.22090 60745 36579
06	.38354 17826 72018	.22098 27839 69213
07	.38353 10187 22934	.22105 94912 49412
08	.38352 02512 40732	.22113 61963 76467
09	.38350 94802 25729	.22121 28993 49673
0.2810	0.38349 87056 78238	0.22128 96001 68322
11	.38348 79275 98575	.22136 62988 31708
12	.38347 71459 87053	.22144 29953 39126
13	.38346 63608 43989	.22151 96896 89868
14	.38345 55721 69697	.22159 63818 83228
0.2815	0.38344 47799 64493	0.22167 30719 18500
16	.38343 39842 28690	.22174 97597 94978
17	.38342 31849 62606	.22182 64455 11956
18	.38341 23821 66555	.22190 31290 68728
19	.38340 15758 40852	.22197 98104 64588
0.2820	0.38339 07659 85814	0.22205 64896 98829
21	.38337 99526 01756	.22213 31667 70747
22	.38336 91356 88994	.22220 98416 79635
23	.38335 83152 47843	.22228 65144 24787
24	.38334 74912 78620	.22236 31850 05499
0.2825	0.38333 66637 81641	0.22243 98534 21063
26	.38332 58327 57222	.22251 65196 70776
27	.38331 49982 05679	.22259 31837 53931
28	.38330 41601 27329	.22266 98456 69823
29	.38329 33185 22488	.22274 65054 17747
0.2830	0.38328 24733 91472	0.22282 31629 96997
31	.38327 16247 34599	.22289 98184 06869
32	.38326 07725 52185	.22297 64716 46656
33	.38324 99168 44548	.22305 31227 15654
34	.38323 90576 12003	.22312 97716 13159
0.2835	0.38322 81948 54868	0.22320 64183 38464
36	.38321 73285 73460	.22328 30628 90866
37	.38320 64587 68097	.22335 97052 69659
38	.38319 55854 39095	.22343 63454 74138
39	.38318 47085 86773	.22351 29835 03599
0.2840	0.38317 38282 11448	0.22358 96193 57338
41	.38316 29443 13437	.22366 62530 34649
42	.38315 20568 93058	.22374 28845 34829
43	.38314 11659 50629	.22381 95138 57172
44	.38313 02714 86468	.22389 61410 00974
0.2845	0.38311 93735 00893	0.22397 27659 65531
46	.38310 84719 94222	.22404 93887 50140
47	.38309 75669 66773	.22412 60093 54094
48	.38308 66584 18865	.22420 26277 76692
49	.38307 57463 50815	.22427 92440 17227
0.2850	0.38306 48307 62944	0.22435 58580 74997

x	$\dfrac{1}{\sqrt{2\pi}}\,e^{-\frac{x^2}{2}}$	$\dfrac{1}{\sqrt{2\pi}}\displaystyle\int_{-x}^{x} e^{-\frac{\alpha^2}{2}}\,d\alpha$
0.2850	0.38306 48307 62944	0.22435 58580 74997
51	.38305 39116 55568	.22443 24699 49298
52	.38304 29890 29007	.22450 90796 39425
53	.38303 20628 83580	.22458 56871 44675
54	.38302 11332 19606	.22466 22924 64344
0.2855	0.38301 02000 37402	0.22473 88955 97728
56	.38299 92633 37290	.22481 54965 44124
57	.38298 83231 19587	.22489 20953 02829
58	.38297 73793 84613	.22496 86918 73138
59	.38296 64321 32688	.22504 52862 54348
0.2860	0.38295 54813 64130	0.22512 18784 45756
61	.38294 45270 79260	.22519 84684 46659
62	.38293 35692 78398	.22527 50562 56353
63	.38292 26079 61862	.22535 16418 74136
64	.38291 16431 29972	.22542 82252 99304
0.2865	0.38290 06747 83050	0.22550 48065 31154
66	.38288 97029 21414	.22558 13855 68983
67	.38287 87275 45385	.22565 79624 12088
68	.38286 77486 55283	.22573 45370 59767
69	.38285 67662 51429	.22581 11095 11316
0.2870	0.38284 57803 34143	0.22588 76797 66033
71	.38283 47909 03745	.22596 42478 23215
72	.38282 37979 60556	.22604 08136 82160
73	.38281 28015 04897	.22611 73773 42165
74	.38280 18015 37088	.22619 39388 02528
0.2875	0.38279 07980 57451	0.22627 04980 62546
76	.38277 97910 66307	.22634 70551 21517
77	.38276 87805 63976	.22642 36099 78739
78	.38275 77665 50780	.22650 01626 33509
79	.38274 67490 27041	.22657 67130 85125
0.2880	0.38273 57279 93079	0.22665 32613 32885
81	.38272 47034 49215	.22672 98073 76088
82	.38271 36753 95773	.22680 63512 14031
83	.38270 26438 33073	.22688 28928 46012
84	.38269 16087 61437	.22695 94322 71330
0.2885	0.38268 05701 81187	0.22703 59694 89283
86	.38266 95280 92645	.22711 25044 99169
87	.38265 84824 96133	.22718 90373 00286
88	.38264 74333 91973	.22726 55678 91934
89	.38263 63807 80487	.22734 20962 73409
0.2890	0.38262 53246 61999	0.22741 86224 44012
91	.38261 42650 36829	.22749 51464 03040
92	.38260 32019 05302	.22757 16681 49793
93	.38259 21352 67739	.22764 81876 83569
94	.38258 10651 24463	.22772 47050 03666
0.2895	0.38256 99914 75797	0.22780 12201 09385
96	.38255 89143 22064	.22787 77330 00023
97	.38254 78336 63587	.22795 42436 74880
98	.38253 67495 00689	.22803 07521 33255
99	.38252 56618 33694	.22810 72583 74447
0.2900	0.38251 45706 62924	0.22818 37623 97755

60

x	$\frac{1}{\sqrt{2\pi}} e^{-\frac{x^2}{2}}$	$\frac{1}{\sqrt{2\pi}} \int_{-x}^{x} e^{-\frac{\alpha^2}{2}} d\alpha$
0.2900	0.38251 45706 62924	0.22818 37623 97755
01	.38250 34759 88703	.22826 02642 02478
02	.38249 23778 11355	.22833 67637 87917
03	.38248 12761 31203	.22841 32611 53369
04	.38247 01709 48571	.22848 97562 98136
0.2905	0.38245 90622 63782	0.22856 62492 21515
06	.38244 79500 77161	.22864 27399 22808
07	.38243 68343 89032	.22871 92284 01313
08	.38242 57151 99718	.22879 57146 56330
09	.38241 45925 09544	.22887 21986 87159
0.2910	0.38240 34663 18834	0.22894 86804 93100
11	.38239 23366 27912	.22902 51600 73453
12	.38238 12034 37103	.22910 16374 27518
13	.38237 00667 46732	.22917 81125 54595
14	.38235 89265 57123	.22925 45854 53984
0.2915	0.38234 77828 68601	0.22933 10561 24984
16	.38233 66356 81490	.22940 75245 66898
17	.38232 54849 96116	.22948 39907 79024
18	.38231 43308 12804	.22956 04547 60663
19	.38230 31731 31878	.22963 69165 11116
0.2920	0.38229 20119 53665	0.22971 33760 29683
21	.38228 08472 78489	.22978 98333 15664
22	.38226 96791 06675	.22986 62883 68361
23	.38225 85074 38550	.22994 27411 87074
24	.38224 73322 74439	.23001 91917 71103
0.2925	0.38223 61536 14667	0.23009 56401 19750
26	.38222 49714 59561	.23017 20862 32316
27	.38221 37858 09446	.23024 85301 08101
28	.38220 25966 64648	.23032 49717 46407
29	.38219 14040 25494	.23040 14111 46534
0.2930	0.38218 02078 92309	0.23047 78483 07784
31	.38216 90082 65420	.23055 42832 29458
32	.38215 78051 45154	.23063 07159 10857
33	.38214 65985 31836	.23070 71463 51283
34	.38213 53884 25793	.23078 35745 50037
0.2935	0.38212 41748 27352	0.23086 00005 06421
36	.38211 29577 36839	.23093 64242 19735
37	.38210 17371 54582	.23101 28456 89283
38	.38209 05130 80908	.23108 92649 14365
39	.38207 92855 16143	.23116 56818 94282
0.2940	0.38206 80544 60614	0.23124 20966 28338
41	.38205 68199 14650	.23131 85091 15834
42	.38204 55818 78576	.23139 49193 56071
43	.38203 43403 52721	.23147 13273 48353
44	.38202 30953 37412	.23154 77330 91980
0.2945	0.38201 18468 32977	0.23162 41365 86255
46	.38200 05948 39743	.23170 05378 30480
47	.38198 93393 58038	.23177 69368 23958
48	.38197 80803 88190	.23185 33335 65991
49	.38196 68179 30528	.23192 97280 55881
0.2950	0.38195 55519 85378	0.23200 61202 92931

x	$\frac{1}{\sqrt{2\pi}}e^{-\frac{x^2}{2}}$	$\frac{1}{\sqrt{2\pi}}\int_{-x}^{x}e^{-\frac{\alpha^2}{2}}d\alpha$
0.2950	0.38195 55519 85378	0.23200 61202 92931
51	.38194 42825 53070	.23208 25102 76443
52	.38193 30096 33931	.23215 88980 05720
53	.38192 17332 28291	.23223 52834 80064
54	.38191 04533 36476	.23231 16666 98779
0.2955	0.38189 91699 58817	.23238 80476 61166
56	.38188 78830 95641	.23246 44263 66530
57	.38187 65927 47278	.23254 08028 14172
58	.38186 52989 14056	.23261 71770 03396
59	.38185 40015 96304	.23269 35489 33505
0.2960	0.38184 27007 94351	0.23276 99186 03803
61	.38183 13965 08527	.23284 62860 13591
62	.38182 00887 39160	.23292 26511 62174
63	.38180 87774 86580	.23299 90140 48854
64	.38179 74627 51116	.23307 53746 72936
0.2965	0.38178 61445 33097	0.23315 17330 33723
66	.38177 48228 32855	.23322 80891 30517
67	.38176 34976 50717	.23330 44429 62624
68	.38175 21689 87014	.23338 07945 29345
69	.38174 08368 42076	.23345 71438 29986
0.2970	0.38172 95012 16232	0.23353 34908 63850
71	.38171 81621 09814	.23360 98356 30241
72	.38170 68195 23150	.23368 61781 28462
73	.38169 54734 56571	.23376 25183 57818
74	.38168 41239 10408	.23383 88563 17613
0.2975	0.38167 27708 84991	0.23391 51920 07150
76	.38166 14143 80651	.23399 15254 25735
77	.38165 00543 97718	.23406 78565 72671
78	.38163 86909 36522	.23414 41854 47262
79	.38162 73239 97396	.23422 05120 48813
0.2980	0.38161 59535 80669	0.23429 68363 76629
81	.38160 45796 86673	.23437 31584 30014
82	.38159 32023 15738	.23444 94782 08272
83	.38158 18214 68197	.23452 57957 10708
84	.38157 04371 44380	.23460 21109 36628
0.2985	0.38155 90493 44619	0.23467 84238 85334
86	.38154 76580 69245	.23475 47345 56134
87	.38153 62633 18589	.23483 10429 48330
88	.38152 48650 92984	.23490 73490 61229
89	.38151 34633 92762	.23498 36528 94136
0.2990	0.38150 20582 18254	0.23505 99544 46355
91	.38149 06495 69791	.23513 62537 17192
92	.38147 92374 47707	.23521 25507 05951
93	.38146 78218 52333	.23528 88454 11939
94	.38145 64027 84002	.23536 51378 34461
0.2995	0.38144 49802 43045	0.23544 14279 72821
96	.38143 35542 29796	.23551 77158 26326
97	.38142 21247 44587	.23559 40013 94282
98	.38141 06917 87750	.23567 02846 75993
99	.38139 92553 59618	.23574 65656 70765
0.3000	0.38138 78154 60524	0.23582 28443 77905

x	$\frac{1}{\sqrt{2\pi}} e^{-\frac{x^2}{2}}$	$\frac{1}{\sqrt{2\pi}} \int_{-x}^{x} e^{-\frac{\alpha^2}{2}} d\alpha$
0.3000	0.38138 78154 60524	0.23582 28443 77905
01	.38137 63720 90801	.23589 91207 96718
02	.38136 49252 50782	.23597 53949 26510
03	.38135 34749 40800	.23605 16667 66587
04	.38134 20211 61188	.23612 79363 16255
0.3005	0.38133 05639 12280	0.23620 42035 74820
06	.38131 91031 94408	.23628 04685 41589
07	.38130 76390 07907	.23635 67312 15867
08	.38129 61713 53110	.23643 29915 96961
09	.38128 47002 30350	.23650 92496 84177
0.3010	0.38127 32256 39961	0.23658 55054 76822
11	.38126 17475 82277	.23666 17589 74202
12	.38125 02660 57633	.23673 80101 75624
13	.38123 87810 66362	.23681 42590 80394
14	.38122 72926 08797	.23689 05056 87819
0.3015	0.38121 58006 85274	0.23696 67499 97206
16	.38120 43052 96127	.23704 29920 07862
17	.38119 28064 41691	.23711 92317 19094
18	.38118 13041 22298	.23719 54691 30208
19	.38116 97983 38285	.23727 17042 40512
0.3020	0.38115 82890 89986	0.23734 79370 49312
21	.38114 67763 77736	.23742 41675 55917
22	.38113 52602 01869	.23750 03957 59632
23	.38112 37405 62721	.23757 66216 59767
24	.38111 22174 60626	.23765 28452 55627
0.3025	0.38110 06908 95921	0.23772 90665 46520
26	.38108 91608 68939	.23780 52855 31754
27	.38107 76273 80017	.23788 15022 10637
28	.38106 60904 29489	.23795 77165 82475
29	.38105 45500 17692	.23803 39286 46578
0.3030	0.38104 30061 44961	0.23811 01384 02252
31	.38103 14588 11632	.23818 63458 48805
32	.38101 99080 18040	.23826 25509 85546
33	.38100 83537 64521	.23833 87538 11782
34	.38099 67960 51412	.23841 49543 26821
0.3035	0.38098 52348 79049	0.23849 11525 29972
36	.38097 36702 47767	.23856 73484 20542
37	.38096 21021 57904	.23864 35419 97840
38	.38095 05306 09794	.23871 97332 61174
39	.38093 89556 03776	.23879 59222 09853
0.3040	0.38092 73771 40185	0.23887 21088 43185
41	.38091 57952 19358	.23894 82931 60479
42	.38090 42098 41632	.23902 44751 61043
43	.38089 26210 07344	.23910 06548 44185
44	.38088 10287 16830	.23917 68322 09215
0.3045	0.38086 94329 70428	0.23925 30072 55442
46	.38085 78337 68474	.23932 91799 82173
47	.38084 62311 11307	.23940 53503 88719
48	.38083 46249 99263	.23948 15184 74387
49	.38082 30154 32679	.23955 76842 38488
0.3050	0.38081 14024 11894	0.23963 38476 80330

x	$\frac{1}{\sqrt{2\pi}}e^{-\frac{x^2}{2}}$	$\frac{1}{\sqrt{2\pi}}\int_{-x}^{x}e^{-\frac{\alpha^2}{2}}\,d\alpha$
0.3050	0.38081 14024 11894	0.23963 38476 80330
51	.38079 97859 37245	.23971 00087 99223
52	.38078 81660 09069	.23978 61675 94475
53	.38077 65426 27704	.23986 23240 65396
54	.38076 49157 93489	.23993 84782 11296
0.3055	0.38075 32855 06760	0.24001 46300 31483
56	.38074 16517 67857	.24009 07795 25268
57	.38073 00145 77117	.24016 69266 91960
58	.38071 83739 34879	.24024 30715 30869
59	.38070 67298 41480	.24031 92140 41304
0.3060	0.38069 50822 97260	0.24039 53542 22575
61	.38068 34313 02556	.24047 14920 73993
62	.38067 17768 57708	.24054 76275 94866
63	.38066 01189 63054	.24062 37607 84506
64	.38064 84576 18933	.24069 98916 42222
0.3065	0.38063 67928 25684	0.24077 60201 67324
66	.38062 51245 83646	.24085 21463 59122
67	.38061 34528 93158	.24092 82702 16927
68	.38060 17777 54559	.24100 43917 40049
69	.38059 00991 68188	.24108 05109 27799
0.0370	0.38057 84171 34385	0.24115 66277 79487
71	.38056 67316 53489	.24123 27422 94423
72	.38055 50427 25840	.24130 88544 71919
73	.38054 33503 51777	.24138 49643 11284
74	.38053 16545 31641	.24146 10718 11830
0.3075	0.38051 99552 65770	0.24153 71769 72867
76	.38050 82525 54505	.24161 32797 93706
77	.38049 65463 98186	.24168 93802 73659
78	.38048 48367 97153	.24176 54784 12036
79	.38047 31237 51746	.24184 15742 08148
0.3080	0.38046 14072 62306	0.24191 76676 61307
81	.38044 96873 29173	.24199 37587 70823
82	.38043 79639 52686	.24206 98475 36009
83	.38042 62371 33188	.24214 59339 56175
84	.38041 45068 71018	.24222 20180 30633
0.3085	0.38040 27731 66518	0.24229 80997 58694
86	.38039 10360 20028	.24237 41791 39670
87	.38037 92954 31888	.24245 02561 72872
88	.38036 75514 02441	.24252 63308 57613
89	.38035 58039 32027	.24260 24031 93204
0.3090	0.38034 40530 20988	0.24267 84731 78957
91	.38033 22986 69665	.24275 45408 14183
92	.38032 05408 78398	.24283 06060 98195
93	.38030 87796 47530	.24290 66690 30305
94	.38029 70149 77403	.24298 27296 09825
0.3095	0.38028 52468 68358	0.24305 87878 36067
96	.38027 34753 20736	.24313 48437 08343
97	.38026 17003 34880	.24321 08972 25966
98	.38024 99219 11131	.24328 69483 88248
99	.38023 81400 49832	.24336 29971 94501
0.3100	0.38022 63547 51325	0.24343 90436 44039

X	$\dfrac{1}{\sqrt{2\pi}} e^{-\frac{x^2}{2}}$	$\dfrac{1}{\sqrt{2\pi}} \displaystyle\int_{-x}^{x} e^{-\frac{\alpha^2}{2}} d\alpha$
0.3100	0.38022 63547 51325	0.24343 90436 44039
01	.38021 45660 15952	.24351 50877 36173
02	.38020 27738 44055	.24359 11294 70216
03	.38019 09782 35977	.24366 71688 45481
04	.38017 91791 92060	.24374 32058 61281
0.3105	0.38016 73767 12646	0.24381 92405 16929
06	.38015 55707 98080	.24389 52728 11737
07	.38014 37614 48703	.24397 13027 45019
08	.38013 19486 64858	.24404 73303 16088
09	.38012 01324 46888	.24412 33555 24256
0.3110	0.38010 83127 95137	0.24419 93783 68838
11	.38009 64897 09947	.24427 53988 49145
12	.38008 46631 91661	.24435 14169 64493
13	.38007 28332 40624	.24442 74327 14193
14	.38006 09998 57178	.24450 34460 97560
0.3115	0.38004 91630 41668	0.24457 94571 13907
16	.38003 73227 94435	.24465 54657 62548
17	.38002 54791 15826	.24473 14720 42796
18	.38001 36320 06182	.24480 74759 53966
19	.38000 17814 65848	.24488 34774 95370
0.3120	0.37998 99274 95169	0.24495 94766 66323
21	.37997 80700 94487	.24503 54734 66139
22	.37996 62092 64148	.24511 14678 94132
23	.37995 43450 04496	.24518 74599 49616
24	.37994 24773 15874	.24526 34496 31906
0.3125	0.37993 06061 98628	0.24533 94369 40314
26	.37991 87316 53101	.24541 54218 74156
27	.37990 68536 79640	.24549 14044 32747
28	.37989 49722 78587	.24556 73846 15400
29	.37988 30874 50289	.24564 33624 21430
0.3130	0.37987 11991 95090	0.24571 93378 50151
31	.37985 93075 13334	.24579 53109 00879
32	.37984 74124 05368	.24587 12815 72928
33	.37983 55138 71536	.24594 72498 65613
34	.37982 36119 12184	.24602 32157 78249
0.3135	0.37981 17065 27657	0.24609 91793 10150
36	.37979 97977 18300	.24617 51404 60631
37	.37978 78854 84459	.24625 10992 29009
38	.37977 59698 26480	.24632 70556 14597
39	.37976 40507 44708	.24640 30096 16711
0.3140	0.37975 21282 39489	0.24647 89612 34667
41	.37974 02023 11170	.24655 49104 67779
42	.37972 82729 60096	.24663 08573 15363
43	.37971 63401 86613	.24670 68017 76735
44	.37970 44039 91067	.24678 27438 51209
0.3145	0.37969 24643 73805	0.24685 86835 38103
46	.37968 05213 35173	.24693 46208 36731
47	.37966 85748 75518	.24701 05557 46409
48	.37965 66249 95186	.24708 64882 66453
49	.37964 46716 94524	.24716 24183 96179
0.3150	0.37963 27149 73878	0.24723 83461 34903

x	$\dfrac{1}{\sqrt{2\pi}}\, e^{-\frac{x^2}{2}}$	$\dfrac{1}{\sqrt{2\pi}} \displaystyle\int_{-x}^{x} e^{-\frac{\alpha^2}{2}}\, d\alpha$
0.3150	0.37963 27149 73878	0.24723 83461 34903
51	.37962 07548 33596	.24731 42714 81940
52	.37960 87912 74024	.24739 01944 36608
53	.37959 68242 95510	.24746 61149 98222
54	.37958 48538 98400	.24754 20331 66099
0.3155	0.37957 28800 83042	0.24761 79489 39554
56	.37956 09028 49783	.24769 38623 17904
57	.37954 89221 98970	.24776 97733 00466
58	.37953 69381 30951	.24784 56818 86556
59	.37952 49506 46073	.24792 15880 75490
0.3160	0.37951 29597 44685	0.24799 74918 66586
61	.37950 09654 27133	.24807 33932 59160
62	.37948 89676 93767	.24814 92922 52529
63	.37947 69665 44932	.24822 51888 46010
64	.37946 49619 80979	.24830 10830 38920
0.3165	0.37945 29540 02254	0.24837 69748 30575
66	.37944 09426 09107	.24845 28642 20293
67	.37942 89278 01884	.24852 87512 07391
68	.37941 69095 80936	.24860 46357 91186
69	.37940 48879 46610	.24868 05179 70996
0.3170	0.37939 28628 99254	0.24875 63977 46137
71	.37938 08344 39218	.24883 22751 15928
72	.37936 88025 66850	.24890 81500 79686
73	.37935 67672 82499	.24898 40226 36727
74	.37934 47285 86515	.24905 98927 86371
0.3175	0.37933 26864 79245	0.24913 57605 27934
76	.37932 06409 61040	.24921 16258 60735
77	.37930 85920 32248	.24928 74887 84092
78	.37929 65396 93218	.24936 33492 97321
79	.37928 44839 44301	.24943 92073 99742
0.3180	0.37927 24247 85846	0.24951 50630 90671
81	.37926 03622 18201	.24959 09163 69429
82	.37924 82962 41718	.24966 67672 35331
83	.37923 62268 56745	.24974 26156 87698
84	.37922 41540 63633	.24981 84617 25847
0.3185	0.37921 20778 62731	0.24989 43053 49096
86	.37919 99982 54390	.24997 01465 56765
87	.37918 79152 38959	.25004 59853 48171
88	.37917 58288 16789	.25012 18217 22633
89	.37916 37389 88231	.25019 76556 79471
0.3190	0.37915 16457 53633	0.25027 34872 18001
91	.37913 95491 13348	.25034 93163 37545
92	.37912 74490 67726	.25042 51430 37420
93	.37911 53456 17117	.25050 09673 16945
94	.37910 32387 61872	.25057 67891 75440
0.3195	0.37909 11285 02342	0.25065 26086 12223
96	.37907 90148 38877	.25072 84256 26614
97	.37906 68977 71830	.25080 42402 17931
98	.37905 47773 01551	.25088 00523 85496
99	.37904 26534 28391	.25095 58621 28625
0.3200	0.37903 05261 52702	0.25103 16694 46640

X	$\dfrac{1}{\sqrt{2\pi}} e^{-\frac{x^2}{2}}$	$\dfrac{1}{\sqrt{2\pi}} \displaystyle\int_{-x}^{x} e^{-\frac{\alpha^2}{2}} \, d\alpha$
0.3200	0.37903 05261 52702	0.25103 16694 46640
01	.37901 83954 74834	.25110 74743 38859
02	.37900 62613 95141	.25118 32768 04603
03	.37899 41239 13972	.25125 90768 43191
04	.37898 19830 31680	.25133 48744 53942
0.3205	0.37896 98387 48616	0.25141 06696 36177
06	.37895 76910 65133	.25148 64623 89215
07	.37894 55399 81583	.25156 22527 12376
08	.37893 33854 98316	.25163 80406 04981
09	.37892 12276 15686	.25171 38260 66349
0.3210	0.37890 90663 34045	0.25178 96090 95800
11	.37889 69016 53745	.25186 53896 92656
12	.37888 47335 75139	.25194 11678 56235
13	.37887 25620 98578	.25201 69435 85859
14	.37886 03872 24416	.25209 27168 80848
0.3215	0.37884 82089 53005	0.25216 84877 40523
16	.37883 60272 84698	.25224 42561 64203
17	.37882 38422 19847	.25232 00221 51210
18	.37881 16537 58807	.25239 57857 00865
19	.37879 94619 01929	.25247 15468 12487
0.3220	0.37878 72666 49567	0.25254 73054 85399
21	.37877 50680 02075	.25262 30617 18921
22	.37876 28659 59804	.25269 88155 12373
23	.37875 06605 23110	.25277 45668 65078
24	.37873 84516 92345	.25285 03157 76356
0.3225	0.37872 62394 67863	0.25292 60622 45529
26	.37871 40238 50017	.25300 18062 71917
27	.37870 18048 39162	.25307 75478 54843
28	.37868 95824 35651	.25315 32869 93627
29	.37867 73566 39838	.25322 90236 87591
0.3230	0.37866 51274 52077	0.25330 47579 36057
31	.37865 28948 72723	.25338 04897 38346
32	.37864 06589 02128	.25345 62190 93780
33	.37862 84195 40649	.25353 19460 01680
34	.37861 61767 88639	.25360 76704 61370
0.3235	0.37860 39306 46453	0.25368 33924 72170
36	.37859 16811 14445	.25375 91120 33403
37	.37857 94281 92969	.25383 48291 44390
38	.37856 71718 82382	.25391 05438 04454
39	.37855 49121 83036	.25398 62560 12917
0.3240	0.37854 26490 95289	0.25406 19657 69101
41	.37853 03826 19493	.25413 76730 72329
42	.37851 81127 56006	.25421 33779 21923
43	.37850 58395 05181	.25428 90803 17206
44	.37849 35628 67374	.25436 47802 57499
0.3245	0.37848 12828 42940	0.25444 04777 42127
46	.37846 89994 32236	.25451 61727 70411
47	.37845 67126 35616	.25459 18653 41674
48	.37844 44224 53436	.25466 75554 55239
49	.37843 21288 86052	.25474 32431 10430
0.3250	0.37841 98319 33819	0.25481 89283 06568

x	$\dfrac{1}{\sqrt{2\pi}}\,e^{-\frac{x^2}{2}}$	$\dfrac{1}{\sqrt{2\pi}}\displaystyle\int_{-x}^{x} e^{-\frac{\alpha^2}{2}}\,d\alpha$
0.3250	0.37841 98319 33819	0.25481 89283 06568
51	.37840 75315 97095	.25489 46110 42978
52	.37839 52278 76234	.25497 02913 18981
53	.37838 29207 71592	.25504 59691 33902
54	.37837 06102 83527	.25512 16444 87064
0.3255	0.37835 82964 12394	0.25519 73173 77790
56	.37834 59791 58549	.25527 29878 05404
57	.37833 36585 22350	.25534 86557 69228
58	.37832 13345 04152	.25542 43212 68587
59	.37830 90071 04313	.25549 99843 02804
0.3260	0.37829 66763 23188	0.25557 56448 71204
61	.37828 43421 61135	.25565 13029 73108
62	.37827 20046 18511	.25572 69586 07843
63	.37825 96636 95673	.25580 26117 74730
64	.37824 73193 92977	.25587 82624 73096
0.3265	0.37823 49717 10782	0.25595 39107 02262
66	.37822 26206 49444	.25602 95564 61555
67	.37821 02662 09320	.25610 51997 50297
68	.37819 79083 90769	.25618 08405 67813
69	.37818 55471 94147	.25625 64789 13428
0.3270	0.37817 31826 19813	0.25633 21147 86466
71	.37816 08146 68123	.25640 77481 86251
72	.37814 84433 39436	.25648 33791 12108
73	.37813 60686 34110	.25655 90075 63361
74	.37812 36905 52503	.25663 46335 39336
0.3275	0.37811 13090 94972	0.25671 02570 39357
76	.37809 89242 61877	.25678 58780 62749
77	.37808 65360 53574	.25686 14966 08837
78	.37807 41444 70423	.25693 71126 76946
79	.37806 17495 12782	.25701 27262 66400
0.3280	0.37804 93511 81010	0.25708 83373 76526
81	.37803 69494 75464	.25716 39460 06648
82	.37802 45443 96505	.25723 95521 56091
83	.37801 21359 44490	.25731 51558 24181
84	.37799 97241 19778	.25739 07570 10244
0.3285	0.37798 73089 22729	0.25746 63557 13605
86	.37797 48903 53702	.25754 19519 33588
87	.37796 24684 13055	.25761 75456 69521
88	.37795 00431 01148	.25769 31369 20729
89	.37793 76144 18340	.25776 87256 86537
0.3290	0.37792 51823 64991	0.25784 43119 66271
91	.37791 27469 41460	.25791 98957 59258
92	.37790 03081 48107	.25799 54770 64823
93	.37788 78659 85292	.25807 10558 82293
94	.37787 54204 53374	.25814 66322 10993
0.3295	0.37786 29715 52712	0.25822 22060 50250
96	.37785 05192 83668	.25829 77773 99389
97	.37783 80636 46601	.25837 33462 57739
98	.37782 56046 41871	.25844 89126 24624
99	.37781 31422 69839	.25852 44764 99371
0.3300	0.37780 06765 30865	0.25860 00378 81307

x	$\dfrac{1}{\sqrt{2\pi}}\,e^{-\frac{x^2}{2}}$	$\dfrac{1}{\sqrt{2\pi}}\displaystyle\int_{-x}^{x} e^{-\frac{\alpha^2}{2}}\,d\alpha$
0.3300	0.37780 06765 30865	0.25860 00378 81307
01	.37778 82074 25308	.25867 55967 69759
02	.37777 57349 53531	.25875 11531 64053
03	.37776 32591 15892	.25882 67070 63516
04	.37775 07799 12754	.25890 22584 67475
0.3305	0.37773 82973 44476	0.25897 78073 75257
06	.37772 58114 11419	.25905 33537 86188
07	.37771 33221 13946	.25912 88976 99597
08	.37770 08294 52415	.25920 44391 14810
09	.37768 83334 27189	.25927 99780 31154
0.3310	0.37767 58340 38629	0.25935 55144 47956
11	.37766 33312 87096	.25943 10483 64545
12	.37765 08251 72952	.25950 65797 80247
13	.37763 83156 96557	.25958 21086 94390
14	.37762 58028 58274	.25965 76351 06301
0.3315	0.37761 32866 58465	0.25973 31590 15309
16	.37760 07670 97490	.25980 86804 20741
17	.37758 82441 75711	.25988 41993 21924
18	.37757 57178 93492	.25995 97157 18187
19	.37756 31882 51193	.26003 52296 08857
0.3320	0.37755 06552 49176	0.26011 07409 93263
21	.37753 81188 87805	.26018 62498 70733
22	.37752 55791 67440	.26026 17562 40595
23	.37751 30360 88446	.26033 72601 02176
24	.37750 04896 51183	.26041 27614 54806
0.3325	0.37748 79398 56015	0.26048 82602 97813
26	.37747 53867 03303	.26056 37566 30525
27	.37746 28301 93412	.26063 92504 52270
28	.37745 02703 26703	.26071 47417 62378
29	.37743 77071 03540	.26079 02305 60177
0.3330	0.37742 51405 24285	0.26086 57168 44996
31	.37741 25705 89302	.26094 12006 16163
32	.37739 99972 98954	.26101 66818 73008
33	.37738 74206 53603	.26109 21606 14859
34	.37737 48406 53614	.26116 76368 41046
0.3335	0.37736 22572 99350	0.26124 31105 50897
36	.37734 96705 91173	.26131 85817 43742
37	.37733 70805 29449	.26139 40504 18910
38	.37732 44871 14540	.26146 95165 75730
39	.37731 18903 46810	.26154 49802 13532
0.3340	0.37729 92902 26624	0.26162 04413 31645
41	.37728 66867 54345	.26169 58999 29399
42	.37727 40799 30336	.26177 13560 06124
43	.37726 14697 54963	.26184 68095 61148
44	.37724 88562 28590	.26192 22605 93802
0.3345	0.37723 62393 51580	0.26199 77091 03416
46	.37722 36191 24299	.26207 31550 89319
47	.37721 09955 47110	.26214 85985 50842
48	.37719 83686 20379	.26222 40394 87315
49	.37718 57383 44469	.26229 94778 98067
0.3350	0.37717 31047 19746	0.26237 49137 82430

x	$\frac{1}{\sqrt{2\pi}}e^{-\frac{x^2}{2}}$	$\frac{1}{\sqrt{2\pi}}\int_{-x}^{x}e^{-\frac{\alpha^2}{2}}\,d\alpha$
0.3350	0.37717 31047 19746	0.26237 49137 82430
51	.37716 04677 46574	.26245 03471 39732
52	.37714 78274 25319	.26252 57779 69305
53	.37713 51837 56345	.26260 12062 70479
54	.37712 25367 40018	.26267 66320 42584
0.3355	0.37710 98863 76703	0.26275 20552 84952
56	.37709 72326 66764	.26282 74759 96912
57	.37708 45756 10568	.26290 28941 77795
58	.37707 19152 08479	.26297 83098 26933
59	.37705 92514 60864	.26305 37229 43656
0.3360	0.37704 65843 68088	0.26312 91335 27294
61	.37703 39139 30517	.26320 45415 77180
62	.37702 12401 48516	.26327 99470 92644
63	.37700 85630 22451	.26335 53500 73017
64	.37699 58825 52689	.26343 07505 17630
0.3365	0.37698 31987 39595	0.26350 61484 25815
66	.37697 05115 83536	.26358 15437 96903
67	.37695 78210 84877	.26365 69366 30225
68	.37694 51272 43986	.26373 23269 25114
69	.37693 24300 61228	.26380 77146 80900
0.3370	0.37691 97295 36971	0.26388 30998 96916
71	.37690 70256 71580	.26395 84825 72492
72	.37689 43184 65422	.26403 38627 06962
73	.37688 16079 18865	.26410 92402 99656
74	.37686 88940 32274	.26418 46153 49906
0.3375	0.37685 61768 06018	0.26425 99878 57046
76	.37684 34562 40462	.26433 53578 20406
77	.37683 07323 35975	.26441 07252 39319
78	.37681 80050 92923	.26448 60901 13118
79	.37680 52745 11673	.26456 14524 41134
0.3380	0.37679 25405 92593	0.26463 68122 22700
81	.37677 98033 36051	.26471 21694 57149
82	.37676 70627 42414	.26478 75241 43812
83	.37675 43188 12050	.26486 28762 82023
84	.37674 15715 45326	.26493 82258 71114
0.3385	0.37672 88209 42611	0.26501 35729 10419
86	.37671 60670 04271	.26508 89173 99269
87	.37670 33097 30676	.26516 42593 36998
88	.37669 05491 22193	.26523 95987 22939
89	.37667 77851 79190	.26531 49355 56425
0.3390	0.37666 50179 02036	0.26539 02698 36788
91	.37665 22472 91099	.26546 56015 63363
92	.37663 94733 46747	.26554 09307 35483
93	.37662 66960 69350	.26561 62573 52480
94	.37661 39154 59275	.26569 15814 13688
0.3395	0.37660 11315 16892	0.26576 69029 18441
96	.37658 83442 42568	.26584 22218 66073
97	.37657 55536 36674	.26591 75382 55916
98	.37656 27596 99577	.26599 28520 87305
99	.37654 99624 31647	.26606 81633 59574
0.3400	0.37653 71618 33254	0.26614 34720 72056

x	$\dfrac{1}{\sqrt{2\pi}}e^{-\frac{x^2}{2}}$	$\dfrac{1}{\sqrt{2\pi}}\displaystyle\int_{-x}^{x}e^{-\frac{\alpha^2}{2}}\,d\alpha$
0.3400	0.37653 71618 33254	0.26614 34720 72056
01	.37652 43579 04766	.26621 87782 24085
02	.37651 15506 46552	.26629 40818 14996
03	.37649 87400 58983	.26636 93828 44122
04	.37648 59261 42427	.26644 46813 10798
0.3405	0.37647 31088 97254	0.26651 99772 14357
06	.37646 02883 23834	.26659 52705 54135
07	.37644 74644 22537	.26667 05613 29465
08	.37643 46371 93732	.26674 58495 39682
09	.37642 18066 37789	.26682 11351 84120
0.3410	0.37640 89727 55079	0.26689 64182 62115
11	.37639 61355 45971	.26697 16987 73001
12	.37638 32950 10835	.26704 69767 16112
13	.37637 04511 50043	.26712 22520 90783
14	.37635 76039 63963	.26719 75248 96350
0.3415	0.37634 47534 52967	0.26727 27951 32147
16	.37633 18996 17426	.26734 80627 97510
17	.37631 90424 57709	.26742 33278 91773
18	.37630 61819 74188	.26749 85904 14271
19	.37629 33181 67233	.26757 38503 64341
0.3420	0.37628 04510 37215	0.26764 91077 41317
21	.37626 75805 84506	.26772 43625 44534
22	.37625 47068 09475	.26779 96147 73329
23	.37624 18297 12495	.26787 48644 27036
24	.37622 89492 93937	.26795 01115 04992
0.3425	0.37621 60655 54172	0.26802 53560 06533
26	.37620 31784 93570	.26810 05979 30993
27	.37619 02881 12505	.26817 58372 77709
28	.37617 73944 11347	.26825 10740 46016
29	.37616 44973 90468	.26832 63082 35252
0.3430	0.37615 15970 50240	0.26840 15398 44751
31	.37613 86933 91034	.26847 67688 73851
32	.37612 57864 13223	.26855 19953 21887
33	.37611 28761 17179	.26862 72191 88195
34	.37609 99625 03273	.26870 24404 72112
0.3435	0.37608 70455 71878	0.26877 76591 72975
36	.37607 41253 23367	.26885 28752 90120
37	.37606 12017 58110	.26892 80888 22883
38	.37604 82748 76482	.26900 32997 70602
39	.37603 53446 78854	.26907 85081 32613
0.3440	0.37602 24111 65599	0.26915 37139 08252
41	.37600 94743 37090	.26922 89170 96858
42	.37599 65341 93699	.26930 41176 97766
43	.37598 35907 35800	.26937 93157 10314
44	.37597 06439 63766	.26945 45111 33840
0.3445	0.37595 76938 77969	0.26952 97039 67679
46	.37594 47404 78782	.26960 48942 11170
47	.37593 17837 66579	.26968 00818 63650
48	.37591 88237 41734	.26975 52669 24456
49	.37590 58604 04618	.26983 04493 92926
0.3450	0.37589 28937 55607	0.26990 56292 68397

x	$\frac{1}{\sqrt{2\pi}}e^{-\frac{x^2}{2}}$	$\frac{1}{\sqrt{2\pi}}\int_{-x}^{x}e^{-\frac{\alpha^2}{2}}d\alpha$
0.3450	0.37589 28937 55607	0.26990 56292 68397
51	.37587 99237 95074	.26998 08065 50207
52	.37586 69505 23392	.27005 59812 37694
53	.37585 39739 40934	.27013 11533 30196
54	.37584 09940 48076	.27020 63228 27050
0.3455	0.37582 80108 45190	0.27028 14897 27594
56	.37581 50243 32651	.27035 66540 31167
57	.37580 20345 10833	.27043 18157 37107
58	.37578 90413 80110	.27050 69748 44751
59	.37577 60449 40856	.27058 21313 53438
0.3460	0.37576 30451 93446	0.27065 72852 62507
61	.37575 00421 38253	.27073 24365 71295
62	.37573 70357 75654	.27080 75852 79142
63	.37572 40261 06021	.27088 27313 85385
64	.37571 10131 29730	.27095 78748 89364
0.3465	0.37569 79968 47156	0.27103 30157 90416
66	.37568 49772 58674	.27110 81540 87882
67	.37567 19543 64658	.27118 32897 81099
68	.37565 89281 65483	.27125 84228 69408
69	.37564 58986 61525	.27133 35533 52145
0.3470	0.37563 28658 53159	0.27140 86812 28652
71	.37561 98297 40760	.27148 38064 98266
72	.37560 67903 24704	.27155 89291 60328
73	.37559 37476 05365	.27163 40492 14176
74	.37558 07015 83120	.27170 91666 59150
0.3475	0.37556 76522 58344	0.27178 42814 94589
76	.37555 45996 31414	.27185 93937 19833
77	.37554 15437 02703	.27193 45033 34221
78	.37552 84844 72590	.27200 96103 37094
79	.37551 54219 41449	.27208 47147 27790
0.3480	0.37550 23561 09656	0.27215 98165 05651
81	.37548 92869 77589	.27223 49156 70014
82	.37547 62145 45623	.27231 00122 20222
83	.37546 31388 14133	.27238 51061 55613
84	.37545 00597 83498	.27246 01974 75527
0.3485	0.37543 69774 54093	0.27253 52861 79306
86	.37542 38918 26295	.27261 03722 66289
87	.37541 08029 00481	.27268 54557 35817
88	.37539 77106 77027	.27276 05365 87229
89	.37538 46151 56310	.27283 56148 19868
0.3490	0.37537 15163 38707	0.27291 06904 33072
91	.37535 84142 24595	.27298 57634 26183
92	.37534 53088 14351	.27306 08337 98542
93	.37533 22001 08353	.27313 59015 49489
94	.37531 90881 06977	.27321 09666 78366
0.3495	0.37530 59728 10602	0.27328 60291 84513
96	.37529 28542 19604	.27336 10890 67270
97	.37527 97323 34361	.27343 61463 25981
98	.37526 66071 55250	.27351 12009 59985
99	.37525 34786 82650	.27358 62529 68623
0.3500	0.37524 03469 16938	0.27366 13023 51238

x	$\dfrac{1}{\sqrt{2\pi}}\,e^{-\frac{x^2}{2}}$	$\dfrac{1}{\sqrt{2\pi}}\displaystyle\int_{-x}^{x} e^{-\frac{\alpha^2}{2}}\,d\alpha$
0.3500	0.37524 03469 16938	0.27366 13023 51238
01	.37522 72118 58492	.27373 63491 07171
02	.37521 40735 07690	.27381 13932 35762
03	.37520 09318 64909	.27388 64347 36354
04	.37518 77869 30529	.27396 14736 08289
0.3505	0.37517 46387 04927	0.27403 65098 50907
06	.37516 14871 88482	.27411 15434 63551
07	.37514 83323 81572	.27418 65744 45563
08	.37513 51742 84575	.27426 16027 96284
09	.37512 20128 97870	.27433 66285 15058
0.3510	0.37510 88482 21836	0.27441 16516 01224
11	.37509 56802 56851	.27448 66720 54127
12	.37508 25090 03295	.27456 16898 73108
13	.37506 93344 61545	.27463 67050 57509
14	.37505 61566 31982	.27471 17176 06673
0.3515	0.37504 29755 14983	0.27478 67275 19943
16	.37502 97911 10929	.27486 17347 96660
17	.37501 66034 20199	.27493 67394 36168
18	.37500 34124 43171	.27501 17414 37809
19	.37499 02181 80226	.27508 67408 00926
0.3520	0.37497 70206 31742	0.27516 17375 24862
21	.37496 38197 98100	.27523 67316 08960
22	.37495 06156 79679	.27531 17230 52562
23	.37493 74082 76858	.27538 67118 55013
24	.37492 41975 90018	.27546 16980 15654
0.3525	0.37491 09836 19539	0.27553 66815 33830
26	.37489 77663 65800	.27561 16624 08883
27	.37488 45458 29181	.27568 66406 40157
28	.37487 13220 10064	.27576 16162 26996
29	.37485 80949 08827	.27583 65891 68743
0.3530	0.37484 48645 25852	0.27591 15594 64741
31	.37483 16308 61518	.27598 65271 14334
32	.37481 83939 16207	.27606 14921 16867
33	.37480 51536 90299	.27613 64544 71682
34	.37479 19101 84174	.27621 14141 78124
0.3535	0.37477 86633 98214	0.27628 63712 35537
36	.37476 54133 32799	.27636 13256 43265
37	.37475 21599 88310	.27643 62774 00651
38	.37473 89033 65128	.27651 12265 07041
39	.37472 56434 63635	.27658 61729 61779
0.3540	0.37471 23802 84211	0.27666 11167 64208
41	.37469 91138 27238	.27673 60579 13674
42	.37468 58440 93097	.27681 09964 09521
43	.37467 25710 82170	.27688 59322 51093
44	.37465 92947 94837	.27696 08654 37735
0.3545	0.37464 60152 31482	0.27703 57959 68792
46	.37463 27323 92485	.27711 07238 43609
47	.37461 94462 78228	.27718 56490 61531
48	.37460 61568 89093	.27726 05716 21902
49	.37459 28642 25462	.27733 54915 24068
0.3550	0.37457 95682 87718	0.27741 04087 67374

X	$\dfrac{1}{\sqrt{2\pi}}\,e^{-\frac{x^2}{2}}$	$\dfrac{1}{\sqrt{2\pi}}\displaystyle\int_{-x}^{x} e^{-\frac{\alpha^2}{2}}\,d\alpha$
0.3550	0.37457 95682 87718	0.27741 04087 67374
51	.37456 62690 76241	.27748 53233 51165
52	.37455 29665 91415	.27756 02352 74787
53	.37453 96608 33622	.27763 51445 37584
54	.37452 63518 03244	.27771 00511 38902
0.3555	0.37451 30395 00663	0.27778 49550 78087
56	.37449 97239 26263	.27785 98563 54484
57	.37448 64050 80425	.27793 47549 67439
58	.37447 30829 63533	.27800 96509 16298
59	.37445 97575 75969	.27808 45442 00407
0.3560	0.37444 64289 18117	0.27815 94348 19110
61	.37443 30969 90358	.27823 43227 71756
62	.37441 97617 93077	.27830 92080 57689
63	.37440 64233 26656	.27838 40906 76255
64	.37439 30815 91478	.27845 89706 26801
0.3565	0.37437 97365 87927	0.27853 38479 08674
66	.37436 63883 16387	.27860 87225 21219
67	.37435 30367 77241	.27868 35944 63783
68	.37433 96819 70871	.27875 84637 35712
69	.37432 63238 97663	.27883 33303 36353
0.3570	0.37431 29625 57999	0.27890 81942 65053
71	.37429 95979 52264	.27898 30555 21159
72	.37428 62300 80842	.27905 79141 04016
73	.37427 28589 44115	.27913 27700 12973
74	.37425 94845 42470	.27920 76232 47376
0.3575	0.37424 61068 76288	0.27928 24738 06573
76	.37423 27259 45956	.27935 73216 89909
77	.37421 93417 51857	.27943 21668 96733
78	.37420 59542 94375	.27950 70094 26392
79	.37419 25635 73896	.27958 18492 78234
0.3580	0.37417 91695 90803	0.27965 66864 51604
81	.37416 57723 45481	.27973 15209 45852
82	.37415 23718 38316	.27980 63527 60325
83	.37413 89680 69691	.27988 11818 94370
84	.37412 55610 39992	.27995 60083 47336
0.3585	0.37411 21507 49604	0.28003 08321 18569
86	.37409 87371 98912	.28010 56532 07418
87	.37408 53203 88301	.28018 04716 13231
88	.37407 19003 18156	.28025 52873 35356
89	.37405 84769 88862	.28033 01003 73141
0.3590	0.37404 50504 00806	0.28040 49107 25934
91	.37403 16205 54372	.28047 97183 93084
92	.37401 81874 49946	.28055 45233 73939
93	.37400 47510 87914	.28062 93256 67847
94	.37399 13114 68662	.28070 41252 74157
0.3595	0.37397 78685 92574	0.28077 89221 92217
96	.37396 44224 60038	.28085 37164 21377
97	.37395 09730 71440	.28092 85079 60984
98	.37393 75204 27164	.28100 32968 10388
99	.37392 40645 27598	.28107 80829 68938
0.3600	0.37391 06053 73128	0.28115 28664 35982

x	$\frac{1}{\sqrt{2\pi}} e^{-\frac{x^2}{2}}$	$\frac{1}{\sqrt{2\pi}} \int_{-x}^{x} e^{-\frac{\alpha^2}{2}} d\alpha$
0.3600	0.37391 06053 73128	0.28115 28664 35982
01	.37389 71429 64140	.28122 76472 10870
02	.37388 36773 01021	.28130 24252 92951
03	.37387 02083 84156	.28137 72006 81574
04	.37385 67362 13934	.28145 19733 76088
0.3605	0.37384 32607 90739	0.28152 67433 75843
06	.37382 97821 14960	.28160 15106 80187
07	.37381 63001 86982	.28167 62752 88472
08	.37380 28150 07193	.28175 10372 00045
09	.37378 93265 75980	.28182 57964 14258
0.3610	0.37377 58348 93730	0.28190 05529 30459
11	.37376 23399 60830	.28197 53067 47999
12	.37374 88417 77667	.28205 00578 66227
13	.37373 53403 44629	.28212 48062 84493
14	.37372 18356 62103	.28219 95520 02148
0.3615	0.37370 83277 30476	0.28227 42950 18541
16	.37369 48165 50137	.28234 90353 33024
17	.37368 13021 21473	.28242 37729 44945
18	.37366 77844 44871	.28249 85078 53656
19	.37365 42635 20720	.28257 32400 58506
0.3620	0.37364 07393 49407	0.28264 79695 58847
21	.37362 72119 31320	.28272 26963 54030
22	.37361 36812 66848	.28279 74204 43404
23	.37360 01473 56378	.28287 21418 26320
24	.37358 66102 00300	.28294 68605 02130
0.3625	0.37357 30697 99001	0.28302 15764 70184
26	.37355 95261 52869	.28309 62897 29833
27	.37354 59792 62294	.28317 10002 80429
28	.37353 24291 27663	.28324 57081 21322
29	.37351 88757 49366	.28332 04132 51863
0.3630	0.37350 53191 27791	0.28339 51156 71405
31	.37349 17592 63327	.28346 98153 79298
32	.37347 81961 56362	.28354 45123 74894
33	.37346 46298 07287	.28361 92066 57545
34	.37345 10602 16490	.28369 38982 26601
0.3635	0.37343 74873 84361	0.28376 85870 81415
36	.37342 39113 11287	.28384 32732 21339
37	.37341 03319 97660	.28391 79566 45724
38	.37339 67494 43868	.28399 26373 53922
39	.37338 31636 50300	.28406 73153 45285
0.3640	0.37336 95746 17347	0.28414 19906 19166
41	.37335 59823 45398	.28421 66631 74916
42	.37334 23868 34843	.28429 13330 11888
43	.37332 87880 86071	.28436 60001 29434
44	.37331 51860 99473	.28444 06645 26907
0.3645	0.37330 15808 75438	0.28451 53262 03658
46	.37328 79724 14357	.28458 99851 59041
47	.37327 43607 16620	.28466 46413 92408
48	.37326 07457 82616	.28473 92949 03112
49	.37324 71276 12737	.28481 39456 90506
0.3650	0.37323 35062 07373	0.28488 85937 53942

x	$\frac{1}{\sqrt{2\pi}}e^{-\frac{x^2}{2}}$	$\frac{1}{\sqrt{2\pi}}\int_{-x}^{x}e^{-\frac{\alpha^2}{2}}d\alpha$
0.3650	0.37323 35062 07373	0.28488 85937 53942
51	.37321 98815 66914	.28496 32390 92773
52	.37320 62536 91751	.28503 78817 06353
53	.37319 26225 82275	.28511 25215 94034
54	.37317 89882 38876	.28518 71587 55170
0.3655	0.37316 53506 61945	0.28526 17931 89114
56	.37315 17098 51873	.28533 64248 95219
57	.37313 80658 09051	.28541 10538 72839
58	.37312 44185 33870	.28548 56801 21327
59	.37311 07680 26721	.28556 03036 40037
0.3660	0.37309 71142 87996	0.28563 49244 28323
61	.37308 34573 18086	.28570 95424 85537
62	.37306 97971 17382	.28578 41578 11034
63	.37305 61336 86275	.28585 87704 04169
64	.37304 24670 25158	.28593 33802 64294
0.3665	0.37302 87971 34422	0.28600 79873 90763
66	.37301 51240 14459	.28608 25917 82932
67	.37300 14476 65660	.28615 71934 40154
68	.37298 77680 88418	.28623 17923 61783
69	.37297 40852 83124	.28630 63885 47174
0.3670	0.37296 03992 50171	0.28638 09819 95681
71	.37294 67099 89950	.28645 55727 06659
72	.37293 30175 02854	.28653 01606 79462
73	.37291 93217 89275	.28660 47459 13445
74	.37290 56228 49606	.28667 93284 07963
0.3675	0.37289 19206 84239	0.28675 39081 62370
76	.37287 82152 93567	.28682 84851 76021
77	.37286 45066 77982	.28690 30594 48272
78	.37285 07948 37876	.28697 76309 78478
79	.37283 70797 73644	.28705 21997 65992
0.3680	0.37282 33614 85678	0.28712 67658 10172
81	.37280 96399 74370	.28720 13291 10372
82	.37279 59152 40114	.28727 58896 65947
83	.37278 21872 83303	.28735 04474 76253
84	.37276 84561 04330	.28742 50025 40646
0.3685	0.37275 47217 03588	0.28749 95548 58480
86	.37274 09840 81471	.28757 41044 29112
87	.37272 72432 38373	.28764 86512 51898
88	.37271 34991 74686	.28772 31953 26193
89	.37269 97518 90805	.28779 77366 51353
0.3690	0.37268 60013 87123	0.28787 22752 26735
91	.37267 22476 64034	.28794 68110 51693
92	.37265 84907 21931	.28802 13441 25586
93	.37264 47305 61210	.28809 58744 47767
94	.37263 09671 82264	.28817 04020 17595
0.3695	0.37261 72005 85486	0.28824 49268 34426
96	.37260 34307 71272	.28831 94488 97615
97	.37258 96577 40015	.28839 39682 06520
98	.37257 58814 92110	.28846 84847 60497
99	.37256 21020 27951	.28854 29985 58902
0.3700	0.37254 83193 47933	0.28861 75096 01094

x	$\frac{1}{\sqrt{2\pi}} e^{-\frac{x^2}{2}}$	$\frac{1}{\sqrt{2\pi}} \int_{-x}^{x} e^{-\frac{\alpha^2}{2}} d\alpha$
0.3700	0.37254 83193 47933	0.28861 75096 01094
01	.37253 45334 52451	.28869 20178 86427
02	.37252 07443 41899	.28876 65234 14260
03	.37250 69520 16672	.28884 10261 83950
04	.37249 31564 77164	.28891 55261 94853
0.3705	0.37247 93577 23771	0.28899 00234 46326
06	.37246 55557 56888	.28906 45179 37728
07	.37245 17505 76910	.28913 90096 68415
08	.37243 79421 84232	.28921 34986 37744
09	.37242 41305 79250	.28928 79848 45074
0.3710	0.37241 03157 62358	0.28936 24682 89762
11	.37239 64977 33952	.28943 69489 71165
12	.37238 26764 94428	.28951 14268 88641
13	.37236 88520 44181	.28958 59020 41549
14	.37235 50243 83607	.28966 03744 29245
0.3715	0.37234 11935 13102	0.28973 48440 51088
16	.37232 73594 33061	.28980 93109 06436
17	.37231 35221 43881	.28988 37749 94648
18	.37229 96816 45957	.28995 82363 15080
19	.37228 58379 39685	.29003 26948 67092
0.3720	0.37227 19910 25463	0.29010 71506 50042
21	.37225 81409 03685	.29018 16036 63288
22	.37224 42875 74749	.29025 60539 06190
23	.37223 04310 39050	.29033 05013 78105
24	.37221 65712 96986	.29040 49460 78392
0.3725	0.37220 27083 48952	0.29047 93880 06410
26	.37218 88421 95346	.29055 38271 61517
27	.37217 49728 36564	.29062 82635 43074
28	.37216 11002 73003	.29070 26971 50438
29	.37214 72245 05060	.29077 71279 82970
0.3730	0.37213 33455 33132	0.29085 15560 40027
31	.37211 94633 57616	.29092 59813 20969
32	.37210 55779 78909	.29100 04038 25156
33	.37209 16893 97408	.29107 48235 51947
34	.37207 77976 13511	.29114 92405 00702
0.3735	0.37206 39026 27615	0.29122 36546 70779
36	.37205 00044 40117	.29129 80660 61539
37	.37203 61030 51415	.29137 24746 72342
38	.37202 21984 61907	.29144 68805 02547
39	.37200 82906 71991	.29152 12835 51513
0.3740	0.37199 43796 82064	0.29159 56838 18602
41	.37198 04654 92523	.29167 00813 03173
42	.37196 65481 03768	.29174 44760 04586
43	.37195 26275 16196	.29181 88679 22201
44	.37193 87037 30205	.29189 32570 55379
0.3745	0.37192 47767 46193	0.29196 76434 03480
46	.37191 08465 64559	.29204 20269 65864
47	.37189 69131 85702	.29211 64077 41893
48	.37188 29766 10018	.29219 07857 30925
49	.37186 90368 37908	.29226 51609 32324
0.3750	0.37185 50938 69769	0.29233 95333 45448

X	$\dfrac{1}{\sqrt{2\pi}}\, e^{-\frac{x^2}{2}}$	$\dfrac{1}{\sqrt{2\pi}} \displaystyle\int_{-x}^{x} e^{-\frac{\alpha^2}{2}}\, d\alpha$
0.3750	0.37185 50938 69769	0.29233 95333 45448
51	.37184 11477 06000	.29241 39029 69658
52	.37182 71983 47001	.29248 82698 04317
53	.37181 32457 93169	.29256 26338 48784
54	.37179 92900 44905	.29263 69951 02421
0.3755	0.37178 53311 02606	0.29271 13535 64589
56	.37177 13689 66672	.29278 57092 34649
57	.37175 74036 37502	.29286 00621 11963
58	.37174 34351 15496	.29293 44121 95892
59	.37172 94634 01052	.29300 87594 85796
0.3760	0.37171 54884 94570	0.29308 31039 81039
61	.37170 15103 96450	.29315 74456 80981
62	.37168 75291 07092	.29323 17845 84985
63	.37167 35446 26894	.29330 61206 92412
64	.37165 95569 56256	.29338 04540 02623
0.3765	0.37164 55660 95579	0.29345 47845 14981
66	.37163 15720 45263	.29352 91122 28849
67	.37161 75748 05706	.29360 34371 43587
68	.37160 35743 77310	.29367 77592 58558
69	.37158 95707 60474	.29375 20785 73125
0.3770	0.37157 55639 55600	0.29382 63950 86650
71	.37156 15539 63086	.29390 07087 98495
72	.37154 75407 83333	.29397 50197 08023
73	.37153 35244 16742	.29404 93278 14596
74	.37151 95048 63714	.29412 36331 17577
0.3775	0.37150 54821 24649	0.29419 79356 16329
76	.37149 14561 99947	.29427 22353 10215
77	.37147 74270 90010	.29434 65321 98597
78	.37146 33947 95239	.29442 08262 80838
79	.37144 93593 16033	.29449 51175 56302
0.3780	0.37143 53206 52795	0.29456 94060 24352
81	.37142 12788 05926	.29464 36916 84351
82	.37140 72337 75826	.29471 79745 35662
83	.37139 31855 62897	.29479 22545 77649
84	.37137 91341 67540	.29486 65318 09675
0.3785	0.37136 50795 90157	0.29494 08062 31104
86	.37135 10218 31149	.29501 50778 41299
87	.37133 69608 90917	.29508 93466 39625
88	.37132 28967 69865	.29516 36126 25444
89	.37130 88294 68392	.29523 78757 98121
0.3790	0.37129 47589 86901	0.29531 21361 57019
91	.37128 06853 25795	.29538 63937 01503
92	.37126 66084 85474	.29546 06484 30937
93	.37125 25284 66341	.29553 49003 44686
94	.37123 84452 68799	.29560 91494 42112
0.3795	0.37122 43588 93248	0.29568 33957 22581
96	.37121 02693 40093	.29575 76391 85458
97	.37119 61766 09734	.29583 18798 30106
98	.37118 20807 02575	.29590 61176 55890
99	.37116 79816 19018	.29598 03526 62175
0.3800	0.37115 38793 59466	0.29605 45848 48326

x	$\dfrac{1}{\sqrt{2\pi}}\,e^{-\frac{x^2}{2}}$	$\dfrac{1}{\sqrt{2\pi}}\displaystyle\int_{-x}^{x} e^{-\frac{\alpha^2}{2}}\,d\alpha$
0.3800	0.37115 38793 59466	0.29605 45848 48326
01	.37113 97739 24321	.29612 88142 13707
02	.37112 56653 13987	.29620 30407 57684
03	.37111 15535 28865	.29627 72644 79621
04	.37109 74385 69359	.29635 14853 78884
0.3805	0.37108 33204 35873	0.29642 57034 54837
06	.37106 91991 28809	.29649 99187 06846
07	.37105 50746 48570	.29657 41311 34277
08	.37104 09469 95559	.29664 83407 36494
09	.37102 68161 70181	.29672 25475 12864
0.3810	0.37101 26821 72838	0.29679 67514 62751
11	.37099 85450 03934	.29687 09525 85521
12	.37098 44046 63872	.29694 51508 80541
13	.37097 02611 53057	.29701 93463 47176
14	.37095 61144 71891	.29709 35389 84791
0.3815	0.37094 19646 20780	0.29716 77287 92753
16	.37092 78116 00126	.29724 19157 70428
17	.37091 36554 10333	.29731 60999 17182
18	.37089 94960 51806	.29739 02812 32381
19	.37088 53335 24949	.29746 44597 15391
0.3820	0.37087 11678 30166	0.29753 86353 65580
21	.37085 69989 67862	.29761 28081 82312
22	.37084 28269 38440	.29768 69781 64956
23	.37082 86517 42305	.29776 11453 12876
24	.37081 44733 79863	.29783 53096 25441
0.3825	0.37080 02918 51516	0.29790 94711 02017
26	.37078 61071 57671	.29798 36297 41971
27	.37077 19192 98731	.29805 77855 44669
28	.37075 77282 75103	.29813 19385 09479
29	.37074 35340 87190	.29820 60886 35768
0.3830	0.37072 93367 35397	0.29828 02359 22903
31	.37071 51362 20131	.29835 43803 70252
32	.37070 09325 41795	.29842 85219 77181
33	.37068 67257 00796	.29850 26607 43058
34	.37067 25156 97538	.29857 67966 67250
0.3835	0.37065 83025 32427	0.29865 09297 49126
36	.37064 40862 05869	.29872 50599 88052
37	.37062 98667 18269	.29879 91873 83397
38	.37061 56440 70032	.29887 33119 34529
39	.37060 14182 61565	.29894 74336 40815
0.3840	0.37058 71892 93274	0.29902 15525 01623
41	.37057 29571 65563	.29909 56685 16321
42	.37055 87218 78839	.29916 97816 84278
43	.37054 44834 33509	.29924 38920 04862
44	.37053 02418 29978	.29931 79994 77441
0.3845	0.37051 59970 68653	0.29939 21041 01384
46	.37050 17491 49939	.29946 62058 76058
47	.37048 74980 74243	.29954 03048 00833
48	.37047 32438 41973	.29961 44008 75078
49	.37045 89864 53533	.29968 84940 98160
0.3850	0.37044 47259 09331	0.29976 25844 69449

x	$\dfrac{1}{\sqrt{2\pi}}\,e^{-\frac{x^2}{2}}$	$\dfrac{1}{\sqrt{2\pi}}\displaystyle\int_{-x}^{x} e^{-\frac{\alpha^2}{2}}\,d\alpha$
0.3850	0.37044 47259 09331	0.29976 25844 69449
51	.37043 04622 09773	.29983 66719 88313
52	.37041 61953 55267	.29991 07566 54122
53	.37040 19253 46219	.29998 48384 66245
54	.37038 76521 83036	.30005 89174 24050
0.3855	0.37037 33758 66124	0.30013 29935 26908
56	.37035 90963 95892	.30020 70667 74187
57	.37034 48137 72746	.30028 11371 65256
58	.37033 05279 97093	.30035 52046 99486
59	.37031 62390 69342	.30042 92693 76245
0.3860	0.37030 19469 89898	0.30050 33311 94903
61	.37028 76517 59170	.30057 73901 54831
62	.37027 33533 77565	.30065 14462 55397
63	.37025 90518 45491	.30072 54994 95972
64	.37024 47471 63355	.30079 95498 75925
0.3865	0.37023 04393 31566	0.30087 35973 94627
66	.37021 61283 50531	.30094 76420 51448
67	.37020 18142 20658	.30102 16838 45757
68	.37018 74969 42355	.30109 57227 76926
69	.37017 31765 16030	.30116 97588 44324
0.3870	0.37015 88529 42092	0.30124 37920 47323
71	.37014 45262 20949	.30131 78223 85291
72	.37013 01963 53008	.30139 18498 57601
73	.37011 58633 38679	.30146 58744 63623
74	.37010 15271 78370	.30153 98962 02727
0.3875	0.37008 71878 72490	0.30161 39150 74284
76	.37007 28454 21446	.30168 79310 77666
77	.37005 84998 25649	.30176 19442 12243
78	.37004 41510 85506	.30183 59544 77387
79	.37002 97992 01427	.30190 99618 72468
0.3880	0.37001 54441 73821	0.30198 39663 96858
81	.37000 10860 03096	.30205 79680 49928
82	.36998 67246 89661	.30213 19668 31050
83	.36997 23602 33927	.30220 59627 39594
84	.36995 79926 36302	.30227 99557 74934
0.3885	0.36994 36218 97196	0.30235 39459 36439
86	.36992 92480 17017	.30242 79332 23483
87	.36991 48709 96176	.30250 19176 35437
88	.36990 04908 35082	.30257 58991 71672
89	.36988 61075 34145	.30264 98778 31562
0.3890	0.36987 17210 93775	0.30272 38536 14477
91	.36985 73315 14381	.30279 78265 19790
92	.36984 29387 96373	.30287 17965 46873
93	.36982 85429 40162	.30294 57636 95099
94	.36981 41439 46157	.30301 97279 63840
0.3895	0.36979 97418 14768	0.30309 36893 52468
96	.36978 53365 46406	.30316 76478 60357
97	.36977 09281 41481	.30324 16034 86878
98	.36975 65166 00403	.30331 55562 31404
99	.36974 21019 23584	.30338 95060 93309
0.3900	0.36972 76841 11432	0.30346 34530 71965

x	$\dfrac{1}{\sqrt{2\pi}} e^{-\frac{x^2}{2}}$	$\dfrac{1}{\sqrt{2\pi}} \displaystyle\int_{-x}^{x} e^{-\frac{\alpha^2}{2}} \, d\alpha$
0.3900	0.36972 76841 11432	0.30346 34530 71965
01	.36971 32631 64360	.30353 73971 66745
02	.36969 88390 82777	.30361 13383 77022
03	.36968 44118 67095	.30368 52767 02169
04	.36966 99815 17724	.30375 92121 41559
0.3905	0.36965 55480 35075	0.30383 31446 94567
06	.36964 11114 19559	.30390 70743 60565
07	.36962 66716 71588	.30398 10011 38926
08	.36961 22287 91572	.30405 49250 29024
09	.36959 77827 79923	.30412 88460 30234
0.3910	0.36958 33336 37051	0.30420 27641 41928
11	.36956 88813 63369	.30427 66793 63480
12	.36955 44259 59288	.30435 05916 94264
13	.36953 99674 25219	.30442 45011 33655
14	.36952 55057 61575	.30449 84076 81026
0.3915	0.36951 10409 68766	0.30457 23113 35751
16	.36949 65730 47204	.30464 62120 97205
17	.36948 21019 97302	.30472 01099 64761
18	.36946 76278 19471	.30479 40049 37795
19	.36945 31505 14123	.30486 78970 15681
0.3920	0.36943 86700 81671	0.30494 17861 97792
21	.36942 41865 22526	.30501 56724 83505
22	.36940 96998 37101	.30508 95558 72193
23	.36939 52100 25809	.30516 34363 63231
24	.36938 07170 89060	.30523 73139 55995
0.3925	0.36936 62210 27269	0.30531 11886 49859
26	.36935 17218 40847	.30538 50604 44197
27	.36933 72195 30208	.30545 89293 38387
28	.36932 27140 95763	.30553 27953 31801
29	.36930 82055 37926	.30560 66584 23817
0.3930	0.36929 36938 57109	0.30568 05186 13808
31	.36927 91790 53726	.30575 43759 01151
32	.36926 46611 28190	.30582 82302 85222
33	.36925 01400 80913	.30590 20817 65395
34	.36923 56159 12309	.30597 59303 41046
0.3935	0.36922 10886 22791	0.30604 97760 11551
36	.36920 65582 12772	.30612 36187 76287
37	.36919 20246 82666	.30619 74586 34628
38	.36917 74880 32886	.30627 12955 85952
39	.36916 29482 63846	.30634 51296 29634
0.3940	0.36914 84053 75960	0.30641 89607 65050
41	.36913 38593 69641	.30649 27889 91576
42	.36911 93102 45302	.30656 66143 08590
43	.36910 47580 03359	.30664 04367 15466
44	.36909 02026 44224	.30671 42562 11583
0.3945	0.36907 56441 68312	0.30678 80727 96316
46	.36906 10825 76037	.30686 18864 69043
47	.36904 65178 67814	.30693 56972 29139
48	.36903 19500 44055	.30700 95050 75982
49	.36901 73791 05176	.30708 33100 08949
0.3950	0.36900 28050 51591	0.30715 71120 27417

x	$\frac{1}{\sqrt{2\pi}} e^{-\frac{x^2}{2}}$	$\frac{1}{\sqrt{2\pi}} \int_{-x}^{x} e^{-\frac{\alpha^2}{2}} d\alpha$
0.3950	0.36900 28050 51591	0.30715 71120 27417
51	.36898 82278 83715	.30723 09111 30762
52	.36897 36476 01962	.30730 47073 18362
53	.36895 90642 06747	.30737 85005 89595
54	.36894 44776 98484	.30745 22909 43838
0.3955	0.36892 98880 77589	0.30752 60783 80467
56	.36891 52953 44476	.30759 98628 98861
57	.36890 06994 99560	.30767 36444 98397
58	.36888 61005 43256	.30774 74231 78454
59	.36887 14984 75979	.30782 11989 38407
0.3960	0.36885 68932 98145	0.30789 49717 77637
61	.36884 22850 10168	.30796 87416 95519
62	.36882 76736 12465	.30804 25086 91433
63	.36881 30591 05450	.30811 62727 64757
64	.36879 84414 89538	.30819 00339 14868
0.3965	0.36878 38207 65147	0.30826 37921 41146
66	.36876 91969 32690	.30833 75474 42967
67	.36875 45699 92585	.30841 12998 19711
68	.36873 99399 45246	.30848 50492 70757
69	.36872 53067 91089	.30855 87957 95482
0.3970	0.36871 06705 30531	0.30863 25393 93266
71	.36869 60311 63988	.30870 62800 63488
72	.36868 13886 91875	.30878 00178 05525
73	.36866 67431 14609	.30885 37526 18757
74	.36865 20944 32606	.30892 74845 02564
0.3975	0.36863 74426 46282	0.30900 12134 56323
76	.36862 27877 56054	.30907 49394 79415
77	.36860 81297 62339	.30914 86625 71219
78	.36859 34686 65552	.30922 23827 31113
79	.36857 88044 66111	.30929 60999 58478
0.3980	0.36856 41371 64431	0.30936 98142 52693
81	.36854 94667 60931	.30944 35256 13137
82	.36853 47932 56027	.30951 72340 39191
83	.36852 01166 50135	.30959 09395 30233
84	.36850 54369 43674	.30966 46420 85644
0.3985	0.36849 07541 37059	0.30973 83417 04804
86	.36847 60682 30708	.30981 20383 87092
87	.36846 13792 25038	.30988 57321 31889
88	.36844 66871 20468	.30995 94229 38576
89	.36843 19919 17413	.31003 31108 06531
0.3990	0.36841 72936 16292	0.31010 67957 35136
91	.36840 25922 17521	.31018 04777 23771
92	.36838 78877 21520	.31025 41567 71817
93	.36837 31801 28705	.31032 78328 78653
94	.36835 84694 39494	.31040 15060 43662
0.3995	0.36834 37556 54305	0.31047 51762 66223
96	.36832 90387 73557	.31054 88435 45717
97	.36831 43187 97666	.31062 25078 81526
98	.36829 95957 27051	.31069 61692 73030
99	.36828 48695 62131	.31076 98277 19610
0.4000	0.36827 01403 03323	0.31084 34832 20648

x	$\dfrac{1}{\sqrt{2\pi}} e^{-\frac{x^2}{2}}$	$\dfrac{1}{\sqrt{2\pi}} \displaystyle\int_{-x}^{x} e^{-\frac{\alpha^2}{2}}\, d\alpha$
0.4000	0.36827 01403 03323	0.31084 34832 20648
01	.36825 54079 51046	.31091 71357 75525
02	.36824 06725 05719	.31099 07853 83623
03	.36822 59339 67758	.31106 44320 44321
04	.36821 11923 37585	.31113 80757 57004
0.4005	0.36819 64476 15616	0.31121 17165 21050
06	.36818 16998 02270	.31128 53543 35844
07	.36816 69488 97967	.31135 89892 00765
08	.36815 21949 03125	.31143 26211 15197
09	.36813 74378 18163	.31150 62500 78520
0.4010	0.36812 26776 43501	0.31157 98760 90118
11	.36810 79143 79556	.31165 34991 49372
12	.36809 31480 26749	.31172 71192 55664
13	.36807 83785 85498	.31180 07364 08377
14	.36806 36060 56223	.31187 43506 06892
0.4015	0.36804 88304 39344	0.31194 79618 50593
16	.36803 40517 35279	.31202 15701 38862
17	.36801 92699 44448	.31209 51754 71082
18	.36800 44850 67271	.31216 87778 46634
19	.36798 96971 04168	.31224 23772 64903
0.4020	0.36797 49060 55558	0.31231 59737 25270
21	.36796 01119 21861	.31238 95672 27119
22	.36794 53147 03497	.31246 31577 69833
23	.36793 05144 00886	.31253 67453 52795
24	.36791 57110 14449	.31261 03299 75388
0.4025	0.36790 09045 44604	0.31268 39116 36995
26	.36788 60949 91773	.31275 74903 37000
27	.36787 12823 56375	.31283 10660 74787
28	.36785 64666 38832	.31290 46388 49737
29	.36784 16478 39563	.31297 82086 61237
0.4030	0.36782 68259 58989	0.31305 17755 08668
31	.36781 20009 97531	.31312 53393 91415
32	.36779 71729 55609	.31319 89003 08862
33	.36778 23418 33644	.31327 24582 60392
34	.36776 75076 32057	.31334 60132 45390
0.4035	0.36775 26703 51269	0.31341 95652 63239
36	.36773 78299 91700	.31349 31143 13325
37	.36772 29865 53772	.31356 66603 95031
38	.36770 81400 37906	.31364 02035 07741
39	.36769 32904 44523	.31371 37436 50841
0.4040	0.36767 84377 74044	0.31378 72808 23714
41	.36766 35820 26891	.31386 08150 25745
42	.36764 87232 03485	.31393 43462 56320
43	.36763 38613 04248	.31400 78745 14822
44	.36761 89963 29601	.31408 13998 00636
0.4045	0.36760 41282 79966	0.31415 49221 13148
46	.36758 92571 55764	.31422 84414 51743
47	.36757 43829 57417	.31430 19578 15806
48	.36755 95056 85348	.31437 54712 04721
49	.36754 46253 39978	.31444 89816 17875
0.4050	0.36752 97419 21728	0.31452 24890 54652

x	$\frac{1}{\sqrt{2\pi}} e^{-\frac{x^2}{2}}$	$\frac{1}{\sqrt{2\pi}} \int_{-x}^{x} e^{-\frac{\alpha^2}{2}} d\alpha$
0.4050	0.36752 97419 21728	0.31452 24890 54652
51	.36751 48554 31023	.31459 59935 14439
52	.36749 99658 68282	.31466 94949 96620
53	.36748 50732 33929	.31474 29935 00581
54	.36747 01775 28387	.31481 64890 25709
0.4055	0.36745 52787 52076	0.31488 99815 71388
56	.36744 03769 05421	.31496 34711 37005
57	.36742 54719 88842	.31503 69577 21946
58	.36741 05640 02764	.31511 04413 25596
59	.36739 56529 47609	.31518 39219 47342
0.4060	0.36738 07388 23799	0.31525 73995 86570
61	.36736 58216 31757	.31533 08742 42667
62	.36735 09013 71907	.31540 43459 15019
63	.36733 59780 44671	.31547 78146 03011
64	.36732 10516 50472	.31555 12803 06032
0.4065	0.36730 61221 89734	0.31562 47430 23467
66	.36729 11896 62879	.31569 82027 54703
67	.36727 62540 70332	.31577 16594 99128
68	.36726 13154 12514	.31584 51132 56127
69	.36724 63736 89851	.31591 85640 25089
0.4070	0.36723 14289 02765	0.31599 20118 05399
71	.36721 64810 51679	.31606 54565 96445
72	.36720 15301 37019	.31613 88983 97615
73	.36718 65761 59206	.31621 23372 08296
74	.36717 16191 18666	.31628 57730 27875
0.4075	0.36715 66590 15822	0.31635 92058 55739
76	.36714 16958 51098	.31643 26356 91277
77	.36712 67296 24917	.31650 60625 33876
78	.36711 17603 37705	.31657 94863 82923
79	.36709 67879 89886	.31665 29072 37807
0.4080	0.36708 18125 81882	0.31672 63250 97915
81	.36706 68341 14120	.31679 97399 62635
82	.36705 18525 87024	.31687 31518 31357
83	.36703 68680 01017	.31694 65607 03466
84	.36702 18803 56524	.31701 99665 78353
0.4085	0.36700 68896 53971	0.31709 33694 55405
86	.36699 18958 93781	.31716 67693 34011
87	.36697 68990 76380	.31724 01662 13559
88	.36696 18992 02192	.31731 35600 93438
89	.36694 68962 71643	.31738 69509 73036
0.4090	0.36693 18902 85157	0.31746 03388 51743
91	.36691 68812 43159	.31753 37237 28946
92	.36690 18691 46075	.31760 71056 04036
93	.36688 68539 94330	.31768 04844 76401
94	.36687 18357 88349	.31775 38603 45430
0.4095	0.36685 68145 28557	0.31782 72332 10513
96	.36684 17902 15381	.31790 06030 71038
97	.36682 67628 49245	.31797 39699 26395
98	.36681 17324 30575	.31804 73337 75974
99	.36679 66989 59797	.31812 06946 19164
0.4100	0.36678 16624 37336	0.31819 40524 55355

x	$\frac{1}{\sqrt{2\pi}} e^{-\frac{x^2}{2}}$	$\frac{1}{\sqrt{2\pi}} \int_{-x}^{x} e^{-\frac{\alpha^2}{2}} d\alpha$
0.4100	0.36678 16624 37336	0.31819 40524 55355
01	.36676 66228 63619	.31826 74072 83936
02	.36675 15802 39071	.31834 07591 04297
03	.36673 65345 64118	.31841 41079 15828
04	.36672 14858 39187	.31848 74537 17919
0.4105	0.36670 64340 64702	0.31856 07965 09960
06	.36669 13792 41092	.31863 41362 91342
07	.36667 63213 68781	.31870 74730 61454
08	.36666 12604 48197	.31878 08068 19686
09	.36664 61964 79765	.31885 41375 65430
0.4110	0.36663 11294 63912	0.31892 74652 98075
11	.36661 60594 01065	.31900 07900 17012
12	.36660 09862 91651	.31907 41117 21632
13	.36658 59101 36095	.31914 74304 11326
14	.36657 08309 34825	.31922 07460 85484
0.4115	0.36655 57486 88268	0.31929 40587 43497
16	.36654 06633 96850	.31936 73683 84756
17	.36652 55750 60999	.31944 06750 08652
18	.36651 04836 81142	.31951 39786 14577
19	.36649 53892 57706	.31958 72792 01922
0.4120	0.36648 02917 91117	0.31966 05767 70077
21	.36646 51912 81805	.31973 38713 18435
22	.36645 00877 30195	.31980 71628 46387
23	.36643 49811 36715	.31988 04513 53325
24	.36641 98715 01792	.31995 37368 38639
0.4125	0.36640 47588 25856	0.32002 70193 01723
26	.36638 96431 09332	.32010 02987 41967
27	.36637 45243 52649	.32017 35751 58764
28	.36635 94025 56234	.32024 68485 51505
29	.36634 42777 20517	.32032 01189 19584
0.4130	0.36632 91498 45923	0.32039 33862 62391
31	.36631 40189 32882	.32046 66505 79319
32	.36629 88849 81821	.32053 99118 69762
33	.36628 37479 93170	.32061 31701 33110
34	.36626 86079 67355	.32068 64253 68756
0.4135	0.36625 34649 04806	0.32075 96775 76094
36	.36623 83188 05950	.32083 29267 54516
37	.36622 31696 71217	.32090 61729 03414
38	.36620 80175 01035	.32097 94160 22182
39	.36619 28622 95832	.32105 26561 10212
0.4140	0.36617 77040 56037	0.32112 58931 66898
41	.36616 25427 82079	.32119 91271 91632
42	.36614 73784 74386	.32127 23581 83809
43	.36613 22111 33389	.32134 55861 42820
44	.36611 70407 59515	.32141 88110 68060
0.4145	0.36610 18673 53194	0.32149 20329 58922
46	.36608 66909 14854	.32156 52518 14799
47	.36607 15114 44926	.32163 84676 35085
48	.36605 63289 43838	.32171 16804 19175
49	.36604 11434 12020	.32178 48901 66461
0.4150	0.36602 59548 49901	0.32185 80968 76338

x	$\frac{1}{\sqrt{2\pi}}e^{-\frac{x^2}{2}}$	$\frac{1}{\sqrt{2\pi}}\int_{-x}^{x}e^{-\frac{\alpha^2}{2}}d\alpha$
0.4150	0.36602 59548 49901	0.32185 80968 76338
51	.36601 07632 57911	.32193 13005 48199
52	.36599 55686 36479	.32200 45011 81439
53	.36598 03709 86034	.32207 76987 75452
54	.36596 51703 07008	.32215 08933 29631
0.4155	0.36594 99665 99829	0.32222 40848 43372
56	.36593 47598 64927	.32229 72733 16069
57	.36591 95501 02732	.32237 04587 47117
58	.36590 43373 13674	.32244 36411 35909
59	.36588 91214 98184	.32251 68204 81840
0.4160	.36587 39026 56692	0.32258 99967 84306
61	.36585 86807 89627	.32266 31700 42701
62	.36584 34558 97420	.32273 63402 56420
63	.36582 82279 80501	.32280 95074 24859
64	.36581 29970 39302	.32288 26715 47411
0.4165	0.36579 77630 74251	0.32295 58326 23473
66	.36578 25260 85781	.32302 89906 52439
67	.36576 72860 74321	.32310 21456 33706
68	.36575 20430 40303	.32317 52975 66667
69	.36573 67969 84157	.32324 84464 50720
0.4170	0.36572 15479 06314	0.32332 15922 85260
71	.36570 62958 07205	.32339 47350 69681
72	.36569 10406 87262	.32346 78748 03381
73	.36567 57825 46914	.32354 10114 85755
74	.36566 05213 86594	.32361 41451 16199
0.4175	0.36564 52572 06733	0.32368 72756 94108
76	.36562 99900 07761	.32376 04032 18880
77	.36561 47197 90111	.32383 35276 89910
78	.36559 94465 54214	.32390 66491 06595
79	.36558 41703 00501	.32397 97674 68331
0.4180	0.36556 88910 29404	0.32405 28827 74514
81	.36555 36087 41355	.32412 59950 24541
82	.36553 83234 36785	.32419 91042 17809
83	.36552 30351 16126	.32427 22103 53715
84	.36550 77437 79811	.32434 53134 31655
0.4185	0.36549 24494 28271	0.32441 84134 51026
86	.36547 71520 61938	.32449 15104 11225
87	.36546 18516 81244	.32456 46043 11650
88	.36544 65482 86622	.32463 76951 51697
89	.36543 12418 78504	.32471 07829 30763
0.4190	0.36541 59324 57322	0.32478 38676 48247
91	.36540 06200 23508	.32485 69493 03545
92	.36538 53045 77496	.32493 00278 96056
93	.36536 99861 19717	.32500 31034 25176
94	.36535 46646 50604	.32507 61758 90303
0.4195	0.36533 93401 70590	0.32514 92452 90835
96	.36532 40126 80108	.32522 23116 26170
97	.36530 86821 79590	.32529 53748 95706
98	.36529 33486 69470	.32536 84350 98842
99	.36527 80121 50180	.32544 14922 34974
0.4200	0.36526 26726 22154	0.32551 45463 03501

x	$\dfrac{1}{\sqrt{2\pi}}\,e^{-\frac{x^2}{2}}$	$\dfrac{1}{\sqrt{2\pi}}\displaystyle\int_{-x}^{x} e^{-\frac{\alpha^2}{2}}\,d\alpha$
0.4200	0.36526 26726 22154	0.32551 45463 03501
01	.36524 73300 85824	.32558 75973 03822
02	.36523 19845 41624	.32566 06452 35335
03	.36521 66359 89988	.32573 36900 97438
04	.36520 12844 31348	.32580 67318 89530
0.4205	0.36518 59298 66137	0.32587 97706 11010
06	.36517 05722 94790	.32595 28062 61276
07	.36515 52117 17740	.32602 58388 39728
08	.36513 98481 35421	.32609 88683 45763
09	.36512 44815 48266	.32617 18947 78782
0.4210	0.36510 91119 56709	0.32624 49181 38182
11	.36509 37393 61184	.32631 79384 23364
12	.36507 83637 62125	.32639 09556 33726
13	.36506 29851 59965	.32646 39697 68669
14	.36504 76035 55140	.32653 69808 27590
0.4215	0.36503 22189 48082	0.32660 99888 09891
16	.36501 68313 39227	.32668 29937 14969
17	.36500 14407 29008	.32675 59955 42226
18	.36498 60471 17861	.32682 89942 91061
19	.36497 06505 06218	.32690 19899 60873
0.4220	0.36495 52508 94516	0.32697 49825 51063
21	.36493 98482 83188	.32704 79720 61031
22	.36492 44426 72669	.32712 09584 90177
23	.36490 90340 63393	.32719 39418 37900
24	.36489 36224 55797	.32726 69221 03602
0.4225	0.36487 82078 50313	0.32733 98992 86683
26	.36486 27902 47378	.32741 28733 86542
27	.36484 73696 47427	.32748 58444 02582
28	.36483 19460 50893	.32755 88123 34202
29	.36481 65194 58214	.32763 17771 80802
0.4230	0.36480 10898 69823	0.32770 47389 41785
31	.36478 56572 86156	.32777 76976 16551
32	.36477 02217 07648	.32785 06532 04500
33	.36475 47831 34736	.32792 36057 05034
34	.36473 93415 67853	.32799 65551 17554
0.4235	0.36472 38970 07437	0.32806 95014 41462
36	.36470 84494 53922	.32814 24446 76158
37	.36469 29989 07744	.32821 53848 21044
38	.36467 75453 69340	.32828 83218 75521
39	.36466 20888 39144	.32836 12558 38992
0.4240	0.36464 66293 17593	0.32843 41867 10858
41	.36463 11668 05123	.32850 71144 90520
42	.36461 57013 02170	.32858 00391 77380
43	.36460 02328 09170	.32865 29607 70841
44	.36458 47613 26560	.32872 58792 70305
0.4245	0.36456 92868 54774	0.32879 87946 75173
46	.36455 38093 94251	.32887 17069 84847
47	.36453 83289 45426	.32894 46161 98731
48	.36452 28455 08736	.32901 75223 16226
49	.36450 73590 84617	.32909 04253 36735
0.4250	0.36449 18696 73506	0.32916 33252 59661

x	$\frac{1}{\sqrt{2\pi}} e^{-\frac{x^2}{2}}$	$\frac{1}{\sqrt{2\pi}} \int_{-x}^{x} e^{-\frac{\alpha^2}{2}} d\alpha$
0.4250	0.36449 18696 73506	0.32916 33252 59661
51	.36447 63772 75840	.32923 62220 84406
52	.36446 08818 92056	.32930 91158 10372
53	.36444 53835 22590	.32938 20064 36963
54	.36442 98821 67879	.32945 48939 63582
0.4255	0.36441 43778 28361	0.32952 77783 89632
56	.36439 88705 04472	.32960 06597 14515
57	.36438 33601 96649	.32967 35379 37634
58	.36436 78469 05330	.32974 64130 58394
59	.36435 23306 30953	.32981 92850 76198
0.4260	0.36433 68113 73953	0.32989 21539 90448
61	.36432 12891 34769	.32996 50198 00549
62	.36430 57639 13839	.33003 78825 05903
63	.36429 02357 11599	.33011 07421 05915
64	.36427 47045 28488	.33018 35985 99989
0.4265	0.36425 91703 64943	0.33025 64519 87528
66	.36424 36332 21402	.33032 93022 67936
67	.36422 80930 98302	.33040 21494 40618
68	.36421 25499 96083	.33047 49935 04977
69	.36419 70039 15181	.33054 78344 60418
0.4270	0.36418 14548 56034	0.33062 06723 06345
71	.36416 59028 19082	.33069 35070 42162
72	.36415 03478 04762	.33076 63386 67274
73	.36413 47898 13512	.33083 91671 81085
74	.36411 92288 45770	.33091 19925 83001
0.4275	0.36410 36649 01976	0.33098 48148 72425
76	.36408 80979 82567	.33105 76340 48763
77	.36407 25280 87983	.33113 04501 11420
78	.36405 69552 18661	.33120 32630 59800
79	.36404 13793 75041	.33127 60728 93309
0.4280	0.36402 58005 57560	0.33134 88796 11352
81	.36401 02187 66659	.33142 16832 13334
82	.36399 46340 02776	.33149 44836 98660
83	.36397 90462 66350	.33156 72810 66737
84	.36396 34555 57819	.33164 00753 16969
0.4285	0.36394 78618 77624	0.33171 28664 48762
86	.36393 22652 26203	.33178 56544 61522
87	.36391 66656 03995	.33185 84393 54654
88	.36390 10630 11440	.33193 12211 27565
89	.36388 54574 48978	.33200 39997 79661
0.4290	0.36386 98489 17047	0.33207 67753 10347
91	.36385 42374 16087	.33214 95477 19030
92	.36383 86229 46538	.33222 23170 05115
93	.36382 30055 08840	.33229 50831 68010
94	.36380 73851 03432	.33236 78462 07121
0.4295	0.36379 17617 30754	0.33244 06061 21854
96	.36377 61353 91246	.33251 33629 11615
97	.36376 05060 85348	.33258 61165 75813
98	.36374 48738 13499	.33265 88671 13852
99	.36372 92385 76141	.33273 16145 25140
0.4300	0.36371 36003 73713	0.33280 43588 09085

X	$\frac{1}{\sqrt{2\pi}} e^{-\frac{x^2}{2}}$	$\frac{1}{\sqrt{2\pi}} \int_{-x}^{x} e^{-\frac{\alpha^2}{2}} d\alpha$
0.4300	0.36371 36003 73713	0.33280 43588 09085
01	.36369 79592 06656	.33287 70999 65092
02	.36368 23150 75409	.33294 98379 92570
03	.36366 66679 80414	.33302 25728 90925
04	.36365 10179 22110	.33309 53046 59564
0.4305	0.36363 53649 00938	0.33316 80332 97896
06	.36361 97089 17339	.33324 07588 05327
07	.36360 40499 71753	.33331 34811 81265
08	.36358 83880 64621	.33338 62004 25118
09	.36357 27231 96384	.33345 89165 36294
0.4310	0.36355 70553 67483	0.33353 16295 14200
11	.36354 13845 78358	.33360 43393 58244
12	.36352 57108 29451	.33367 70460 67834
13	.36351 00341 21203	.33374 97496 42378
14	.36349 43544 54055	.33382 24500 81285
0.4315	0.36347 86718 28448	0.33389 51473 83962
16	.36346 29862 44824	.33396 78415 49819
17	.36344 72977 03623	.33404 05325 78263
18	.36343 16062 05287	.33411 32204 68703
19	.36341 59117 50258	.33418 59052 20548
0.4320	0.36340 02143 38977	0.33425 85868 33206
21	.36338 45139 71886	.33433 12653 06087
22	.36336 88106 49427	.33440 39406 38598
23	.36335 31043 72041	.33447 66128 30150
24	.36333 73951 40170	.33454 92818 80150
0.4325	0.36332 16829 54257	0.33462 19477 88009
26	.36330 59678 14742	.33469 46105 53135
27	.36329 02497 22069	.33476 72701 74938
28	.36327 45286 76679	.33483 99266 52827
29	.36325 88046 79014	.33491 25799 86212
0.4330	0.36324 30777 29517	0.33498 52301 74502
31	.36322 73478 28630	.33505 78772 17107
32	.36321 16149 76795	.33513 05211 13436
33	.36319 58791 74456	.33520 31618 62901
34	.36318 01404 22054	.33527 57994 64909
0.4335	0.36316 43987 20032	0.33534 84339 18873
36	.36314 86540 68832	.33542 10652 24201
37	.36313 29064 68898	.33549 36933 80304
38	.36311 71559 20673	.33556 63183 86592
39	.36310 14024 24598	.33563 89402 42475
0.4340	0.36308 56459 81118	0.33571 15589 47365
41	.36306 98865 90675	.33578 41745 00671
42	.36305 41242 53712	.33585 67869 01805
43	.36303 83589 70672	.33592 93961 50177
44	.36302 25907 41999	.33600 20022 45197
0.4345	0.36300 68195 68136	0.33607 46051 86277
46	.36299 10454 49527	.33614 72049 72828
47	.36297 52683 86614	.33621 98016 04260
48	.36295 94883 79841	.33629 23950 79986
49	.36294 37054 29652	.33636 49853 99416
0.4350	0.36292 79195 36491	0.33643 75725 61962

x	$\frac{1}{\sqrt{2\pi}}e^{-\frac{x^2}{2}}$	$\frac{1}{\sqrt{2\pi}}\int_{-x}^{x}e^{-\frac{\alpha^2}{2}}\,d\alpha$
0.4350	0.36292 79195 36491	0.33643 75725 61962
51	.36291 21307 00800	.33651 01565 67035
52	.36289 63389 23025	.33658 27374 14046
53	.36288 05442 03609	.33665 53151 02408
54	.36286 47465 42995	.33672 78896 31531
0.4355	0.36284 89459 41628	0.33680 04610 00829
56	.36283 31423 99951	.33687 30292 09712
57	.36281 73359 18410	.33694 55942 57593
58	.36280 15264 97447	.33701 81561 43883
59	.36278 57141 37508	.33709 07148 67996
0.4360	0.36276 98988 39037	0.33716 32704 29343
61	.36275 40806 02478	.33723 58228 27336
62	.36273 82594 28275	.33730 83720 61388
63	.36272 24353 16873	.33738 09181 30911
64	.36270 66082 68717	.33745 34610 35319
0.4365	0.36269 07782 84252	0.33752 60007 74023
66	.36267 49453 63921	.33759 85373 46437
67	.36265 91095 08171	.33767 10707 51973
68	.36264 32707 17445	.33774 36009 90044
69	.36262 74289 92189	.33781 61280 60064
0.4370	0.36261 15843 32848	0.33788 86519 61446
71	.36259 57367 39867	.33796 11726 93602
72	.36257 98862 13691	.33803 36902 55946
73	.36256 40327 54765	.33810 62046 47892
74	.36254 81763 63535	.33817 87158 68852
0.4375	0.36253 23170 40445	0.33825 12239 18242
76	.36251 64547 85942	.33832 37287 95473
77	.36250 05896 00471	.33839 62304 99961
78	.36248 47214 84477	.33846 87290 31118
79	.36246 88504 38406	.33854 12243 88359
0.4380	0.36245 29764 62704	0.33861 37165 71098
81	.36243 70995 57917	.33868 62055 78749
82	.36242 12197 24190	.33875 86914 10726
83	.36240 53369 62269	.33883 11740 66443
84	.36238 94512 72500	.33890 36535 45316
0.4385	0.36237 35626 55330	0.33897 61298 46757
86	.36235 76711 11204	.33904 86029 70183
87	.36234 17766 40569	.33912 10729 15007
88	.36232 58792 43870	.33919 35396 80644
89	.36230 99789 21555	.33926 60032 66509
0.4390	0.36229 40756 74069	0.33933 84636 72017
91	.36227 81695 01860	.33941 09208 96584
92	.36226 22604 05373	.33948 33749 39623
93	.36224 63483 85055	.33955 58258 00551
94	.36223 04334 41352	.33962 82734 78782
0.4395	0.36221 45155 74713	0.33970 07179 73733
96	.36219 85947 85582	.33977 31592 84817
97	.36218 26710 74408	.33984 55974 11452
98	.36216 67444 41637	.33991 80323 53052
99	.36215 08148 87716	.33999 04641 09034
0.4400	0.36213 48824 13092	0.34006 28926 78813

x	$\dfrac{1}{\sqrt{2\pi}}\,e^{-\frac{x^2}{2}}$	$\dfrac{1}{\sqrt{2\pi}}\displaystyle\int_{-x}^{x}e^{-\frac{\alpha^2}{2}}\,d\alpha$
0.4400	0.36213 48824 13092	0.34006 28926 78813
01	.36211 89470 18213	.34013 53180 61804
02	.36210 30087 03525	.34020 77402 57425
03	.36208 70674 69476	.34028 01592 65091
04	.36207 11233 16513	.34035 25750 84218
0.4405	0.36205 51762 45083	0.34042 49877 14223
06	.36203 92262 55634	.34049 73971 54522
07	.36202 32733 48615	.34056 98034 04531
08	.36200 73175 24471	.34064 22064 63667
09	.36199 13587 83651	.34071 46063 31346
0.4410	0.36197 53971 26602	0.34078 70030 06986
11	.36195 94325 53774	.34085 93964. 90003
12	.36194 34650 65612	.34093 17867 79813
13	.36192 74946 62565	.34100 41738 75835
14	.36191 15213 45082	.34107 65577 77484
0.4415	0.36189 55451 13610	0.34114 89384 84178
16	.36187 95659 68598	.34122 13159 95335
17	.36186 35839 10494	.34129 36903 10372
18	.36184 75989 39745	.34136 60614 28705
19	.36183 16110 56801	.34143 84293 49753
0.4420	0.36181 56202 62109	0.34151 07940 72934
21	.36179 96265 56119	.34158 31555 97664
22	.36178 36299 39279	.34165 55139 23362
23	.36176 76304 12037	.34172 78690 49446
24	.36175 16279 74842	.34180 02209 75333
0.4425	0.36173 56226 28143	0.34187 25697 00442
26	.36171 96143 72389	.34194 49152 24190
27	.36170 36032 08029	.34201 72575 45997
28	.36168 75891 35511	.34208 95966 65280
29	.36167 15721 55284	.34216 19325 81457
0.4430	0.36165 55522 67799	0.34223 42652 93948
31	.36163 95294 73503	.34230 65948 02170
32	.36162 35037 72847	.34237 89211 05544
33	.36160 74751 66279	.34245 12442 03486
34	.36159 14436 54248	.34252 35640 95416
0.4435	0.36157 54092 37205	0.34259 58807 80754
36	.36155 93719 15599	.34266 81942 58918
37	.36154 33316 89879	.34274 05045 29327
38	.36152 72885 60494	.34281 28115 91400
39	.36151 12425 27896	.34288 51154 44557
0.4440	0.36149 51935 92533	0.34295 74160 88218
41	.36147 91417 54855	.34302 97135 21801
42	.36146 30870 15312	.34310 20077 44726
43	.36144 70293 74354	.34317 42987 56413
44	.36143 09688 32432	.34324 65865 56282
0.4445	0.36141 49053 89995	0.34331 88711 43753
46	.36139 88390 47493	.34339 11525 18245
47	.36138 27698 05377	.34346 34306 79179
48	.36136 66976 64096	.34353 57056 25974
49	.36135 06226 24103	.34360 79773 58051
0.4450	0.36133 45446 85845	0.34368 02458 74830

x	$\dfrac{1}{\sqrt{2\pi}}e^{-\frac{x^2}{2}}$	$\dfrac{1}{\sqrt{2\pi}}\displaystyle\int_{-x}^{x}e^{-\frac{\alpha^2}{2}}\,d\alpha$
0.4450	0.36133 45446 85845	0.34368 02458 74830
51	.36131 84638 49776	.34375 25111 75732
52	.36130 23801 16344	.34382 47732 60177
53	.36128 62934 86000	.34389 70321 27586
54	.36127 02039 59196	.34396 92877 77378
0.4455	0.36125 41115 36382	0.34404 15402 08976
56	.36123 80162 18009	.34411 37894 21800
57	.36122 19180 04527	.34418 60354 15270
58	.36120 58168 96388	.34425 82781 88809
59	.36118 97128 94043	.34433 05177 41836
0.4460	0.36117 36059 97942	0.34440 27540 73773
61	.36115 74962 08538	.34447 49871 84042
62	.36114 13835 26281	.34454 72170 72064
63	.36112 52679 51623	.34461 94437 37260
64	.36110 91494 85014	.34469 16671 79052
0.4465	0.36109 30281 26907	0.34476 38873 96861
66	.36107 69038 77753	.34483 61043 90110
67	.36106 07767 38003	.34490 83181 58220
68	.36104 46467 08110	.34498 05287 00612
69	.36102 85137 88524	.34505 27360 16710
0.4470	0.36101 23779 79698	0.34512 49401 05935
71	.36099 62392 82083	.34519 71409 67710
72	.36098 00976 96132	.34526 93386 01456
73	.36096 39532 22296	.34534 15330 06595
74	.36094 78058 61028	.34541 37241 82552
0.4475	0.36093 16556 12778	0.34548 59121 28747
76	.36091 55024 78001	.34555 80968 44605
77	.36089 93464 57147	.34563 02783 29546
78	.36088 31875 50670	.34570 24565 82995
79	.36086 70257 59021	.34577 46316 04374
0.4480	0.36085 08610 82653	0.34584 68033 93106
81	.36083 46935 22019	.34591 89719 48615
82	.36081 85230 77571	.34599 11372 70323
83	.36080 23497 49761	.34606 32993 57654
84	.36078 61735 39043	.34613 54582 10031
0.4485	0.36076 99944 45869	0.34620 76138 26877
86	.36075 38124 70692	.34627 97662 07617
87	.36073 76276 13965	.34635 19153 51673
88	.36072 14398 76141	.34642 40612 58470
89	.36070 52492 57673	.34649 62039 27432
0.4490	0.36068 90557 59014	0.34656 83433 57981
91	.36067 28593 80617	.34664 04795 49543
92	.36065 66601 22935	.34671 26125 01542
93	.36064 04579 86422	.34678 47422 13401
94	.36062 42529 71532	.34685 68686 84544
0.4495	0.36060 80450 78717	0.34692 89919 14397
96	.36059 18343 08430	.34700 11119 02384
97	.36057 56206 61127	.34707 32286 47929
98	.36055 94041 37259	.34714 53421 50457
99	.36054 31847 37282	.34721 74524 09392
0.4500	0.36052 69624 61648	0.34728 95594 24160

x	$\dfrac{1}{\sqrt{2\pi}}\,e^{-\frac{x^2}{2}}$	$\dfrac{1}{\sqrt{2\pi}}\displaystyle\int_{-x}^{x} e^{-\frac{\alpha^2}{2}}\,d\alpha$
0.4500	0.36052 69624 61648	0.34728 95594 24160
01	.36051 07373 10812	.34736 16631 94185
02	.36049 45092 85227	.34743 37637 18893
03	.36047 82783 85347	.34750 58609 97708
04	.36046 20446 11626	.34757 79550 30055
0.4505	0.36044 58079 64520	0.34765 00458 15361
06	.36042 95684 44480	.34772 21333 53049
07	.36041 33260 51963	.34779 42176 42547
08	.36039 70807 87421	.34786 62986 83279
09	.36038 08326 51310	.34793 83764 74670
0.4510	0.36036 45816 44084	0.34801 04510 16148
11	.36034 83277 66198	.34808 25223 07137
12	.36033 20710 18105	.34815 45903 47063
13	.36031 58114 00261	.34822 66551 35353
14	.36029 95489 13119	.34829 87166 71432
0.4515	0.36028 32835 57136	0.34837 07749 54727
16	.36026 70153 32766	.34844 28299 84663
17	.36025 07442 40463	.34851 48817 60669
18	.36023 44702 80683	.34858 69302 82168
19	.36021 81934 53880	.34865 89755 48590
0.4520	0.36020 19137 60510	0.34873 10175 59359
21	.36018 56312 01028	.34880 30563 13903
22	.36016 93457 75889	.34887 50918 11648
23	.36015 30574 85548	.34894 71240 52022
24	.36013 67663 30460	.34901 91530 34452
0.4525	0.36012 04723 11082	0.34909 11787 58363
26	.36010 41754 27868	.34916 32012 23185
27	.36008 78756 81274	.34923 52204 28344
28	.36007 15730 71756	.34930 72363 73267
29	.36005 52675 99769	.34937 92490 57382
0.4530	0.36003 89592 65768	0.34945 12584 80116
31	.36002 26480 70211	.34952 32646 40897
32	.36000 63340 13552	.34959 52675 39153
33	.35999 00170 96248	.34966 72671 74312
34	.35997 36973 18754	.34973 92635 45801
0.4535	0.35995 73746 81527	0.34981 12566 53049
36	.35994 10491 85023	.34988 32464 95483
37	.35992 47208 29697	.34995 52330 72532
38	.35990 83896 16007	.35002 72163 83624
39	.35989 20555 44408	.35009 91964 28188
0.4540	0.35987 57186 15357	0.35017 11732 05652
41	.35985 93788 29310	.35024 31467 15444
42	.35984 30361 86724	.35031 51169 56993
43	.35982 66906 88055	.35038 70839 29728
44	.35981 03423 33760	.35045 90476 33078
0.4545	0.35979 39911 24296	0.35053 10080 66471
46	.35977 76370 60119	.35060 29652 29337
47	.35976 12801 41686	.35067 49191 21105
48	.35974 49203 69455	.35074 68697 41204
49	.35972 85577 43882	.35081 88170 89062
0.4550	0.35971 21922 65424	0.35089 07611 64111

X	$\dfrac{1}{\sqrt{2\pi}}\,e^{-\frac{x^2}{2}}$	$\dfrac{1}{\sqrt{2\pi}}\displaystyle\int_{-x}^{x} e^{-\frac{\alpha^2}{2}}\,d\alpha$
0.4550	0.35971 21922 65424	0.35089 07611 64111
51	.35969 58239 34538	.35096 27019 65778
52	.35967 94527 51682	.35103 46394 93495
53	.35966 30787 17312	.35110 65737 46689
54	.35964 67018 31886	.35117 85047 24791
0.4555	0.35963 03220 95862	0.35125 04324 27232
56	.35961 39395 09696	.35132 23568 53440
57	.35959 75540 73846	.35139 42780 02846
58	.35958 11657 88770	.35146 61958 74879
59	.35956 47746 54925	.35153 81104 68971
0.4560	0.35954 83806 72770	0.35161 00217 84551
61	.35953 19838 42761	.35168 19298 21050
62	.35951 55841 65356	.35175 38345 77899
63	.35949 91816 41014	.35182 57360 54527
64	.35948 27762 70192	.35189 76342 50365
0.4565	0.35946 63680 53349	0.35196 95291 64845
66	.35944 99569 90942	.35204 14207 97397
67	.35943 35430 83429	.35211 33091 47452
68	.35941 71263 31269	.35218 51942 14441
69	.35940 07067 34920	.35225 70759 97795
0.4570	0.35938 42842 94840	0.35232 89544 96945
71	.35936 78590 11488	.35240 08297 11323
72	.35935 14308 85322	.35247 27016 40360
73	.35933 49999 16801	.35254 45702 83488
74	.35931 85661 06383	.35261 64356 40137
0.4575	0.35930 21294 54527	0.35268 82977 09741
76	.35928 56899 61691	.35276 01564 91730
77	.35926 92476 28334	.35283 20119 85536
78	.35925 28024 54916	.35290 38641 90592
79	.35923 63544 41894	.35297 57131 06329
0.4580	0.35921 99035 89729	0.35304 75587 32179
81	.35920 34498 98879	.35311 94010 67575
82	.35918 69933 69802	.35319 12401 11950
83	.35917 05340 02959	.35326 30758 64734
84	.35915 40717 98809	.35333 49083 25362
0.4585	0.35913 76067 57810	0.35340 67374 93265
86	.35912 11388 80422	.35347 85633 67876
87	.35910 46681 67105	.35355 03859 48628
88	.35908 81946 18318	.35362 22052 34954
89	.35907 17182 34520	.35369 40212 26286
0.4590	0.35905 52390 16171	0.35376 58339 22058
91	.35903 87569 63731	.35383 76433 21704
92	.35902 22720 77660	.35390 94494 24655
93	.35900 57843 58417	.35398 12522 30346
94	.35898 92938 06462	.35405 30517 38209
0.4595	0.35897 28004 22255	0.35412 48479 47680
96	.35895 63042 06257	.35419 66408 58190
97	.35893 98051 58926	.35426 84304 69173
98	.35892 33032 80724	.35434 02167 80064
99	.35890 67985 72110	.35441 19997 90297
0.4600	0.35889 02910 33545	0.35448 37794 99305

x	$\dfrac{1}{\sqrt{2\pi}}e^{-\frac{x^2}{2}}$	$\dfrac{1}{\sqrt{2\pi}}\displaystyle\int_{-x}^{x}e^{-\frac{\alpha^2}{2}}\,d\alpha$
0.4600	0.35889 02910 33545	0.35448 37794 99305
01	.35887 37806 65488	.35455 55559 06522
02	.35885 72674 68401	.35462 73290 11382
03	.35884 07514 42744	.35469 90988 13320
04	.35882 42325 88977	.35477 08653 11771
0.4605	0.35880 77109 07561	0.35484 26285 06168
06	.35879 11863 98956	.35491 43883 95945
07	.35877 46590 63623	.35498 61449 80539
08	.35875 81289 02023	.35505 78982 59382
09	.35874 15959 14617	.35512 96482 31911
0.4610	0.35872 50601 01866	0.35520 13948 97560
11	.35870 85214 64229	.35527 31382 55763
12	.35869 19800 02170	.35534 48783 05957
13	.35867 54357 16148	.35541 66150 47576
14	.35865 88886 06624	.35548 83484 80055
0.4615	0.35864 23386 74061	0.35556 00786 02831
16	.35862 57859 18919	.35563 18054 15337
17	.35860 92303 41659	.35570 35289 17010
18	.35859 26719 42743	.35577 52491 07285
19	.35857 61107 22632	.35584 69659 85599
0.4620	0.35855 95466 81788	0.35591 86795 51386
21	.35854 29798 20672	.35599 03898 04084
22	.35852 64101 39747	.35606 20967 43127
23	.35850 98376 39473	.35613 38003 67952
24	.35849 32623 20313	.35620 55006 77995
0.4625	0.35847 66841 82727	0.35627 71976 72692
26	.35846 01032 27180	.35634 88913 51480
27	.35844 35194 54131	.35642 05817 13795
28	.35842 69328 64043	.35649 22687 59074
29	.35841 03434 57379	.35656 39524 86753
0.4630	0.35839 37512 34600	0.35663 56328 96269
31	.35837 71561 96169	.35670 73099 87059
32	.35836 05583 42547	.35677 89837 58560
33	.35834 39576 74198	.35685 06542 10208
34	.35832 73541 91583	.35692 23213 41442
0.4635	0.35831 07478 95166	0.35699 39851 51697
36	.35829 41387 85408	.35706 56456 40412
37	.35827 75268 62772	.35713 73028 07024
38	.35826 09121 27721	.35720 89566 50970
39	.35824 42945 80717	.35728 06071 71688
0.4640	0.35822 76742 22224	0.35735 22543 68615
41	.35821 10510 52703	.35742 38982 41189
42	.35819 44250 72619	.35749 55387 88848
43	.35817 77962 82434	.35756 71760 11031
44	.35816 11646 82611	.35763 88099 07174
0.4645	0.35814 45302 73613	0.35771 04404 76717
46	.35812 78930 55903	.35778 20677 19096
47	.35811 12530 29944	.35785 36916 33752
48	.35809 46101 96201	.35792 53122 20121
49	.35807 79645 55135	.35799 69294 77643
0.4650	0.35806 13161 07211	0.35806 85434 05756

x	$\frac{1}{\sqrt{2\pi}}e^{-\frac{x^2}{2}}$	$\frac{1}{\sqrt{2\pi}}\int_{-x}^{x}e^{-\frac{\alpha^2}{2}}d\alpha$
0.4650	0.35806 13161 07211	0.35806 85434 05756
51	.35804 46648 52892	.35814 01540 03899
52	.35802 80107 92641	.35821 17612 71510
53	.35801 13539 26922	.35828 33652 08029
54	.35799 46942 56199	.35835 49658 12894
0.4655	0.35797 80317 80935	0.35842 65630 85544
56	.35796 13665 01595	.35849 81570 25419
57	.35794 46984 18641	.35856 97476 31958
58	.35792 80275 32539	.35864 13349 04600
59	.35791 13538 43751	.35871 29188 42784
0.4660	0.35789 46773 52742	0.35878 44994 45951
61	.35787 79980 59976	.35885 60767 13539
62	.35786 13159 65918	.35892 76506 44988
63	.35784 46310 71030	.35899 92212 39738
64	.35782 79433 75779	.35907 07884 97230
0.4665	0.35781 12528 80627	0.35914 23524 16902
66	.35779 45595 86040	.35921 39129 98195
67	.35777 78634 92481	.35928 54702 40550
68	.35776 11646 00416	.35935 70241 43406
69	.35774 44629 10309	.35942 85747 06203
0.4670	0.35772 77584 22625	0.35950 01219 28383
71	.35771 10511 37827	.35957 16658 09386
72	.35769 43410 56382	.35964 32063 48652
73	.35767 76281 78754	.35971 47435 45622
74	.35766 09125 05408	.35978 62773 99737
0.4675	0.35764 41940 36808	0.35985 78079 10438
76	.35762 74727 73420	.35992 93350 77165
77	.35761 07487 15709	.36000 08588 99361
78	.35759 40218 64140	.36007 23793 76465
79	.35757 72922 19179	.36014 38965 07920
0.4680	0.35756 05597 81290	0.36021 54102 93167
81	.35754 38245 50938	.36028 69207 31647
82	.35752 70865 28590	.36035 84278 22801
83	.35751 03457 14711	.36042 99315 66072
84	.35749 36021 09766	.36050 14319 60901
0.4685	0.35747 68557 14221	0.36057 29290 06730
86	.35746 01065 28541	.36064 44227 03001
87	.35744 33545 53192	.36071 59130 49155
88	.35742 65997 88640	.36078 74000 44636
89	.35740 98422 35351	.36085 88836 88885
0.4690	0.35739 30818 93791	0.36093 03639 81344
91	.35737 63187 64425	.36100 18409 21457
92	.35735 95528 47719	.36107 33145 08664
93	.35734 27841 44141	.36114 47847 42410
94	.35732 60126 54155	.36121 62516 22136
0.4695	0.35730 92383 78228	0.36128 77151 47286
96	.35729 24613 16827	.36135 91753 17302
97	.35727 56814 70417	.36143 06321 31627
98	.35725 88988 39465	.36150 20855 89704
99	.35724 21134 24437	.36157 35356 90977
0.4700	0.35722 53252 25801	0.36164 49824 34888

x	$\frac{1}{\sqrt{2\pi}} e^{-\frac{x^2}{2}}$	$\frac{1}{\sqrt{2\pi}} \int_{-x}^{x} e^{-\frac{\alpha^2}{2}} d\alpha$
0.4700	0.35722 53252 25801	0.36164 49824 34888
01	.35720 85342 44022	.36171 64258 20882
02	.35719 17404 79567	.36178 78658 48400
03	.35717 49439 32903	.36185 93025 16888
04	.35715 81446 04496	.36193 07358 25788
0.4705	0.35714 13424 94814	0.36200 21657 74544
06	.35712 45376 04323	.36207 35923 62601
07	.35710 77299 33490	.36214 50155 89401
08	.35709 09194 82783	.36221 64354 54389
09	.35707 41062 52667	.36228 78519 57009
0.4710	0.35705 72902 43611	0.36235 92650 96705
11	.35704 04714 56082	.36243 06748 72921
12	.35702 36498 90547	.36250 20812 85102
13	.35700 68255 47472	.36257 34843 32692
14	.35698 99984 27326	.36264 48840 15136
0.4715	0.35697 31685 30576	0.36271 62803 31878
16	.35695 63358 57690	.36278 76732 82363
17	.35693 95004 09134	.36285 90628 66036
18	.35692 26621 85377	.36293 04490 82341
19	.35690 58211 86886	.36300 18319 30725
0.4720	0.35688 89774 14129	0.36307 32114 10631
21	.35687 21308 67574	.36314 45875 21506
22	.35685 52815 47689	.36321 59602 62793
23	.35683 84294 54941	.36328 73296 33940
24	.35682 15745 89798	.36335 86956 34391
0.4725	0.35680 47169 52730	0.36343 00582 63591
26	.35678 78565 44202	.36350 14175 20987
27	.35677 09933 64685	.36357 27734 06024
28	.35675 41274 14646	.36364 41259 18148
29	.35673 72586 94553	.36371 54750 56805
0.4730	0.35672 03872 04875	0.36378 68208 21441
31	.35670 35129 46079	.36385 81632 11503
32	.35668 66359 18636	.36392 95022 26435
33	.35666 97561 23012	.36400 08378 65685
34	.35665 28735 59677	.36407 21701 28700
0.4735	0.35663 59882 29100	0.36414 34990 14925
36	.35661 91001 31748	.36421 48245 23807
37	.35660 22092 68092	.36428 61466 54793
38	.35658 53156 38599	.36435 74654 07330
39	.35656 84192 43738	.36442 87807 80864
0.4740	0.35655 15200 83979	0.36450 00927 74843
41	.35653 46181 59790	.36457 14013 88713
42	.35651 77134 71641	.36464 27066 21923
43	.35650 08060 20001	.36471 40084 73918
44	.35648 38958 05339	.36478 53069 44146
0.4745	0.35646 69828 28124	0.36485 66020 32056
46	.35645 00670 88825	.36492 78937 37094
47	.35643 31485 87912	.36499 91820 58707
48	.35641 62273 25854	.36507 04669 96345
49	.35639 93033 03122	.36514 17485 49454
0.4750	0.35638 23765 20183	0.36521 30267 17482

x	$\frac{1}{\sqrt{2\pi}}e^{-\frac{x^2}{2}}$	$\frac{1}{\sqrt{2\pi}}\int_{-x}^{x}e^{-\frac{\alpha^2}{2}}\,d\alpha$
0.4750	0.35638 23765 20183	0.36521 30267 17482
51	.35636 54469 77509	.36528 43014 99878
52	.35634 85146 75568	.36535 55728 96089
53	.35633 15796 14831	.36542 68409 05564
54	.35631 46417 95766	.36549 81055 27751
0.4755	0.35629 77012 18845	0.36556 93667 62098
56	.35628 07578 84537	.36564 06246 08055
57	.35626 38117 93312	.36571 18790 65068
58	.35624 68629 45640	.36578 31301 32588
59	.35622 99113 41991	.36585 43778 10063
0.4760	0.35621 29569 82835	0.36592 56220 96941
61	.35619 59998 68643	.36599 68629 92672
62	.35617 90399 99884	.36606 81004 96705
63	.35616 20773 77030	.36613 93346 08489
64	.35614 51120 00550	.36621 05653 27472
0.4765	0.35612 81438 70915	0.36628 17926 53105
66	.35611 11729 88596	.36635 30165 84837
67	.35609 41993 54063	.36642 42371 22117
68	.35607 72229 67787	.36649 54542 64395
69	.35606 02438 30238	.36656 66680 11121
0.4770	0.35604 32619 41887	0.36663 78783 61744
71	.35602 62773 03205	.36670 90853 15715
72	.35600 92899 14664	.36678 02888 72482
73	.35599 22997 76733	.36685 14890 31497
74	.35597 53068 89884	.36692 26857 92210
0.4775	0.35595 83112 54588	0.36699 38791 54070
76	.35594 13128 71316	.36706 50691 16528
77	.35592 43117 40540	.36713 62556 79035
78	.35590 73078 62730	.36720 74388 41041
79	.35589 03012 38357	.36727 86186 01997
0.4780	0.35587 32918 67894	0.36734 97949 61354
81	.35585 62797 51812	.36742 09679 18561
82	.35583 92648 90582	.36749 21374 73071
83	.35582 22472 84675	.36756 33036 24335
84	.35580 52269 34564	.36763 44663 71802
0.4785	0.35578 82038 40719	0.36770 56257 14925
86	.35577 11780 03613	.36777 67816 53156
87	.35575 41494 23718	.36784 79341 85944
88	.35573 71181 01505	.36791 90833 12742
89	.35572 00840 37446	.36799 02290 33002
0.4790	0.35570 30472 32013	0.36806 13713 46174
91	.35568 60076 85678	.36813 25102 51712
92	.35566 89653 98914	.36820 36457 49066
93	.35565 19203 72192	.36827 47778 37689
94	.35563 48726 05985	.36834 59065 17032
0.4795	0.35561 78221 00764	0.36841 70317 86549
96	.35560 07688 57003	.36848 81536 45690
97	.35558 37128 75173	.36855 92720 93909
98	.35556 66541 55747	.36863 03871 30658
99	.35554 95926 99197	.36870 14987 55389
0.4800	0.35553 25285 05997	0.36877 26069 67555

x	$\dfrac{1}{\sqrt{2\pi}}\,e^{-\frac{x^2}{2}}$	$\dfrac{1}{\sqrt{2\pi}}\displaystyle\int_{-x}^{x} e^{-\frac{\alpha^2}{2}}\,d\alpha$
0.4800	0.35553 25285 05997	0.36877 26069 67555
01	.35551 54615 76618	.36884 37117 66609
02	.35549 83919 11534	.36891 48131 52003
03	.35548 13195 11217	.36898 59111 23191
04	.35546 42443 76139	.36905 70056 79625
0.4805	0.35544 71665 06775	0.36912 80968 20759
06	.35543 00859 03596	.36919 91845 46046
07	.35541 30025 67075	.36927 02688 54938
08	.35539 59164 97687	.36934 13497 46890
09	.35537 88276 95903	.36941 24272 21355
0.4810	0.35536 17361 62197	0.36948 35012 77787
11	.35534 46418 97042	.36955 45719 15638
12	.35532 75449 00911	.36962 56391 34363
13	.35531 04451 74278	.36969 67029 33416
14	.35529 33427 17616	.36976 77633 12251
0.4815	0.35527 62375 31399	0.36983 88202 70321
16	.35525 91296 16100	.36990 98738 07082
17	.35524 20189 72192	.36998 09239 21986
18	.35522 49056 00150	.37005 19706 14489
19	.35520 77895 00447	.37012 30138 84044
0.4820	0.35519 06706 73556	0.37019 40537 30107
21	.35517 35491 19952	.37026 50901 52132
22	.35515 64248 40108	.37033 61231 49573
23	.35513 92978 34498	.37040 71527 21886
24	.35512 21681 03597	.37047 81788 68525
0.4825	0.35510 50356 47877	0.37054 92015 88946
26	.35508 79004 67815	.37062 02208 82603
27	.35507 07625 63882	.37069 12367 48951
28	.35505 36219 36555	.37076 22491 87447
29	.35503 64785 86306	.37083 32581 97545
0.4830	0.35501 93325 13611	0.37090 42637 78700
31	.35500 21837 18944	.37097 52659 30369
32	.35498 50322 02778	.37104 62646 52006
33	.35496 78779 65590	.37111 72599 43068
34	.35495 07210 07852	.37118 82518 03011
0.4835	0.35493 35613 30041	0.37125 92402 31290
36	.35491 63989 32630	.37133 02252 27362
37	.35489 92338 16094	.37140 12067 90682
38	.35488 20659 80909	.37147 21849 20707
39	.35486 48954 27548	.37154 31596 16893
0.4840	0.35484 77221 56488	0.37161 41308 78697
41	.35483 05461 68202	.37168 50987 05574
42	.35481 33674 63166	.37175 60630 96983
43	.35479 61860 41855	.37182 70240 52379
44	.35477 90019 04744	.37189 79815 71219
0.4845	0.35476 18150 52309	0.37196 89356 52959
46	.35474 46254 85024	.37203 98862 97058
47	.35472 74332 03365	.37211 08335 02973
48	.35471 02382 07808	.37218 17772 70159
49	.35469 30404 98827	.37225 27175 98075
0.4850	0.35467 58400 76899	0.37232 36544 86178

x	$\dfrac{1}{\sqrt{2\pi}}e^{-\frac{x^2}{2}}$	$\dfrac{1}{\sqrt{2\pi}}\displaystyle\int_{-x}^{x}e^{-\frac{\alpha^2}{2}}\,d\alpha$
0.4850	0.35467 58400 76899	0.37232 36544 86178
51	.35465 86369 42498	.37239 45879 33925
52	.35464 14310 96101	.37246 55179 40774
53	.35462 42225 38183	.37253 64445 06182
54	.35460 70112 69220	.37260 73676 29608
0.4855	0.35458 97972 89688	0.37267 82873 10509
56	.35457 25806 00062	.37274 92035 48343
57	.35455 53612 00819	.37282 01163 42569
58	.35453 81390 92434	.37289 10256 92643
59	.35452 09142 75383	.37296 19315 98025
0.4860	0.35450 36867 50143	0.37303 28340 58173
61	.35448 64565 17190	.37310 37330 72545
62	.35446 92235 76999	.37317 46286 40599
63	.35445 19879 30048	.37324 55207 61795
64	.35443 47495 76812	.37331 64094 35591
0.4865	0.35441 75085 17768	0.37338 72946 61445
66	.35440 02647 53392	.37345 81764 38818
67	.35438 30182 84161	.37352 90547 67166
68	.35436 57691 10551	.37359 99296 45951
69	.35434 85172 33039	.37367 08010 74630
0.4870	0.35433 12626 52102	0.37374 16690 52664
71	.35431 40053 68216	.37381 25335 79511
72	.35429 67453 81858	.37388 33946 54631
73	.35427 94826 93505	.37395 42522 77484
74	.35426 22173 03634	.37402 51064 47528
0.4875	0.35424 49492 12721	0.37409 59571 64225
76	.35422 76784 21244	.37416 68044 27033
77	.35421 04049 29680	.37423 76482 35413
78	.35419 31287 38507	.37430 84885 88825
79	.35417 58498 48200	.37437 93254 86729
0.4880	0.35415 85682 59237	0.37445 01589 28585
81	.35414 12839 72097	.37452 09889 13853
82	.35412 39969 87255	.37459 18154 41994
83	.35410 67073 05190	.37466 26385 12468
84	.35408 94149 26379	.37473 34581 24736
0.4885	0.35407 21198 51299	0.37480 42742 78259
86	.35405 48220 80429	.37487 50869 72497
87	.35403 75216 14245	.37494 58962 06911
88	.35402 02184 53225	.37501 67019 80963
89	.35400 29125 97848	.37508 75042 94113
0.4890	0.35398 56040 48591	0.37515 83031 45822
91	.35396 82928 05931	.37522 90985 35553
92	.35395 09788 70348	.37529 98904 62765
93	.35393 36622 42318	.37537 06789 26921
94	.35391 63429 22320	.37544 14639 27483
0.4895	0.35389 90209 10832	0.37551 22454 63911
96	.35388 16962 08332	.37558 30235 35668
97	.35386 43688 15299	.37565 37981 42215
98	.35384 70387 32210	.37572 45692 83014
99	.35382 97059 59544	.37579 53369 57528
0.4900	0.35381 23704 97780	0.37586 61011 65219

x	$\dfrac{1}{\sqrt{2\pi}}\,e^{-\frac{x^2}{2}}$	$\dfrac{1}{\sqrt{2\pi}}\displaystyle\int_{-x}^{x} e^{-\frac{\alpha^2}{2}}\,d\alpha$
0.4900	0.35381 23704 97780	0.37586 61011 65219
01	.35379 50323 47395	.37593 68619 05548
02	.35377 76915 08868	.37600 76191 77979
03	.35376 03479 82679	.37607 83729 81973
04	.35374 30017 69305	.37614 91233 16993
0.4905	0.35372 56528 69225	0.37621 98701 82501
06	.35370 83012 82918	.37629 06135 77961
07	.35369 09470 10863	.37636 13535 02835
08	.35367 35900 53538	.37643 20899 56587
09	.35365 62304 11423	.37650 28229 38678
0.4910	0.35363 88680 84996	0.37657 35524 48572
11	.35362 15030 74736	.37664 42784 85733
12	.35360 41353 81124	.37671 50010 49623
13	.35358 67650 04636	.37678 57201 39706
14	.35356 93919 45754	.37685 64357 55446
0.4915	0.35355 20162 04956	0.37692 71478 96306
16	.35353 46377 82721	.37699 78565 61749
17	.35351 72566 79529	.37706 85617 51240
18	.35349 98728 95859	.37713 92634 64242
19	.35348 24864 32190	.37720 99617 00220
0.4920	0.35346 50972 89003	0.37728 06564 58637
21	.35344 77054 66777	.37735 13477 38957
22	.35343 03109 65991	.37742 20355 40645
23	.35341 29137 87125	.37749 27198 63165
24	.35339 55139 30660	.37756 34007 05981
0.4925	0.35337 81113 97074	0.37763 40780 68559
26	.35336 07061 86847	.37770 47519 50362
27	.35334 32983 00460	.37777 54223 50855
28	.35332 58877 38392	.37784 60892 69503
29	.35330 84745 01125	.37791 67527 05772
0.4930	0.35329 10585 89136	0.37798 74126 59126
31	.35327 36400 02908	.37805 80691 29029
32	.35325 62187 42919	.37812 87221 14948
33	.35323 87948 09651	.37819 93716 16348
34	.35322 13682 03583	.37827 00176 32694
0.4935	0.35320 39389 25197	0.37834 06601 63452
36	.35318 65069 74972	.37841 12992 08086
37	.35316 90723 53388	.37848 19347 66063
38	.35315 16350 60928	.37855 25668 36849
39	.35313 41950 98070	.37862 31954 19910
0.4940	0.35311 67524 65296	0.37869 38205 14711
41	.35309 93071 63087	.37876 44421 20718
42	.35308 18591 91922	.37883 50602 37398
43	.35306 44085 52284	.37890 56748 64217
44	.35304 69552 44653	.37897 62860 00641
0.4945	0.35302 94992 69510	0.37904 68936 46137
46	.35301 20406 27336	.37911 74978 00171
47	.35299 45793 18612	.37918 80984 62210
48	.35297 71153 43819	.37925 86956 31721
49	.35295 96487 03438	.37932 92893 08170
0.4950	0.35294 21793 97950	0.37939 98794 91024

x	$\dfrac{1}{\sqrt{2\pi}} e^{-\frac{x^2}{2}}$	$\dfrac{1}{\sqrt{2\pi}} \displaystyle\int_{-x}^{x} e^{-\frac{\alpha^2}{2}}\, d\alpha$
0.4950	0.35294 21793 97950	0.37939 98794 91024
51	.35292 47074 27838	.37947 04661 79751
52	.35290 72327 93581	.37954 10493 73818
53	.35288 97554 95662	.37961 16290 72691
54	.35287 22755 34562	.37968 22052 75839
0.4955	0.35285 47929 10763	0.37975 27779 82728
56	.35283 73076 24745	.37982 33471 92825
57	.35281 98196 76992	.37989 39129 05600
58	.35280 23290 67983	.37996 44751 20519
59	.35278 48357 98202	.38003 50338 37050
0.4960	0.35276 73398 68129	0.38010 55890 54661
61	.35274 98412 78248	.38017 61407 72820
62	.35273 23400 29038	.38024 66889 90995
63	.35271 48361 20984	.38031 72337 08654
64	.35269 73295 54566	.38038 77749 25266
0.4965	0.35267 98203 30266	0.38045 83126 40299
66	.35266 23084 48568	.38052 88468 53221
67	.35264 47939 09952	.38059 93775 63501
68	.35262 72767 14901	.38066 99047 70608
69	.35260 97568 63898	.38074 04284 74010
0.4970	0.35259 22343 57425	.38081 09486 73176
71	.35257 47091 95964	.38088 14653 67576
72	.35255 71813 79998	.38095 19785 56678
73	.35253 96509 10008	.38102 24882 39951
74	.35252 21177 86479	.38109 29944 16865
0.4975	0.35250 45820 09892	0.38116 34970 86889
76	.35248 70435 80730	.38123 39962 49492
77	.35246 95024 99476	.38130 44919 04144
78	.35245 19587 66612	.38137 49840 50315
79	.35243 44123 82622	.38144 54726 87474
0.4980	0.35241 68633 47988	0.38151 59578 15091
81	.35239 93116 63193	.38158 64394 32637
82	.35238 17573 28721	.38165 69175 39580
83	.35236 42003 45054	.38172 73921 35391
84	.35234 66407 12676	.38179 78632 19541
0.4985	0.35232 90784 32069	0.38186 83307 91500
86	.35231 15135 03717	.38193 87948 50738
87	.35229 39459 28103	.38200 92553 96725
88	.35227 63757 05711	.38207 97124 28932
89	.35225 88028 37024	.38215 01659 46831
0.4990	0.35224 12273 22525	0.38222 06159 49891
91	.35222 36491 62699	.38229 10624 37583
92	.35220 60683 58027	.38236 15054 09380
93	.35218 84849 08995	.38243 19448 64750
94	.35217 08988 16085	.38250 23808 03167
0.4995	0.35215 33100 79782	0.38257 28132 24101
96	.35213 57187 00570	.38264 32421 27023
97	.35211 81246 78931	.38271 36675 11405
98	.35210 05280 15351	.38278 40893 76718
99	.35208 29287 10312	.38285 45077 22435
0.5000	0.35206 53267 64299	0.38292 49225 48026

x	$\dfrac{1}{\sqrt{2\pi}}\,e^{-\frac{x^2}{2}}$	$\dfrac{1}{\sqrt{2\pi}}\displaystyle\int_{-x}^{x}e^{-\frac{\alpha^2}{2}}\,d\alpha$
0.5000	0.35206 53267 64299	0.38292 49225 48026
01	.35204 77221 77797	.38299 53338 52964
02	.35203 01149 51289	.38306 57416 36721
03	.35201 25050 85259	.38313 61458 98769
04	.35199 48925 80191	.38320 65466 38579
0.5005	0.35197 72774 36571	0.38327 69438 55625
06	.35195 96596 54881	.38334 73375 49378
07	.35194 20392 35607	.38341 77277 19311
08	.35192 44161 79234	.38348 81143 64897
09	.35190 67904 86244	.38355 84974 85607
0.5010	0.35188 91621 57124	0.38362 88770 80915
11	.35187 15311 92358	.38369 92531 50294
12	.35185 38975 92430	.38376 96256 93217
13	.35183 62613 57825	.38383 99947 09156
14	.35181 86224 89028	.38391 03601 97584
0.5015	0.35180 09809 86523	0.38398 07221 57976
16	.35178 33368 50796	.38405 10805 89803
17	.35176 56900 82332	.38412 14354 92540
18	.35174 80406 81615	.38419 17868 65661
19	.35173 03886 49131	.38426 21347 08638
0.5020	0.35171 27339 85364	0.38433 24790 20945
21	.35169 50766 90800	.38440 28198 02056
22	.35167 74167 65925	.38447 31570 51446
23	.35165 97542 11222	.38454 34907 68587
24	.35164 20890 27178	.38461 38209 52955
0.5025	0.35162 44212 14279	0.38468 41476 04023
26	.35160 67507 73008	.38475 44707 21266
27	.35158 90777 03853	.38482 47903 04157
28	.35157 14020 07298	.38489 51063 52172
29	.35155 37236 83829	.38496 54188 64785
0.5030	0.35153 60427 33932	0.38503 57278 41470
31	.35151 83591 58092	.38510 60332 81703
32	.35150 06729 56795	.38517 63351 84959
33	.35148 29841 30527	.38524 66335 50711
34	.35146 52926 79774	.38531 69283 78436
0.5035	0.35144 75986 05022	0.38538 72196 67608
36	.35142 99019 06757	.38545 75074 17703
37	.35141 22025 85464	.38552 77916 28196
38	.35139 45006 41630	.38559 80722 98562
39	.35137 67960 75742	.38566 83494 28278
0.5040	0.35135 90888 88284	0.38573 86230 16818
41	.35134 13790 79744	.38580 88930 63658
42	.35132 36666 50607	.38587 91595 68275
43	.35130 59516 01361	.38594 94225 30144
44	.35128 82339 32491	.38601 96819 48741
0.5045	0.35127 05136 44484	0.38608 99378 23542
46	.35125 27907 37826	.38616 01901 54024
47	.35123 50652 13005	.38623 04389 39663
48	.35121 73370 70506	.38630 06841 79935
49	.35119 96063 10816	.38637 09258 74317
0.5050	0.35118 18729 34423	0.38644 11640 22285

x	$\frac{1}{\sqrt{2\pi}} e^{-\frac{x^2}{2}}$	$\frac{1}{\sqrt{2\pi}} \int_{-x}^{x} e^{-\frac{a^2}{2}} \, da$
0.5050	0.35118 18729 34423	0.38644 11640 22285
51	.35116 41369 41812	.38651 13986 23316
52	.35114 63983 33471	.38658 16296 76887
53	.35112 86571 09887	.38665 18571 82475
54	.35111 09132 71546	.38672 20811 39557
0.5055	0.35109 31668 18936	0.38679 23015 47609
56	.35107 54177 52543	.38686 25184 06110
57	.35105 76660 72855	.38693 27317 14536
58	.35103 99117 80359	.38700 29414 72365
59	.35102 21548 75542	.38707 31476 79074
0.5060	0.35100 43953 58891	0.38714 33503 34141
61	.35098 66332 30894	.38721 35494 37044
62	.35096 88684 92038	.38728 37449 87259
63	.35095 11011 42810	.38735 39369 84266
64	.35093 33311 83699	.38742 41254 27543
0.5065	0.35091 55586 15191	0.38749 43103 16566
66	.35089 77834 37773	.38756 44916 50815
67	.35088 00056 51935	.38763 46694 29767
68	.35086 22252 58163	.38770 48436 52902
69	.35084 44422 56946	.38777 50143 19697
0.5070	0.35082 66566 48770	0.38784 51814 29631
71	.35080 88684 34124	.38791 53449 82182
72	.35079 10776 13496	.38798 55049 76830
73	.35077 32841 87374	.38805 56614 13054
74	.35075 54881 56245	.38812 58142 90332
0.5075	0.35073 76895 20598	0.38819 59636 08143
76	.35071 98882 80921	.38826 61093 65966
77	.35070 20844 37703	.38833 62515 63282
78	.35068 42779 91430	.38840 63901 99568
79	.35066 64689 42593	.38847 65252 74305
0.5080	0.35064 86572 91678	0.38854 66567 86972
81	.35063 08430 39175	.38861 67847 37048
82	.35061 30261 85571	.38868 69091 24014
83	.35059 52067 31356	.38875 70299 47349
84	.35057 73846 77018	.38882 71472 06533
0.5085	0.35055 95600 23045	0.38889 72609 01046
86	.35054 17327 69926	.38896 73710 30369
87	.35052 39029 18150	.38903 74775 93981
88	.35050 60704 68206	.38910 75805 91363
89	.35048 82354 20583	.38917 76800 21995
0.5090	0.35047 03977 75768	0.38924 77758 85358
91	.35045 25575 34252	.38931 78681 80932
92	.35043 47146 96523	.38938 79569 08199
93	.35041 68692 63070	.38945 80420 66638
94	.35039 90212 34383	.38952 81236 55731
0.5095	0.35038 11706 10950	0.38959 82016 74959
96	.35036 33173 93261	.38966 82761 23802
97	.35034 54615 81804	.38973 83470 01743
98	.35032 76031 77070	.38980 84143 08262
99	.35030 97421 79547	.38987 84780 42841
0.5100	0.35029 18785 89726	0.38994 85382 04961

x	$\frac{1}{\sqrt{2\pi}} e^{-\frac{x^2}{2}}$	$\frac{1}{\sqrt{2\pi}} \int_{-x}^{x} e^{-\frac{\alpha^2}{2}} d\alpha$
0.5100	0.35029 18785 89726	0.38994 85382 04961
01	.35027 40124 08095	.39001 85947 94104
02	.35025 61436 35143	.39008 86478 09752
03	.35023 82722 71361	.39015 86972 51385
04	.35022 03983 17238	.39022 87431 18488
0.5105	0.35020 25217 73264	0.39029 87854 10540
06	.35018 46426 39929	.39036 88241 27024
07	.35016 67609 17721	.39043 88592 67423
08	.35014 88766 07132	.39050 88908 31219
09	.35013 09897 08650	.39057 89188 17893
0.5110	0.35011 31002 22767	0.39064 89432 26930
11	.35009 52081 49971	.39071 89640 57810
12	.35007 73134 90753	.39078 89813 10017
13	.35005 94162 45603	.39085 89949 83034
14	.35004 15164 15011	.39092 90050 76343
0.5115	0.35002 36139 99467	0.39099 90115 89428
16	.35000 57089 99462	.39106 90145 21771
17	.34998 78014 15486	.39113 90138 72855
18	.34996 98912 48029	.39120 90096 42165
19	.34995 19784 97581	.39127 90018 29182
0.5120	0.34993 40631 64634	0.39134 89904 33391
21	.34991 61452 49677	.39141 89754 54276
22	.34989 82247 53201	.39148 89568 91319
23	.34988 03016 75697	.39155 89347 44005
24	.34986 23760 17655	.39162 89090 11817
0.5125	0.34984 44477 79566	0.39169 88796 94240
26	.34982 65169 61921	.39176 88467 90757
27	.34980 85835 65210	.39183 88103 00853
28	.34979 06475 89926	.39190 87702 24011
29	.34977 27090 36557	.39197 87265 59717
0.5130	0.34975 47679 05596	0.39204 86793 07454
31	.34973 68241 97534	.39211 86284 66708
32	.34971 88779 12861	.39218 85740 36962
33	.34970 09290 52069	.39225 85160 17701
34	.34968 29776 15648	.39232 84544 08411
0.5135	0.34966 50236 04091	0.39239 83892 08576
36	.34964 70670 17888	.39246 83204 17681
37	.34962 91078 57531	.39253 82480 35211
38	.34961 11461 23510	.39260 81720 60652
39	.34959 31818 16319	.39267 80924 93489
0.5140	0.34957 52149 36447	0.39274 80093 33207
41	.34955 72454 84387	.39281 79225 79292
42	.34953 92734 60630	.39288 78322 31229
43	.34952 12988 65668	.39295 77382 88505
44	.34950 33216 99993	.39302 76407 50604
0.5145	0.34948 53419 64096	0.39309 75396 17014
46	.34946 73596 58469	.39316 74348 87219
47	.34944 93747 83604	.39323 73265 60706
48	.34943 13873 39992	.39330 72146 36961
49	.34941 33973 28127	.39337 70991 15470
0.5150	0.34939 54047 48500	0.39344 69799 95721

x	$\dfrac{1}{\sqrt{2\pi}}e^{-\frac{x^2}{2}}$	$\dfrac{1}{\sqrt{2\pi}}\displaystyle\int_{-x}^{x}e^{-\frac{\alpha^2}{2}}\,d\alpha$
0.5150	0.34939 54047 48500	0.39344 69799 95721
51	.34937 74096 01602	.39351 68572 77199
52	.34935 94118 87926	.39358 67309 59390
53	.34934 14116 07965	.39365 66010 41783
54	.34932 34087 62210	.39372 64675 23863
0.5155	0.34930 54033 51154	0.39379 63304 05117
56	.34928 73953 75289	.39386 61896 85032
57	.34926 93848 35107	.39393 60453 63096
58	.34925 13717 31101	.39400 58974 38795
59	.34923 33560 63763	.39407 57459 11617
0.5160	0.34921 53378 33587	0.39414 55907 81050
61	.34919 73170 41063	.39421 54320 46580
62	.34917 92936 86686	.39428 52697 07695
63	.34916 12677 70947	.39435 51037 63884
64	.34914 32392 94340	.39442 49342 14633
0.5165	0.34912 52082 57357	0.39449 47610 59431
66	.34910 71746 60491	.39456 45842 97765
67	.34908 91385 04236	.39463 44039 29124
68	.34907 10997 89083	.39470 42199 52996
69	.34905 30585 15526	.39477 40323 68870
0.5170	0.34903 50146 84058	0.39484 38411 76232
71	.34901 69682 95172	.39491 36463 74573
72	.34899 89193 49361	.39498 34479 63380
73	.34898 08678 47119	.39505 32459 42142
74	.34896 28137 88938	.39512 30403 10348
0.5175	0.34894 47571 75312	0.39519 28310 67487
76	.34892 66980 06735	.39526 26182 13048
77	.34890 86362 83699	.39533 24017 46520
78	.34889 05720 06698	.39540 21816 67391
79	.34887 25051 76227	.39547 19579 75152
0.5180	0.34885 44357 92777	0.39554 17306 69291
81	.34883 63638 56843	.39561 14997 49299
82	.34881 82893 68919	.39568 12652 14664
83	.34880 02123 29497	.39575 10270 64876
84	.34878 21327 39073	.39582 07852 99426
0.5185	0.34876 40505 98140	0.39589 05399 17802
86	.34874 59659 07191	.39596 02909 19495
87	.34872 78786 66720	.39603 00383 03995
88	.34870 97888 77222	.39609 97820 70792
89	.34869 16965 39191	.39616 95222 19376
0.5190	0.34867 36016 53120	0.39623 92587 49238
91	.34865 55042 19504	.39630 89916 59867
92	.34863 74042 38837	.39637 87209 50756
93	.34861 93017 11613	.39644 84466 21393
94	.34860 11966 38326	.39651 81686 71271
0.5195	0.34858 30890 19471	0.39658 78870 99879
96	.34856 49788 55542	.39665 76019 06709
97	.34854 68661 47033	.39672 73130 91251
98	.34852 87508 94439	.39679 70206 52998
99	.34851 06330 98255	.39686 67245 91440
0.5200	0.34849 25127 58974	0.39693 64249 06068

x	$\dfrac{1}{\sqrt{2\pi}}\,e^{-\frac{x^2}{2}}$	$\dfrac{1}{\sqrt{2\pi}}\displaystyle\int_{-x}^{x} e^{-\frac{\alpha^2}{2}}\,d\alpha$
0.5200	0.34849 25127 58974	0.39693 64249 06068
01	.34847 43898 77093	.39700 61215 96374
02	.34845 62644 53104	.39707 58146 61849
03	.34843 81364 87504	.39714 55041 01985
04	.34842 00059 80786	.39721 51899 16275
0.5205	0.34840 18729 33446	0.39728 48721 04208
06	.34838 37373 45979	.39735 45506 65279
07	.34836 55992 18879	.39742 42255 98977
08	.34834 74585 52641	.39749 38969 04797
09	.34832 93153 47761	.39756 35645 82229
0.5210	0.34831 11696 04733	0.39763 32286 30767
11	.34829 30213 24053	.39770 28890 49902
12	.34827 48705 06216	.39777 25458 39127
13	.34825 67171 51717	.39784 21989 97935
14	.34823 85612 61051	.39791 18485 25819
0.5215	0.34822 04028 34714	0.39798 14944 22271
16	.34820 22418 73200	.39805 11366 86784
17	.34818 40783 77007	.39812 07753 18851
18	.34816 59123 46628	.39819 04103 17966
19	.34814 77437 82559	.39826 00416 83621
0.5220	0.34812 95726 85297	0.39832 96694 15310
21	.34811 13990 55336	.39839 92935 12526
22	.34809 32228 93173	.39846 89139 74763
23	.34807 50441 99303	.39853 85308 01514
24	.34805 68629 74221	.39860 81439 92274
0.5225	0.34803 86792 18424	0.39867 77535 46535
26	.34802 04929 32408	.39874 73594 63793
27	.34800 23041 16668	.39881 69617 43540
28	.34798 41127 71701	.39888 65603 85271
29	.34796 59188 98002	.39895 61553 88480
0.5230	0.34794 77224 96068	0.39902 57467 52661
31	.34792 95235 66395	.39909 53344 77310
32	.34791 13221 09478	.39916 49185 61919
33	.34789 31181 25814	.39923 44990 05985
34	.34787 49116 15900	.39930 40758 09001
0.5235	0.34785 67025 80232	0.39937 36489 70463
36	.34783 84910 19306	.39944 32184 89865
37	.34782 02769 33618	.39951 27843 66703
38	.34780 20603 23665	.39958 23466 00470
39	.34778 38411 89944	.39965 19051 90664
0.5240	0.34776 56195 32951	0.39972 14601 36778
41	.34774 73953 53182	.39979 10114 38309
42	.34772 91686 51135	.39986 05590 94751
43	.34771 09394 27307	.39993 01031 05601
44	.34769 27076 82193	.39999 96434 70354
0.5245	0.34767 44734 16290	0.40006 91801 88506
46	.34765 62366 30097	.40013 87132 59553
47	.34763 79973 24109	.40020 82426 82990
48	.34761 97554 98823	.40027 77684 58314
49	.34760 15111 54737	.40034 72905 85022
0.5250	0.34758 32642 92348	0.40041 68090 62608

x	$\dfrac{1}{\sqrt{2\pi}}\,e^{-\frac{x^2}{2}}$	$\dfrac{1}{\sqrt{2\pi}}\displaystyle\int_{-x}^{x} e^{-\frac{\alpha^2}{2}}\,d\alpha$
0.5250	0.34758 32642 92348	0.40041 68090 62608
51	.34756 50149 12152	.40048 63238 90571
52	.34754 67630 14648	.40055 58350 68405
53	.34752 85086 00331	.40062 53425 95609
54	.34751 02516 69700	.40069 48464 71678
0.5255	0.34749 19922 23251	0.40076 43466 96109
56	.34747 37302 61483	.40083 38432 68399
57	.34745 54657 84892	.40090 33361 88046
58	.34743 71987 93976	.40097 28254 54546
59	.34741 89292 89233	.40104 23110 67396
0.5260	0.34740 06572 71159	0.40111 17930 26094
61	.34738 23827 40254	.40118 12713 30137
62	.34736 41056 97013	.40125 07459 79022
63	.34734 58261 41936	.40132 02169 72248
64	.34732 75440 75520	.40138 96843 09312
0.5265	0.34730 92594 98262	0.40145 91479 89711
66	.34729 09724 10660	.40152 86080 12944
67	.34727 26828 13214	.40159 80643 78508
68	.34725 43907 06419	.40166 75170 85902
69	.34723 60960 90775	.40173 69661 34623
0.5270	0.34721 77989 66779	0.40180 64115 24171
71	.34719 94993 34930	.40187 58532 54043
72	.34718 11971 95725	.40194 52913 23738
73	.34716 28925 49663	.40201 47257 32754
74	.34714 45853 97243	.40208 41564 80590
0.5275	0.34712 62757 38962	0.40215 35835 66746
76	.34710 79635 75319	.40222 30069 90719
77	.34708 96489 06811	.40229 24267 52009
78	.34707 13317 33939	.40236 18428 50115
79	.34705 30120 57200	.40243 12552 84535
0.5280	0.34703 46898 77092	0.40250 06640 54771
81	.34701 63651 94115	.40257 00691 60319
82	.34699 80380 08767	.40263 94706 00681
83	.34697 97083 21546	.40270 88683 75356
84	.34696 13761 32952	.40277 82624 83843
0.5285	0.34694 30414 43483	0.40284 76529 25643
86	.34692 47042 53637	.40291 70397 00254
87	.34690 63645 63915	.40298 64228 07177
88	.34688 80223 74815	.40305 58022 45913
89	.34686 96776 86835	.40312 51780 15961
0.5290	0.34685 13305 00475	0.40319 45501 16821
91	.34683 29808 16235	.40326 39185 47994
92	.34681 46286 34612	.40333 32833 08981
93	.34679 62739 56106	.40340 26443 99282
94	.34677 79167 81217	.40347 20018 18397
0.5295	0.34675 95571 10444	0.40354 13555 65828
96	.34674 11949 44286	.40361 07056 41075
97	.34672 28302 83242	.40368 00520 43639
98	.34670 44631 27812	.40374 93947 73022
99	.34668 60934 78495	.40381 87338 28724
0.5300	0.34666 77213 35792	0.40388 80692 10247

X	$\frac{1}{\sqrt{2\pi}} e^{-\frac{x^2}{2}}$	$\frac{1}{\sqrt{2\pi}} \int_{-x}^{x} e^{-\frac{\alpha^2}{2}} d\alpha$
0.5300	0.34666 77213 35792	0.40388 80692 10247
01	.34664 93467 00200	.40395 74009 17092
02	.34663 09695 72221	.40402 67289 48761
03	.34661 25899 52353	.40409 60533 04755
04	.34659 42078 41097	.40416 53739 84576
0.5305	0.34657 58232 38952	0.40423 46909 87725
06	.34655 74361 46418	.40430 40043 13705
07	.34653 90465 63995	.40437 33139 62018
08	.34652 06544 92183	.40444 26199 32165
09	.34650 22599 31481	.40451 19222 23649
0.5310	0.34648 38628 82390	0.40458 12208 35972
11	.34646 54633 45409	.40465 05157 68636
12	.34644 70613 21040	.40471 98070 21144
13	.34642 86568 09781	.40478 90945 92999
14	.34641 02498 12134	.40485 83784 83702
0.5315	0.34639 18403 28598	0.40492 76586 92758
16	.34637 34283 59674	.40499 69352 19668
17	.34635 50139 05862	.40506 62080 63936
18	.34633 65969 67662	.40513 54772 25065
19	.34631 81775 45575	.40520 47427 02557
0.5320	0.34629 97556 40101	0.40527 40044 95917
21	.34628 13312 51742	.40534 32626 04648
22	.34626 29043 80996	.40541 25170 28253
23	.34624 44750 28366	.40548 17677 66235
24	.34622 60431 94352	.40555 10148 18099
0.5325	0.34620 76088 79454	0.40562 02581 83347
26	.34618 91720 84173	.40568 94978 61485
27	.34617 07328 09010	.40575 87338 52016
28	.34615 22910 54467	.40582 79661 54443
29	.34613 38468 21043	.40589 71947 68272
0.5330	0.34611 54001 09239	0.40596 64196 93006
31	.34609 69509 19558	.40603 56409 28151
32	.34607 84992 52499	.40610 48584 73209
33	.34606 00451 08565	.40617 40723 27687
34	.34604 15884 88255	.40624 32824 91087
0.5335	0.34602 31293 92072	0.40631 24889 62917
36	.34600 46678 20516	.40638 16917 42679
37	.34598 62037 74089	.40645 08908 29880
38	.34596 77372 53292	.40652 00862 24024
39	.34594 92682 58627	.40658 92779 24616
0.5340	0.34593 07967 90595	0.40665 84659 31163
41	.34591 23228 49697	.40672 76502 43168
42	.34589 38464 36435	.40679 68308 60138
43	.34587 53675 51311	.40686 60077 81578
44	.34585 68861 94826	.40693 51810 06993
0.5345	0.34583 84023 67482	0.40700 43505 35891
46	.34581 99160 69780	.40707 35163 67776
47	.34580 14273 02223	.40714 26785 02154
48	.34578 29360 65312	.40721 18369 38532
49	.34576 44423 59549	.40728 09916 76416
0.5350	0.34574 59461 85435	0.40735 01427 15311

X	$\frac{1}{\sqrt{2\pi}} e^{-\frac{x^2}{2}}$	$\frac{1}{\sqrt{2\pi}} \int_{-x}^{x} e^{-\frac{\alpha^2}{2}} d\alpha$
0.5350	0.34574 59461 85435	0.40735 01427 15311
51	.34572 74475 43474	.40741 92900 54725
52	.34570 89464 34167	.40748 84336 94164
53	.34569 04428 58015	.40755 75736 33134
54	.34567 19368 15522	.40762 67098 71143
0.5355	0.34565 34283 07188	0.40769 58424 07696
56	.34563 49173 33517	.40776 49712 42301
57	.34561 64038 95011	.40783 40963 74465
58	.34559 78879 92171	.40790 32178 03695
59	.34557 93696 25501	.40797 23355 29498
0.5360	0.34556 08487 95502	0.40804 14495 51381
61	.34554 23255 02678	.40811 05598 68852
62	.34552 37997 47530	.40817 96664 81418
63	.34550 52715 30560	.40824 87693 88587
64	.34548 67408 52273	.40831 78685 89866
0.5365	0.34546 82077 13169	0.40838 69640 84764
66	.34544 96721 13753	.40845 60558 72787
67	.34543 11340 54526	.40852 51439 53445
68	.34541 25935 35991	.40859 42283 26245
69	.34539 40505 58651	.40866 33089 90696
0.5370	0.34537 55051 23009	0.40873 23859 46305
71	.34535 69572 29569	.40880 14591 92581
72	.34533 84068 78832	.40887 05287 29033
73	.34531 98540 71301	.40893 95945 55169
74	.34530 12988 07481	.40900 86566 70498
0.5375	0.34528 27410 87873	0.40907 77150 74528
76	.34526 41809 12981	.40914 67697 66769
77	.34524 56182 83309	.40921 58207 46730
78	.34522 70531 99359	.40928 48680 13919
79	.34520 84856 61635	.40935 39115 67846
0.5380	0.34518 99156 70639	0.40942 29514 08020
81	.34517 13432 26876	.40949 19875 33950
82	.34515 27683 30849	.40956 10199 45147
83	.34513 41909 83061	.40963 00486 41119
84	.34511 56111 84016	.40969 90736 21377
0.5385	0.34509 70289 34217	0.40976 80948 85430
86	.34507 84442 34167	.40983 71124 32787
87	.34505 98570 84372	.40990 61262 62960
88	.34504 12674 85333	.40997 51363 75458
89	.34502 26754 37555	.41004 41427 69791
0.5390	0.34500 40809 41542	0.41011 31454 45470
91	.34498 54839 97798	.41018 21444 02004
92	.34496 68846 06826	.41025 11396 38906
93	.34494 82827 69130	.41032 01311 55684
94	.34492 96784 85214	.41038 91189 51850
0.5395	0.34491 10717 55583	0.41045 81030 26915
96	.34489 24625 80740	.41052 70833 80389
97	.34487 38509 61189	.41059 60600 11784
98	.34485 52368 97435	.41066 50329 20611
99	.34483 66203 89982	.41073 40021 06380
0.5400	0.34481 80014 39333	0.41080 29675 68604

x	$\dfrac{1}{\sqrt{2\pi}}\,e^{-\frac{x^2}{2}}$	$\dfrac{1}{\sqrt{2\pi}}\displaystyle\int_{-x}^{x} e^{-\frac{\alpha^2}{2}}\,d\alpha$
0.5400	0.34481 80014 39333	0.41080 29675 68604
01	.34479 93800 45994	.41087 19293 06793
02	.34478 07562 10469	.41094 08873 20460
03	.34476 21299 33261	.41100 98416 09115
04	.34474 35012 14876	.41107 87921 72270
0.5405	0.34472 48700 55818	0.41114 77390 09438
06	.34470 62364 56592	.41121 66821 20130
07	.34468 76004 17701	.41128 56215 03858
08	.34466 89619 39651	.41135 45571 60134
09	.34465 03210 22946	.41142 34890 88471
0.5410	0.34463 16776 68091	0.41149 24172 88381
11	.34461 30318 75590	.41156 13417 59376
12	.34459 43836 45949	.41163 02625 00969
13	.34457 57329 79673	.41169 91795 12672
14	.34455 70798 77265	.41176 80927 93998
0.5415	0.34453 84243 39232	0.41183 70023 44460
16	.34451 97663 66078	.41190 59081 63571
17	.34450 11059 58307	.41197 48102 50844
18	.34448 24431 16426	.41204 37086 05792
19	.34446 37778 40940	.41211 26032 27929
0.5420	0.34444 51101 32352	0.41218 14941 16767
21	.34442 64399 91170	.41225 03812 71820
22	.34440 77674 17897	.41231 92646 92601
23	.34438 90924 13039	.41238 81443 78625
24	.34437 04149 77102	.41245 70203 29404
0.5425	0.34435 17351 10591	0.41252 58925 44453
26	.34433 30528 14011	.41259 47610 23286
27	.34431 43680 87868	.41266 36257 65417
28	.34429 56809 32668	.41273 24867 70360
29	.34427 69913 48915	.41280 13440 37628
0.5430	0.34425 82993 37116	0.41287 01975 66737
31	.34423 96048 97775	.41293 90473 57201
32	.34422 09080 31400	.41300 78934 08535
33	.34420 22087 38495	.41307 67357 20252
34	.34418 35070 19567	.41314 55742 91868
0.5435	0.34416 48028 75121	0.41321 44091 22898
36	.34414 60963 05663	.41328 32402 12857
37	.34412 73873 11699	.41335 20675 61259
38	.34410 86758 93736	.41342 08911 67620
39	.34408 99620 52278	.41348 97110 31455
0.5440	0.34407 12457 87832	0.41355 85271 52279
41	.34405 25271 00905	.41362 73395 29608
42	.34403 38059 92002	.41369 61481 62958
43	.34401 50824 61630	.41376 49530 51844
44	.34399 63565 10294	.41383 37541 95781
0.5445	0.34397 76281 38501	0.41390 25515 94286
46	.34395 88973 46758	.41397 13452 46875
47	.34394 01641 35571	.41404 01351 53064
48	.34392 14285 05446	.41410 89213 12368
49	.34390 26904 56890	.41417 77037 24305
0.5450	0.34388 39499 90409	0.41424 64823 88390

x	$\dfrac{1}{\sqrt{2\pi}}e^{-\frac{x^2}{2}}$	$\dfrac{1}{\sqrt{2\pi}}\displaystyle\int_{-x}^{x}e^{-\frac{\alpha^2}{2}}\,d\alpha$
0.5450	0.34388 39499 90409	0.41424 64823 88390
51	.34386 52071 06510	.41431 52573 04140
52	.34384 64618 05699	.41438 40284 71071
53	.34382 77140 88484	.41445 27958 88701
54	.34380 89639 55370	.41452 15595 56546
0.5455	0.34379 02114 06864	0.41459 03194 74122
56	.34377 14564 43474	.41465 90756 40947
57	.34375 26990 65706	.41472 78280 56539
58	.34373 39392 74067	.41479 65767 20413
59	.34371 51770 69064	.41486 53216 32087
0.5460	0.34369 64124 51204	0.41493 40627 91079
61	.34367 76454 20993	.41500 28001 96907
62	.34365 88759 78940	.41507 15338 49087
63	.34364 01041 25550	.41514 02637 47138
64	.34362 13298 61332	.41520 89898 90577
0.5465	0.34360 25531 86792	0.41527 77122 78922
66	.34358 37741 02438	.41534 64309 11691
67	.34356 49926 08776	.41541 51457 88402
68	.34354 62087 06315	.41548 38569 08574
69	.34352 74223 95561	.41555 25642 71724
0.5470	0.34350 86336 77023	0.41562 12678 77371
71	.34348 98425 51206	.41568 99677 25034
72	.34347 10490 18620	.41575 86638 14231
73	.34345 22530 79771	.41582 73561 44481
74	.34343 34547 35167	.41589 60447 15303
0.5475	0.34341 46539 85316	0.41596 47295 26215
76	.34339 58508 30725	.41603 34105 76737
77	.34337 70452 71902	.41610 20878 66387
78	.34335 82373 09355	.41617 07613 94685
79	.34333 94269 43592	.41623 94311 61151
0.5480	0.34332 06141 75120	0.41630 80971 65302
81	.34330 17990 04447	.41637 67594 06660
82	.34328 29814 32082	.41644 54178 84744
83	.34326 41614 58532	.41651 40725 99073
84	.34324 53390 84306	.41658 27235 49167
0.5485	0.34322 65143 09911	0.41665 13707 34547
86	.34320 76871 35856	.41672 00141 54731
87	.34318 88575 62648	.41678 86538 09241
88	.34317 00255 90796	.41685 72896 97597
89	.34315 11912 20809	.41692 59218 19318
0.5490	0.34313 23544 53193	0.41699 45501 73925
91	.34311 35152 88459	.41706 31747 60939
92	.34309 46737 27114	.41713 17955 79881
93	.34307 58297 69666	.41720 04126 30270
94	.34305 69834 16625	.41726 90259 11629
0.5495	0.34303 81346 68498	0.41733 76354 23477
96	.34301 92835 25794	.41740 62411 65337
97	.34300 04299 89022	.41747 48431 36728
98	.34298 15740 58691	.41754 34413 37173
99	.34296 27157 35308	.41761 20357 66192
0.5500	0.34294 38550 19384	0.41768 06264 23307

x	$\dfrac{1}{\sqrt{2\pi}} e^{-\frac{x^2}{2}}$	$\dfrac{1}{\sqrt{2\pi}} \displaystyle\int_{-x}^{x} e^{-\frac{\alpha^2}{2}} \, d\alpha$
0.5500	0.34294 38550 19384	0.41768 06264 23307
01	.34292 49919 11426	.41774 92133 08040
02	.34290 61264 11943	.41781 77964 19912
03	.34288 72585 21445	.41788 63757 58446
04	.34286 83882 40440	.41795 49513 23162
0.5505	0.34284 95155 69437	0.41802 35231 13582
06	.34283 06405 08946	.41809 20911 29230
07	.34281 17630 59474	.41816 06553 69627
08	.34279 28832 21532	.41822 92158 34295
09	.34277 40009 95628	.41829 77725 22756
0.5510	0.34275 51163 82272	0.41836 63254 34534
11	.34273 62293 81973	.41843 48745 69150
12	.34271 73399 95239	.41850 34199 26127
13	.34269 84482 22581	.41857 19615 04989
14	.34267 95540 64508	.41864 04993 05257
0.5515	0.34266 06575 21529	0.41870 90333 26456
16	.34264 17585 94153	.41877 75635 68107
17	.34262 28572 82891	.41884 60900 29735
18	.34260 39535 88251	.41891 46127 10861
19	.34258 50475 10742	.41898 31316 11011
0.5520	0.34256 61390 50876	0.41905 16467 29707
21	.34254 72282 09161	.41912 01580 66473
22	.34252 83149 86107	.41918 86656 20832
23	.34250 93993 82224	.41925 71693 92308
24	.34249 04813 98021	.41932 56693 80426
0.5525	0.34247 15610 34009	0.41939 41655 84709
26	.34245 26382 90697	.41946 26580 04681
27	.34243 37131 68595	.41953 11466 39866
28	.34241 47856 68213	.41959 96314 89790
29	.34239 58557 90062	.41966 81125 53975
0.5530	0.34237 69235 34650	0.41973 65898 31947
31	.34235 79889 02489	.41980 50633 23231
32	.34233 90518 94088	.41987 35330 27350
33	.34232 01125 09957	.41994 19989 43830
34	.34230 11707 50608	.42001 04610 72196
0.5535	0.34228 22266 16549	0.42007 89194 11972
36	.34226 32801 08291	.42014 73739 62684
37	.34224 43312 26345	.42021 58247 23857
38	.34222 53799 71221	.42028 42716 95016
39	.34220 64263 43430	.42035 27148 75687
0.5540	0.34218 74703 43481	0.42042 11542 65395
41	.34216 85119 71886	.42048 95898 63666
42	.34214 95512 29155	.42055 80216 70026
43	.34213 05881 15798	.42062 64496 84000
44	.34211 16226 32326	.42069 48739 05114
0.5545	0.34209 26547 79251	0.42076 32943 32895
46	.34207 36845 57082	.42083 17109 66868
47	.34205 47119 66330	.42090 01238 06560
48	.34203 57370 07506	.42096 85328 51497
49	.34201 67596 81122	.42103 69381 01205
0.5550	0.34199 77799 87687	0.42110 53395 55211

x	$\dfrac{1}{\sqrt{2\pi}} e^{-\frac{x^2}{2}}$	$\dfrac{1}{\sqrt{2\pi}} \displaystyle\int_{-x}^{x} e^{-\frac{\alpha^2}{2}} \, d\alpha$
0.5550	0.34199 77799 87687	0.42110 53395 55211
51	.34197 87979 27713	.42117 37372 13042
52	.34195 98135 01712	.42124 21310 74225
53	.34194 08267 10193	.42131 05211 38285
54	.34192 18375 53668	.42137 89074 04751
0.5555	0.34190 28460 32648	0.42144 72898 73149
56	.34188 38521 47644	.42151 56685 43007
57	.34186 48558 99167	.42158 40434 13851
58	.34184 58572 87729	.42165 24144 85209
59	.34182 68563 13842	.42172 07817 56608
0.5560	0.34180 78529 78015	0.42178 91452 27577
61	.34178 88472 80761	.42185 75048 97642
62	.34176 98392 22591	.42192 58607 66332
63	.34175 08288 04016	.42199 42128 33174
64	.34173 18160 25549	.42206 25610 97696
0.5565	0.34171 28008 87699	0.42213 09055 59427
66	.34169 37833 90980	.42219 92462 17894
67	.34167 47635 35903	.42226 75830 72626
68	.34165 57413 22979	.42233 59161 23151
69	.34163 67167 52720	.42240 42453 68998
0.5570	0.34161 76898 25638	0.42247 25708 09695
71	.34159 86605 42244	.42254 08924 44771
72	.34157 96289 03051	.42260 92102 73755
73	.34156 05949 08569	.42267 75242 96175
74	.34154 15585 59313	.42274 58345 11561
0.5575	0.34152 25198 55792	0.42281 41409 19442
76	.34150 34787 98519	.42288 24435 19347
77	.34148 44353 88007	.42295 07423 10805
78	.34146 53896 24767	.42301 90372 93345
79	.34144 63415 09311	.42308 73284 66498
0.5580	0.34142 72910 42152	0.42315 56158 29792
81	.34140 82382 23802	.42322 38993 82758
82	.34138 91830 54772	.42329 21791 24925
83	.34137 01255 35576	.42336 04550 55823
84	.34135 10656 66726	.42342 87271 74982
0.5585	0.34133 20034 48733	0.42349 69954 81933
86	.34131 29388 82111	.42356 52599 76205
87	.34129 38719 67372	.42363 35206 57329
88	.34127 48027 05029	.42370 17775 24836
89	.34125 57310 95593	.42377 00305 78255
0.5590	0.34123 66571 39578	0.42383 82798 17118
91	.34121 75808 37495	.42390 65252 40954
92	.34119 85021 89859	.42397 47668 49296
93	.34117 94211 97181	.42404 30046 41674
94	.34116 03378 59975	.42411 12386 17619
0.5595	0.34114 12521 78753	0.42417 94687 76662
96	.34112 21641 54027	.42424 76951 18334
97	.34110 30737 86311	.42431 59176 42167
98	.34108 39810 76118	.42438 41363 47692
99	.34106 48860 23961	.42445 23512 34441
0.5600	0.34104 57886 30353	0.42452 05623 01946

x	$\dfrac{1}{\sqrt{2\pi}} e^{-\frac{x^2}{2}}$	$\dfrac{1}{\sqrt{2\pi}} \displaystyle\int_{-x}^{x} e^{-\frac{\alpha^2}{2}} d\alpha$
0.5600	0.34104 57886 30353	0.42452 05623 01946
01	.34102 66888 95806	.42458 87695 49738
02	.34100 75868 20833	.42465 69729 77348
03	.34098 84824 05949	.42472 51725 84310
04	.34096 93756 51666	.42479 33683 70155
0.5605	0.34095 02665 58497	0.42486 15603 34415
06	.34093 11551 26956	.42492 97484 76622
07	.34091 20413 57556	.42499 79327 96310
08	.34089 29252 50809	.42506 61132 93009
09	.34087 38068 07231	.42513 42899 66254
0.5610	0.34085 46860 27333	0.42520 24628 15576
11	.34083 55629 11629	.42527 06318 40509
12	.34081 64374 60634	.42533 87970 40585
13	.34079 73096 74860	.42540 69584 15338
14	.34077 81795 54821	.42547 51159 64300
0.5615	0.34075 90471 01031	0.42554 32696 87004
16	.34073 99123 14003	.42561 14195 82985
17	.34072 07751 94251	.42567 95656 51774
18	.34070 16357 42289	.42574 77078 92907
19	.34068 24939 58630	.42581 58463 05916
0.5620	0.34066 33498 43789	0.42588 39808 90335
21	.34064 42033 98279	.42595 21116 45698
22	.34062 50546 22614	.42602 02385 71539
23	.34060 59035 17309	.42608 83616 67392
24	.34058 67500 82876	.42615 64809 32791
0.5625	0.34056 75943 19831	0.42622 45963 67270
26	.34054 84362 28686	.42629 27079 70363
27	.34052 92758 09958	.42636 08157 41606
28	.34051 01130 64158	.42642 89196 80532
29	.34049 09479 91803	.42649 70197 86676
0.5630	0.34047 17805 93405	0.42656 51160 59574
31	.34045 26108 69479	.42663 32084 98759
32	.34043 34388 20540	.42670 12971 03767
33	.34041 42644 47102	.42676 93818 74132
34	.34039 50877 49679	.42683 74628 09390
0.5635	0.34037 59087 28786	0.42690 55399 09077
36	.34035 67273 84937	.42697 36131 72727
37	.34033 75437 18646	.42704 16825 99876
38	.34031 83577 30429	.42710 97481 90060
39	.34029 91694 20800	.42717 78099 42814
0.5640	0.34027 99787 90274	0.42724 58678 57673
41	.34026 07858 39364	.42731 39219 34175
42	.34024 15905 68587	.42738 19721 71854
43	.34022 23929 78456	.42745 00185 70248
44	.34020 31930 69487	.42751 80611 28891
0.5645	0.34018 39908 42194	0.42758 60998 47321
46	.34016 47862 97092	.42765 41347 25074
47	.34014 55794 34697	.42772 21657 61685
48	.34012 63702 55523	.42779 01929 56693
49	.34010 71587 60085	.42785 82163 09633
0.5650	0.34008 79449 48898	0.42792 62358 20043

x	$\frac{1}{\sqrt{2\pi}} e^{-\frac{x^2}{2}}$	$\frac{1}{\sqrt{2\pi}} \int_{-x}^{x} e^{-\frac{\alpha^2}{2}} d\alpha$
0.5650	0.34008 79449 48898	0.42792 62358 20043
51	.34006 87288 22477	.42799 42514 87458
52	.34004 95103 81338	.42806 22633 11417
53	.34003 02896 25995	.42813 02712 91457
54	.34001 10665 56965	.42819 82754 27113
0.5655	0.33999 18411 74761	0.42826 62757 17925
56	.33997 26134 79899	.42833 42721 63429
57	.33995 33834 72896	.42840 22647 63163
58	.33993 41511 54265	.42847 02535 16664
59	.33991 49165 24523	.42853 82384 23471
0.5660	0.33989 56795 84185	0.42860 62194 83120
61	.33987 64403 33766	.42867 41966 95150
62	.33985 71987 73782	.42874 21700 59100
63	.33983 79549 04749	.42881 01395 74506
64	.33981 87087 27181	.42887 81052 40908
0.5665	0.33979 94602 41596	0.42894 60670 57843
66	.33978 02094 48508	.42901 40250 24850
67	.33976 09563 48433	.42908 19791 41469
68	.33974 17009 41887	.42914 99294 07236
69	.33972 24432 29386	.42921 78758 21692
0.5670	0.33970 31832 11446	0.42928 58183 84374
71	.33968 39208 88582	.42935 37570 94822
72	.33966 46562 61311	.42942 16919 52576
73	.33964 53893 30148	.42948 96229 57173
74	.33962 61200 95609	.42955 75501 08154
0.5675	0.33960 68485 58211	0.42962 54734 05058
76	.33958 75747 18470	.42969 33928 47424
77	.33956 82985 76901	.42976 13084 34792
78	.33954 90201 34022	.42982 92201 66701
79	.33952 97393 90347	.42989 71280 42692
0.5680	0.33951 04563 46394	0.42996 50320 62304
81	.33949 11710 02678	.43003 29322 25078
82	.33947 18833 59717	.43010 08285 30552
83	.33945 25934 18025	.43016 87209 78268
84	.33943 33011 78121	.43023 66095 67766
0.5685	0.33941 40066 40520	0.43030 44942 98586
86	.33939 47098 05738	.43037 23751 70269
87	.33937 54106 74293	.43044 02521 82355
88	.33935 61092 46700	.43050 81253 34386
89	.33933 68055 23477	.43057 59946 25901
0.5690	0.33931 74995 05140	0.43064 38600 56442
91	.33929 81911 92205	.43071 17216 25550
92	.33927 88805 85191	.43077 95793 32766
93	.33925 95676 84612	.43084 74331 77631
94	.33924 02524 90986	.43091 52831 59687
0.5695	0.33922 09350 04831	0.43098 31292 78475
96	.33920 16152 26662	.43105 09715 33536
97	.33918 22931 56996	.43111 88099 24413
98	.33916 29687 96352	.43118 66444 50646
99	.33914 36421 45245	.43125 44751 11779
0.5700	0.33912 43132 04192	0.43132 23019 07352

x	$\dfrac{1}{\sqrt{2\pi}}\,e^{-\frac{x^2}{2}}$	$\dfrac{1}{\sqrt{2\pi}}\displaystyle\int_{-x}^{x} e^{-\frac{\alpha^2}{2}}\,d\alpha$
0.5700	0.33912 43132 04192	0.43132 23019 07352
01	.33910 49819 73712	.43139 01248 36908
02	.33908 56484 54320	.43145 79438 99989
03	.33906 63126 46534	.43152 57590 96137
04	.33904 69745 50872	.43159 35704 24895
0.5705	0.33902 76341 67850	0.43166 13778 85805
06	.33900 82914 97986	.43172 91814 78409
07	.33898 89465 41797	.43179 69812 02251
08	.33896 95992 99800	.43186 47770 56874
09	.33895 02497 72513	.43193 25690 41819
0.5710	0.33893 08979 60453	0.43200 03571 56630
11	.33891 15438 64138	.43206 81414 00851
12	.33889 21874 84086	.43213 59217 74024
I3	.33887 28288 20813	.43220 36982 75692
14	.33885 34678 74837	.43227 14709 05400
0.5715	0.33883 41046 46677	0.43233 92396 62690
16	.33881 47391 36849	.43240 70045 47106
17	.33879 53713 45871	.43247 47655 58193
18	.33877 60012 74262	.43254 25226 95493
19	.33875 66289 22538	.43261 02759 58550
0.5720	0.33873 72542 91218	0.43267 80253 46910
21	.33871 78773 80820	.43274 57708 60115
22	.33869 84981 91861	.43281 35124 97710
23	.33867 91167 24859	.43288 12502 59240
24	.33865 97329 80333	.43294 89841 44248
0.5725	0.33864 03469 58800	0.43301 67141 52280
26	.33862 09586 60779	.43308 44402 82880
27	.33860 15680 86787	.43315 21625 35593
28	.33858 21752 37343	.43321 98809 09963
29	.33856 27801 12965	.43328 75954 05536
0.5730	0.33854 33827 14170	0.43335 53060 21857
31	.33852 39830 41478	.43342 30127 58470
32	.33850 45810 95407	.43349 07156 14922
33	.33848 51768 76474	.43355 84145 90757
34	.33846 57703 85199	.43362 61096 85521
0.5735	0.33844 63616 22099	0.43369 38008 98759
36	.33842 69505 87694	.43376 14882 30018
37	.33840 75372 82501	.43382 91716 78843
38	.33838 81217 07039	.43389 68512 44780
39	.33836 87038 61827	.43396 45269 27375
0.5740	0.33834 92837 47383	0.43403 21987 26173
41	.33832 98613 64225	.43409 98666 40722
42	.33831 04367 12874	.43416 75306 70568
43	.33829 10097 93846	.43423 51908 15256
44	.33827 15806 07662	.43430 28470 74334
0.5745	0.33825 21491 54839	0.43437 04994 47348
46	.33823 27154 35897	.43443 81479 33845
47	.33821 32794 51354	.43450 57925 33372
48	.33819 38412 01729	.43457 34332 45475
49	.33817 44006 87542	.43464 10700 69701
0.5750	0.33815 49579 09311	0.43470 87030 05599

X	$\frac{1}{\sqrt{2\pi}} e^{-\frac{x^2}{2}}$	$\frac{1}{\sqrt{2\pi}} \int_{-x}^{x} e^{-\frac{\alpha^2}{2}} d\alpha$
0.5750	0.33815 49579 09311	0.43470 87030 05599
51	.33813 55128 67556	.43477 63320 52714
52	.33811 60655 62794	.43484 39572 10595
53	.33809 66159 95546	.43491 15784 78788
54	.33807 71641 66331	.43497 91958 56842
0.5755	0.33805 77100 75667	0.43504 68093 44304
56	.33803 82537 24074	.43511 44189 40722
57	.33801 87951 12072	.43518 20246 45643
58	.33799 93342 40178	.43524 96264 58616
59	.33797 98711 08914	.43531 72243 79189
0.5760	0.33796 04057 18797	0.43538 48184 06909
61	.33794 09380 70348	.43545 24085 41326
62	.33792 14681 64086	.43551 99947 81987
63	.33790 19960 00530	.43558 75771 28441
64	.33788 25215 80200	.43565 51555 80236
0.5765	0.33786 30449 03615	0.43572 27301 36922
66	.33784 35659 71296	.43579 03007 98047
67	.33782 40847 83761	.43585 78675 63160
68	.33780 46013 41530	.43592 54304 31811
69	.33778 51156 45123	.43599 29894 03547
0.5770	0.33776 56276 95060	0.43606 05444 77918
71	.33774 61374 91860	.43612 80956 54475
72	.33772 66450 36044	.43619 56429 32765
73	.33770 71503 28131	.43626 31863 12339
74	.33768 76533 68640	.43633 07257 92746
0.5775	0.33766 81541 58093	0.43639 82613 73536
76	.33764 86526 97009	.43646 57930 54259
77	.33762 91489 85907	.43653 33208 34465
78	.33760 96430 25308	.43660 08447 13704
79	.33759 01348 15732	.43666 83646 91525
0.5780	0.33757 06243 57699	0.43673 58807 67480
81	.33755 11116 51730	.43680 33929 41119
82	.33753 15966 98344	.43687 09012 11991
83	.33751 20794 98061	.43693 84055 79648
84	.33749 25600 51402	.43700 59060 43640
0.5785	0.33747 30383 58888	0.43707 34026 03519
86	.33745 35144 21038	.43714 08952 58834
87	.33743 39882 38372	.43720 83840 09138
88	.33741 44598 11412	.43727 58688 53980
89	.33739 49291 40678	.43734 33497 92913
0.5790	0.33737 53962 26690	0.43741 08268 25487
91	.33735 58610 69969	.43747 82999 51254
92	.33733 63236 71034	.43754 57691 69765
93	.33731 67840 30408	.43761 32344 80573
94	.33729 72421 48610	.43768 06958 83228
0.5795	0.33727 76980 26161	0.43774 81533 77283
96	.33725 81516 63583	.43781 56069 62289
97	.33723 86030 61394	.43788 30566 37799
98	.33721 90522 20117	.43795 05024 03364
99	.33719 94991 40272	.43801 79442 58538
0.5800	0.33717 99438 22381	0.43808 53822 02871

X	$\frac{1}{\sqrt{2\pi}} e^{-\frac{x^2}{2}}$	$\frac{1}{\sqrt{2\pi}} \int_{-x}^{x} e^{-\frac{\alpha^2}{2}} d\alpha$
0.5800	0.33717 99438 22381	0.43808 53822 02871
01	.33716 03862 66963	.43815 28162 35918
02	.33714 08264 74539	.43822 02463 57229
03	.33712 12644 45632	.43928 76725 66358
04	.33710 17001 80762	.43835 50948 62858
0.5805	0.33708 21336 80449	0.43842 25132 46282
06	.33706 25649 45215	.43848 99277 16181
07	.33704 29939 75581	.43855 73382 72111
08	.33702 34207 72068	.43862 47449 13623
09	.33700 38453 35198	.43869 21476 40271
0.5810	0.33698 42676 65491	0.43875 95464 51608
11	.33696 46877 63469	.43882 69413 47188
12	.33694 51056 29653	.43889 43323 26564
13	.33692 55212 64564	.43896 17193 89291
14	.33690 59346 68725	.43902 91025 34922
0.5815	0.33688 63458 42655	0.43909 64817 63010
16	.33686 67547 86877	.43916 38570 73110
17	.33684 71615 01912	.43923 12284 64776
18	.33682 75659 88282	.43929 85959 37562
19	.33680 79682 46507	.43936 59594 91023
0.5820	0.33678 83682 77111	0.43943 33191 24712
21	.33676 87660 80614	.43950 06748 38185
22	.33674 91616 57538	.43956 80266 30996
23	.33672 95550 08404	.43963 53745 02700
24	.33670 99461 33735	.43970 27184 52851
0.5825	0.33669 03350 34053	0.43977 00584 81005
26	.33667 07217 09878	.43983 73945 86716
27	.33665 11061 61733	.43990 47267 69541
28	.33663 14883 90140	.43997 20550 29033
29	.33661 18683 95620	.44003 93793 64748
0.5830	0.33659 22461 78696	0.44010 66997 76243
31	.33657 26217 39890	.44017 40162 63072
32	.33655 29950 79723	.44024 13288 24791
33	.33653 33661 98718	.44030 86374 60956
34	.33651 37350 97396	.44037 59421 71122
0.5835	0.33649 41017 76281	0.44044 32429 54847
36	.33647 44662 35893	.44051 05398 11685
37	.33645 48284 76756	.44057 78327 41193
38	.33643 51884 99391	.44064 51217 42928
39	.33641 55463 04320	.44071 24068 16445
0.5840	0.33639 59018 92067	0.44077 96879 61302
41	.33637 62552 63154	.44084 69651 77054
42	.33635 66064 18102	.44091 42384 63259
43	.33633 69553 57434	.44098 15078 19474
44	.33631 73020 81673	.44104 87732 45254
0.5845	0.33629 76465 91341	0.44111 60347 40159
46	.33627 79888 86960	.44118 32923 03743
47	.33625 83289 69054	.44125 05459 35566
48	.33623 86668 38145	.44131 77956 35183
49	.33621 90024 94755	.44138 50414 02154
0.5850	0.33619 93359 39407	0.44145 22832 36034

x	$\dfrac{1}{\sqrt{2\pi}}\,e^{-\frac{x^2}{2}}$	$\dfrac{1}{\sqrt{2\pi}}\displaystyle\int_{-x}^{x} e^{-\frac{\alpha^2}{2}}\,d\alpha$
0.5850	0.33619 93359 39407	0.44145 22832 36034
51	.33617 96671 72624	.44151 95211 36382
52	.33615 99961 94929	.44158 67551 02756
53	.33614 03230 06844	.44165 39851 34713
54	.33612 06476 08892	.44172 12112 31811
0.5855	0.33610 09700 01596	0.44178 84333 93609
56	.33608 12901 85479	.44185 56516 19664
57	.33606 16081 61064	.44192 28659 09536
58	.33604 19239 28874	.44199 00762 62782
59	.33602 22374 89431	.44205 72826 78960
0.5860	0.33600 25488 43259	0.44212 44851 57630
61	.33598 28579 90881	.44219 16836 98350
62	.33596 31649 32820	.44225 88783 00680
63	.33594 34696 69598	.44232 60689 64177
64	.33592 37722 01741	.44239 32556 88400
0.5865	0.33590 40725 29769	0.44246 04384 72910
66	.33588 43706 54207	.44252 76173 17265
67	.33586 46665 75578	.44259 47922 21025
68	.33584 49602 94406	.44266 19631 83749
69	.33582 52518 11213	.44272 91302 04996
0.5870	0.33580 55411 26523	0.44279 62932 84326
71	.33578 58282 40859	.44286 34524 21300
72	.33576 61131 54745	.44293 06076 15476
73	.33574 63958 68704	.44299 77588 66415
74	.33572 66763 83261	.44306 49061 73677
0.5875	0.33570 69546 98937	0.44313 20495 36822
76	.33568 72308 16258	.44319 91889 55410
77	.33566 75047 35746	.44326 63244 29002
78	.33564 77764 57926	.44333 34559 57158
79	.33562 80459 83321	.44340 05835 39439
0.5880	0.33560 83133 12454	0.44346 77071 75405
81	.33558 85784 45850	.44353 48268 64617
82	.33556 88413 84032	.44360 19426 06637
83	.33554 91021 27524	.44366 90544 01024
84	.33552 93606 76850	.44373 61622 47341
0.5885	0.33550 96170 32534	0.44380 32661 45149
86	.33548 98711 95100	.44387 03660 94008
87	.33547 01231 65072	.44393 74620 93481
88	.33545 03729 42973	.44400 45541 43128
89	.33543 06205 29329	.44407 16422 42512
0.5890	0.33541 08659 24662	0.44413 87263 91194
91	.33539 11091 29497	.44420 58065 88736
92	.33537 13501 44359	.44427 28828 34700
93	.33535 15889 69771	.44433 99551 28648
94	.33533 18256 06258	.44440 70234 70142
0.5895	0.33531 20600 54343	0.44447 40878 58744
96	.33529 22923 14552	.44454 11482 94017
97	.33527 25223 87408	.44460 82047 75524
98	.33525 27502 73437	.44467 52573 02827
99	.33523 29759 73161	.44474 23058 75488
0.5900	0.33521 31994 87106	0.44480 93504 93070

X	$\dfrac{1}{\sqrt{2\pi}}\,e^{-\frac{x^2}{2}}$	$\dfrac{1}{\sqrt{2\pi}}\displaystyle\int_{-x}^{x} e^{-\frac{\alpha^2}{2}}\,d\alpha$
0.5900	0.33521 31994 87106	0.44480 93504 93070
01	.33519 34208 15796	.44487 63911 55137
02	.33517 36399 59756	.44494 34278 61251
03	.33515 38569 19510	.44501 04606 10975
04	.33513 40716 95583	.44507 74894 03873
0.5905	0.33511 42842 88499	0.44514 45142 39508
06	.33509 44946 98784	.44521 15351 17443
07	.33507 47029 26960	.44527 85520 37242
08	.33505 49089 73555	.44534 55649 98468
09	.33503 51128 39091	.44541 25740 00686
0.5910	0.33501 53145 24094	0.44547 95790 43459
11	.33499 55140 29089	.44554 65801 26350
12	.33497 57113 54601	.44561 35772 48925
13	.33495 59065 01154	.44568 05704 10747
14	.33493 60994 69273	.44574 75596 11380
0.5915	0.33491 62902 59483	0.44581 45448 50389
16	.33489 64788 72310	.44588 15261 27339
17	.33487 66653 08278	.44594 85034 41793
18	.33485 68495 67913	.44601 54767 93317
19	.33483 70316 51738	.44608 24461 81475
0.5920	0.33481 72115 60281	0.44614 94116 05833
21	.33479 73892 94065	.44621 63730 65954
22	.33477 75648 53616	.44628 33305 61405
23	.33475 77382 39459	.44635 02840 91751
24	.33473 79094 52119	.44641 72336 56556
0.5925	0.33471 80784 92122	0.44648 41792 55387
26	.33469 82453 59993	.44655 11208 87808
27	.33467 84100 56257	.44661 80585 53386
28	.33465 85725 81440	.44668 49922 51686
29	.33463 87329 36067	.44675 19219 82274
0.5930	0.33461 88911 20663	0.44681 88477 44716
31	.33459 90471 35755	.44688 57695 38578
32	.33457 92009 81867	.44695 26873 63426
33	.33455 93526 59526	.44701 96012 18826
34	.33453 95021 69256	.44708 65111 04345
0.5935	0.33451 96495 11583	0.44715 34170 19549
36	.33449 97946 87034	.44722 03189 64005
37	.33447 99376 96133	.44728 72169 37279
38	.33446 00785 39407	.44735 41109 38939
39	.33444 02172 17381	.44742 10009 68551
0.5940	0.33442 03537 30582	0.44748 78870 25682
41	.33440 04880 79533	.44755 47691 09899
42	.33438 06202 64763	.44762 16472 20769
43	.33436 07502 86797	.44768 85213 57860
44	.33434 08781 46159	.44775 53915 20740
0.5945	0.33432 10038 43378	0.44782 22577 08975
46	.33430 11273 78978	.44788 91199 22133
47	.33428 12487 53485	.44795 59781 59782
48	.33426 13679 67426	.44802 28324 21490
49	.33424 14850 21327	.44808 96827 06825
0.5950	0.33422 15999 15714	0.44815 65290 15355

X	$\frac{1}{\sqrt{2\pi}} e^{-\frac{x^2}{2}}$	$\frac{1}{\sqrt{2\pi}} \int_{-x}^{x} e^{-\frac{\alpha^2}{2}} d\alpha$
0.5950	0.33422 15999 15714	0.44815 65290 15355
51	.33420 17126 51113	.44822 33713 46648
52	.33418 18232 28050	.44829 02097 00272
53	.33416 19316 47051	.44835 70440 75795
54	.33414 20379 08643	.44842 38744 72787
0.5955	0.33412 21420 13352	0.44849 07008 90815
56	.33410 22439 61705	.44855 75233 29448
57	.33408 23437 54227	.44862 43417 88256
58	.33406 24413 91445	.44869 11562 66806
59	.33404 25368 73886	.44875 79667 64669
0.5960	0.33402 26302 02076	0.44882 47732 81412
61	.33400 27213 76542	.44889 15758 16606
62	.33398 28103 97809	.44895 83743 69819
63	.33396 28972 66405	.44902 51689 40621
64	.33394 29819 82857	.44909 19595 28582
0.5965	0.33392 30645 47690	0.44915 87461 33271
66	.33390 31449 61432	.44922 55287 54258
67	.33388 32232 24609	.44929 23073 91112
68	.33386 32993 37748	.44935 90820 43404
69	.33384 33733 01375	.44942 58527 10704
0.5970	0.33382 34451 16019	0.44949 26193 92582
71	.33380 35147 82204	.44955 93820 88607
72	.33378 35823 00459	.44962 61407 98351
73	.33376 36476 71310	.44969 28955 21384
74	.33374 37108 95284	.44975 96462 57277
0.5975	0.33372 37719 72908	0.44982 63930 05599
76	.33370 38309 04709	.44989 31357 65923
77	.33368 38876 91214	.44995 98745 37818
78	.33366 39423 32950	.45002 66093 20856
79	.33364 39948 30444	.45009 33401 14608
0.5980	0.33362 40451 84224	0.45016 00669 18646
81	.33360 40933 94816	.45022 67897 32539
82	.33358 41394 62748	.45029 35085 55861
83	.33356 41833 88546	.45036 02233 88182
84	.33354 42251 72739	.45042 69342 29073
0.5985	0.33352 42648 15853	0.45049 36410 78108
86	.33350 43023 18416	.45056 03439 34857
87	.33348 43376 80956	.45062 70427 98893
88	.33346 43709 03998	.45069 37376 69787
89	.33344 44019 88072	.45076 04285 47112
0.5990	0.33342 44309 33704	0.45082 71154 30439
91	.33340 44577 41422	.45089 37983 19343
92	.33338 44824 11753	.45096 04772 13393
93	.33336 45049 45226	.45102 71521 12165
94	.33334 45253 42366	.45109 38230 15229
0.5995	0.33332 45436 03703	0.45116 04899 22159
96	.33330 45597 29764	.45122 71528 32528
97	.33328 45737 21076	.45129 38117 45909
98	.33326 45855 78168	.45136 04666 61874
99	.33324 45953 01566	.45142 71175 79998
0.6000	0.33322 46028 91800	0.45149 37644 99853

x	$\dfrac{1}{\sqrt{2\pi}}e^{-\frac{x^2}{2}}$	$\dfrac{1}{\sqrt{2\pi}}\displaystyle\int_{-x}^{x} e^{-\frac{\alpha^2}{2}}\,d\alpha$
0.6000	0.33322 46028 91800	0.45149 37644 99853
01	.33320 46083 49395	.45156 04074 21012
02	.33318 46116 74881	.45162 70463 43050
03	.33316 46128 68786	.45169 36812 65540
04	.33314 46119 31636	.45176 03121 88056
0.6005	0.33312 46088 63961	0.45182 69391 10171
06	.33310 46036 66288	.45189 35620 31459
07	.33308 45963 39145	.45196 01809 51496
08	.33306 45868 83060	.45202 67958 69853
09	.33304 45752 98561	.45209 34067 86107
0.6010	0.33302 45615 86176	0.45216 00136 99831
11	.33300 45457 46434	.45222 66166 10599
12	.33298 45277 79863	.45229 32155 17988
13	.33296 45076 86990	.45235 98104 21570
14	.33294 44854 68344	.45242 64013 20921
0.6015	0.33292 44611 24454	0.45249 29882 15615
16	.33290 44346 55847	.45255 95711 05229
17	.33288 44060 63052	.45262 61499 89336
18	.33286 43753 46598	.45269 27248 67512
19	.33284 43425 07012	.45275 92957 39333
0.6020	0.33282 43075 44823	0.45282 58626 04374
21	.33280 42704 60560	.45289 24254 62210
22	.33278 42312 54750	.45295 89843 12417
23	.33276 41899 27923	.45302 55391 54570
24	.33274 41464 80608	.45309 20899 88246
0.6025	0.33272 41009 13332	0.45315 86368 13021
26	.33270 40532 26624	.45322 51796 28470
27	.33268 40034 21013	.45329 17184 34170
28	.33266 39514 97028	.45335 82532 29698
29	.33264 38974 55197	.45342 47840 14628
0.6030	0.33262 38412 96049	0.45349 13107 88538
31	.33260 37830 20113	.45355 78335 51005
32	.33258 37226 27917	.45362 43523 01605
33	.33256 36601 19991	.45369 08670 39915
34	.33254 35954 96863	.45375 73777 65512
0.6035	0.33252 35287 59063	0.45382 38844 77973
36	.33250 34599 07119	.45389 03871 76875
37	.33248 33889 41559	.45395 68858 61795
38	.33246 33158 62914	.45402 33805 32311
39	.33244 32406 71712	.45408 98711 87999
0.6040	0.33242 31633 68482	0.45415 63578 28439
41	.33240 30839 53753	.45422 28404 53206
42	.33238 30024 28055	.45428 93190 61879
43	.33236 29187 91916	.45435 57936 54037
44	.33234 28330 45866	.45442 22642 29256
0.6045	0.33232 27451 90434	0.45448 87307 87114
46	.33230 26552 26149	.45455 51933 27191
47	.33228 25631 53541	.45462 16518 49064
48	.33226 24689 73138	.45468 81063 52312
49	.33224 23726 85470	.45475 45568 36513
0.6050	0.33222 22742 91067	0.45482 10033 01246

x	$\dfrac{1}{\sqrt{2\pi}}e^{-\frac{x^2}{2}}$	$\dfrac{1}{\sqrt{2\pi}}\displaystyle\int_{-x}^{x}e^{-\frac{\alpha^2}{2}}\,d\alpha$
0.6050	0.33222 22742 91067	0.45482 10033 01246
51	.33220 21737 90457	.45488 74457 46089
52	.33218 20711 84171	.45495 38841 70622
53	.33216 19664 72738	.45502 03185 74422
54	.33214 18596 56687	.45508 67489 57070
0.6055	0.33212 17507 36547	0.45515 31753 18145
56	.33210 16397 12849	.45521 95976 57225
57	.33208 15265 86122	.45528 60159 73890
58	.33206 14113 56895	.45535 24302 67719
59	.33204 12940 25698	.45541 88405 38292
0.6060	0.33202 11745 93061	0.45548 52467 85189
61	.33200 10530 59514	.45555 16490 07990
62	.33198 09294 25586	.45561 80472 06273
63	.33196 08036 91807	.45568 44413 79620
64	.33194 06758 58707	.45575 08315 27610
0.6065	0.33192 05459 26816	0.45581 72176 49823
66	.33190 04138 96663	.45588 35997 45841
67	.33188 02797 68778	.45594 99778 15242
68	.33186 01435 43692	.45601 63518 57608
69	.33184 00052 21934	.45608 27218 72520
0.6070	0.33181 98648 04035	0.45614 90878 59557
71	.33179 97222 90524	.45621 54498 18302
72	.33177 95776 81931	.45628 18077 48334
73	.33175 94309 78787	.45634 81616 49235
74	.33173 92821 81621	.45641 45115 20586
0.6075	0.33171 91312 90964	0.45648 08573 61968
76	.33169 89783 07346	.45654 71991 72963
77	.33167 88232 31297	.45661 35369 53151
78	.33165 86660 63347	.45667 98707 02116
79	.33163 85068 04027	.45674 62004 19437
0.6080	0.33161 83454 53867	0.45681 25261 04698
81	.33159 81820 13397	.45687 88477 57480
82	.33157 80164 83147	.45694 51653 77364
83	.33155 78488 63649	.45701 14789 63933
84	.33153 76791 55431	.45707 77885 16770
0.6085	0.33151 75073 59026	0.45714 40940 35456
86	.33149 73334 74962	.45721 03955 19575
87	.33147 71575 03772	.45727 66929 68707
88	.33145 69794 45985	.45734 29863 82437
89	.33143 67993 02131	.45740 92757 60347
0.6090	0.33141 66170 72743	0.45747 55611 02019
91	.33139 64327 58349	.45754 18424 07037
92	.33137 62463 59481	.45760 81196 74983
93	.33135 60578 76669	.45767 43929 05442
94	.33133 58673 10445	.45774 06620 97995
0.6095	0.33131 56746 61338	0.45780 69272 52227
96	.33129 54799 29881	.45787 31883 67721
97	.33127 52831 16602	.45793 94454 44060
98	.33125 50842 22034	.45800 56984 80829
99	.33123 48832 46708	.45807 19474 77610
0.6100	0.33121 46801 91153	0.45813 81924 33989

X	$\frac{1}{\sqrt{2\pi}} e^{-\frac{x^2}{2}}$	$\frac{1}{\sqrt{2\pi}} \int_{-x}^{x} e^{-\frac{\alpha^2}{2}} d\alpha$
0.6100	0.33121 46801 91153	0.45813 81924 33989
01	.33119 44750 55901	.45820 44333 49548
02	.33117 42678 41484	.45827 06702 23872
03	.33115 40585 48431	.45833 69030 56546
04	.33113 38471 77274	.45840 31318 47153
0.6105	0.33111 36337 28545	0.45846 93565 95278
06	.33109 34182 02773	.45853 55773 00506
07	.33107 32006 00491	.45860 17939 62421
08	.33105 29809 22229	.45866 80065 80608
09	.33103 27591 68518	.45873 42151 54652
0.6110	0.33101 25353 39891	0.45880 04196 84137
11	.33099 23094 36877	.45886 66201 68649
12	.33097 20814 60008	.45893 28166 07774
13	.33095 18514 09816	.45899 90090 01095
14	.33093 16192 86832	.45906 51973 48199
0.6115	0.33091 13850 91587	0.45913 13816 48672
16	.33089 11488 24612	.45919 75619 02098
17	.33087 09104 86440	.45926 37381 08063
18	.33085 06700 77601	.45932 99102 66154
19	.33083 04275 98626	.45939 60783 75956
0.6120	0.33081 01830 50048	0.45946 22424 37056
21	.33078 99364 32398	.45952 84024 49038
22	.33076 96877 46207	.45959 45584 11491
23	.33074 94369 92008	.45966 07103 23999
24	.33072 91841 70331	.45972 68581 86150
0.6125	0.33070 89292 81708	0.45979 30019 97529
26	.33068 86723 26671	.45985 91417 57725
27	.33066 84133 05752	.45992 52774 66322
28	.33064 81522 19482	.45999 14091 22909
29	.33062 78890 68393	.46005 75367 27073
0.6130	0.33060 76238 53017	0.46012 36602 78399
31	.33058 73565 73886	.46018 97797 76476
32	.33056 70872 31531	.46025 58952 20891
33	.33054 68158 26485	.46032 20066 11231
34	.33052 65423 59279	.46038 81139 47084
0.6135	0.33050 62668 30446	0.46045 42172 28038
36	.33048 59892 40516	.46052 03164 53679
37	.33046 57095 90023	.46058 64116 23596
38	.33044 54278 79499	.46065 25027 37378
39	.33042 51441 09474	.46071 85897 94611
0.6140	0.33040 48582 80482	0.46078 46727 94884
41	.33038 45703 93055	.46085 07517 37786
42	.33036 42804 47724	.46091 68266 22904
43	.33034 39884 45022	.46098 28974 49828
44	.33032 36943 85481	.46104 89642 18145
0.6145	0.33030 33982 69633	0.46111 50269 27445
46	.33028 31000 98011	.46118 10855 77316
47	.33026 27998 71147	.46124 71401 67347
48	.33024 24975 89572	.46131 31906 97127
49	.33022 21932 53820	.46137 92371 66246
0.6150	0.33020 18868 64423	0.46144 52795 74292

x	$\frac{1}{\sqrt{2\pi}}e^{-\frac{x^2}{2}}$	$\frac{1}{\sqrt{2\pi}}\int_{-x}^{x}e^{-\frac{\alpha^2}{2}}d\alpha$
0.6150	0.33020 18868 64423	0.46144 52795 74292
51	.33018 15784 21914	.46151 13179 20855
52	.33016 12679 26823	.46157 73522 05524
53	.33014 09553 79685	.46164 33824 27889
54	.33012 06407 81032	.46170 94085 87539
0.6155	0.33010 03241 31396	0.46177 54306 84064
56	.33008 00054 31309	.46184 14487 17055
57	.33005 96846 81304	.46190 74626 86100
58	.33003 93618 81915	.46197 34725 90791
59	.33001 90370 33673	.46203 94784 30716
0.6160	0.32999 87101 37111	0.46210 54802 05468
61	.32997 83811 92761	.46217 14779 14635
62	.32995 80502 01158	.46223 74715 57808
63	.32993 77171 62832	.46230 34611 34579
64	.32991 73820 78318	.46236 94466 44537
0.6165	0.32989 70449 48147	0.46243 54280 87274
66	.32987 67057 72853	.46250 14054 62380
67	.32985 63645 52969	.46256 73787 69447
68	.32983 60212 89027	.46263 33480 08065
69	.32981 56759 81560	.46269 93131 77826
0.6170	0.32979 53286 31102	0.46276 52742 78321
71	.32977 49792 38185	.46283 12313 09142
72	.32975 46278 03342	.46289 71842 69880
73	.32973 42743 27106	.46296 31331 60127
74	.32971 39188 10011	.46302 90779 79475
0.6175	0.32969 35612 52589	0.46309 50187 27515
76	.32967 32016 55374	.46316 09554 03840
77	.32965 28400 18899	.46322 68880 08042
78	.32963 24763 43696	.46329 28165 39712
79	.32961 21106 30299	.46335 87409 98443
0.6180	0.32959 17428 79242	0.46342 46613 83828
81	.32957 13730 91057	.46349 05776 95459
82	.32955 10012 66278	.46355 64899 32929
83	.32953 06274 05438	.46362 23980 95830
84	.32951 02515 09071	.46368 83021 83755
0.6185	0.32948 98735 77710	0.46375 42021 96298
86	.32946 94936 11887	.46382 00981 33051
87	.32944 91116 12138	.46388 59899 93607
88	.32942 87275 78994	.46395 18777 77560
89	.32940 83415 12990	.46401 77614 84503
0.6190	0.32938 79534 14660	0.46408 36411 14030
91	.32936 75632 84536	.46414 95166 65734
92	.32934 71711 23152	.46421 53881 39208
93	.32932 67769 31042	.46428 12555 34047
94	.32930 63807 08739	.46434 71188 49845
0.6195	0.32928 59824 56777	0.46441 29780 86196
96	.32926 55821 75690	.46447 88332 42693
97	.32924 51798 66012	.46454 46843 18931
98	.32922 47755 28276	.46461 05313 14504
99	.32920 43691 63015	.46467 63742 29007
0.6200	0.32918 39607 70765	0.46474 22130 62034

x	$\dfrac{1}{\sqrt{2\pi}}e^{-\frac{x^2}{2}}$	$\dfrac{1}{\sqrt{2\pi}}\displaystyle\int_{-x}^{x}e^{-\frac{\alpha^2}{2}}\,d\alpha$
0.6200	0.32918 39607 70765	0.46474 22130 62034
01	.32916 35503 52058	.46480 80478 13180
02	.32914 31379 07428	.46487 38784 82040
03	.32912 27234 37410	.46493 97050 68208
04	.32910 23069 42536	.46500 55275 71280
0.6205	0.32908 18884 23342	0.46507 13459 90850
06	.32906 14678 80361	.46513 71603 26514
07	.32904 10453 14127	.46520 29705 77867
08	.32902 06207 25174	.46526 87767 44505
09	.32900 01941 14036	.46533 45788 26023
0.6210	0.32897 97654 81247	0.46540 03768 22016
11	.32895 93348 27341	.46546 61707 32080
12	.32893 89021 52852	.46553 19605 55812
13	.32891 84674 58316	.46559 77462 92807
14	.32889 80307 44264	.46566 35279 42661
0.6215	0.32887 75920 11233	0.46572 93055 04970
16	.32885 71512 59755	.46579 50789 79331
17	.32883 67084 90366	.46586 08483 65339
18	.32881 62637 03600	.46592 66136 62592
19	.32879 58168 99990	.46599 23748 70686
0.6220	0.32877 53680 80072	0.46605 81319 89218
21	.32875 49172 44379	.46612 38850 17784
22	.32873 44643 93446	.46618 96339 55981
23	.32871 40095 27808	.46625 53788 03407
24	.32869 35526 47999	.46632 11195 59658
0.6225	0.32867 30937 54553	0.46638 68562 24332
26	.32865 26328 48004	.46645 25887 97026
27	.32863 21699 28889	.46651 83172 77337
28	.32861 17049 97740	.46658 40416 64863
29	.32859 12380 55092	.46664 97619 59202
0.6230	0.32857 07691 01481	0.46671 54781 59951
31	.32855 02981 37440	.46678 11902 66708
32	.32852 98251 63505	.46684 68982 79072
33	.32850 93501 80210	.46691 26021 96640
34	.32848 88731 88090	.46697 83020 19010
0.6235	0.32846 83941 87679	0.46704 39977 45781
36	.32844 79131 79513	.46710 96893 76551
37	.32842 74301 64126	.46717 53769 10919
38	.32840 69451 42053	.46724 10603 48483
39	.32838 64581 13828	.46730 67396 88842
0.6240	0.32836 59690 79988	0.46737 24149 31595
41	.32834 54780 41065	.46743 80860 76341
42	.32832 49849 97597	.46750 37531 22678
43	.32830 44899 50117	.46756 94160 70206
44	.32828 39928 99160	.46763 50749 18524
0.6245	0.32826 34938 45262	0.46770 07296 67232
46	.32824 29927 88957	.46776 63803 15929
47	.32822 24897 30781	.46783 20268 64214
48	.32820 19846 71268	.46789 76693 11688
49	.32818 14776 10955	.46796 33076 57949
0.6250	0.32816 09685 50375	0.46802 89419 02599

x	$\frac{1}{\sqrt{2\pi}} e^{-\frac{x^2}{2}}$	$\frac{1}{\sqrt{2\pi}} \int_{-x}^{x} e^{-\frac{\alpha^2}{2}} d\alpha$
0.6250	0.32816 09685 50375	0.46802 89419 02599
51	.32814 04574 90064	.46809 45720 45236
52	.32811 99444 30558	.46816 01980 85462
53	.32809 94293 72391	.46822 58200 22875
54	.32807 89123 16099	.46829 14378 57077
0.6255	0.32805 83932 62217	0.46835 70515 87669
56	.32803 78722 11280	.46842 26612 14249
57	.32801 73491 63825	.46848 82667 36420
58	.32799 68241 20385	.46855 38681 53782
59	.32797 62970 81496	.46861 94654 65935
0.6260	0.32795 57680 47694	0.46868 50586 72481
61	.32793 52370 19515	.46875 06477 73021
62	.32791 47039 97493	.46881 62327 67156
63	.32789 41689 82165	.46888 18136 54487
64	.32787 36319 74065	.46894 73904 34616
0.6265	0.32785 30929 73730	0.46901 29631 07144
66	.32783 25519 81694	.46907 85316 71673
67	.32781 20089 98494	.46914 40961 27804
68	.32779 14640 24665	.46920 96564 75140
69	.32777 09170 60742	.46927 52127 13281
0.6270	0.32775 03681 07262	0.46934 07648 41831
71	.32772 98171 64760	.46940 63128 60392
72	.32770 92642 33772	.46947 18567 68565
73	.32768 87093 14833	.46953 73965 65953
74	.32766 81524 08480	.46960 29322 52158
0.6275	0.32764 75935 15248	0.46966 84638 26783
76	.32762 70326 35672	.46973 39912 89432
77	.32760 64697 70290	.46979 95146 39705
78	.32758 59049 19636	.46986 50338 77207
79	.32756 53380 84247	.46993 05490 01541
0.6280	0.32754 47692 64658	0.46999 60600 12309
81	.32752 41984 61406	.47006 15669 09115
82	.32750 36256 75026	.47012 70696 91561
83	.32748 30509 06055	.47019 25683 59252
84	.32746 24741 55028	.47025 80629 11791
0.6285	0.32744 18954 22482	0.47032 35533 48782
86	.32742 13147 08952	.47038 90396 69828
87	.32740 07320 14975	.47045 45218 74534
88	.32738 01473 41087	.47051 99999 62502
89	.32735 95606 87824	.47058 54739 33338
0.6290	0.32733 89720 55722	0.47065 09437 86646
91	.32731 83814 45318	.47071 64095 22029
92	.32729 77888 57148	.47078 18711 39092
93	.32727 71942 91747	.47084 73286 37440
94	.32725 65977 49653	.47091 27820 16677
0.6295	0.32723 59992 31401	0.47097 82312 76408
96	.32721 53987 37529	.47104 36764 16238
97	.32719 47962 68571	.47110 91174 35771
98	.32717 41918 25065	.47117 45543 34613
99	.32715 35854 07548	.47123 99871 12370
0.6300	0.32713 29770 16554	0.47130 54157 68645

X	$\frac{1}{\sqrt{2\pi}} e^{-\frac{x^2}{2}}$	$\frac{1}{\sqrt{2\pi}} \int_{-x}^{x} e^{-\frac{\alpha^2}{2}} \, d\alpha$
0.6300	0.32713 29770 16554	0.47130 54157 68645
01	.32711 23666 52622	.47137 08403 03045
02	.32709 17543 16288	.47143 62607 15174
03	.32707 11400 08087	.47150 16770 04640
04	.32705 05237 28557	.47156 70891 71046
0.6305	0.32702 99054 78234	0.47163 24972 14000
06	.32700 92852 57655	.47169 79011 33106
07	.32698 86630 67357	.47176 33009 27972
08	.32696 80389 07875	.47182 86965 98202
09	.32694 74127 79747	.47189 40881 43403
0.6310	0.32692 67846 83509	0.47195 94755 63183
11	.32690 61546 19699	.47202 48588 57146
12	.32688 55225 88852	.47209 02380 24899
13	.32686 48885 91506	.47215 56130 66050
14	.32684 42526 28197	.47222 09839 80205
0.6315	0.32682 36146 99463	0.47228 63507 66970
16	.32680 29748 05840	.47235 17134 25954
17	.32678 23329 47864	.47241 70719 56762
18	.32676 16891 26074	.47248 24263 59002
19	.32674 10433 41006	.47254 77766 32281
0.6320	0.32672 03955 93196	0.47261 31227 76207
21	.32669 97458 83182	.47267 84647 90388
22	.32667 90942 11500	.47274 38026 74430
23	.32665 84405 78688	.47280 91364 27942
24	.32663 77849 85284	.47287 44660 50531
0.6325	0.32661 71274 31823	0.47293 97915 41805
26	.32659 64679 18842	.47300 51129 01373
27	.32657 58064 46880	.47307 04301 28842
28	.32655 51430 16474	.47313 57432 23821
29	.32653 44776 28159	.47320 10521 85918
0.6330	0.32651 38102 82475	0.47326 63570 14742
31	.32649 31409 79957	.47333 16577 09901
32	.32647 24697 21143	.47339 69542 71003
33	.32645 17965 06570	.47346 22466 97659
34	.32643 11213 36776	.47352 75349 89476
0.6335	0.32641 04442 12298	0.47359 28191 46063
36	.32638 97651 33674	.47365 80991 67030
37	.32636 90841 01440	.47372 33750 51986
38	.32634 84011 16134	.47378 86468 00541
39	.32632 77161 78294	.47385 39144 12303
0.6340	0.32630 70292 88456	0.47391 91778 86882
41	.32628 63404 47159	.47398 44372 23888
42	.32626 56496 54940	.47404 96924 22931
43	.32624 49569 12336	.47411 49434 83620
44	.32622 42622 19885	.47418 01904 05566
0.6345	0.32620 35655 7812E	0.47424 54331 88378
46	.32618 28669 87592	.47431 06718 31667
47	.32616 21664 48826	.47437 59063 35043
48	.32614 14639 62362	.47444 11366 98117
49	.32612 07595 28740	.47450 63629 20498
0.6350	0.32610 00531 48497	0.47457 15850 01798

X	$\dfrac{1}{\sqrt{2\pi}} e^{-\frac{x^2}{2}}$	$\dfrac{1}{\sqrt{2\pi}} \displaystyle\int_{-x}^{x} e^{-\frac{\alpha^2}{2}}\, d\alpha$
C.6350	0.32610 00531 48497	0.47457 15850 01798
51	.32607 93448 22170	.47463 68029 41628
52	.32605 86345 50297	.47470 20167 39597
53	.32603 79223 33416	.47476 72263 95318
54	.32601 72081 72064	.47483 24319 08401
0.6355	0.32599 64920 66780	0.47489 76332 78457
56	.32597 57740 18102	.47496 28305 05098
57	.32595 50540 26567	.47502 80235 87935
58	.32593 43320 92712	.47509 32125 26579
59	.32591 36082 17077	.47515 83973 20643
0.6360	0.32589 28824 00199	0.47522 35779 69737
61	.32587 21546 42615	.47528 87544 73473
62	.32585 14249 44864	.47535 39268 31465
63	.32583 06933 07484	.47541 90950 43322
64	.32580 99597 31013	.47548 42591 08658
0.6365	0.32578 92242 15989	0.47554 94190 27085
66	.32576 84867 62950	.47561 45747 98215
67	.32574 77473 72434	.47567 97264 21661
68	.32572 70060 44979	.47574 48738 97035
69	.32570 62627 81123	.47581 00172 23950
0.6370	0.32568 55175 81405	0.47587 51564 02019
71	.32566 47704 46363	.47594 02914 30854
72	.32564 40213 76534	.47600 54223 10068
73	.32562 32703 72458	.47607 05490 39275
74	.32560 25174 34672	.47613 56716 18088
0.6375	0.32558 17625 63715	0.47620 07900 46120
76	.32556 10057 60125	.47626 59043 22985
77	.32554 02470 24440	.47633 10144 48296
78	.32551 94863 57199	.47639 61204 21666
79	.32549 87237 58940	.47646 12222 42710
0.6380	0.32547 79592 30201	0.47652 63199 11041
81	.32545 71927 71521	.47659 14134 26273
82	.32543 64243 83439	.47665 65027 88021
83	.32541 56540 66492	.47672 15879 95898
84	.32539 48818 21220	.47678 66690 49519
0.6385	0.32537 41076 48161	0.47685 17459 48498
86	.32535 33315 47853	.47691 68186 92450
87	.32533 25535 20835	.47698 18872 80989
88	.32531 17735 67646	.47704 69517 13730
89	.32529 09916 88824	.47711 20119 90287
0.6390	0.32527 02078 84907	0.47717 70681 10277
91	.32524 94221 56436	.47724 21200 73313
92	.32522 86345 03947	.47730 71678 79011
93	.32520 78449 27980	.47737 22115 26986
94	.32518 70534 29074	.47743 72510 16854
0.6395	0.32516 62600 07767	0.47750 22863 48230
96	.32514 54646 64599	.47756 73175 20729
97	.32512 46674 00107	.47763 23445 33968
98	.32510 38682 14831	.47769 73673 87561
99	.32508 30671 09310	.47776 23860 81125
0.6400	0.32506 22640 84082	0.47782 74006 14277

X	$\dfrac{1}{\sqrt{2\pi}}\,e^{-\frac{x^2}{2}}$	$\dfrac{1}{\sqrt{2\pi}}\displaystyle\int_{-x}^{x} e^{-\frac{\alpha^2}{2}}\,d\alpha$
0.6400	0.32506 22640 84082	0.47782 74006 14277
01	.32504 14591 39687	.47789 24109 86631
02	.32502 06522 76663	.47795 74171 97805
03	.32499 98434 95549	.47802 24192 47414
04	.32497 90327 96884	.47808 74171 35075
0.6405	0.32495 82201 81208	0.47815 24108 60405
06	.32493 74056 49059	.47821 74004 23020
07	.32491 65892 00976	.47828 23858 22537
08	.32489 57708 37498	.47834 73670 58573
09	.32487 49505 59165	.47841 23441 30744
0.6410	0.32485 41283 66515	0.47847 73170 38669
11	.32483 33042 60088	.47854 22857 81963
12	.32481 24782 40423	.47860 72503 60245
13	.32479 16503 08058	.47867 22107 73132
14	.32477 08204 63534	.47873 71670 20241
0.6415	0.32474 99887 07389	0.47880 21191 01190
16	.32472 91550 40163	.47886 70670 15596
17	.32470 83194 62394	.47893 20107 63079
18	.32468 74819 74623	.47899 69503 43254
19	.32466 66425 77388	.47906 18857 55741
0.6420	0.32464 58012 71228	0.47912 68170 00158
21	.32462 49580 56684	.47919 17440 76122
22	.32460 41129 34294	.47925 66669 83253
23	.32458 32659 04599	.47932 15857 21169
24	.32456 24169 68136	.47938 65002 89488
0.6425	0.32454 15661 25446	0.47945 14106 87829
26	.32452 07133 77069	.47951 63169 15811
27	.32449 98587 23543	.47958 12189 73053
28	.32447 90021 65408	.47964 61168 59174
29	.32445 81437 03204	.47971 10105 73792
0.6430	0.32443 72833 37471	0.47977 59001 16528
31	.32441 64210 68747	.47984 07854 87000
32	.32439 55568 97573	.47990 56666 84829
33	.32437 46908 24488	.47997 05437 09632
34	.32435 38228 50031	.48003 54165 61032
0.6435	0.32433 29529 74743	0.48010 02852 38646
36	.32431 20811 99163	.48016 51497 42095
37	.32429 12075 23831	.48023 00100 70999
38	.32427 03319 49287	.48029 48662 24978
39	.32424 94544 76069	.48035 97182 03652
0.6440	0.32422 85751 04719	0.48042 45660 06642
41	.32420 76938 35776	.48048 94096 33567
42	.32418 68106 69779	.48055 42490 84049
43	.32416 59256 07269	.48061 90843 57709
44	.32414 50386 48785	.48068 39154 54166
0.6445	0.32412 41497 94868	0.48074 87423 73042
46	.32410 32590 46057	.48081 35651 13958
47	.32408 23664 02892	.48087 83836 76534
48	.32406 14718 65913	.48094 31980 60392
49	.32404 05754 35660	.48100 80082 65154
0.6450	0.32401 96771 12673	0.48107 28142 90441

X	$\dfrac{1}{\sqrt{2\pi}}\,e^{-\frac{x^2}{2}}$	$\dfrac{1}{\sqrt{2\pi}}\displaystyle\int_{-x}^{x} e^{-\frac{\alpha^2}{2}}\,d\alpha$
0.6450	0.32401 96771 12673	0.48107 28142 90441
51	.32399 87768 97492	.48113 76161 35873
52	.32397 78747 90658	.48120 24138 01073
53	.32395 69707 92709	.48126 72072 85663
54	.32393 60649 04187	.48133 19965 89264
0.6455	0.32391 51571 25632	0.48139 67817 11499
56	.32389 42474 57582	.48146 15626 51989
57	.32387 33359 00580	.48152 63394 10356
58	.32385 24224 55164	.48159 11119 86223
59	.32383 15071 21876	.48165 58803 79212
0.6460	0.32381 05899 01254	0.48172 06445 88946
61	.32378 96707 93841	.48178 54046 15047
62	.32376 87498 00174	.48185 01604 57138
63	.32374 78269 20796	.48191 49121 14841
64	.32372 69021 56247	.48197 96595 87780
0.6465	0.32370 59755 07066	0.48204 44028 75578
66	.32368 50469 73794	.48210 91419 77858
67	.32366 41165 56971	.48217 38768 94242
68	.32364 31842 57138	.48223 86076 24355
69	.32362 22500 74836	.48230 33341 67820
0.6470	0.32360 13140 10604	0.48236 80565 24259
71	.32358 03760 64983	.48243 27746 93298
72	.32355 94362 38514	.48249 74886 74560
73	.32353 84945 31737	.48256 21984 67668
74	.32351 75509 45192	.48262 69040 72247
0.6475	0.32349 66054 79420	0.48269 16054 87921
76	.32347 56581 34962	.48275 63027 14314
77	.32345 47089 12359	.48282 09957 51050
78	.32343 37578 12150	.48288 56845 97754
79	.32341 28048 34877	.48295 03692 54050
0.6480	0.32339 18499 81080	0.48301 50497 19563
81	.32337 08932 51300	.48307 97259 93917
82	.32334 99346 46077	.48314 43980 76738
83	.32332 89741 65952	.48320 90659 67650
84	.32330 80118 11467	.48327 37296 66279
0.6485	0.32328 70475 83161	0.48333 83891 72250
86	.32326 60814 81576	.48340 30444 85188
87	.32324 51135 07251	.48346 76956 04718
88	.32322 41436 60729	.48353 23425 30466
89	.32320 31719 42550	.48359 69852 62057
0.6490	0.32318 21983 53255	0.48366 16237 99118
91	.32316 12228 93384	.48372 62581 41274
92	.32314 02455 63479	.48379 08882 88151
93	.32311 92663 64081	.48385 55142 39375
94	.32309 82852 95730	.48392 01359 94572
0.6495	0.32307 73023 58967	0.48398 47535 53369
96	.32305 63175 54333	.48404 93669 15391
97	.32303 53308 82370	.48411 39760 80266
98	.32301 43423 43619	.48417 85810 47619
99	.32299 33519 38620	.48424 31818 17079
0.6500	0.32297 23596 67914	0.48430 77783 88271

x	$\dfrac{1}{\sqrt{2\pi}}\,e^{-\frac{x^2}{2}}$	$\dfrac{1}{\sqrt{2\pi}}\displaystyle\int_{-x}^{x} e^{-\frac{\alpha^2}{2}}\,d\alpha$
0.6500	0.32297 23596 67914	0.48430 77783 88271
01	.32295 13655 32043	.48437 23707 60822
02	.32293 03695 31548	.48443 69589 34359
03	.32290 93716 66970	.48450 15429 08510
04	.32288 83719 38850	.48456 61226 82902
0.6505	0.32286 73703 47728	0.48463 06982 57161
06	.32284 63668 94148	.48469 52696 30917
07	.32282 53615 78649	.48475 98368 03795
08	.32280 43544 01772	.48482 43997 75424
09	.32278 33453 64060	.48488 89585 45431
0.6510	0.32276 23344 66053	0.48495 35131 13446
11	.32274 13217 08293	.48501 80634 79094
12	.32272 03070 91321	.48508 26096 42005
13	.32269 92906 15678	.48514 71516 01807
14	.32267 82722 81906	.48521 16893 58127
0.6515	0.32265 72520 90545	0.48527 62229 10595
16	.32263 62300 42139	.48534 07522 58840
17	.32261 52061 37227	.48540 52774 02489
18	.32259 41803 76351	.48546 97983 41171
19	.32257 31527 60053	.48553 43150 74515
0.6520	0.32255 21232 88875	0.48559 88276 02151
21	.32253 10919 63357	.48566 33359 23707
22	.32251 00587 84042	.48572 78400 38813
23	.32248 90237 51470	.48579 23399 47097
24	.32246 79868 66183	.48585 68356 48190
0.6525	0.32244 69481 28724	0.48592 13271 41720
26	.32242 59075 39633	.48598 58144 27318
27	.32240 48650 99453	.48605 02975 04613
28	.32238 38208 08724	.48611 47763 73235
29	.32236 27746 67988	.48617 92510 32813
0.6530	0.32234 17266 77788	0.48624 37214 82978
31	.32232 06768 38665	.48630 81877 23361
32	.32229 96251 51160	.48637 26497 53591
33	.32227 85716 15816	.48643 71075 73298
34	.32225 75162 33173	.48650 15611 82114
0.6535	0.32223 64590 03775	0.48656 60105 79668
36	.32221 53999 28162	.48663 04557 65592
37	.32219 43390 06877	.48669 48967 39517
38	.32217 32762 40461	.48675 93335 01072
39	.32215 22116 29456	.48682 37660 49890
0.6540	0.32213 11451 74405	0.48688 81943 85601
41	.32211 00768 75848	.48695 26185 07837
42	.32208 90067 34328	.48701 70384 16228
43	.32206 79347 50388	.48708 14541 10407
44	.32204 68609 24568	.48714 58655 90006
0.6545	0.32202 57852 57411	0.48721 02728 54655
46	.32200 47077 49458	.48727 46759 03986
47	.32198 36284 01253	.48733 90747 37632
48	.32196 25472 13336	.48740 34693 55224
49	.32194 14641 86250	.48746 78597 56394
0.6550	0.32192 03793 20538	0.48753 22459 40776

X	$\frac{1}{\sqrt{2\pi}} e^{-\frac{x^2}{2}}$	$\frac{1}{\sqrt{2\pi}} \int_{-x}^{x} e^{-\frac{\alpha^2}{2}} d\alpha$
0.6550	0.32192 03793 20538	0.48753 22459 40776
51	.32189 92926 16740	.48759 66279 08000
52	.32187 82040 75400	.48766 10056 57700
53	.32185 71136 97059	.48772 53791 89508
54	.32183 60214 82259	.48778 97485 03056
0.6555	0.32181 49274 31543	0.48785 41135 97978
56	.32179 38315 45454	.48791 84744 73907
57	.32177 27338 24532	.48798 28311 30474
58	.32175 16342 69321	.48804 71835 67314
59	.32173 05328 80362	.48811 15317 84060
0.6560	0.32170 94296 58198	0.48817 58757 80344
61	.32168 83246 03372	.48824 02155 55801
62	.32166 72177 16425	.48830 45511 10063
63	.32164 61089 97899	.48836 88824 42765
64	.32162 49984 48338	.48843 32095 53540
0.6565	0.32160 38860 68284	0.48849 75324 42022
66	.32158 27718 58278	.48856 18511 07846
67	.32156 16558 18864	.48862 61655 50644
68	.32154 05379 50584	.48869 04757 70051
69	.32151 94182 53980	.48875 47817 65702
0.6570	0.32149 82967 29594	0.48881 90835 37231
71	.32147 71733 77970	.48888 33810 84272
72	.32145 60481 99650	.48894 76744 06460
73	.32143 49211 95176	.48901 19635 03430
74	.32141 37923 65090	.48907 62483 74817
0.6575	0.32139 26617 09937	0.48914 05290 20255
76	.32137 15292 30256	.48920 48054 39379
77	.32135 03949 26593	.48926 90776 31825
78	.32132 92587 99489	.48933 33455 97228
79	.32130 81208 49486	.48939 76093 35223
0.6580	0.32128 69810 77128	0.48946 18688 45446
81	.32126 58394 82957	.48952 61241 27533
82	.32124 46960 67516	.48959 03751 81118
83	.32122 35508 31348	.48965 46220 05838
84	.32120 24037 74995	.48971 88646 01329
0.6585	0.32118 12548 99000	0.48978 31029 67227
86	.32116 01042 03906	.48984 73371 03168
87	.32113 89516 90255	.48991 15670 08787
88	.32111 77973 58591	.48997 57926 83723
89	.32109 66412 09456	.49004 00141 27610
0.6590	0.32107 54832 43393	0.49010 42313 40085
91	.32105 43234 60945	.49016 84443 20786
92	.32103 31618 62656	.49023 26530 69349
93	.32101 19984 49066	.49029 68575 85410
94	.32099 08332 20721	.49036 10578 68607
0.6595	0.32096 96661 78162	0.49042 52539 18577
96	.32094 84973 21933	.49048 94457 34958
97	.32092 73266 52577	.49055 36333 17385
98	.32090 61541 70636	.49061 78166 65498
99	.32088 49798 76653	.49068 19957 78933
0.6600	0.32086 38037 71172	0.49074 61706 57328

x	$\dfrac{1}{\sqrt{2\pi}}\,e^{-\frac{x^2}{2}}$	$\dfrac{1}{\sqrt{2\pi}}\displaystyle\int_{-x}^{x} e^{-\frac{\alpha^2}{2}}\,d\alpha$
0.6600	0.32086 38037 71172	0.49074 61706 57328
01	.32084 26258 54736	.49081 03413 00320
02	.32082 14461 27888	.49087 45077 07549
03	.32080 02645 91171	.49093 86698 78651
04	.32077 90812 45127	.49100 28278 13265
0.6605	0.32075 78960 90301	0.49106 69815 11028
06	.32073 67091 27235	.49113 11309 71580
07	.32071 55203 56472	.49119 52761 94559
08	.32069 43297 78556	.49125 94171 79602
09	.32067 31373 94030	.49132 35539 26350
0.6610	0.32065 19432 03436	0.49138 76864 34440
11	.32063 07472 07319	.49145 18147 03511
12	.32060 95494 06222	.49151 59387 33202
13	.32058 83498 00687	.49158 00585 23153
14	.32056 71483 91258	.49164 41740 73002
0.6615	0.32054 59451 78479	0.49170 82853 82389
16	.32052 47401 62892	.49177 23924 50953
17	.32050 35333 45042	.49183 64952 78334
18	.52048 23247 25470	.49190 05938 64171
19	.32046 11143 04722	.49196 46882 08104
0.6620	0.32043 99020 83340	0.49202 87783 09773
21	.32041 86880 61867	.49209 28641 68818
22	.32039 74722 40848	.49215 69457 84878
23	.32037 62546 20825	.49222 10231 57594
24	.32035 50352 02342	.49228 50962 86606
0.6625	0.32033 38139 85942	0.49234 91651 71555
26	.32031 25909 72170	.49241 32298 12081
27	.32029 13661 61568	.49247 72902 07824
28	.32027 01395 54680	.49254 13463 58426
29	.32024 89111 52050	.49260 53982 63526
0.6630	0.32022 76809 54221	0.49266 94459 22767
31	.32020 64489 61736	.49273 34893 35788
32	.32018 52151 75141	.49279 75285 02232
33	.32016 39795 94977	.49286 15634 21739
34	.32014 27422 21789	.49292 55940 93951
0.6635	0.32012 15030 56120	0.49298 96205 18508
36	.32010 02620 98514	.49305 36426 95054
37	.32007 90193 49516	.49311 76606 23228
38	.32005 77748 09667	.49318 16743 02674
39	.32003 65284 79513	.49324 56837 33033
0.6640	0.32001 52803 59597	0.49330 96889 13946
41	.31999 40304 50463	.49337 36898 45057
42	.31997 27787 52654	.49343 76865 26007
43	.31995 15252 66714	.49350 16789 56439
44	.31993 02699 93188	.49356 56671 35995
0.6645	0.31990 90129 32619	0.49362 96510 64317
46	.31988 77540 85551	.49369 36307 41049
47	.31986 64934 52527	.49375 76061 65832
48	.31984 52310 34092	.49382 15773 38311
49	.31982 39668 30790	.49388 55442 58127
0.6650	0.31980 27008 43165	0.49394 95069 24924

x	$\frac{1}{\sqrt{2\pi}} e^{-\frac{x^2}{2}}$	$\frac{1}{\sqrt{2\pi}} \int_{-x}^{x} e^{-\frac{\alpha^2}{2}} d\alpha$
0.6650	0.31980 27008 43165	0.49394 95069 24924
51	.31978 14330 71759	.49401 34653 38345
52	.31976 01635 17119	.49407 74194 98034
53	.31973 88921 79786	.49414 13694 03633
54	.31971 76190 60307	.49420 53150 54787
0.6655	0.31969 63441 59223	0.49426 92564 51139
56	.31967 50674 77080	.49433 31935 92332
57	.31965 37890 14422	.49439 71264 78011
58	.31963 25087 71792	.49446 10551 07819
59	.31961 12267 49735	.49452 49794 81401
0.6660	0.31958 99429 48795	0.49458 88995 98400
61	.31956 86573 69516	.49465 28154 58462
62	.31954 73700 12442	.49471 67270 61230
63	.31952 60808 78117	.49478 06344 06348
64	.31950 47899 67085	.49484 45374 93463
0.6665	0.31948 34972 79892	0.49490 84363 22217
66	.31946 22028 17079	.49497 23308 92256
67	.31944 09065 79193	.49503 62212 03225
68	.31941 96085 66778	.49510 01072 54769
69	.31939 83087 80376	.49516 39890 46534
0.6670	0.31937 70072 20534	0.49522 78665 78163
71	.31935 57038 87795	.49529 17398 49304
72	.31933 43987 82703	.49535 56088 59600
73	.31931 30919 05802	.49541 94736 08699
74	.31929 17832 57638	.49548 33340 96245
0.6675	0.31927 04728 38755	0.49554 71903 21884
76	.31924 91606 49696	.49561 10422 85262
77	.31922 78466 91006	.49567 48899 86026
78	.31920 65309 63230	.49573 87334 23821
79	.31918 52134 66912	.49580 25725 98293
0.6680	0.31916 38942 02597	0.49586 64075 09089
81	.31914 25731 70828	.49593 02381 55856
82	.31912 12503 72151	.49599 40645 38240
83	.31909 99258 07110	.49605 78866 55887
84	.31907 85994 76249	.49612 17045 08445
0.6685	0.31905 72713 80113	0.49618 55180 95560
86	.31903 59415 19247	.49624 93274 16880
87	.31901 46098 94195	.49631 31324 72050
88	.31899 32765 05502	.49637 69332 60720
89	.31897 19413 53711	.49644 07297 82535
0.6690	0.31895 06044 39369	0.49650 45220 37144
91	.31892 92657 63019	.49656 83100 24193
92	.31890 79253 25206	.49663 20937 43331
93	.31888 65831 26475	.49669 58731 94206
94	.31886 52391 67370	.49675 96483 76465
0.6695	0.31884 38934 48437	0.49682 34192 89756
96	.31882 25459 70219	.49688 71859 33727
97	.31880 11967 33262	.49695 09483 08026
98	.31877 98457 38110	.49701 47064 12303
99	.31875 84929 85308	.49707 84602 46204
0.6700	0.31873 71384 75402	0.49714 22098 09380

x	$\dfrac{1}{\sqrt{2\pi}}\,e^{-\frac{x^2}{2}}$	$\dfrac{1}{\sqrt{2\pi}}\displaystyle\int_{-x}^{x} e^{-\frac{\alpha^2}{2}}\,d\alpha$
0.6700	0.31873 71384 75402	0.49714 22098 09380
01	.31871 57822 08934	.49720 59551 01477
02	.31869 44241 86451	.49726 96961 22146
03	.31867 30644 08498	.49733 34328 71035
04	.31865 17028 75619	.49739 71653 47793
0.6705	0.31863 03395 88358	0.49746 08935 52068
06	.31860 89745 47261	.49752 46174 83511
07	.31858 76077 52873	.49758 83371 41770
08	.31856 62392 05739	.49765 20525 26495
09	.31854 48689 06403	.49771 57636 37336
0.6710	0.31852 34968 55411	0.49777 94704 73941
11	.31850 21230 53307	.49784 31730 35961
12	.31848 07475 00636	.49790 68713 23046
13	.31845 93701 97944	.49797 05653 34845
14	.31843 79911 45775	.49803 42550 71008
0.6715	0.31841 66103 44675	0.49809 79405 31187
16	.31839 52277 95188	.49816 16217 15030
17	.31837 38434 97859	.49822 52986 22188
18	.31835 24574 53234	.49828 89712 52312
19	.31833 10696 61857	.49835 26396 05053
0.6720	0.31830 96801 24274	0.49841 63036 80061
21	.31828 82888 41030	.49847 99634 76986
22	.31826 68958 12670	.49854 36189 95481
23	.31824 55010 39739	.49860 72702 35195
24	.31822 41045 22782	.49867 09171 95780
0.6725	0.31820 27062 62344	0.49873 45598 76888
26	.31818 13062 58971	.49879 81982 78169
27	.31815 99045 13208	.49886 18323 99275
28	.31813 85010 25600	.49892 54622 39858
29	.31811 70957 96692	.49898 90877 99569
0.6730	0.31809 56888 27029	0.49905 27090 78061
31	.31807 42801 17157	.49911 63260 74984
32	.31805 28696 67622	.49917 99387 89992
33	.31803 14574 78967	.49924 35472 22735
34	.31801 00435 51739	.49930 71513 72867
0.6735	0.31798 86278 86483	0.49937 07512 40040
36	.31796 72104 83745	.49943 43468 23906
37	.31794 57913 44069	.49949 79381 24118
38	.31792 43704 68001	.49956 15251 40328
39	.31790 29478 56086	.49962 51078 72189
0.6740	0.31788 15235 08871	0.49968 86863 19355
41	.31786 00974 26899	.49975 22604 81477
42	.31783 86696 10717	.49981 58303 58210
43	.31781 72400 60871	.49987 93959 49206
44	.31779 58087 77905	.49994 29572 54119
0.6745	0.31777 43757 62365	0.50000 65142 72602
46	.31775 29410 14796	.50007 00670 04308
47	.31773 15045 35745	.50013 36154 48892
48	.31771 00663 25756	.50019 71596 06007
49	.31768 86263 85375	.50026 06994 75307
0.6750	0.31766 71847 15148	0.50032 42350 56446

X	$\frac{1}{\sqrt{2\pi}} e^{-\frac{x^2}{2}}$	$\frac{1}{\sqrt{2\pi}} \int_{-x}^{x} e^{-\frac{\alpha^2}{2}} d\alpha$
0.6750	0.31766 71847 15148	0.50032 42350 56446
51	.31764 57413 15621	.50038 77663 49078
52	.31762 42961 87338	.50045 12933 52857
53	.31760 28493 30845	.50051 48160 67438
54	.31758 14007 46689	.50057 83344 92474
0.6755	0.31755 99504 35414	0.50064 18486 27621
56	.31753 84983 97567	.50070 53584 72533
57	.31751 70446 33693	.50076 88640 26865
58	.31749 55891 44337	.50083 23652 90272
59	.31747 41319 30046	.50089 58622 62408
0.6760	0.31745 26729 91365	0.50095 93549 42929
61	.31743 12123 28839	.50102 28433 31489
62	.31740 97499 43015	.50108 63274 27745
63	.31738 82858 34439	.50114 98072 31352
64	.31736 68200 03655	.50121 32827 41964
0.6765	0.31734 53524 51211	0.50127 67539 59238
66	.31732 38831 77651	.50134 02208 82830
67	.31730 24121 83521	.50140 36835 12395
68	.31728 09394 69368	.50146 71418 47589
69	.31725 94650 35736	.50153 05958 88068
0.6770	0.31723 79888 83173	0.50159 40456 33488
71	.31721 65110 12224	.50165 74910 83507
72	.31719 50314 23434	.50172 09322 37779
73	.31717 35501 17350	.50178 43690 95962
74	.31715 20670 94517	.50184 78016 57711
0.6775	0.31713 05823 55482	0.50191 12299 22685
76	.31710 90959 00790	.50197 46538 90539
77	.31708 76077 30987	.50203 80735 60931
78	.31706 61178 46620	.50210 14889 33517
79	.31704 46262 48234	.50216 49000 07955
0.6780	0.31702 31329 36375	0.50222 83067 83902
81	.31700 16379 11590	.50229 17092 61016
82	.31698 01411 74424	.50235 51074 38953
83	.31695 86427 25423	.50241 85013 17371
84	.31693 71425 65133	.50248 18908 95929
0.6785	0.31691 56406 94102	0.50254 52761 74283
86	.31689 41371 12873	.50260 86571 52093
87	.31687 26318 21995	.50267 20338 29014
88	.31685 11248 22012	.50273 54062 04707
89	.31682 96161 13471	.50279 87742 78829
0.6790	0.31680 81056 96918	0.50286 21380 51039
91	.31678 65935 72899	.50292 54975 20994
92	.31676 50797 41961	.50298 88526 88354
93	.31674 35642 04649	.50305 22035 52777
94	.31672 20469 61510	.50311 55501 13922
0.6795	0.31670 05280 13090	0.50317 88923 71448
96	.31667 90073 59935	.50324 22303 25014
97	.31665 74850 02592	.50330 55639 74279
98	.31663 59609 41606	.50336 88933 18901
99	.31661 44351 77524	.50343 22183 58542
0.6800	0.31659 29077 10893	0.50349 55390 92859

x	$\dfrac{1}{\sqrt{2\pi}}\,e^{-\frac{x^2}{2}}$	$\dfrac{1}{\sqrt{2\pi}}\displaystyle\int_{-x}^{x} e^{-\frac{\alpha^2}{2}}\,d\alpha$
0.6800	0.31659 29077 10893	0.50349 55390 92859
01	.31657 13785 42258	.50355 88555 21513
02	.31654 98476 72166	.50362 21676 44162
03	.31652 83151 01163	.50368 54754 60468
04	.31650 67808 29795	.50374 87789 70090
0.6805	0.31648 52448 58609	0.50381 20781 72687
06	.31646 37071 88152	.50387 53730 67920
07	.31644 21678 18969	.50393 86636 55449
08	.31642 06267 51607	.50400 19499 34934
09	.31639 90839 86613	.50406 52319 06036
0.6810	0.31637 75395 24532	0.50412 85095 68416
11	.31635 59933 65912	.50419 17829 21733
12	.31633 44455 11298	.50425 50519 65649
13	.31631 28959 61237	.50431 83166 99824
14	.31629 13447 16276	.50438 15771 23920
0.6815	0.31626 97917 76962	0.50444 48332 37598
16	.31624 82371 43839	.50450 80850 40518
17	.31622 66808 17456	.50457 13325 32343
18	.31620 51227 98359	.50463 45757 12732
19	.31618 35630 87094	.50469 78145 81349
0.6820	0.31616 20016 84207	0.50476 10491 37854
21	.31614 04385 90246	.50482 42793 81910
22	.31611 88738 05757	.50488 75053 13178
23	.31609 73073 31286	.50495 07269 31320
24	.31607 57391 67381	.50501 39442 35998
0.6825	0.31605 41693 14587	0.50507 71572 26874
26	.31603 25977 73451	.50514 03659 03611
27	.31601 10245 44521	.50520 35702 65871
28	.31598 94496 28342	.50526 67703 13316
29	.31596 78730 25462	.50532 99660 45610
0.6830	0.31594 62947 36427	0.50539 31574 62414
31	.31592 47147 61783	.50545 63445 63392
32	.31590 31331 02078	.50551 95273 48206
33	.31588 15497 57858	.50558 27058 16521
34	.31585 99647 29671	.50564 58799 67997
0.6835	0.31583 83780 18061	0.50570 90498 02300
36	.31581 67896 23578	.50577 22153 19092
37	.31579 51995 46766	.50583 53765 18037
38	.31577 36077 88174	.50589 85333 98799
39	.31575 20143 48348	.50596 16859 61041
0.6840	0.31573 04192 27834	0.50602 48342 04426
41	.31570 88224 27179	.50608 79781 28620
42	.31568 72239 46932	.50615 11177 33285
43	.31566 56237 87637	.50621 42530 18087
44	.31564 40219 49842	.50627 73839 82688
0.6845	0.31562 24184 34095	0.50634 05106 26755
46	.31560 08132 40941	.50640 36329 49950
47	.31557 92063 70928	.50646 67509 51939
48	.31555 75978 24603	.50652 98646 32387
49	.31553 59876 02512	.50659 29739 90957
0.6850	0.31551 43757 05203	0.50665 60790 27316

x	$\frac{1}{\sqrt{2\pi}} e^{-\frac{x^2}{2}}$	$\frac{1}{\sqrt{2\pi}} \int_{-x}^{x} e^{-\frac{\alpha^2}{2}} d\alpha$
0.6850	0.31551 43757 05203	0.50665 60790 27316
51	.31549 27621 33223	.50671 91797 41128
52	.31547 11468 87118	.50678 22761 32058
53	.31544 95299 67436	.50684 53681 99771
54	.31542 79113 74723	.50690 84559 43933
0.6855	0.31540 62911 09527	0.50697 15393 64209
56	.31538 46691 72394	.50703 46184 60266
57	.31536 30455 63872	.50709 76932 31767
58	.31534 14202 84508	.50716 07636 78380
59	.31531 97933 34849	.50722 38297 99769
0.6860	0.31529 81647 15441	0.50728 68915 95602
61	.31527 65344 26832	.50734 99490 65544
62	.31525 49024 69569	.50741 30022 09262
63	.31523 32688 44199	.50747 60510 26421
64	.31521 16335 51270	.50753 90955 16688
0.6865	0.31518 99965 91328	0.50760 21356 79730
66	.31516 83579 64920	.50766 51715 15214
67	.31514 67176 72595	.50772 82030 22805
68	.31512 50757 14898	.50779 12302 02172
69	.31510 34320 92377	.50785 42530 52980
0.6870	0.31508 17868 05579	0.50791 72715 74898
71	.31506 01398 55052	.50798 02857 67592
72	.31503 84912 41343	.50804 32956 30729
73	.31501 68409 64998	.50810 63011 63977
74	.31499 51890 26566	.50816 93023 67004
0.6875	0.31497 35354 26593	0.50823 22992 39477
76	.31495 18801 65627	.50829 52917 81064
77	.31493 02232 44215	.50835 82799 91433
78	.31490 85646 62905	.50842 12638 70251
79	.31488 69044 22243	.50848 42434 17187
0.6880	0.31486 52425 22777	0.50854 72186 31909
81	.31484 35789 65054	.50861 01895 14086
82	.31482 19137 49622	.50867 31560 63385
83	.31480 02468 77028	.50873 61182 79475
84	.31477 85783 47819	.50879 90761 62025
0.6885	0.31475 69081 62544	0.50886 20297 10704
86	.31473 52363 21748	.50892 49789 25180
87	.31471 35628 25980	.50898 79238 05122
88	.31469 18876 75787	.50905 08643 50200
89	.31467 02108 71716	.50911 38005 60082
0.6890	0.31464 85324 14315	0.50917 67324 34438
91	.31462 68523 04132	.50923 96599 72938
92	.31460 51705 41713	.50930 25831 75250
93	.31458 34871 27607	.50936 55020 41044
94	.31456 18020 62360	.50942 84165 69991
0.6895	0.31454 01153 46521	0.50949 13267 61759
96	.31451 84269 80637	.50955 42326 16019
97	.31449 67369 65254	.50961 71341 32442
98	.31447 50453 00922	.50968 00313 10696
99	.31445 33519 88187	.50974 29241 50452
0.6900	0.31443 16570 27597	0.50980 58126 51381

X	$\dfrac{1}{\sqrt{2\pi}}\,e^{-\frac{x^2}{2}}$	$\dfrac{1}{\sqrt{2\pi}}\displaystyle\int_{-x}^{x} e^{-\frac{\alpha^2}{2}}\,d\alpha$
0.6900	0.31443 16570 27597	0.50980 58126 51381
01	.31440 99604 19700	.50986 86968 13153
02	.31438 82621 65043	.50993 15766 35439
03	.31436 65622 64173	.50999 44521 17910
04	.31434 48607 17639	.51005 73232 60235
0.6905	0.31432 31575 25988	0.51012 01900 62087
06	.31430 14526 89767	.51018 30525 23136
07	.31427 97462 09525	.51024 59106 43053
08	.31425 80380 85808	.51030 87644 21510
09	.31423 63283 19166	.51037 16138 58178
0.6910	0.31421 46169 10144	0.51043 44589 52728
11	.31419 29038 59291	.51049 72997 04833
12	.31417 11891 67155	.51056 01361 14163
13	.31414 94728 34283	.51062 29681 80390
14	.31412 77548 61223	.51068 57959 03187
0.6915	0.31410 60352 48524	0.51074 86192 82225
16	.31408 43139 96731	.51081 14383 17177
17	.31406 25911 06394	.51087 42530 07715
18	.31404 08665 78060	.51093 70633 53510
19	.31401 91404 12277	.51099 98693 54237
0.6920	0.31399 74126 09592	0.51106 26710 09566
21	.31397 56831 70554	.51112 54683 19172
22	.31395 39520 95711	.51118 82612 82725
23	.31393 22193 85609	.51125 10498 99901
24	.31391 04850 40797	.51131 38341 70371
0.6925	0.31388 87490 61823	0.51137 66140 93808
26	.31386 70114 49235	.51143 93896 69887
27	.31384 52722 03580	.51150 21608 98279
28	.31382 35313 25406	.51156 49277 78659
29	.31380 17888 15262	.51162 76903 10700
0.6930	0.31378 00446 73695	0.51169 04484 94076
31	.31375 82989 01253	.51175 32023 28461
32	.31373 65514 98484	.51181 59518 13528
33	.31371 48024 65936	.51187 86969 48952
34	.31369 30518 04156	.51194 14377 34406
0.6935	0.31367 12995 13694	0.51200 41741 69565
36	.31364 95455 95097	.51206 69062 54103
37	.31362 77900 48912	.51212 96339 87694
38	.31360 60328 75688	.51219 23573 70014
39	.31358 42740 75973	.51225 50764 00736
0.6940	0.31356 25136 50314	0.51231 77910 79536
41	.31354 07515 99261	.51238 05014 06088
42	.31351 89879 23360	.51244 32073 80067
43	.31349 72226 23160	.51250 59090 01149
44	.31347 54556 99209	.51256 86062 69008
0.6945	0.31345 36871 52055	0.51263 12991 83321
46	.31343 19169 82246	.51269 39877 43761
47	.31341 01451 90331	.51275 66719 50005
48	.31338 83717 76856	.51281 93518 01729
49	.31336 65967 42371	.51288 20272 98608
0.6950	0.31334 48200 87424	0.51294 46984 40318

x	$\dfrac{1}{\sqrt{2\pi}}\,e^{-\frac{x^2}{2}}$	$\dfrac{1}{\sqrt{2\pi}}\displaystyle\int_{-x}^{x} e^{-\frac{\alpha^2}{2}}\,d\alpha$
0.6950	0.31334 48200 87424	0.51294 46984 40318
51	.31332 30418 12562	.51300 73652 26535
52	.31330 12619 18334	.51307 00276 56935
53	.31327 94804 05288	.51313 26857 31194
54	.31325 76972 73971	.51319 53394 48989
0.6955	0.31323 59125 24933	0.51325 79888 09996
56	.31321 41261 58722	.51332 06338 13891
57	.31319 23381 75885	.51338 32744 60352
58	.31317 05485 76971	.51344 59107 49054
59	.31314 87573 62528	.51350 85426 79675
0.6960	0.31312 69645 33104	0.51357 11702 51891
61	.31310 51700 89247	.51363 37934 65381
62	.31308 33740 31507	.51369 64123 19820
63	.31306 15763 60430	.51375 90268 14886
64	.31303 97770 76566	.51382 16369 50256
0.6965	0.31301 79761 80462	0.51388 42427 25609
66	.31299 61736 72666	.51394 68441 40621
67	.31297 43695 53728	.51400 94411 94970
68	.31295 25638 24196	.51407 20338 88335
69	.31293 07564 84617	.51413 46222 20393
0.6970	0.31290 89475 35539	0.51419 72061 90822
71	.31288 71369 77513	.51425 97857 99300
72	.31286 53248 11085	.51432 23610 45505
73	.31284 35110 36804	.51438 49319 29117
74	.31282 16956 55218	.51444 74984 49813
0.6975	0.31279 98786 66877	0.51451 00606 07272
76	.31277 80600 72327	.51457 26184 01173
77	.31275 62398 72118	.51463 51718 31194
78	.31273 44180 66798	.51469 77208 97014
79	.31271 25946 56916	.51476 02655 98314
0.6980	0.31269 07696 43019	0.51482 28059 34770
81	.31266 89430 25656	.51488 53419 06064
82	.31264 71148 05376	.51494 78735 11874
83	.31262 52849 82728	.51501 04007 51879
84	.31260 34535 58259	.51507 29236 25760
0.6985	0.31258 16205 32518	0.51513 54421 33196
86	.31255 97859 06053	.51519 79562 73866
87	.31253 79496 79414	.51526 04660 47452
88	.31251 61118 53148	.51532 29714 53631
89	.31249 42724 27804	.51538 54724 92086
0.6990	0.31247 24314 03931	0.51544 79691 62496
91	.31245 05887 82076	.51551 04614 64541
92	.31242 87445 62790	.51557 29493 97902
93	.31240 68987 46620	.51563 54329 62260
94	.31238 50513 34114	.51569 79121 57295
0.6995	0.31236 32023 25822	0.51576 03869 82687
96	.31234 13517 22292	.51582 28574 38119
97	.31231 94995 24072	.51588 53235 23270
98	.31229 76457 31711	.51594 77852 37822
99	.31227 57903 45758	.51601 02425 81456
0.7000	0.31225 39333 66761	0.51607 26955 53854

x	$\dfrac{1}{\sqrt{2\pi}}\,e^{-\frac{x^2}{2}}$	$\dfrac{1}{\sqrt{2\pi}}\displaystyle\int_{-x}^{x} e^{-\frac{\alpha^2}{2}}\,d\alpha$
0.7000	0.31225 39333 66761	0.51607 26955 53854
01	.31223 20747 95269	.51613 51441 54697
02	.31221 02146 31831	.51619 75883 83666
03	.31218 83528 76995	.51626 00282 40443
04	.31216 64895 31310	.51632 24637 24711
0.7005	0.31214 46245 95325	0.51638 48948 36150
06	.31212 27580 69587	.51644 73215 74443
07	.31210 08899 54647	.51650 97439 39272
08	.31207 90202 51052	.51657 21619 30319
09	.31205 71489 59351	.51663 45755 47266
0.7010	0.31203 52760 80094	0.51669 69847 89797
11	.31201 34016 13828	.51675 93896 57593
12	.31199 15255 61102	.51682 17901 50336
13	.31196 96479 22466	.51688 41862 67711
14	.31194 77686 98468	.51694 65780 09400
0.7015	0.31192 58878 89656	0.51700 89653 75085
16	.31190 40054 96580	.51707 13483 64450
17	.31188 21215 19788	.51713 37269 77178
18	.31186 02359 59829	.51719 61012 12952
19	.31183 83488 17251	.51725 84710 71456
0.7020	0.31181 64600 92605	0.51732 08365 52374
21	.31179 45697 86437	.51738 31976 55388
22	.31177 26778 99298	.51744 55543 80183
23	.31175 07844 31736	.51750 79067 26442
24	.31172 88893 84300	.51757 02546 93850
0.7025	0.31170 69927 57538	0.51763 25982 82091
26	.31168 50945 52000	.51769 49374 90848
27	.31166 31947 68235	.51775 72723 19806
28	.31164 12934 06790	.51781 96027 68650
29	.31161 93904 68216	.51788 19288 37064
0.7030	0.31159 74859 53061	0.51794 42505 24732
31	.31157 55798 61874	.51800 65678 31340
32	.31155 36721 95204	.51806 88807 56572
33	.31153 17629 53600	.51813 11893 00113
34	.31150 98521 37610	.51819 34934 61649
0.7035	0.31148 79397 47784	0.51825 57932 40863
36	.31146 60257 84671	.51831 80886 37443
37	.31144 41102 48819	.51838 03796 51072
38	.31142 21931 40777	.51844 26662 81438
39	.31140 02744 61095	.51850 49485 28224
0.7040	0.31137 83542 10322	0.51856 72263 91117
41	.31135 64323 89005	.51862 94998 69803
42	.31133 45089 97695	.51869 17689 63968
43	.31131 25840 36941	.51875 40336 73298
44	.31129 06575 07291	.51881 62939 97478
0.7045	0.31126 87294 09294	0.51887 85499 36196
46	.31124 67997 43500	.51894 08014 89138
47	.31122 48685 10458	.51900 30486 55989
48	.31120 29357 10715	.51906 52914 36437
49	.31118 10013 44823	.51912 75298 30169
0.7050	0.31115 90654 13329	0.51918 97638 36871

x	$\dfrac{1}{\sqrt{2\pi}}\,e^{-\frac{x^2}{2}}$	$\dfrac{1}{\sqrt{2\pi}}\displaystyle\int_{-x}^{x} e^{-\frac{\alpha^2}{2}}\,d\alpha$
0.7050	0.31115 90654 13329	0.51918 97638 36871
51	.31113 71279 16783	.51925 19934 56230
52	.31111 51888 55733	.51931 42186 87933
53	.31109 32482 30729	.51937 64395 31668
54	.31107 13060 42321	.51943 86559 87121
0.7055	0.31104 93622 91056	0.51950 08680 53981
56	.31102 74169 77484	.51956 30757 31934
57	.31100 54701 02155	.51962 52790 20668
58	.31098 35216 65617	.51968 74779 19870
59	.31096 15716 68420	.51974 96724 29230
0.7060	0.31093 96201 11112	0.51981 18625 48434
61	.31091 76669 94243	.51987 40482 77170
62	.31089 57123 18362	.51993 62296 15128
63	.31087 37560 84018	.51999 84065 61994
64	.31085 17982 91761	.52006 05791 17457
0.7065	0.31082 98389 42139	0.52012 27472 81207
66	.31080 78780 35701	.52018 49110 52930
67	.31078 59155 72998	.52024 70704 32317
68	.31076 39515 54577	.52030 92254 19056
69	.31074 19859 80989	.52037 13760 12835
0.7070	0.31072 00188 52783	0.52043 35222 13345
71	.31069 80501 70507	.52049 56640 20273
72	.31067 60799 34710	.52055 78014 33309
73	.31065 41081 45944	.52061 99344 52143
74	.31063 21348 04755	.52068 20630 76464
0.7075	0.31061 01599 11695	0.52074 41873 05962
76	.31058 81834 67311	.52080 63071 40325
77	.31056 62054 72153	.52086 84225 79245
78	.31054 42259 26771	.52093 05336 22411
79	.31052 22448 31714	.52099 26402 69513
0.7080	0.31050 02621 87531	0.52105 47425 20240
81	.31047 82779 94772	.52111 68403 74284
82	.31045 62922 53985	.52117 89338 31335
83	.31043 43049 65720	.52124 10228 91083
84	.31041 23161 30526	.52130 31075 53218
0.7085	0.31039 03257 48954	0.52136 51878 17432
86	.31036 83338 21551	.52142 72636 83415
87	.31034 63403 48868	.52148 93351 50857
88	.31032 43453 31453	.52155 14022 19451
89	.31030 23487 69856	.52161 34648 88887
0.7090	0.31028 03506 64627	0.52167 55231 58856
91	.31025 83510 16315	.52173 75770 29050
92	.31023 63498 25469	.52179 96264 99160
93	.31021 43470 92639	.52186 16715 68877
94	.31019 23428 18374	.52192 37122 37894
0.7095	0.31017 03370 03223	0.52198 57485 05902
96	.31014 83296 47736	.52204 77803 72593
97	.31012 63207 52463	.52210 98078 37659
98	.31010 43103 17952	.52217 18309 00791
99	.31008 22983 44753	.52223 38495 61683
0.7100	0.31006 02848 33416	0.52229 58638 20027

x	$\dfrac{1}{\sqrt{2\pi}}\,e^{-\frac{x^2}{2}}$	$\dfrac{1}{\sqrt{2\pi}}\displaystyle\int_{-x}^{x}e^{-\frac{\alpha^2}{2}}\,d\alpha$
0.7100	0.31006 02848 33416	0.52229 58638 20027
01	.31003 82697 84490	.52235 78736 75514
02	.31001 62531 98524	.52241 98791 27838
03	.30999 42350 76069	.52248 18801 76691
04	.30997 22154 17673	.52254 38768 21766
0.7105	0.30995 01942 23886	0.52260 58690 62756
06	.30992 81714 95257	.52266 78568 99353
07	.30990 61472 32336	.52272 98403 31251
08	.30988 41214 35672	.52279 18193 58144
09	.30986 20941 05816	.52285 37939 79724
0.7110	0.30984 00652 43315	0.52291 57641 95684
11	.30981 80348 48721	.52297 77300 05719
12	.30979 60029 22582	.52303 96914 09521
13	.30977 39694 65449	.52310 16484 06786
14	.30975 19344 77869	.52316 36009 97206
0.7115	0.30972 98979 60394	0.52322 55491 80475
16	.30970 78599 13573	.52328 74929 56288
17	.30968 58203 37955	.52334 94323 24338
18	.30966 37792 34089	.52341 13672 84321
19	.30964 17366 02526	.52347 32978 35930
0.7120	0.30961 96924 43815	0.52353 52239 78860
21	.30959 76467 58505	.52359 71457 12806
22	.30957 55995 47147	.52365 90630 37462
23	.30955 35508 10289	.52372 09759 52523
24	.30953 15005 48482	.52378 28844 57684
0.7125	0.30950 94487 62274	0.52384 47885 52641
26	.30948 73954 52216	.52390 66882 37088
27	.30946 53406 18857	.52396 85835 10720
28	.30944 32842 62748	.52403 04743 73234
29	.30942 12263 84436	.52409 23608 24324
0.7130	0.30939 91669 84473	0.52415 42428 63686
31	.30937 71060 63407	.52421 61204 91016
32	.30935 50436 21789	.52427 79937 06010
33	.30933 29796 60168	.52433 98625 08364
34	.30931 09141 79094	.52440 17268 97773
0.7135	0.30928 88471 79117	0.52446 35868 73934
36	.30926 67786 60785	.52452 54424 36543
37	.30924 47086 24649	.52458 72935 85297
38	.30922 26370 71259	.52464 91403 19892
39	.30920 05640 01164	.52471 09826 40024
0.7140	0.30917 84894 14914	0.52477 28205 45391
41	.30915 64133 13059	.52483 46540 35689
42	.30913 43356 96148	.52489 64831 10616
43	.30911 22565 64731	.52495 83077 69867
44	.30909 01759 19359	.52502 01280 13140
0.7145	0.30906 80937 60579	0.52508 19438 40134
46	.30904 60100 88943	.52514 37552 50544
47	.30902 39249 05001	.52520 55622 44068
48	.30900 18382 09301	.52526 73648 20405
49	.30897 97500 02394	.52532 91629 79251
0.7150	0.30895 76602 84829	0.52539 09567 20305

x	$\frac{1}{\sqrt{2\pi}} e^{-\frac{x^2}{2}}$	$\frac{1}{\sqrt{2\pi}} \int_{-x}^{x} e^{-\frac{\alpha^2}{2}} d\alpha$
0.7150	0.30895 76602 84829	0.52539 09567 20305
51	.30893 55690 57156	.52545 27460 43265
52	.30891 34763 19925	.52551 45309 47828
53	.30889 13820 73687	.52557 63114 33692
54	.30886 92863 18989	.52563 80875 00556
0.7155	0.30884 71890 56383	0.52569 98591 48119
56	.30882 50902 86418	.52576 16263 76079
57	.30880 29900 09645	.52582 33891 84133
58	.30878 08882 26612	.52588 51475 71982
59	.30875 87849 37869	.52594 69015 39323
0.7160	0.30873 66801 43968	0.52600 86510 85857
61	.30871 45738 45456	.52607 03962 11281
62	.30869 24660 42885	.52613 21369 15295
63	.30867 03567 36803	.52619 38731 97598
64	.30864 82459 27762	.52625 56050 57889
0.7165	0.30862 61336 16310	0.52631 73324 95869
66	.30860 40198 02998	.52637 90555 11236
67	.30858 19044 88375	.52644 07741 03690
68	.30855 97876 72992	.52650 24882 72931
69	.30853 76693 57398	.52656 41980 18659
0.7170	0.30851 55495 42143	0.52662 59033 40574
71	.30849 34282 27777	.52668 76042 38376
72	.30847 13054 14850	.52674 93007 11765
73	.30844 91811 03911	.52681 09927 60442
74	.30842 70552 95512	.52687 26803 84107
0.7175	0.30840 49279 90201	0.52693 43635 82460
76	.30838 27991 88529	.52699 60423 55203
77	.30836 06688 91045	.52705 77167 02036
78	.30833 85370 98299	.52711 93866 22660
79	.30831 64038 10842	.52718 10521 16776
0.7180	0.30829 42690 29223	0.52724 27131 84085
81	.30827 21327 53993	.52730 43698 24288
82	.30824 99949 85701	.52736 60220 37087
83	.30822 78557 24896	.52742 76698 22183
84	.30820 57149 72130	.52748 93131 79277
0.7185	0.30818 35727 27953	0.52755 09521 08072
86	.30816 14289 92913	.52761 25866 08269
87	.30813 92837 67561	.52767 42166 79570
88	.30811 71370 52447	.52773 58423 21677
89	.30809 49888 48122	.52779 74635 34292
0.7190	0.30807 28391 55134	0.52785 90803 17117
91	.30805 06879 74035	.52792 06926 69854
92	.30802 85353 05373	.52798 23005 92207
93	.30800 63811 49700	.52804 39040 83877
94	.30798 42255 07564	.52810 55031 44568
0.7195	0.30796 20683 79517	0.52816 70977 73981
96	.30793 99097 66108	.52822 86879 71821
97	.30791 77496 67887	.52829 02737 37789
98	.30789 55880 85404	.52835 18550 71589
99	.30787 34250 19209	.52841 34319 72924
0.7200	0.30785 12604 69853	0.52847 50044 41498

x	$\frac{1}{\sqrt{2\pi}} e^{-\frac{x^2}{2}}$	$\frac{1}{\sqrt{2\pi}} \int_{-x}^{x} e^{-\frac{\alpha^2}{2}} d\alpha$
0.7200	0.30785 12604 69853	0.52847 50044 41498
01	.30782 90944 37885	.52853 65724 77013
02	.30780 69269 23855	.52859 81360 79174
03	.30778 47579 28314	.52865 96952 47684
04	.30776 25874 51812	.52872 12499 82247
0.7205	0.30774 04154 94897	0.52878 28002 82566
06	.30771 82420 58122	.52884 43461 48346
07	.30769 60671 42035	.52890 58875 79291
08	.30767 38907 47188	.52896 74245 75104
09	.30765 17128 74129	.52902 89571 35491
0.7210	0.30762 95335 23409	0.52909 04852 60155
11	.30760 73526 95578	.52915 20089 48802
12	.30758 51703 91186	.52921 35282 01135
13	.30756 29866 10784	.52927 50430 16860
14	.30754 08013 54921	.52933 65533 95681
0.7215	0.30751 86146 24148	0.52939 80593 37304
16	.30749 64264 19014	.52945 95608 41432
17	.30747 42367 40071	.52952 10579 07773
18	.30745 20455 87867	.52958 25505 36030
19	.30742 98529 62953	.52964 40387 25910
0.7220	0.30740 76588 65879	0.52970 55224 77117
21	.30738 54632 97196	.52976 70017 89358
22	.30736 32662 57453	.52982 84766 62338
23	.30734 10677 47201	.52988 99470 95763
24	.30731 88677 66990	.52995 14130 89339
0.7225	0.30729 66663 17370	0.53001 28746 42772
26	.30727 44633 98890	.53007 43317 55768
27	.30725 22590 12103	.53013 57844 28034
28	.30723 00531 57556	.53019 72326 59275
29	.30720 78458 35802	.53025 86764 49199
0.7230	0.30718 56370 47389	0.53032 01157 97511
31	.30716 34267 92868	.53038 15507 03920
32	.30714 12150 72789	.53044 29811 68131
33	.30711 90018 87703	.53050 44071 89851
34	.30709 67872 38160	.53056 58287 68788
0.7235	0.30707 45711 24709	0.53062 72459 04649
36	.30705 23535 47901	.53068 86585 97141
37	.30703 01345 08287	.53075 00668 45971
38	.30700 79140 06416	.53081 14706 50847
39	.30698 56920 42839	.53087 28700 11476
0.7240	0.30696 34686 18105	0.53093 42649 27566
41	.30694 12437 32766	.53099 56553 98826
42	.30691 90173 87371	.53105 70414 24962
43	.30689 67895 82471	.53111 84230 05683
44	.30687 45603 18616	.53117 98001 40698
0.7245	0.30685 23295 96356	0.53124 11728 29714
46	.30683 00974 16241	.53130 25410 72439
47	.30680 78637 78822	.53136 39048 68583
48	.30678 56286 84648	.53142 52642 17854
49	.30676 33921 34271	.53148 66191 19960
0.7250	0.30674 11541 28240	0.53154 79695 74610

x	$\dfrac{1}{\sqrt{2\pi}} e^{-\frac{x^2}{2}}$	$\dfrac{1}{\sqrt{2\pi}} \displaystyle\int_{-x}^{x} e^{-\frac{\alpha^2}{2}} \, d\alpha$
0.7250	0.30674 11541 28240	0.53154 79695 74610
51	.30671 89146 67106	.53160 93155 81514
52	.30669 66737 51418	.53167 06571 40380
53	.30667 44313 81728	.53173 19942 50918
54	.30665 21875 58586	.53179 33269 12836
0.7255	0.30662 99422 82541	0.53185 46551 25844
56	.30660 76955 54144	.53191 59788 89652
57	.30658 54473 73945	.53197 72982 03969
58	.30656 31977 42495	.53203 86130 68505
59	.30654 09466 60344	.53209 99234 82969
0.7260	0.30651 86941 28043	0.53216 12294 47072
61	.30649 64401 46140	.53222 25309 60524
62	.30647 41847 15188	.53228 38280 23034
63	.30645 19278 35736	.53234 51206 34313
64	.30642 96695 08334	.53240 64087 94072
0.7265	0.30640 74097 33533	0.53246 76925 02020
66	.30638 51485 11883	.53252 89717 57869
67	.30636 28858 43935	.53259 02465 61329
68	.30634 06217 30238	.53265 15169 12110
69	.30631 83561 71344	.53271 27828 09924
0.7270	0.30629 60891 67801	0.53277 40442 54482
71	.30627 38207 20162	.53283 53012 45495
72	.30625 15508 28976	.53289 65537 82674
73	.30622 92794 94793	.53295 78018 65731
74	.30620 70067 18164	.53301 90454 94376
0.7275	0.30618 47324 99639	0.53308 02846 68322
76	.30616 24568 39769	.53314 15193 87280
77	.30614 01797 39103	.53320 27496 50962
78	.30611 79011 98193	.53326 39754 59079
79	.30609 56212 17588	.53332 51968 11345
0.7280	0.30607 33397 97839	0.53338 64137 07470
81	.30605 10569 39497	.53344 76261 47168
82	.30602 87726 43111	.53350 88341 30150
83	.30600 64869 09233	.53357 00376 56130
84	.30598 41997 38412	.53363 12367 24818
0.7285	0.30596 19111 31198	0.53369 24313 35929
86	.30593 96210 88143	.53375 36214 89175
87	.30591 73296 09797	.53381 48071 84269
88	.30589 50366 96709	.53387 59884 20923
89	.30587 27423 49431	.53393 71651 98852
0.7290	0.30585 04465 68513	0.53399 83375 17767
91	.30582 81493 54505	.53405 95053 77384
92	.30580 58507 07958	.53412 06687 77414
93	.30578 35506 29421	.53418 18277 17571
94	.30576 12491 19446	.53424 29821 97570
0.7295	0.30573 89461 78583	0.53430 41322 17124
96	.30571 66418 07382	.53436 52777 75946
97	.30569 43360 06394	.53442 64188 73751
98	.30567 20287 76169	.53448 75555 10253
99	.30564 97201 17258	.53454 86876 85167
0.7300	0.30562 74100 30210	0.53460 98153 98205

x	$\dfrac{1}{\sqrt{2\pi}}\,e^{-\frac{x^2}{2}}$	$\dfrac{1}{\sqrt{2\pi}}\displaystyle\int_{-x}^{x} e^{-\frac{\alpha^2}{2}}\,d\alpha$
0.7300	0.30562 74100 30210	0.53460 98153 98205
01	.30560 50985 15577	.53467 09386 49084
02	.30558 27855 73908	.53473 20574 37516
03	.30556 04712 05755	.53479 31717 63218
04	.30553 81554 11667	.53485 42816 25903
0.7305	0.30551 58381 92196	0.53491 53870 25288
06	.30549 35195 47891	.53497 64879 61085
07	.30547 11994 79303	.53503 75844 33012
08	.30544 88779 86982	.53509 86764 40782
09	.30542 65550 71480	.53515 97639 84112
0.7310	0.30540 42307 33346	0.53522 08470 62716
11	.30538 19049 73130	.53528 19256 76310
12	.30535 95777 91384	.53534 29998 24610
13	.30533 72491 88657	.53540 40695 07332
14	.30531 49191 65501	.53546 51347 24191
0.7315	0.30529 25877 22465	0.53552 61954 74904
16	.30527 02548 60101	.53558 72517 59186
17	.30524 79205 78958	.53564 83035 76753
18	.30522 55848 79587	.53570 93509 27323
19	.30520 32477 62538	.53577 03938 10610
0.7320	0.30518 09092 28363	0.53583 14322 26333
21	.30515 85692 77611	.53589 24661 74207
22	.30513 62279 10833	.53595 34956 53950
23	.30511 38851 28579	.53601 45206 65277
24	.30509 15409 31400	.53607 55412 07907
0.7325	0.30506 91953 19847	0.53613 65572 81556
26	.30504 68482 94469	.53619 75688 85941
27	.30502 44998 55818	.53625 85760 20779
28	.30500 21500 04444	.53631 95786 85789
29	.30497 97987 40897	.53638 05768 80687
0.7330	0.30495 74460 65728	0.53644 15706 05191
31	.30493 50919 79487	.53650 25598 59019
32	.30491 27364 82725	.53656 35446 41889
33	.30489 03795 75993	.53662 45249 53518
34	.30486 80212 59840	.53668 55007 93625
0.7335	0.30484 56615 34818	0.53674 64721 61928
36	.30482 33004 01477	.53680 74390 58145
37	.30480 09378 60367	.53686 84014 81995
38	.30477 85739 12039	.53692 93594 33196
39	.30475 62085 57043	.53699 03129 11466
0.7340	0.30473 38417 95930	0.53705 12619 16525
41	.30471 14736 29251	.53711 22064 48091
42	.30468 91040 57555	.53717 31465 05883
43	.30466 67330 81394	.53723 40820 89620
44	.30464 43607 01319	.53729 50131 99022
0.7345	0.30462 19869 17878	0.53735 59398 33807
46	.30459 96117 31624	.53741 68619 93695
47	.30457 72351 43106	.53747 77796 78406
48	.30455 48571 52875	.53753 86928 87659
49	.30453 24777 61482	.53759 96016 21174
0.7350	0.30451 00969 69477	0.53766 05058 78670

x	$\dfrac{1}{\sqrt{2\pi}}\,e^{-\frac{x^2}{2}}$	$\dfrac{1}{\sqrt{2\pi}}\displaystyle\int_{-x}^{x} e^{-\frac{\alpha^2}{2}}\,d\alpha$
0.7350	0.30451 00969 69477	0.53766 05058 78670
51	.30448 77147 77411	.53772 14056 59868
52	.30446 53311 85834	.53778 23009 64488
53	.30444 29461 95297	.53784 31917 92249
54	.30442 05598 06350	.53790 40781 42873
0.7355	0.30439 81720 19544	0.53796 49600 16079
56	.30437 57828 35430	.53802 58374 11587
57	.30435 33922 54557	.53808 67103 29120
58	.30433 10002 77477	.53814 75787 68396
59	.30430 86069 04740	.53820 84427 29138
0.7360	0.30428 62121 36896	0.53826 93022 11065
61	.30426 38159 74497	.53833 01572 13899
62	.30424 14184 18092	.53839 10077 37362
63	.30421 90194 68233	.53845 18537 81174
64	.30419 66191 25469	.53851 26953 45056
0.7365	0.30417 42173 90351	0.53857 35324 28731
66	.30415 18142 63431	.53863 43650 31920
67	.30412 94097 45257	.53869 51931 54344
68	.30410 70038 36382	.53875 60167 95725
69	.30408 45965 37356	.53881 68359 55786
0.7370	0.30406 21878 48728	0.53887 76506 34247
71	.30403 97777 71050	.53893 84608 30833
72	.30401 73663 04873	.53899 92665 45263
73	.30399 49534 50746	.53906 00677 77262
74	.30397 25392 09220	.53912 08645 26551
0.7375	0.30395 01235 80847	0.53918 16567 92853
76	.30392 77065 66176	.53924 24445 75891
77	.30390 52881 65758	.53930 32278 75387
78	.30388 28683 80143	.53936 40066 91065
79	.30386 04472 09883	.53942 47810 22647
0.7380	0.30383 80246 55528	0.53948 55508 69857
81	.30381 56007 17627	.53954 63162 32417
82	.30379 31753 96733	.53960 70771 10051
83	.30377 07486 93395	.53966 78335 02484
84	.30374 83206 08165	.53972 85854 09437
0.7385	0.30372 58911 41591	0.53978 93328 30635
86	.30370 34602 94226	.53985 00757 65801
87	.30368 10280 66620	.53991 08142 14660
88	.30365 85944 59323	.53997 15481 76936
89	.30363 61594 72886	.54003 22776 52352
0.7390	0.30361 37231 07860	0.54009 30026 40633
91	.30359 12853 64795	.54015 37231 41503
92	.30356 88462 44241	.54021 44391 54687
93	.30354 64057 46749	.54027 51506 79909
94	.30352 39638 72871	.54033 58577 16894
0.7395	0.30350 15206 23155	0.54039 65602 65367
96	.30347 90759 98154	.54045 72583 25052
97	.30345 66299 98417	.54051 79518 95674
98	.30343 41826 24496	.54057 86409 76960
99	.30341 17338 76940	.54063 93255 68633
0.7400	0.30338 92837 56300	0.54070 00056 70419

x	$\dfrac{1}{\sqrt{2\pi}}\,e^{-\frac{x^2}{2}}$	$\dfrac{1}{\sqrt{2\pi}}\displaystyle\int_{-x}^{x} e^{-\frac{\alpha^2}{2}}\,d\alpha$
0.7400	0.30338 92837 56300	0.54070 00056 70419
01	.30336 68322 63127	.54076 06812 82044
02	.30334 43793 97972	.54082 13524 03233
03	.30332 19251 61385	.54088 20190 33711
04	.30329 94695 53916	.54094 26811 73206
0.7405	0.30327 70125 76117	0.54100 33388 21442
06	.30325 45542 28537	.54106 39919 78145
07	.30323 20945 11728	.54112 46406 43042
08	.30320 96334 26240	.54118 52848 15858
09	.30318 71709 72623	.54124 59244 96321
0.7410	0.30316 47071 51429	0.54130 65596 84156
11	.30314 22419 63207	.54136 71903 79090
12	.30311 97754 08508	.54142 78165 80850
13	.30309 73074 87884	.54148 84382 89163
14	.30307 48382 01884	.54154 90555 03755
0.7415	0.30305 23675 51059	0.54160 96682 24353
16	.30302 98955 35959	.54167 02764 50684
17	.30300 74221 57136	.54173 08801 82476
18	.30298 49474 15140	.54179 14794 19456
19	.30296 24713 10521	.54185 20741 61351
0.7420	0.30293 99938 43831	0.54191 26644 07889
21	.30291 75150 15618	.54197 32501 58798
22	.30289 50348 26436	.54203 38314 13805
23	.30287 25532 76832	.54209 44081 72638
24	.30285 00703 67360	.54215 49804 35025
0.7425	0.30282 75860 98568	0.54221 55482 00694
26	.30280 51004 71007	.54227 61114 69374
27	.30278 26134 85229	.54233 66702 40792
28	.30276 01251 41784	.54239 72245 14677
29	.30273 76354 41222	.54245 77742 90758
0.7430	0.30271 51443 84094	0.54251 83195 68763
31	.30269 26519 70950	.54257 88603 48422
32	.30267 01582 02341	.54263 93966 29461
33	.30264 76630 78818	.54269 99284 11612
34	.30262 51666 00931	.54276 04556 94603
0.7435	0.30260 26687 69231	0.54282 09784 78162
36	.30258 01695 84269	.54288 14967 62020
37	.30255 76690 46594	.54294 20105 45906
38	.30253 51671 56758	.54300 25198 29549
39	.30251 26639 15312	.54306 30246 12678
0.7440	0.30249 01593 22805	0.54312 35248 95025
41	.30246 76533 79788	.54318 40206 76317
42	.30244 51460 86812	.54324 45119 56287
43	.30242 26374 44428	.54330 49987 34662
44	.30240 01274 53186	.54336 54810 11174
0.7445	0.30237 76161 13636	0.54342 59587 85554
46	.30235 51034 26330	.54348 64320 57530
47	.30233 25893 91818	.54354 69008 26834
48	.30231 00740 10649	.54360 73650 93197
49	.30228 75572 83376	.54366 78248 56349
0.7450	0.30226 50392 10549	0.54372 82801 16021

x	$\frac{1}{\sqrt{2\pi}}e^{-\frac{x^2}{2}}$	$\frac{1}{\sqrt{2\pi}}\int_{-x}^{x}e^{-\frac{\alpha^2}{2}}d\alpha$
0.7450	0.30226 50392 10549	0.54372 82801 16021
51	.30224 25197 92718	.54378 87308 71943
52	.30221 99990 30433	.54384 91771 23848
53	.30219 74769 24246	.54390 96188 71466
54	.30217 49534 74706	.54397 00561 14528
0.7455	0.30215 24286 82365	0.54403 04888 52766
56	.30212 99025 47773	.54409 09170 85912
57	.30210 73750 71481	.54415 13408 13696
58	.30208 48462 54039	.54421 17600 35851
59	.30206 23160 95997	.54427 21747 52108
0.7460	0.30203 97845 97907	0.54433 25849 62200
61	.30201 72517 60319	.54439 29906 65858
62	.30199 47175 83783	.54445 33918 62815
63	.30197 21820 68850	.54451 37885 52802
64	.30194 96452 16071	.54457 41807 35553
0.7465	0.30192 71070 25996	0.54463 45684 10800
66	.30190 45674 99175	.54469 49515 78274
67	.30188 20266 36160	.54475 53302 37710
68	.30185 94844 37501	.54481 57043 88840
69	.30183 69409 03748	.54487 60740 31396
0.7470	0.30181 43960 35452	0.54493 64391 65112
71	.30179 18498 33164	.54499 67997 89722
72	.30176 93022 97434	.54505 71559 04957
73	.30174 67534 28812	.54511 75075 10552
74	.30172 42032 27850	.54517 78546 06239
0.7475	0.30170 16516 95097	0.54523 81971 91754
76	.30167 90988 31105	.54529 85352 66829
77	.30165 65446 36423	.54535 88688 31198
78	.30163 39891 11603	.54541 91978 84595
79	.30161 14322 57195	.54547 95224 26754
0.7480	0.30158 88740 73750	0.54553 98424 57409
81	.30156 63145 61817	.54560 01579 76295
82	.30154 37537 21949	.54566 04689 83145
83	.30152 11915 54694	.54572 07754 77695
84	.30149 86280 60604	.54578 10774 59679
0.7485	0.30147 60632 40229	0.54584 13749 28831
86	.30145 34970 94120	.54590 16678 84886
87	.30143 09296 22828	.54596 19563 27580
88	.30140 83608 26902	.54602 22402 56647
89	.30138 57907 06894	.54608 25196 71823
0.7490	0.30136 32192 63354	0.54614 27945 72842
91	.30134 06464 96832	.54620 30649 59440
92	.30131 80724 07879	.54626 33308 31352
93	.30129 54969 97046	.54632 35921 88315
94	.30127 29202 64883	.54638 38490 30063
0.7495	0.30125 03422 11940	0.54644 41013 56333
96	.30122 77628 38769	.54650 43491 66860
97	.30120 51821 45919	.54656 45924 61380
98	.30118 26001 33941	.54662 48312 39630
99	.30116 00168 03386	.54668 50655 01346
0.7500	0.30113 74321 54804	0.54674 52952 46264

x	$\dfrac{1}{\sqrt{2\pi}}\,e^{-\frac{x^2}{2}}$	$\dfrac{1}{\sqrt{2\pi}}\displaystyle\int_{-x}^{x} e^{-\frac{\alpha^2}{2}}\,d\alpha$
0.7500	0.30113 74321 54804	0.54674 52952 46264
01	.30111 48461 88746	.54680 55204 74120
02	.30109 22589 05763	.54686 57411 84651
03	.30106 96703 06404	.54692 59573 77594
04	.30104 70803 91220	.54698 61690 52686
0.7505	0.30102 44891 60762	0.54704 63762 09663
06	.30100 18966 15580	.54710 65788 48263
07	.30097 93027 56226	.54716 67769 68222
08	.30095 67075 83248	.54722 69705 69278
09	.30093 41110 97198	.54728 71596 51168
0.7510	0.30091 15132 98627	0.54734 73442 13629
11	.30088 89141 88085	.54740 75242 56400
12	.30086 63137 66121	.54746 76997 79217
13	.30084 37120 33288	.54752 78707 81819
14	.30082 11089 90135	.54758 80372 63943
0.7515	0.30079 85046 37212	0.54764 81992 25327
16	.30077 58989 75071	.54770 83566 65710
17	.30075 32920 04262	.54776 85095 84830
18	.30073 06837 25335	.54782 86579 82425
19	.30070 80741 38840	.54788 88018 58233
0.7520	0.30068 54632 45329	0.54794 89412 11993
21	.30066 28510 45352	.54800 90760 43444
22	.30064 02375 39458	.54806 92063 52324
23	.30061 76227 28200	.54812 93321 38373
24	.30059 50066 12126	.54818 94534 01329
0.7525	0.30057 23891 91788	0.54824 95701 40931
26	.30054 97704 67736	.54830 96823 56919
27	.30052 71504 40521	.54836 97900 49031
28	.30050 45291 10693	.54842 98932 17008
29	.30048 19064 78802	.54848 99918 60589
0.7530	0.30045 92825 45398	0.54855 00859 79513
31	.30043 66573 11034	.54861 01755 73520
32	.30041 40307 76258	.54867 02606 42350
33	.30039 14029 41621	.54873 03411 85744
34	.30036 87738 07674	.54879 04172 03440
0.7535	0.30034 61433 74967	0.54885 04886 95180
36	.30032 35116 44051	.54891 05556 60704
37	.30030 08786 15476	.54897 06180 99751
38	.30027 82442 89792	.54903 06760 12064
39	.30025 56086 67550	.54909 07293 97381
0.7540	0.30023 29717 49300	0.54915 07782 55444
41	.30021 03335 35594	.54921 08225 85994
42	.30018 76940 26980	.54927 08623 88772
43	.30016 50532 24010	.54933 08976 63519
44	.30014 24111 27234	.54939 09284 09975
0.7545	0.30011 97677 37203	0.54945 09546 27883
46	.30009 71230 54466	.54951 09763 16984
47	.30007 44770 79575	.54957 09934 77019
48	.30005 18298 13079	.54963 10061 07730
49	.30002 91812 55530	.54969 10142 08858
0.7550	0.30000 65314 07477	0.54975 10177 80146

x	$\dfrac{1}{\sqrt{2\pi}}\,e^{-\frac{x^2}{2}}$	$\dfrac{1}{\sqrt{2\pi}}\displaystyle\int_{-x}^{x} e^{-\frac{\alpha^2}{2}}\,d\alpha$
0.7550	0.30000 65314 07477	0.54975 10177 80146
51	.29998 38802 69471	.54981 10168 21335
52	.29996 12278 42062	.54987 10113 32168
53	.29993 85741 25801	.54993 10013 12386
54	.29991 59191 21238	.54999 09867 61732
0.7555	0.29989 32628 28924	0.55005 09676 79949
56	.29987 06052 49408	.55011 09440 66778
57	.29984 79463 83242	.55017 09159 21963
58	.29982 52862 30975	.55023 08832 45246
59	.29980 26247 93158	.55029 08460 36369
0.7560	0.29977 99620 70342	0.55035 08042 95077
61	.29975 72980 63077	.55041 07580 21112
62	.29973 46327 71913	.55047 07072 14217
63	.29971 19661 97400	.55053 06518 74135
64	.29968 92983 40089	.55059 05920 00610
0.7565	0.29966 66292 00530	0.55065 05275 93386
66	.29964 39587 79274	.55071 04586 52205
67	.29962 12870 76871	.55077 03851 76812
68	.29959 86140 93872	.55083 03071 66950
69	.29957 59398 30826	.55089 02246 22364
0.7570	0.29955 32642 88284	0.55095 01375 42797
71	.29953 05874 66796	.55101 00459 27994
72	.29950 79093 66913	.55106 99497 77699
73	.29948 52299 89185	.55112 98490 91656
74	.29946 25493 34162	.55118 97438 69609
0.7575	0.29943 98674 02395	0.55124 96341 11304
76	.29941 71841 94434	.55130 95198 16485
77	.29939 44997 10829	.55136 94009 84897
78	.29937 18139 52131	.55142 92776 16285
79	.29934 91269 18890	.55148 91497 10393
0.7580	0.29932 64386 11656	0.55154 90172 66967
81	.29930 37490 30980	.55160 88802 85753
82	.29928 10581 77412	.55166 87387 66495
83	.29925 83660 51502	.55172 85927 08939
84	.29923 56726 53800	.55178 84421 12831
0.7585	0.29921 29779 84857	0.55184 82869 77916
86	.29919 02820 45223	.55190 81273 03940
87	.29916 75848 35448	.55196 79630 90649
88	.29914 48863 56083	.55202 77943 37789
89	.29912 21866 07678	.55208 76210 45107
0.7590	0.29909 94855 90784	0.55214 74432 12348
91	.29907 67833 05949	.55220 72608 39259
92	.29905 40797 53725	.55226 70739 25586
93	.29903 13749 34663	.55232 68824 71076
94	.29900 86688 49311	.55238 66864 75475
0.7595	0.29898 59614 98221	0.55244 64859 38531
96	.29896 32528 81943	.55250 62808 59990
97	.29894 05430 01027	.55256 60712 39600
98	.29891 78318 56023	.55262 58570 77106
99	.29889 51194 47482	.55268 56383 72258
0.7600	0.29887 24057 75953	0.55274 54151 24801

154

x	$\frac{1}{\sqrt{2\pi}}e^{-\frac{x^2}{2}}$	$\frac{1}{\sqrt{2\pi}}\int_{-x}^{x}e^{-\frac{\alpha^2}{2}}d\alpha$
0.7600	0.29887 24057 75953	0.55274 54151 24801
01	.29884 96908 41987	.55280 51873 34484
02	.29882 69746 46134	.55286 49550 01054
03	.29880 42571 88945	.55292 47181 24258
04	.29878 15384 70970	.55298 44767 03845
0.7605	0.29875 88184 92758	0.55304 42307 39563
06	.29873 60972 54860	.55310 39802 31158
07	.29871 33747 57827	.55316 37251 78381
08	.29869 06510 02208	.55322 34655 80978
09	.29866 79259 88554	.55328 32014 38698
0.7610	0.29864 51997 17414	0.55334 29327 51289
11	.29862 24721 89340	.55340 26595 18501
12	.29859 97434 04881	.55346 23817 40081
13	.29857 70133 64588	.55352 20994 15779
14	.29855 42820 69010	.55358 18125 45343
0.7615	0.29853 15495 18698	0.55364 15211 28523
16	.29850 88157 14201	.55370 12251 65067
17	.29848 60806 56071	.55376 09246 54725
18	.29846 33443 44858	.55382 06195 97246
19	.29844 06067 81110	.55388 03099 92380
0.7620	0.29841 78679 65380	0.55393 99958 39875
21	.29839 51278 98216	.55399 96771 39482
22	.29837 23865 80169	.55405 93538 90951
23	.29834 96440 11789	.55411 90260 94031
24	.29832 69001 93626	.55417 86937 48472
0.7625	0.29830 41551 26231	0.55423 83568 54025
26	.29828 14088 10153	.55429 80154 10440
27	.29825 86612 45942	.55435 76694 17466
28	.29823 59124 34150	.55441 73188 74855
29	.29821 31623 75325	.55447 69637 82357
0.7630	0.29819 04110 70018	0.55453 66041 39722
31	.29816 76585 18779	.55459 62399 46702
32	.29814 49047 22158	.55465 58712 03046
33	.29812 21496 80706	.55471 54979 08507
34	.29809 93933 94971	.55477 51200 62836
0.7635	0.29807 66358 65505	0.55483 47376 65782
36	.29805 38770 92858	.55489 43507 17099
37	.29803 11170 77579	.55495 39592 16537
38	.29800 83558 20219	.55501 35631 63847
39	.29798 55933 21327	.55507 31625 58782
0.7640	0.29796 28295 81455	0.55513 27574 01093
41	.29794 00646 01151	.55519 23476 90532
42	.29791 72983 80966	.55525 19334 26851
43	.29789 45309 21449	.55531 15146 09802
44	.29787 17622 23152	.55537 10912 39137
0.7645	0.29784 89922 86624	0.55543 06633 14608
46	.29782 62211 12415	.55549 02308 35969
47	.29780 34487 01075	.55554 97938 02971
48	.29778 06750 53154	.55560 93522 15367
49	.29775 79001 69202	.55566 89060 72910
0.7650	0.29773 51240 49769	0.55572 84553 75352

155

x	$\frac{1}{\sqrt{2\pi}} e^{-\frac{x^2}{2}}$	$\frac{1}{\sqrt{2\pi}} \int_{-x}^{x} e^{-\frac{\alpha^2}{2}} d\alpha$
0.7650	0.29773 51240 49769	0.55572 84553 75352
51	.29771 23466 95406	.55578 80001 22447
52	.29768 95681 06661	.55584 75403 13948
53	.29766 67882 84086	.55590 70759 49608
54	.29764 40072 28230	.55596 66070 29180
0.7655	0.29762 12249 39643	0.55602 61335 52417
56	.29759 84414 18875	.55608 56555 19073
57	.29757 56566 66476	.55614 51729 28902
58	.29755 28706 82996	.55620 46857 81658
59	.29753 00834 68986	.55626 41940 77094
0.7660	0.29750 72950 24994	0.55632 36978 14963
61	.29748 45053 51571	.55638 31969 95022
62	.29746 17144 49267	.55644 26916 17022
63	.29743 89223 18632	.55650 21816 80719
64	.29741 61289 60216	.55656 16671 85868
0.7665	0.29739 33343 74569	0.55662 11481 32222
66	.29737 05385 62240	.55668 06245 19536
67	.29734 77415 23780	.55674 00963 47565
68	.29732 49432 59738	.55679 95636 16064
69	.29730 21437 70665	.55685 90263 24787
0.7670	0.29727 93430 57110	0.55691 84844 73490
71	.29725 65411 19623	.55697 79380 61928
72	.29723 37379 58754	.55703 73870 89857
73	.29721 09335 75054	.55709 68315 57030
74	.29718 81279 69071	.55715 62714 63205
0.7675	0.29716 53211 41356	0.55721 57068 08136
76	.29714 25130 92459	.55727 51375 91580
77	.29711 97038 22930	.55733 45638 13292
78	.29709 68933 33318	.55739 39854 73028
79	.29707 40816 24173	.55745 34025 70544
0.7680	0.29705 12686 96045	0.55751 28151 05596
81	.29702 84545 49484	.55757 22230 77941
82	.29700 56391 85040	.55763 16264 87335
83	.29698 28226 03263	.55769 10253 33534
84	.29696 00048 04703	.55775 04196 16295
0.7685	0.29693 71857 89909	0.55780 98093 35375
86	.29691 43655 59430	.55786 91944 90530
87	.29689 15441 13818	.55792 85750 81518
88	.29686 87214 53621	.55798 79511 08095
89	.29684 58975 79390	.55804 73225 70018
0.7690	0.29682 30724 91675	0.55810 66894 67046
91	.29680 02461 91024	.55816 60517 98934
92	.29677 74186 77989	.55822 54095 65441
93	.29675 45899 53118	.55828 47627 66324
94	.29673 17600 16962	.55834 41114 01342
0.7695	0.29670 89288 70070	0.55840 34554 70250
96	.29668 60965 12992	.55846 27949 72809
97	.29666 32629 46278	.55852 21299 08775
98	.29664 04281 70477	.55858 14602 77907
99	.29661 75921 86140	.55864 07860 79963
0.7700	0.29659 47549 93816	0.55870 01073 14701

x	$\dfrac{1}{\sqrt{2\pi}}\,e^{-\frac{x^2}{2}}$	$\dfrac{1}{\sqrt{2\pi}}\displaystyle\int_{-x}^{x} e^{-\frac{\alpha^2}{2}}\,d\alpha$
0.7700	0.29659 47549 93816	0.55870 01073 14701
01	.29657 19165 94054	.55875 94239 81880
02	.29654 90769 87405	.55881 87360 81258
03	.29652 62361 74418	.55887 80436 12594
04	.29650 33941 55643	.55893 73465 75647
0.7705	0.29648 05509 31630	0.55899 66449 70176
06	.29645 77065 02928	.55905 59387 95940
07	.29643 48608 70087	.55911 52280 52697
08	.29641 20140 33657	.55917 45127 40207
09	.29638 91659 94187	.55923 37928 58230
0.7710	0.29636 63167 52227	0.55929 30684 06525
11	.29634 34663 08327	.55935 23393 84851
12	.29632 06146 63036	.55941 16057 92968
13	.29629 77618 16904	.55947 08676 30636
14	.29627 49077 70481	.55953 01248 97615
0.7715	0.29625 20525 24317	0.55958 93775 93664
16	.29622 91960 78960	.55964 86257 18545
17	.29620 63384 34961	.55970 78692 72016
18	.29618 34795 92869	.55976 71082 53839
19	.29616 06195 53234	.55982 63426 63773
0.7720	0.29613 77583 16606	0.55988 55725 01580
21	.29611 48958 83533	.55994 47977 67020
22	.29609 20322 54567	.56000 40184 59854
23	.29606 91674 30255	.56006 32345 79842
24	.29604 63014 11149	.56012 24461 26746
0.7725	0.29602 34341 97796	0.56018 16531 00327
26	.29600 05657 90748	.56024 08555 00346
27	.29597 76961 90554	.56030 00533 26564
28	.29595 48253 97762	.56035 92465 78743
29	.29593 19534 12923	.56041 84352 56644
0.7730	0.29590 90802 36587	0.56047 76193 60028
31	.29588 62058 69302	.56053 67988 88659
32	.29586 33303 11618	.56059 59738 42297
33	.29584 04535 64086	.56065 51442 20704
34	.29581 75756 27253	.56071 43100 23643
0.7735	0.29579 46965 01671	0.56077 34712 50876
36	.29577 18161 87888	.56083 26279 02165
37	.29574 89346 86454	.56089 17799 77272
38	.29572 60519 97918	.56095 09274 75960
39	.29570 31681 22829	.56101 00703 97992
0.7740	0.29568 02830 61739	0.56106 92087 43130
41	.29565 73968 15195	.56112 83425 11138
42	.29563 45093 83747	.56118 74717 01777
43	.29561 16207 67945	.56124 65963 14812
44	.29558 87309 68338	.56130 57163 50005
0.7745	0.29556 58399 85476	0.56136 48318 07121
46	.29554 29478 19907	.56142 39426 85921
47	.29552 00544 72182	.56148 30489 86170
48	.29549 71599 42851	.56154 21507 07631
49	.29547 42642 32461	.56160 12478 50068
0.7750	0.29545 13673 41563	0.56166 03404 13245

x	$\frac{1}{\sqrt{2\pi}}e^{-\frac{x^2}{2}}$	$\frac{1}{\sqrt{2\pi}}\int_{-x}^{x}e^{-\frac{\alpha^2}{2}}d\alpha$
0.7750	0.29545 13673 41563	0.56166 03404 13245
51	.29542 84692 70706	.56171 94283 96926
52	.29540 55700 20440	.56177 85118 00875
53	.29538 26695 91313	.56183 75906 24856
54	.29535 97679 83876	.56189 66648 68633
0.7755	0.29533 68651 98677	0.56195 57345 31971
56	.29531 39612 36267	.56201 47996 14634
57	.29529 10560 97194	.56207 38601 16387
58	.29526 81497 82007	.56213 29160 36994
59	.29524 52422 91256	.56219 19673 76221
0.7760	0.29522 23336 25491	0.56225 10141 33832
61	.29519 94237 85261	.56231 00563 09593
62	.29517 65127 71115	.56236 90939 03268
63	.29515 36005 83601	.56242 81269 14623
64	.29513 06872 23271	.56248 71553 43424
0.7765	0.29510 77726 90673	0.56254 61791 89434
66	.29508 48569 86355	.56260 51984 52422
67	.29506 19401 10868	.56266 42131 32151
68	.29503 90220 64762	.56272 32232 28388
69	.29501 61028 48584	.56278 22287 40899
0.7770	0.29499 31824 62884	0.56284 12296 69449
71	.29497 02609 08212	.56290 02260 13806
72	.29494 73381 85117	.56295 92177 73735
73	.29492 44142 94148	.56301 82049 49002
74	.29490 14892 35854	.56307 71875 39375
0.7775	0.29487 85630 10784	0.56313 61655 44619
76	.29485 56356 19489	.56319 51389 64501
77	.29483 27070 62516	.56325 41077 98789
78	.29480 97773 40415	.56331 30720 47249
79	.29478 68464 53736	.56337 20317 09647
0.7780	0.29476 39144 03027	0.56343 09867 85752
81	.29474 09811 88838	.56348 99372 75331
82	.29471 80468 11717	.56354 88831 78150
83	.29469 51112 72215	.56360 78244 93978
84	.29467 21745 70880	.56366 67612 22582
0.7785	0.29464 92367 08261	0.56372 56933 63729
86	.29462 62976 84907	.56378 46209 17188
87	.29460 33575 01368	.56384 35438 82726
88	.29458 04161 58193	.56390 24622 60111
89	.29455 74736 55931	.56396 13760 49112
0.7790	0.29453 45299 95130	0.56402 02852 49496
91	.29451 15851 76340	.56407 91898 61033
92	.29448 86392 00111	.56413 80898 83490
93	.29446 56920 66990	.56419 69853 16636
94	.29444 27437 77528	.56425 58761 60239
0.7795	0.29441 97943 32273	0.56431 47624 14070
96	.29439 68437 31775	.56437 36440 77895
97	.29437 38919 76582	.56443 25211 51485
98	.29435 09390 67243	.56449 13936 34609
99	.29432 79850 04308	.56455 02615 27035
0.7800	0.29430 50297 88325	.56460 91248 28534

x	$\frac{1}{\sqrt{2\pi}} e^{-\frac{x^2}{2}}$	$\frac{1}{\sqrt{2\pi}} \int_{-x}^{x} e^{-\frac{\alpha^2}{2}} \, d\alpha$
0.7800	0.29430 50297 88325	0.56460 91248 28534
01	.29428 20734 19844	.56466 79835 38874
02	.29425 91158 99413	.56472 68376 57825
03	.29423 61572 27582	.56478 56871 85157
04	.29421 31974 04899	.56484 45321 20639
0.7805	0.29419 02364 31914	0.56490 33724 64042
06	.29416 72743 09175	.56496 22082 15135
07	.29414 43110 37232	.56502 10393 73689
08	.29412 13466 16633	.56507 98659 39474
09	.29409 83810 47927	.56513 86879 12259
0.7810	0.29407 54143 31664	0.56519 75052 91816
11	.29405 24464 68392	.56525 63180 77915
12	.29402 94774 58659	.56531 51262 70327
13	.29400 65073 03016	.56537 39298 68822
14	.29398 35360 02011	.56543 27288 73172
0.7815	0.29396 05635 56193	0.56549 15232 83147
16	.29393 75899 66110	.56555 03130 98518
17	.29391 46152 32312	.56560 90983 19057
18	.29389 16393 55348	.56566 78789 44535
19	.29386 86623 35766	.56572 66549 74723
0.7820	0.29384 56841 74115	0.56578 54264 09393
21	.29382 27048 70944	.56584 41932 48317
22	.29379 97244 26802	.56590 29554 91265
23	.29377 67428 42237	.56596 17131 38011
24	.29375 37601 17800	.56602 04661 88326
0.7825	0.29373 07762 54037	0.56607 92146 41983
26	.29370 77912 51499	.56613 79584 98752
27	.29368 48051 10733	.56619 66977 58407
28	.29366 18178 32290	.56625 54324 20720
29	.29363 88294 16716	.56631 41624 85464
0.7830	0.29361 58398 64563	0.56637 28879 52411
31	.29359 28491 76377	.56643 16088 21334
32	.29356 98573 52707	.56649 03250 92006
33	.29354 68643 94104	.56654 90367 64200
34	.29352 38703 01114	.56660 77438 37688
0.7835	0.29350 08750 74288	0.56666 64463 12245
36	.29347 78787 14173	.56672 51441 87642
37	.29345 48812 21319	.56678 38374 63655
38	.29343 18825 96273	.56684 25261 40055
39	.29340 88828 39586	.56690 12102 16618
0.7840	0.29338 58819 51805	0.56695 98896 93116
41	.29336 28799 33479	.56701 85645 69323
42	.29333 98767 85156	.56707 72348 45014
43	.29331 68725 07387	.56713 59005 19962
44	.29329 38671 00718	.56719 45615 93942
0.7845	0.29327 08605 65699	0.56725 32180 66727
46	.29324 78529 02878	.56731 18699 38093
47	.29322 48441 12804	.56737 05172 07813
48	.29320 18341 96026	.56742 91598 75663
49	.29317 88231 53092	.56748 77979 41416
0.7850	0.29315 58109 84550	0.56754 64314 04849

x	$\dfrac{1}{\sqrt{2\pi}}\,e^{-\frac{x^2}{2}}$	$\dfrac{1}{\sqrt{2\pi}}\displaystyle\int_{-x}^{x} e^{-\frac{\alpha^2}{2}}\,d\alpha$
0.7850	0.29315 58109 84550	0.56754 64314 04849
51	.29313 27976 90950	.56760 50602 65735
52	.29310 97832 72839	.56766 36845 23850
53	.29308 67677 30767	.56772 23041 78969
54	.29306 37510 65282	.56778 09192 30868
0.7855	0.29304 07332 76933	0.56783 95296 79321
56	.29301 77143 66268	.56789 81355 24104
57	.29299 46943 33835	.56795 67367 64992
58	.29297 16731 80183	.56801 53334 01763
59	.29294 86509 05860	.56807 39254 34190
0.7860	0.29292 56275 11416	0.56813 25128 62050
61	.29290 26029 97398	.56819 10956 85120
62	.29287 95773 64356	.56824 96739 03175
63	.29285 65506 12837	.56830 82475 15991
64	.29283 35227 43389	.56836 68165 23345
0.7865	0.29281 04937 56562	0.56842 53809 25014
66	.29278 74636 52904	.56848 39407 20773
67	.29276 44324 32963	.56854 24959 10401
68	.29274 14000 97288	.56860 10464 93672
69	.29271 83666 46427	.56865 95924 70365
0.7870	0.29269 53320 80928	0.56871 81338 40256
71	.29267 22964 01340	.56877 66706 03123
72	.29264 92596 08211	.56883 52027 58743
73	.29262 62217 02090	.56889 37303 06892
74	.29260 31826 83525	.56895 22532 47349
0.7875	0.29258 01425 53064	0.56901 07715 79892
76	.29255 71013 11255	.56906 92853 04297
77	.29253 40589 58648	.56912 77944 20342
78	.29251 10154 95790	.56918 62989 27806
79	.29248 79709 23229	.56924 47988 26466
0.7880	0.29246 49252 41515	0.56930 32941 16101
81	.29244 18784 51194	.56936 17847 96489
82	.29241 88305 52816	.56942 02708 67408
83	.29239 57815 46928	.56947 87523 28636
84	.29237 27314 34080	.56953 72291 79953
0.7885	0.29234 96802 14819	0.56959 57014 21136
86	.29232 66278 89693	.56965 41690 51965
87	.29230 35744 59251	.56971 26320 72218
88	.29228 05199 24040	.56977 10904 81675
89	.29225 74642 84610	.56982 95442 80114
0.7890	0.29223 44075 41508	0.56988 79934 67315
91	.29221 13496 95283	.56994 64380 43057
92	.29218 82907 46482	.57000 48780 07120
93	.29216 52306 95654	.57006 33133 59283
94	.29214 21695 43347	.57012 17440 99325
0.7895	0.29211 91072 90109	0.57018 01702 27027
96	.29209 60439 36489	.57023 85917 42168
97	.29207 29794 83034	.57029 70086 44528
98	.29204 99139 30292	.57035 54209 33887
99	.29202 68472 78812	.57041 38286 10027
0.7900	0.29200 37795 29141	0.57047 22316 72726

x	$\dfrac{1}{\sqrt{2\pi}}\,e^{-\frac{x^2}{2}}$	$\dfrac{1}{\sqrt{2\pi}}\displaystyle\int_{-x}^{x} e^{-\frac{\alpha^2}{2}}\,d\alpha$
0.7900	0.29200 37795 29141	0.57047 22316 72726
01	.29198 07106 81829	.57053 06301 21765
02	.29195 76407 37422	.57058 90239 56925
03	.29193 45696 96469	.57064 74131 77987
04	.29191 14975 59519	.57070 57977 84731
0.7905	0.29188 84243 27118	0.57076 41777 76938
06	.29186 53499 99815	.57082 25531 54389
07	.29184 22745 78159	.57088 09239 16865
08	.29181 91980 62696	.57093 92900 64147
09	.29179 61204 53976	.57099 76515 96017
0.7910	0.29177 30417 52545	0.57105 60085 12256
11	.29174 99619 58953	.57111 43608 12645
12	.29172 68810 73747	.57117 27084 96967
13	.29170 37990 97475	.57123 10515 65002
14	.29168 07160 30684	.57128 93900 16533
0.7915	0.29165 76318 73924	0.57134 77238 51342
16	.29163 45466 27741	.57140 60530 69210
17	.29161 14602 92684	.57146 43776 69920
18	.29158 83728 69301	.57152 26976 53254
19	.29156 52843 58140	.57158 10130 18995
0.7920	0.29154 21947 59747	0.57163 93237 66925
21	.29151 91040 74672	.57169 76298 96827
22	.29149 60123 03462	.57175 59314 08483
23	.29147 29194 46665	.57181 42283 01676
24	.29144 98255 04829	.57187 25205 76189
0.7925	0.29142 67304 78502	0.57193 08082 31805
26	.29140 36343 68231	.57198 90912 68308
27	.29138 05371 74565	.57204 73696 85480
28	.29135 74388 98050	.57210 56434 83106
29	.29133 43395 39236	.57216 39126 60967
0.7930	0.29131 12390 98669	0.57222 21772 18849
31	.29128 81375 76897	.57228 04371 56535
32	.29126 50349 74469	.57233 86924 73808
33	.29124 19312 91931	.57239 69431 70453
34	.29121 88265 29832	.57245 51892 46253
0.7935	0.29119 57206 88720	0.57251 34307 00993
36	.29117 26137 69142	.57257 16675 34456
37	.29114 95057 71645	.57262 98997 46428
38	.29112 63966 96778	.57268 81273 36693
39	.29110 32865 45088	.57274 63503 05035
0.7940	0.29108 01753 17123	0.57280 45686 51240
41	.29105 70630 13430	.57286 27823 75090
42	.29103 39496 34558	.57292 09914 76373
43	.29101 08351 81053	.57297 91959 54873
44	.29098 77196 53463	.57303 73958 10374
0.7945	0.29096 46030 52337	0.57309 55910 42662
46	.29094 14853 78221	.57315 37816 51523
47	.29091 83666 31663	.57321 19676 36742
48	.29089 52468 13211	.57327 01489 98105
49	.29087 21259 23412	.57332 83257 35396
0.7950	0.29084 90039 62814	0.57338 64978 48403

x	$\dfrac{1}{\sqrt{2\pi}}\,e^{-\frac{x^2}{2}}$	$\dfrac{1}{\sqrt{2\pi}}\displaystyle\int_{-x}^{x}e^{-\frac{\alpha^2}{2}}\,d\alpha$
0.7950	0.29084 90039 62814	0.57338 64978 48403
51	.29082 58809 31965	.57344 46653 36910
52	.29080 27568 31411	.57350 28282 00704
53	.29077 96316 61701	.57356 09864 39571
54	.29075 65054 23381	.57361 91400 53298
0.7955	0.29073 33781 17000	0.57367 72890 41669
56	.29071 02497 43105	.57373 54334 04473
57	.29068 71203 02244	.57379 35731 41495
58	.29066 39897 94963	.57385 17082 52523
59	.29064 08582 21811	.57390 98387 37342
0.7960	0.29061 77255 83334	0.57396 79645 95741
61	.29059 45918 80080	.57402 60858 27505
62	.29057 14571 12597	.57408 42024 32422
63	.29054 83212 81432	.57414 23144 10279
64	.29052 51843 87132	.57420 04217 60863
0.7965	0.29050 20464 30245	0.57425 85244 83963
66	.29047 89074 11318	.57431 66225 79365
67	.29045 57673 30899	.57437 47160 46857
68	.29043 26261 89534	.57443 28048 86226
69	.29040 94839 87772	.57449 08890 97262
0.7970	0.29038 63407 26159	0.57454 89686 79751
71	.29036 31964 05243	.57460 70436 33482
72	.29034 00510 25570	.57466 51139 58242
73	.29031 69045 87689	.57472 31796 53821
74	.29029 37570 92147	.57478 12407 20007
0.7975	0.29027 06085 39491	0.57483 92971 56588
76	.29024 74589 30268	.57489 73489 63352
77	.29022 43082 65025	.57495 53961 40089
78	.29020 11565 44309	.57501 34386 86588
79	.29017 80037 68669	.57507 14766 02637
0.7980	0.29015 48499 38650	0.57512 95098 88025
81	.29013 16950 54801	.57518 75385 42542
82	.29010 85391 17668	.57524 55625 65977
83	.29008 53821 27799	.57530 35819 58119
84	.29006 22240 85740	.57536 15967 18758
0.7985	0.29003 90649 92039	0.57541 96068 47683
86	.29001 59048 47243	.57547 76123 44684
87	.28999 27436 51899	.57553 56132 09552
88	.28996 95814 06555	.57559 36094 42075
89	.28994 64181 11756	.57565 16010 42045
0.7990	0.28992 32537 68051	0.57570 95880 09250
91	.28990 00883 75986	.57576 75703 43482
92	.28987 69219 36109	.57582 55480 44531
93	.28985 37544 48966	.57588 35211 12187
94	.28983 05859 15105	.57594 14895 46240
0.7995	0.28980 74163 35073	0.57599 94533 46483
96	.28978 42457 09416	.57605 74125 12705
97	.28976 10740 38681	.57611 53670 44697
98	.28973 79013 23416	.57617 33169 42251
99	.28971 47275 64168	.57623 12622 05157
0.8000	0.28969 15527 61483	0.57628 92028 33207

x	$\frac{1}{\sqrt{2\pi}} e^{-\frac{x^2}{2}}$	$\frac{1}{\sqrt{2\pi}} \int_{-x}^{x} e^{-\frac{\alpha^2}{2}} d\alpha$
0.8000	0.28969 15527 61483	0.57628 92028 33207
01	.28966 83769 15908	.57634 71388 26192
02	.28964 52000 27991	.57640 50701 83904
03	.28962 20220 98278	.57646 29969 06133
04	.28959 88431 27316	.57652 09189 92673
0.8005	0.28957 56631 15652	0.57657 88364 43315
06	.28955 24820 63834	.57663 67492 57850
07	.28952 92999 72407	.57669 46574 36071
08	.28950 61168 41918	.57675 25609 77770
09	.28948 29326 72916	.57681 04598 82739
0.8010	0.28945 97474 65945	0.57686 83541 50770
11	.28943 65612 21554	.57692 62437 81656
12	.28941 33739 40288	.57698 41287 75189
13	.28939 01856 22696	.57704 20091 31163
14	.28936 69962 69323	.57709 98848 49369
0.8015	0.28934 38058 80716	0.57715 77559 29602
16	.28932 06144 57422	.57721 56223 71653
17	.28929 74219 99989	.57727 34841 75316
18	.28927 42285 08961	.57733 13413 40384
19	.28925 10339 84887	.57738 91938 66650
0.8020	0.28922 78384 28313	0.57744 70417 53909
21	.28920 46418 39785	.57750 48850 01953
22	.28918 14442 19851	.57756 27236 10576
23	.28915 82455 69057	.57762 05575 79572
24	.28913 50458 87949	.57767 83869 08735
0.8025	0.28911 18451 77075	0.57773 62115 97859
26	.28908 86434 36981	.57779 40316 46737
27	.28906 54406 68213	.57785 18470 55165
28	.28904 22368 71318	.57790 96578 22936
29	.28901 90320 46843	.57796 74639 49845
0.8030	0.28899 58261 95334	0.57802 52654 35686
31	.28897 26193 17338	.57808 30622 80255
32	.28894 94114 13402	.57814 08544 83345
33	.28892 62024 84071	.57819 86420 44752
34	.28890 29925 29893	.57825 64249 64270
0.8035	0.28887 97815 51413	0.57831 42032 41695
36	.28885 65695 49179	.57837 19768 76822
37	.28883 33565 23738	.57842 97458 69447
38	.28881 01424 75634	.57848 75102 19364
39	.28878 69274 05415	.57854 52699 26369
0.8040	0.28876 37113 13628	0.57860 30249 90258
41	.28874 04942 00818	.57866 07754 10826
42	.28871 72760 67533	.57871 85211 87870
43	.28869 40569 14318	.57877 62623 21185
44	.28867 08367 41720	.57883 39988 10568
0.8045	0.28864 76155 50285	0.57889 17306 55814
46	.28862 43933 40560	.57894 94578 56720
47	.28860 11701 13091	.57900 71804 13082
48	.28857 79458 68424	.57906 48983 24698
49	.28855 47206 07106	.57912 26115 91362
0.8050	0.28853 14943 29683	0.57918 03202 12873

x	$\dfrac{1}{\sqrt{2\pi}}\,e^{-\frac{x^2}{2}}$	$\dfrac{1}{\sqrt{2\pi}}\displaystyle\int_{-x}^{x} e^{-\frac{\alpha^2}{2}}\,d\alpha$
0.8050	0.28853 14943 29683	0.57918 03202 12873
51	.28850 82670 36701	.57923 80241 89026
52	.28848 50387 28706	.57929 57235 19620
53	.28846 18094 06246	.57935 34182 04450
54	.28843 85790 69865	.57941 11082 43315
0.8055	0.28841 53477 20111	0.57946 87936 36010
56	.28839 21153 57530	.57952 64743 82335
57	.28836 88819 82667	.57958 41504 82086
58	.28834 56475 96069	.57964 18219 35061
59	.28832 24121 98283	.57969 94887 41057
0.8060	0.28829 91757 89853	0.57975 71508 99873
61	.28827 59383 71327	.57981 48084 11306
62	.28825 26999 43251	.57987 24612 75154
63	.28822 94605 06170	.57993 01094 91216
64	.28820 62200 60632	.57998 77530 59289
0.8065	0.28818 29786 07181	0.58004 53919 79173
66	.28815 97361 46364	.58010 30262 50665
67	.28813 64926 78728	.58016 06558 73564
68	.28811 32482 04818	.58021 82808 47669
69	.28809 00027 25180	.58027 59011 72779
0.8070	0.28806 67562 40360	0.58033 35168 48692
71	.28804 35087 50904	.58039 11278 75208
72	.28802 02602 57359	.58044 87342 52126
73	.28799 70107 60271	.58050 63359 79244
74	.28797 37602 60184	.58056 39330 56363
0.8075	0.28795 05087 57646	0.58062 15254 83281
76	.28792 72562 53202	.58067 91132 59799
77	.28790 40027 47398	.58073 66963 85716
78	.28788 07482 40780	.58079 42748 60831
79	.28785 74927 33894	.58085 18486 84946
0.8080	0.28783 42362 27286	0.58090 94178 57858
81	.28781 09787 21501	.58096 69823 79370
82	.28778 77202 17087	.58102 45422 49280
83	.28776 44607 14588	.58108 20974 67390
84	.28774 12002 14550	.58113 96480 33500
0.8085	0.28771 79387 17519	0.58119 71939 47410
86	.28769 46762 24041	.58125 47352 08920
87	.28767 14127 34662	.58131 22718 17833
88	.28764 81482 49927	.58136 98037 73948
89	.28762 48827 70383	.58142 73310 77066
0.8090	0.28760 16162 96574	0.58148 48537 26990
91	.28757 83488 29048	.58154 23717 23519
92	.28755 50803 68349	.58159 98850 66455
93	.28753 18109 15023	.58165 73937 55600
94	.28750 85404 69616	.58171 48977 90755
0.8095	0.28748 52690 32674	0.58177 23971 71722
96	.28746 19966 04742	.58182 98918 98302
97	.28743 87231 86365	.58188 73819 70298
98	.28741 54487 78091	.58194 48673 87511
99	.28739 21733 80463	.58200 23481 49743
0.8100	0.28736 88969 94028	0.58205 98242 56797

x	$\dfrac{1}{\sqrt{2\pi}}e^{-\frac{x^2}{2}}$	$\dfrac{1}{\sqrt{2\pi}}\displaystyle\int_{-x}^{x}e^{-\frac{\alpha^2}{2}}\,d\alpha$
0.8100	0.28736 88969 94028	0.58205 98242 56797
01	.28734 56196 19332	.58211 72957 08475
02	.28732 23412 56919	.58217 47625 04579
03	.28729 90619 07336	.58223 22246 44912
04	.28727 57815 71129	.58228 96821 29276
0.8105	0.28725 25002 48841	0.58234 71349 57474
06	.28722 92179 41020	.58240 45831 29310
07	.28720 59346 48210	.58246 20266 44585
08	.28718 26503 70958	.58251 94655 03103
09	.28715 93651 09808	.58257 68997 04668
0.8110	0.28713 60788 65306	0.58263 43292 49082
11	.28711 27916 37998	.58269 17541 36148
12	.28708 95034 28429	.58274 91743 65671
13	.28706 62142 37144	.58280 65899 37454
14	.28704 29240 64688	.58286 40008 51301
0.8115	0.28701 96329 11608	0.58292 14071 07015
16	.28699 63407 78449	.58297 88087 04400
17	.28697 30476 65755	.58303 62056 43261
18	.28694 97535 74072	.58309 35979 23401
19	.28692 64585 03946	.58315 09855 44625
0.8120	0.28690 31624 55922	0.58320 83685 06738
21	.28687 98654 30545	.58326 57468 09543
22	.28685 65674 28361	.58332 31204 52845
23	.28683 32684 49914	.58338 04894 36449
24	.28680 99684 95750	.58343 78537 60160
0.8125	0.28678 66675 66414	0.58349 52134 23782
26	.28676 33656 62452	.58355 25684 27121
27	.28674 00627 84409	.58360 99187 69982
28	.28671 67589 32829	.58366 72644 52170
29	.28669 34541 08258	.58372 46054 73490
0.8130	0.28667 01483 11242	0.58378 19418 33749
31	.28664 68415 42325	.58383 92735 32750
32	.28662 35338 02052	.58389 66005 70301
33	.28660 02250 90969	.58395 39229 46206
34	.28657 69154 09620	.58401 12406 60272
0.8135	0.28655 36047 58552	0.58406 85537 12305
36	.28653 02931 38308	.58412 58621 02111
37	.28650 69805 49434	.58418 31658 29496
38	.28648 36669 92475	.58424 04648 94266
39	.28646 03524 67976	.58429 77592 96229
0.8140	0.28643 70369 76482	0.58435 50490 35189
41	.28641 37205 18538	.58441 23341 10955
42	.28639 04030 94689	.58446 96145 23332
43	.28636 70847 05479	.58452 68902 72128
44	.28634 37653 51455	.58458 41613 57150
0.8145	0.28632 04450 33161	0.58464 14277 78205
46	.28629 71237 51141	.58469 86895 35099
47	.28627 38015 05941	.58475 59466 27641
48	.28625 04782 98105	.58481 31990 55637
49	.28622 71541 28179	.58487 04468 18896
0.8150	0.28620 38289 96707	0.58492 76899 17224

x	$\frac{1}{\sqrt{2\pi}}e^{-\frac{x^2}{2}}$	$\frac{1}{\sqrt{2\pi}}\int_{-x}^{x}e^{-\frac{\alpha^2}{2}}\,d\alpha$
0.8150	0.28620 38289 96707	0.58492 76899 17224
51	.28618 05029 04234	.58498 49283 50431
52	.28615 71758 51305	.58504 21621 18322
53	.28613 38478 38465	.58509 93912 20707
54	.28611 05188 66258	.58515 66156 57394
0.8155	0.28608 71889 35230	0.58521 38354 28190
56	.28606 38580 45924	.58527 10505 32904
57	.28604 05261 98887	.58532 82609 71344
58	.28601 71933 94662	.58538 54667 43320
59	.28599 38596 33794	.58544 26678 48638
0.8160	0.28597 05249 16828	0.58549 98642 87109
61	.28594 71892 44309	.58555 70560 58541
62	.28592 38526 16781	.58561 42431 62743
63	.28590 05150 34790	.58567 14255 99524
64	.28587 71764 98878	.58572 86033 68694
0.8165	0.28585 38370 09592	0.58578 57764 70060
66	.28583 04965 67476	.58584 29449 03434
67	.28580 71551 73075	.58590 01086 68624
68	.28578 38128 26932	.58595 72677 65440
69	.28576 04695 29593	.58601 44221 93691
0.8170	0.28573 71252 81602	0.58607 15719 53188
71	.28571 37800 83503	.58612 87170 43741
72	.28569 04339 35842	.58618 58574 65158
73	.28566 70868 39162	.58624 29932 17252
74	.28564 37387 94009	.58630 01242 99831
0.8175	0.28562 03898 00926	0.58635 72507 12706
76	.28559 70398 60458	.58641 43724 55688
77	.28557 36889 73149	.58647 14895 28587
78	.28555 03371 39544	.58652 86019 31214
79	.28552 69843 60188	.58658 57096 63380
0.8180	0.28550 36306 35624	0.58664 28127 24895
81	.28548 02759 66398	.58669 99111 15571
82	.28545 69203 53052	.58675 70048 35219
83	.28543 35637 96132	.58681 40938 83649
84	.28541 02062 96183	.58687 11782 60674
0.8185	0.28538 68478 53747	0.58692 82579 66105
86	.28536 34884 69370	.58698 53329 99753
87	.28534 01281 43596	.58704 24033 61430
88	.28531 67668 76970	.58709 94690 50948
89	.28529 34046 70034	.58715 65300 68118
0.8190	0.28527 00415 23334	0.58721 35864 12753
91	.28524 66774 37414	.58727 06380 84665
92	.28522 33124 12818	.58732 76850 83666
93	.28519 99464 50090	.58738 47274 09567
94	.28517 65795 49774	.58744 17650 62183
0.8195	0.28515 32117 12414	0.58749 87980 41325
96	.28512 98429 38556	.58755 58263 46806
97	.28510 64732 28741	.58761 28499 78438
98	.28508 31025 83516	.58766 98689 36035
99	.28505 97310 03423	.58772 68832 19409
0.8200	0.28503 63584 89007	0.58778 38928 28374

X	$\frac{1}{\sqrt{2\pi}}e^{-\frac{x^2}{2}}$	$\frac{1}{\sqrt{2\pi}}\int_{-x}^{x}e^{-\frac{\alpha^2}{2}}d\alpha$
0.8200	0.28503 63584 89007	0.58778 38928 28374
01	.28501 29850 40812	.58784 08977 62742
02	.28498 96106 59382	.58789 78980 22328
03	.28496 62353 45261	.58795 48936 06944
04	.28494 28590 98993	.58801 18845 16404
0.8205	0.28491 94819 21121	0.58806 88707 50521
06	.28489 61038 12191	.58812 58523 09110
07	.28487 27247 72745	.58818 28291 91984
08	.28484 93448 03328	.58823 98013 98957
09	.28482 59639 04483	.58829 67689 29844
0.8210	0.28480 25820 76755	0.58835 37317 84457
11	.28477 91993 20688	.58841 06899 62612
12	.28475 58156 36824	.58846 76434 64124
13	.28473 24310 25709	.58852 45922 88805
14	.28470 90454 87885	.58858 15364 36472
0.8215	0.28468 56590 23897	0.58863 84759 06939
16	.28466 22716 34289	.58869 54107 00020
17	.28463 88833 19604	.58875 23408 15531
18	.28461 54940 80385	.58880 92662 53286
19	.28459 21039 17178	.58886 61870 13101
0.8220	0.28456 87128 30525	0.58892 31030 94792
21	.28454 53208 20970	.58898 00144 98172
22	.28452 19278 89056	.58903 69212 23058
23	.28449 85340 35329	.58909 38232 69266
24	.28447 51392 60330	.58915 07206 36611
0.8225	0.28445 17435 64604	0.58920 76133 24909
26	.28442 83469 48695	.58926 45013 33976
27	.28440 49494 13146	.58932 13846 63627
28	.28438 15509 58500	.58937 82633 13680
29	.28435 81515 85301	.58943 51372 83949
0.8230	0.28433 47512 94093	0.58949 20065 74253
31	.28431 13500 85419	.58954 88711 84406
32	.28428 79479 59823	.58960 57311 14226
33	.28426 45449 17848	.58966 25863 63529
34	.28424 11409 60038	.58971 94369 32132
0.8235	0.28421 77360 86936	0.58977 62828 19852
36	.28419 43302 99086	.58983 31240 26505
37	.28417 09235 97030	.58988 99605 51910
38	.28414 75159 81314	.58994 67923 95883
39	.28412 41074 52479	.59000 36195 58242
0.8240	0.28410 06980 11069	0.59006 04420 38804
41	.28407 72876 57627	.59011 72598 37386
42	.28405 38763 92698	.59017 40729 53806
43	.28403 04642 16824	.59023 08813 87882
44	.28400 70511 30548	.59028 76851 39432
0.8245	0.28398 36371 34415	0.59034 44842 08274
46	.28396 02222 28966	.59040 12785 94225
47	.28393 68064 14746	.59045 80682 97105
48	.28391 33896 92297	.59051 48533 16730
49	.28388 99720 62163	.59057 16336 52921
0.8250	0.28386 65535 24887	0.59062 84093 05495

X	$\dfrac{1}{\sqrt{2\pi}}\,e^{-\frac{x^2}{2}}$	$\dfrac{1}{\sqrt{2\pi}}\displaystyle\int_{-x}^{x} e^{-\frac{\alpha^2}{2}}\,d\alpha$
0.8250	0.28386 65535 24887	0.59062 84093 05495
51	.28384 31340 81013	.59068 51802 74270
52	.28381 97137 31082	.59074 19465 59067
53	.28379 62924 75639	.59079 87081 59702
54	.28377 28703 15227	.59085 54650 75997
0.8255	0.28374 94472 50389	0.59091 22173 07768
56	.28372 60232 81667	.59096 89648 54837
57	.28370 25984 09606	.59102 57077 17021
58	.28367 91726 34747	.59108 24458 94140
59	.28365 57459 57634	.59113 91793 86014
0.8260	0.28363 23183 78811	0.59119 59081 92463
61	.28360 88898 98819	.59125 26323 13306
62	.28358 54605 18203	.59130 93517 48363
63	.28356 20302 37504	.59136 60664 97453
64	.28353 85990 57266	.59142 27765 60398
0.8265	0.28351 51669 78033	0.59147 94819 37016
66	.28349 17340 00346	.59153 61826 27129
67	.28346 83001 24749	.59159 28786 30556
68	.28344 48653 51784	.59164 95699 47119
69	.28342 14296 81995	.59170 62565 76637
0.8270	0.28339 79931 15924	0.59176 29385 18932
71	.28337 45556 54115	.59181 96157 73824
72	.28335 11172 97109	.59187 62883 41134
73	.28332 76780 45450	.59193 29562 20683
74	.28330 42378 99681	.59198 96194 12293
0.8275	0.28328 07968 60343	0.59204 62779 15784
76	.28325 73549 27981	.59210 29317 30977
77	.28323 39121 03137	.59215 95808 57695
78	.28321 04683 86352	.59221 62252 95759
79	.28318 70237 78171	.59227 28650 44990
0.8280	0.28316 35782 79136	0.59232 95001 05211
81	.28314 01318 89789	.59238 61304 76243
82	.28311 66846 10673	.59244 27561 57908
83	.28309 32364 42331	.59249 93771 50028
84	.28306 97873 85305	.59255 59934 52425
0.8285	0.28304 63374 40138	0.59261 26050 64923
86	.28302 28866 07372	.59266 92119 87342
87	.28299 94348 87550	.59272 58142 19506
88	.28297 59822 81215	.59278 24117 61238
89	.28295 25287 88908	.59283 90046 12360
0.8290	0.28292 90744 11173	0.59289 55927 72695
91	.28290 56191 48552	.59295 21762 42065
92	.28288 21630 01587	.59300 87550 20295
93	.28285 87059 70820	.59306 53291 07207
94	.28283 52480 56795	.59312 18985 02624
0.8295	0.28281 17892 60053	0.59317 84632 06371
96	.28278 83295 81138	.59323 50232 18270
97	.28276 48690 20590	.59329 15785 38145
98	.28274 14075 78953	.59334 81291 65819
99	.28271 79452 56769	.59340 46751 01117
0.8300	0.28269 44820 54580	0.59346 12163 43863

x	$\dfrac{1}{\sqrt{2\pi}}\,e^{-\frac{x^2}{2}}$	$\dfrac{1}{\sqrt{2\pi}}\displaystyle\int_{-x}^{x} e^{-\frac{\alpha^2}{2}}\,d\alpha$
0.8300	0.28269 44820 54580	0.59346 12163 43863
01	.28267 10179 72929	.59351 77528 93881
02	.28264 75530 12357	.59357 42847 50994
03	.28262 40871 73407	.59363 08119 15027
04	.28260 06204 56622	.59368 73343 85805
0.8305	0.28257 71528 62543	0.59374 38521 63151
06	.28255 36843 91712	.59380 03652 46891
07	.28253 02150 44672	.59385 68736 36849
08	.28250 67448 21965	.59391 33773 32851
09	.28248 32737 24133	.59396 98763 34720
0.8310	0.28245 98017 51719	0.59402 63706 42282
11	.28243 63289 05263	.59408 28602 55362
12	.28241 28551 85309	.59413 93451 73786
13	.28238 93805 92398	.59419 58253 97378
14	.28236 59051 27072	.59425 23009 25965
0.8315	0.28234 24287 89874	0.59430 87717 59371
16	.28231 89515 81345	.59436 52378 97423
17	.28229 54735 02027	.59442 16993 39945
18	.28227 19945 52463	.59447 81560 86765
19	.28224 85147 33194	.59453 46081 37708
0.8320	0.28222 50340 44763	0.59459 10554 92601
21	.28220 15524 87710	.59464 74981 51268
22	.28217 80700 62578	.59470 39361 13538
23	.28215 45867 69909	.59476 03693 79236
24	.28213 11026 10245	.59481 67979 48188
0.8325	0.28210 76175 84127	0.59487 32218 20222
26	.28208 41316 92098	.59492 96409 95164
27	.28206 06449 34699	.59498 60554 72841
28	.28203 71573 12471	.59504 24652 53080
29	.28201 36688 25957	.59509 88703 35708
0.8330	0.28199 01794 75699	0.59515 52707 20553
31	.28196 66892 62237	.59521 16664 07441
32	.28194 31981 86114	.59526 80573 96200
33	.28191 97062 47872	.59532 44436 86658
34	.28189 62134 48052	.59538 08252 78642
0.8335	0.28187 27197 87195	0.59543 72021 71980
36	.28184 92252 65844	.59549 35743 66500
37	.28182 57298 84539	.59554 99418 62029
38	.28180 22336 43823	.59560 63046 58396
39	.28177 87365 44237	.59566 26627 55429
0.8340	0.28175 52385 86323	0.59571 90161 52957
41	.28173 17397 70621	.59577 53648 50807
42	.28170 82400 97675	.59583 17088 48808
43	.28168 47395 68024	.59588 80481 46789
44	.28166 12381 82211	.59594 43827 44578
0.8345	0.28163 77359 40777	0.59600 07126 42004
46	.28161 42328 44263	.59605 70378 38897
47	.28159 07288 93211	.59611 33583 35085
48	.28156 72240 88162	.59616 96741 30397
49	.28154 37184 29657	.59622 59852 24663
0.8350	0.28152 02119 18239	0.59628 22916 17712

x	$\frac{1}{\sqrt{2\pi}} e^{-\frac{x^2}{2}}$	$\frac{1}{\sqrt{2\pi}} \int_{-x}^{x} e^{-\frac{\alpha^2}{2}} d\alpha$
0.8350	0.28152 02119 18239	0.59628 22916 17712
51	.28149 67045 54448	.59633 85933 09374
52	.28147 31963 38825	.59639 48902 99477
53	.28144 96872 71912	.59645 11825 87853
54	.28142 61773 54249	.59650 74701 74330
0.8355	0.28140 26665 86380	0.59656 37530 58738
56	.28137 91549 68843	.59662 00312 40907
57	.28135 56425 02182	.59667 63047 20669
58	.28133 21291 86936	.59673 25734 97852
59	.28130 86150 23647	.59678 88375 72287
0.8360	0.28128 51000 12857	0.59684 50969 43805
61	.28126 15841 55105	.59690 13516 12236
62	.28123 80674 50935	.59695 76015 77410
63	.28121 45499 00885	.59701 38468 39160
64	.28119 10315 05498	.59707 00873 97314
0.8365	0.28116 75122 65315	0.59712 63232 51705
66	.28114 39921 80877	.59718 25544 02164
67	.28112 04712 52724	.59723 87808 48522
68	.28109 69494 81398	.59729 50025 90609
69	.28107 34268 67439	.59735 12196 28258
0.8370	0.28104 99034 11389	0.59740 74319 61300
71	.28102 63791 13788	.59746 36395 89566
72	.28100 28539 75178	.59751 98425 12889
73	.28097 93279 96099	.59757 60407 31100
74	.28095 58011 77092	.59763 22342 44032
0.8375	0.28093 22735 18698	0.59768 84230 51515
76	.28090 87450 21458	.59774 46071 53383
77	.28088 52156 85912	.59780 07865 49468
78	.28086 16855 12602	.59785 69612 39602
79	.28083 81545 02068	.59791 31312 23617
0.8380	0.28081 46226 54851	0.59796 92965 01347
81	.28079 10899 71491	.59802 54570 72623
82	.28076 75564 52530	.59808 16129 37280
83	.28074 40220 98508	.59813 77640 95149
84	.28072 04869 09965	.59819 39105 46064
0.8385	0.28069 69508 87443	0.59825 00522 89857
86	.28067 34140 31482	.59830 61893 26363
87	.28064 98763 42622	.59836 23216 55414
88	.28062 63378 21404	.59841 84492 76845
89	.28060 27984 68369	.59847 45721 90487
0.8390	0.28057 92582 84057	0.59853 06903 96176
91	.28055 57172 69009	.59858 68038 93746
92	.28053 21754 23765	.59864 29126 83029
93	.28050 86327 48866	.59869 90167 63860
94	.28048 50892 44852	.59875 51161 36073
0.8395	0.28046 15449 12264	0.59881 12107 99502
96	.28043 79997 51642	.59886 73007 53983
97	.28041 44537 63526	.59892 33859 99348
98	.28039 09069 48457	.59897 94665 35433
99	.28036 73593 06975	.59903 55423 62072
0.8400	0.28034 38108 39621	0.59909 16134 79101

x	$\dfrac{1}{\sqrt{2\pi}}\,e^{-\frac{x^2}{2}}$	$\dfrac{1}{\sqrt{2\pi}}\displaystyle\int_{-x}^{x} e^{-\frac{\alpha^2}{2}}\,d\alpha$
0.8400	0.28034 38108 39621	0.59909 16134 79101
01	.28032 02615 46934	.59914 76798 86353
02	.28029 67114 29456	.59920 37415 83664
03	.28027 31604 87725	.59925 97985 70870
04	.28024 96087 22284	.59931 58508 47805
0.8405	0.28022 60561 33672	0.59937 18984 14304
06	.28020 25027 22428	.59942 79412 70203
07	.28017 89484 89094	.59948 39794 15338
08	.28015 53934 34209	.59954 00128 49544
09	.28013 18375 58314	.59959 60415 72657
0.8410	0.28010 82808 61949	0.59965 20655 84513
11	.28008 47233 45653	.59970 80848 84947
12	.28006 11650 09967	.59976 40994 73796
13	.28003 76058 55432	.59982 01093 50897
14	.28001 40458 82586	.59987 61145 16084
0.8415	0.27999 04850 91971	0.59993 21149 69195
16	.27996 69234 84125	.59998 81107 10066
17	.27994 33610 59590	.60004 41017 38534
18	.27991 97978 18904	.60010 00880 54436
19	.27989 62337 62609	.60015 60696 57607
0.8420	0.27987 26688 91243	0.60021 20465 47886
21	.27984 91032 05348	.60026 80187 25110
22	.27982 55367 05462	.60032 39861 89114
23	.27980 19693 92125	.60037 99489 39738
24	.27977 84012 65878	.60043 59069 76817
0.8425	0.27975 48323 27260	0.60049 18603 00190
26	.27973 12625 76811	.60054 78089 09694
27	.27970 76920 15070	.60060 37528 05166
28	.27968 41206 42578	.60065 96919 86446
29	.27966 05484 59875	.60071 56264 53369
0.8430	0.27963 69754 67499	0.60077 15562 05776
31	.27961 34016 65991	.60082 74812 43503
32	.27958 98270 55890	.60088 34015 66388
33	.27956 62516 37736	.60093 93171 74271
34	.27954 26754 12068	.60099 52280 66989
0.8435	0.27951 90983 79427	0.60105 11342 44382
36	.27949 55205 40352	.60110 70357 06287
37	.27947 19418 95381	.60116 29324 52544
38	.27944 83624 45056	.60121 88244 82992
39	.27942 47821 89915	.60127 47117 97469
0.8440	0.27940 12011 30498	0.60133 05943 95814
41	.27937 76192 67344	.60138 64722 77867
42	.27935 40366 00993	.60144 23454 43468
43	.27933 04531 31984	.60149 82138 92454
44	.27930 68688 60857	.60155 40776 24667
0.8445	0.27928 32837 88151	0.60160 99366 39945
46	.27925 96979 14405	.60166 57909 38129
47	.27923 61112 40159	.60172 16405 19058
48	.27921 25237 65952	.60177 74853 82572
49	.27918 89354 92323	.60183 33255 28511
0.8450	0.27916 53464 19812	0.60188 91609 56715

x	$\dfrac{1}{\sqrt{2\pi}}e^{-\frac{x^2}{2}}$	$\dfrac{1}{\sqrt{2\pi}}\displaystyle\int_{-x}^{x}e^{-\frac{\alpha^2}{2}}\,d\alpha$
0.8450	0.27916 53464 19812	0.60188 91609 56715
51	.27914 17565 48958	.60194 49916 67025
52	.27911 81658 80300	.60200 08176 59282
53	.27909 45744 14377	.60205 66389 33324
54	.27907 09821 51729	.60211 24554 88994
0.8455	0.27904 73890 92895	0.60216 82673 26132
56	.27902 37952 38413	.60222 40744 44578
57	.27900 02005 88824	.60227 98768 44174
58	.27897 66051 44665	.60233 56745 24761
59	.27895 30089 06477	.60239 14674 86179
0.8460	0.27892 94118 74798	0.60244 72557 28271
61	.27890 58140 50168	.60250 30392 50876
62	.27888 22154 33124	.60255 88180 53838
63	.27885 86160 24207	.60261 45921 36997
64	.27883 50158 23956	.60267 03615 00195
0.8465	0.27881 14148 32908	0.60272 61261 43274
66	.27878 78130 51604	.60278 18860 66075
67	.27876 42104 80582	.60283 76412 68442
68	.27874 06071 20381	.60289 33917 50215
69	.27871 70029 71540	.60294 91375 11237
0.8470	0.27869 33980 34597	0.60300 48785 51351
71	.27866 97923 10092	.60306 06148 70399
72	.27864 61857 98564	.60311 63464 68223
73	.27862 25785 00550	.60317 20733 44666
74	.27859 89704 16591	.60322 77954 99570
0.8475	0.27857 53615 47223	0.60328 35129 32780
76	.27855 17518 92988	.60333 92256 44137
77	.27852 81414 54422	.60339 49336 33485
78	.27850 45302 32065	.60345 06369 00666
79	.27848 09182 26456	.60350 63354 45525
0.8480	0.27845 73054 38132	0.60356 20292 67905
81	.27843 36918 67633	.60361 77183 67648
82	.27841 00775 15497	.60367 34027 44600
83	.27838 64623 82263	.60372 90823 98603
84	.27836 28464 68469	.60378 47573 29501
0.8485	0.27833 92297 74653	0.60384 04275 37138
86	.27831 56123 01355	.60389 60930 21359
87	.27829 19940 49113	.60395 17537 82007
88	.27826 83750 18465	.60400 74098 18926
89	.27824 47552 09949	.60406 30611 31962
0.8490	0.27822 11346 24105	0.60411 87077 20958
91	.27819 75132 61470	.60417 43495 85760
92	.27817 38911 22582	.60422 99867 26211
93	.27815 02682 07981	.60428 56191 42157
94	.27812 66445 18204	.60434 12468 33443
0.8495	0.27810 30200 53789	0.60439 68697 99913
96	.27807 93948 15276	.60445 24880 41413
97	.27805 57688 03202	.60450 81015 57787
98	.27803 21420 18105	.60456 37103 48882
99	.27800 85144 60524	.60461 93144 14543
0.8500	0.27798 48861 30996	0.60467 49137 54615

x	$\dfrac{1}{\sqrt{2\pi}} e^{-\frac{x^2}{2}}$	$\dfrac{1}{\sqrt{2\pi}} \displaystyle\int_{-x}^{x} e^{-\frac{\alpha^2}{2}} d\alpha$
0.8500	0.27798 48861 30996	0.60467 49137 54615
01	.27796 12570 30061	.60473 05083 68944
02	.27793 76271 58256	.60478 60982 57376
03	.27791 39965 16118	.60484 16834 19756
04	.27789 03651 04187	.60489 72638 55931
0.8505	0.27786 67329 23001	0.60495 28395 65747
06	.27784 30999 73097	.60500 84105 49049
07	.27781 94662 55013	.60506 39768 05685
08	.27779 58317 69287	.60511 95383 35500
09	.27777 21965 16458	.60517 50951 38341
0.8510	0.27774 85604 97063	0.60523 06472 14055
11	.27772 49237 11641	.60528 61945 62489
12	.27770 12861 60728	.60534 17371 83489
13	.27767 76478 44864	.60539 72750 76902
14	.27765 40087 64586	.60545 28082 42576
0.8515	0.27763 03689 20431	0.60550 83366 80357
16	.27760 67283 12938	.60556 38603 90093
17	.27758 30869 42644	.60561 93793 71631
18	.27755 94448 10087	.60567 48936 24819
19	.27753 58019 15805	.60573 04031 49505
0.8520	0.27751 21582 60336	0.60578 59079 45535
21	.27748 85138 44217	.60584 14080 12758
22	.27746 48686 67986	.60589 69033 51022
23	.27744 12227 32181	.60595 23939 60175
24	.27741 75760 37338	.60600 78798 40064
0.8525	0.27739 39285 83997	0.60606 33609 90539
26	.27737 02803 72694	.60611 88374 11447
27	.27734 66314 03967	.60617 43091 02638
28	.27732 29816 78353	.60622 97760 63958
29	.27729 93311 96391	.60628 52382 95259
0.8530	0.27727 56799 58617	0.60634 06957 96387
31	.27725 20279 65569	.60639 61485 67192
32	.27722 83752 17785	.60645 15966 07523
33	.27720 47217 15801	.60650 70399 17228
34	.27718 10674 60156	.60656 24784 96159
0.8535	0.27715 74124 51386	0.60661 79123 44162
36	.27713 37566 90030	.60667 33414 61089
37	.27711 01001 76623	.60672 87658 46788
38	.27708 64429 11704	.60678 41855 01110
39	.27706 27848 95811	.60683 96004 23903
0.8540	0.27703 91261 29479	0.60689 50106 15018
41	.27701 54666 13247	.60695 04160 74305
42	.27699 18063 47651	.60700 58168 01613
43	.27696 81453 33229	.60706 12127 96794
44	.27694 44835 70519	.60711 66040 59697
0.8545	0.27692 08210 60056	0.60717 19905 90172
46	.27689 71578 02379	.60722 73723 88071
47	.27687 34937 98023	.60728 27494 53243
48	.27684 98290 47528	.60733 81217 85540
49	.27682 61635 51428	.60739 34893 84813
0.8550	0.27680 24973 10263	0.60744 88522 50911

X	$\frac{1}{\sqrt{2\pi}}e^{-\frac{x^2}{2}}$	$\frac{1}{\sqrt{2\pi}}\int_{-x}^{x}e^{-\frac{\alpha^2}{2}}\,d\alpha$
0.8550	0.27680 24973 10263	0.60744 88522 50911
51	.27677 88303 24567	.60750 42103 83687
52	.27675 51625 94880	.60755 95637 82991
53	.27673 14941 21736	.60761 49124 48675
54	.27670 78249 05674	.60767 02563 80591
0.8555	0.27668 41549 47230	0.60772 55955 78588
56	.27666 04842 46942	.60778 09300 42520
57	.27663 68128 05345	.60783 62597 72238
58	.27661 31406 22977	.60789 15847 67593
59	.27658 94677 00375	.60794 69050 28437
0.8560	0.27656 57940 38075	0.60800 22205 54624
61	.27654 21196 36614	.60805 75313 46003
62	.27651 84444 96530	.60811 28374 02429
63	.27649 47686 18358	.60816 81387 23753
64	.27647 10920 02635	.60822 34353 09827
0.8565	0.27644 74146 49898	0.60827 87271 60505
66	.27642 37365 60684	.60833 40142 75638
67	.27640 00577 35530	.60838 92966 55080
68	.27637 63781 74971	.60844 45742 98683
69	.27635 26978 79544	.60849 98472 06301
0.8570	0.27632 90168 49787	0.60855 51153 77786
71	.27630 53350 86235	.60861 03788 12992
72	.27628 16525 89425	.60866 56375 11772
73	.27625 79693 59894	.60872 08914 73979
74	.27623 42853 98178	.60877 61406 99467
0.8575	0.27621 06007 04813	0.60883 13851 88089
76	.27618 69152 80336	.60888 66249 39700
77	.27616 32291 25283	.60894 18599 54153
78	.27613 95422 40190	.60899 70902 31301
79	.27611 58546 25595	.60905 23157 71000
0.8580	0.27609 21662 82032	0.60910 75365 73103
81	.27606 84772 10040	.60916 27526 37464
82	.27604 47874 10152	.60921 79639 63939
83	.27602 10968 82907	.60927 31705 52380
84	.27599 74056 28840	.60932 83724 02643
0.8585	0.27597 37136 48488	0.60938 35695 14583
86	.27595 00209 42386	.60943 87618 88054
87	.27592 63275 11070	.60949 39495 22912
88	.27590 26333 55077	.60954 91324 19010
89	.27587 89384 74944	.60960 43105 76205
0.8590	0.27585 52428 71205	0.60965 94839 94352
91	.27583 15465 44397	.60971 46526 73306
92	.27580 78494 95056	.60976 98166 12922
93	.27578 41517 23719	.60982 49758 13056
94	.27576 04532 30920	.60988 01302 73563
0.8595	0.27573 67540 17196	0.60993 52799 94300
96	.27571 30540 83083	.60999 04249 75122
97	.27568 93534 29117	.61004 55652 15885
98	.27566 56520 55833	.61010 07007 16446
99	.27564 19499 63768	.61015 58314 76660
0.8600	0.27561 82471 53457	0.61021 09574 96383

X	$\frac{1}{\sqrt{2\pi}} e^{-\frac{x^2}{2}}$	$\frac{1}{\sqrt{2\pi}} \int_{-x}^{x} e^{-\frac{\alpha^2}{2}} d\alpha$
0.8600	0.27561 82471 53457	0.61021 09574 96383
01	.27559 45436 25436	.61026 60787 75473
02	.27557 08393 80241	.61032 11953 13786
03	.27554 71344 18407	.61037 63071 11177
04	.27552 34287 40471	.61043 14141 67505
0.8605	0.27549 97223 46968	0.61048 65164 82626
06	.27547 60152 38434	.61054 16140 56396
07	.27545 23074 15404	.61059 67068 88674
08	.27542 85988 78414	.61065 17949 79315
09	.27540 48896 28000	.61070 68783 28177
0.8610	0.27538 11796 64696	0.61076 19569 35119
11	.27535 74689 89040	.61081 70307 99996
12	.27533 37576 01566	.61087 20999 22667
13	.27531 00455 02809	.61092 71643 02989
14	.27528 63326 93306	.61098 22239 40821
0.8615	0.27526 26191 73591	0.61103 72788 36019
16	.27523 89049 44201	.61109 23289 88443
17	.27521 51900 05670	.61114 73743 97949
18	.27519 14743 58534	.61120 24150 64398
19	.27516 77580 03328	.61125 74509 87646
0.8620	0.27514 40409 40587	0.61131 24821 67552
21	.27512 03231 70848	.61136 75086 03975
22	.27509 66046 94645	.61142 25302 96773
23	.27507 28855 12513	.61147 75472 45806
24	.27504 91656 24988	.61153 25594 50931
0.8625	0.27502 54450 32604	0.61158 75669 12009
26	.27500 17237 35898	.61164 25696 28897
27	.27497 80017 35404	.61169 75676 01456
28	.27495 42790 31657	.61175 25608 29544
29	.27493 05556 25192	.61180 75493 13022
0.8630	0.27490 68315 16545	0.61186 25330 51748
31	.27488 31067 06251	.61191 75120 45582
32	.27485 93811 94844	.61197 24862 94383
33	.27483 56549 82860	.61202 74557 98013
34	.27481 19280 70833	.61208 24205 56330
0.8635	0.27478 82004 59299	0.61213 73805 69195
36	.27476 44721 48792	.61219 23358 36467
37	.27474 07431 39848	.61224 72863 58008
38	.27471 70134 33000	.61230 22321 33676
39	.27469 32830 28785	.61235 71731 63334
0.8640	0.27466 95519 27737	0.61241 21094 46842
41	.27464 58201 30390	.61246 70409 84059
42	.27462 20876 37280	.61252 19677 74847
43	.27459 83544 48941	.61257 68898 19068
44	.27457 46205 65908	.61263 18071 16581
0.8645	0.27455 08859 88716	0.61268 67196 67248
46	.27452 71507 17899	.61274 16274 70930
47	.27450 34147 53992	.61279 65305 27489
48	.27447 96780 97530	.61285 14288 36785
49	.27445 59407 49047	.61290 63223 98681
0.8650	0.27443 22027 09077	0.61296 12112 13039

x	$\frac{1}{\sqrt{2\pi}}e^{-\frac{x^2}{2}}$	$\frac{1}{\sqrt{2\pi}}\int_{-x}^{x}e^{-\frac{\alpha^2}{2}}d\alpha$
0.8650	0.27443 22027 09077	0.61296 12112 13039
51	.27440 84639 78156	.61301 60952 79719
52	.27438 47245 56818	.61307 09745 98584
53	.27436 09844 45597	.61312 58491 69496
54	.27433 72436 45028	.61318 07189 92316
0.8655	0.27431 35021 55645	0.61323 55840 66908
56	.27428 97599 77983	.61329 04443 93133
57	.27426 60171 12576	.61334 52999 70853
58	.27424 22735 59958	.61340 01507 99932
59	.27421 85293 20664	.61345 49968 80231
0.8660	0.27419 47843 95229	0.61350 98382 11614
61	.27417 10387 84185	.61356 46747 93944
62	.27414 72924 88068	.61361 95066 27082
63	.27412 35455 07413	.61367 43337 10893
64	.27409 97978 42752	.61372 91560 45240
0.8665	0.27407 60494 94620	0.61378 39736 29985
66	.27405 23004 63552	.61383 87864 64992
67	.27402 85507 50082	.61389 35945 50125
68	.27400 48003 54743	.61394 83978 85247
69	.27398 10492 78071	.61400 31964 70221
0.8670	0.27395 72975 20598	0.61405 79903 04912
71	.27393 35450 82859	.61411 27793 89184
72	.27390 97919 65387	.61416 75637 22900
73	.27388 60381 68718	.61422 23433 05925
74	.27386 22836 93385	.61427 71181 38123
0.8675	0.27383 85285 39921	0.61433 18882 19357
76	.27381 47727 08861	.61438 66535 49493
77	.27379 10162 00738	.61444 14141 28396
78	.27376 72590 16087	.61449 61699 55929
79	.27374 35011 55442	.61455 09210 31957
0.8680	0.27371 97426 19335	0.61460 56673 56346
81	.27369 59834 08301	.61466 04089 28960
82	.27367 22235 22873	.61471 51457 49664
83	.27364 84629 63586	.61476 98778 18324
84	.27362 47017 30973	.61482 46051 34805
0.8685	0.27360 09398 25567	0.61487 93276 98971
86	.27357 71772 47903	.61493 40455 10690
87	.27355 34139 98514	.61498 87585 69826
88	.27352 96500 77933	.61504 34668 76245
89	.27350 58854 86694	.61509 81704 29812
0.8690	0.27348 21202 25331	0.61515 28692 30395
91	.27345 83542 94377	.61520 75632 77858
92	.27343 45876 94365	.61526 22525 72068
93	.27341 08204 25830	.61531 69371 12891
94	.27338 70524 89304	.61537 16169 00194
0.8695	0.27336 32838 85321	0.61542 62919 33842
96	.27333 95146 14414	.61548 09622 13703
97	.27331 57446 77117	.61553 56277 39644
98	.27329 19740 73963	.61559 02885 11530
99	.27326 82028 05485	.61564 49445 29229
0.8700	0.27324 44308 72216	0.61569 95957 92608

x	$\frac{1}{\sqrt{2\pi}} e^{-\frac{x^2}{2}}$	$\frac{1}{\sqrt{2\pi}} \int_{-x}^{x} e^{-\frac{\alpha^2}{2}} d\alpha$
0.8700	0.27324 44308 72216	0.61569 95957 92608
01	.27322 06582 74691	.61575 42423 01533
02	.27319 68850 13441	.61580 88840 55873
03	.27317 31110 89001	.61586 35210 55495
04	.27314 93365 01903	.61591 81533 00265
0.8705	0.27312 55612 52680	0.61597 27807 90051
06	.27310 17853 41866	.61602 74035 24722
07	.27307 80087 69994	.61608 20215 04144
08	.27305 42315 37597	.61613 66347 28186
09	.27303 04536 45207	.61619 12431 96715
0.8710	0.27300 66750 93358	0.61624 58469 09600
11	.27298 28958 82584	.61630 04458 66708
12	.27295 91160 13415	.61635 50400 67909
13	.27293 53354 86387	.61640 96295 13070
14	.27291 15543 02031	.61646 42142 02060
0.8715	0.27288 77724 60881	0.61651 87941 34747
16	.27286 39899 63469	.61657 33693 11000
17	.27284 02068 10328	.61662 79397 30688
18	.27281 64230 01991	.61668 25053 93681
19	.27279 26385 38991	.61673 70662 99846
0.8720	0.27276 88534 21860	0.61679 16224 49053
21	.27274 50676 51132	.61684 61738 41171
22	.27272 12812 27338	.61690 07204 76070
23	.27269 74941 51012	.61695 52623 53618
24	.27267 37064 22686	.61700 97994 73686
0.8725	0.27264 99180 42893	0.61706 43318 36144
26	.27262 61290 12165	.61711 88594 40860
27	.27260 23393 31035	.61717 33822 87705
28	.27257 85490 00036	.61722 79003 76549
29	.27255 47580 19699	.61728 24137 07262
0.8730	0.27253 09663 90558	0.61733 69222 79714
31	.27250 71741 13145	.61739 14260 93775
32	.27248 33811 87992	.61744 59251 49316
33	.27245 95876 15632	.61750 04194 46207
34	.27243 57933 96597	.61755 49089 84319
0.8735	0.27241 19985 31419	0.61760 93937 63523
36	.27238 82030 20631	.61766 38737 83689
37	.27236 44068 64764	.61771 83490 44688
38	.27234 06100 64352	.61777 28195 46392
39	.27231 68126 19927	.61782 72852 88671
0.8740	0.27229 30145 32020	0.61788 17462 71397
41	.27226 92158 01164	.61793 62024 94441
42	.27224 54164 27891	.61799 06539 57674
43	.27222 16164 12733	.61804 51006 60969
44	.27219 78157 56223	.61809 95426 04197
0.8745	0.27217 40144 58891	0.61815 39797 87229
46	.27215 02125 21271	.61820 84122 09938
47	.27212 64099 43894	.61826 28398 72195
48	.27210 26067 27293	.61831 72627 73872
49	.27207 88028 71999	.61837 16809 14843
0.8750	0.27205 49983 78544	0.61842 60942 94979

X	$\frac{1}{\sqrt{2\pi}} e^{-\frac{x^2}{2}}$	$\frac{1}{\sqrt{2\pi}} \int_{-x}^{x} e^{-\frac{\alpha^2}{2}} d\alpha$
0.8750	0.27205 49983 78544	0.61842 60942 94979
51	.27203 11932 47460	.61848 05029 14152
52	.27200 73874 79279	.61853 49067 72235
53	.27198 35810 74532	.61858 93058 69101
54	.27195 97740 33753	.61864 37002 04623
0.8755	0.27193 59663 57472	0.61869 80897 78672
56	.27191 21580 46221	.61875 24745 91123
57	.27188 83491 00532	.61880 68546 41849
58	.27186 45395 20937	.61886 12299 30721
59	.27184 07293 07967	.61891 56004 57615
0.8760	0.27181 69184 62154	0.61896 99662 22402
61	.27179 31069 84029	.61902 43272 24957
62	.27176 92948 74125	.61907 86834 65154
63	.27174 54821 32973	.61913 30349 42865
64	.27172 16687 61104	.61918 73816 57965
0.8765	0.27169 78547 59050	0.61924 17236 10327
66	.27167 40401 27342	.61929 60607 99827
67	.27165 02248 66512	.61935 03932 26336
68	.27162 64089 77091	.61940 47208 89731
69	.27160 25924 59611	.61945 90437 89885
0.8770	0.27157 87753 14602	0.61951 33619 26673
71	.27155 49575 42598	.61956 76752 99969
72	.27153 11391 44127	.61962 19839 09649
73	.27150 73201 19723	.61967 62877 55585
74	.27148 35004 69916	.61973 05868 37655
0.8775	0.27145 96801 95238	0.61978 48811 55732
76	.27143 58592 96219	.61983 91707 09691
77	.27141 20377 73391	.61989 34554 99409
78	.27138 82156 27285	.61994 77355 24759
79	.27136 43928 58433	.62000 20107 85618
0.8780	0.27134 05694 67364	0.62005 62812 81861
81	.27131 67454 54611	.62011 05470 13363
82	.27129 29208 20705	.62016 48079 80001
83	.27126 90955 66175	.62021 90641 81650
84	.27124 52696 91554	.62027 33156 18186
0.8785	0.27122 14431 97373	0.62032 75622 89486
86	.27119 76160 84162	.62038 18041 95424
87	.27117 37883 52451	.62043 60413 35878
88	.27114 99600 02773	.62049 02737 10724
89	.27112 61310 35658	.62054 45013 19838
0.8790	0.27110 23014 51637	0.62059 87241 63097
91	.27107 84712 51240	.62065 29422 40378
92	.27105 46404 34998	.62070 71555 51557
93	.27103 08090 03443	.62076 13640 96511
94	.27100 69769 57104	.62081 55678 75117
0.8795	0.27098 31442 96513	0.62086 97668 87252
96	.27095 93110 22199	.62092 39611 32795
97	.27093 54771 34694	.62097 81506 11620
98	.27091 16426 34529	.62103 23353 23608
99	.27088 78075 22233	.62108 65152 68633
0.8800	0.27086 39717 98338	0.62114 06904 46576

x	$\dfrac{1}{\sqrt{2\pi}} e^{-\frac{x^2}{2}}$	$\dfrac{1}{\sqrt{2\pi}} \displaystyle\int_{-x}^{x} e^{-\frac{\alpha^2}{2}} d\alpha$
0.8800	0.27086 39717 98338	0.62114 06904 46576
01	.27084 01354 63374	.62119 48608 57312
02	.27081 62985 17871	.62124 90265 00720
03	.27079 24609 62359	.62130 31873 76679
04	.27076 86227 97370	.62135 73434 85065
0.8805	0.27074 47840 23434	0.62141 14948 25757
06	.27072 09446 41081	.62146 56413 98634
07	.27069 71046 50841	.62151 97832 03573
08	.27067 32640 53244	.62157 39202 40453
09	.27064 94228 48822	.62162 80525 09154
0.8810	0.27062 55810 38103	0.62168 21800 09552
11	.27060 17386 21620	.62173 63027 41529
12	.27057 78955 99900	.62179 04207 04961
13	.27055 40519 73476	.62184 45338 99728
14	.27053 02077 42876	.62189 86423 25710
0.8815	0.27050 63629 08631	0.62195 27459 82785
16	.27048 25174 71272	.62200 68448 70833
17	.27045 86714 31328	.62206 09389 89733
18	.27043 48247 89328	.62211 50283 39366
19	.27041 09775 45804	.62216 91129 19609
0.8820	0.27038 71297 01286	0.62222 31927 30344
21	.27036 32812 56302	.62227 72677 71450
22	.27033 94322 11383	.62233 13380 42806
23	.27031 55825 67059	.62238 54035 44294
24	.27029 17323 23860	.62243 94642 75793
0.8825	0.27026 78814 82315	0.62249 35202 37184
26	.27024 40300 42955	.62254 75714 28346
27	.27022 01780 06309	.62260 16178 49161
28	.27019 63253 72906	.62265 56594 99509
29	.27017 24721 43277	.62270 96963 79271
0.8830	0.27014 86183 17952	0.62276 37284 88327
31	.27012 47638 97459	.62281 77558 26558
32	.27010 09088 82329	.62287 17783 93846
33	.27007 70532 73090	.62292 57961 90071
34	.27005 31970 70274	.62297 98092 15116
0.8835	0.27002 93402 74409	0.62303 38174 68860
36	.27000 54828 86024	.62308 78209 51186
37	.26998 16249 05649	.62314 18196 61975
38	.26995 77663 33815	.62319 58136 01109
39	.26993 39071 71049	.62324 98027 68469
0.8840	0.26991 00474 17881	0.62330 37871 63938
41	.26988 61870 74842	.62335 77667 87397
42	.26986 23261 42459	.62341 17416 38728
43	.26983 84646 21263	.62346 57117 17815
44	.26981 46025 11783	.62351 96770 24538
0.8845	0.26979 07398 14547	0.62357 36375 58780
46	.26976 68765 30086	.62362 75933 20424
47	.26974 30126 58928	.62368 15443 09353
48	.26971 91482 01602	.62373 54905 25449
49	.26969 52831 58638	.62378 94319 68595
0.8850	0.26967 14175 30565	0.62384 33686 38673

x	$\dfrac{1}{\sqrt{2\pi}}\,e^{-\frac{x^2}{2}}$	$\dfrac{1}{\sqrt{2\pi}}\displaystyle\int_{-x}^{x} e^{-\frac{\alpha^2}{2}}\,d\alpha$
0.8850	0.26967 14175 30565	0.62384 33686 38673
51	.26964 75513 17912	.62389 73005 35568
52	.26962 36845 21207	.62395 12276 59162
53	.26959 98171 40981	.62400 51500 09337
54	.26957 59491 77761	.6240E 90675 85979
0.8855	0.26955 20806 32077	0.62411 29803 88970
56	.26952 82115 04457	.62416 68884 18193
57	.26950 43417 95431	.62422 07916 73533
58	.26948 04715 05528	.62427 46901 54873
59	.26945 66006 35276	.62432 85838 62096
0.8860	0.26943 27291 85203	0.62438 24727 95088
61	.26940 88571 55840	.62443 63569 53732
62	.26938 49845 47714	.62449 02363 37912
63	.26936 11113 61355	.62454 41109 47512
64	.26933 72375 97291	.62459 79807 82418
0.8865	0.26931 33632 56050	0.62465 18458 42513
66	.26928 94883 38162	.62470 57061 27682
67	.26926 56128 44154	.62475 95616 37810
68	.26924 17367 74556	.62481 34123 72781
69	.26921 78601 29896	.62486 72583 32481
0.8870	0.26919 39829 10702	0.62492 10995 16795
71	.26917 01051 17504	.62497 49359 25607
72	.26914 62267 50829	.62502 87675 58803
73	.26912 23478 11205	.62508 25944 16269
74	.26909 84682 99162	.62513 64164 97890
0.8875	0.26907 45882 15228	0.62519 02338 03551
76	.26905 07075 59930	.62524 40463 33138
77	.26902 68263 33798	.62529 78540 86537
78	.26900 29445 37359	.62535 16570 63633
79	.26897 90621 71142	.62540 54552 64314
0.8880	0.26895 51792 35675	0.62545 92486 88464
81	.26893 12957 31486	.62551 30373 35970
82	.26890 74116 59103	.62556 68212 06719
83	.26888 35270 19054	.62562 06003 00596
84	.26885 96418 11869	.62567 43746 17488
0.8885	0.26883 57560 38073	0.62572 81441 57283
86	.26881 18696 98197	.62578 19089 19866
87	.26878 79827 92767	.62583 56689 05124
88	.26876 40953 22311	.62588 94241 12945
89	.26874 02072 87358	.62594 31745 43216
0.8890	0.26871 63186 88435	0.62599 69201 95823
91	.26869 24295 26071	.62605 06610 70653
92	.26866 85398 00793	.62610 43971 67595
93	.26864 46495 13129	.62615 81284 86536
94	.26862 07586 63607	.62621 18550 27363
0.8895	0.26859 68672 52754	0.62626 55767 89964
96	.26857 29752 81098	.62631 92937 74227
97	.26854 90827 49168	.62637 30059 80039
98	.26852 51896 57490	.62642 67134 07289
99	.26850 12960 06592	.62648 04160 55865
0.8900	0.26847 74017 97002	0.62653 41139 25655

x	$\frac{1}{\sqrt{2\pi}}e^{-\frac{x^2}{2}}$	$\frac{1}{\sqrt{2\pi}}\int_{-x}^{x}e^{-\frac{\alpha^2}{2}}d\alpha$
0.8900	0.26847 74017 97002	0.62653 41139 25655
01	.26845 35070 29248	.62658 78070 16547
02	.26842 96117 03857	.62664 14953 28429
03	.26840 57158 21356	.62669 51788 61191
04	.26838 18193 82274	.62674 88576 14721
0.8905	0.26835 79223 87136	0.62680 25315 88907
06	.26833 40248 36472	.62685 62007 83639
07	.26831 01267 30808	.62690 98651 98805
08	.26828 62280 70672	.62696 35248 34294
09	.26826 23288 56591	.62701 71796 89996
0.8910	0.26823 84290 89092	0.62707 08297 65800
11	.26821 45287 68703	.62712 44750 61595
12	.26819 06278 95951	.62717 81155 77270
13	.26816 67264 71363	.62723 17513 12716
14	.26814 28244 95466	.62728 53822 67822
0.8915	0.26811 89219 68787	0.62733 90084 42478
16	.26809 50188 91854	.62739 26298 36573
17	.26807 11152 65194	.62744 62464 49998
18	.26804 72110 89334	.62749 98582 82642
19	.26802 33063 64800	.62755 34653 34397
0.8920	0.26799 94010 92120	0.62760 70676 05152
21	.26797 54952 71821	.62766 06650 94797
22	.26795 15889 04429	.62771 42578 03224
23	.26792 76819 90472	.62776 78457 30323
24	.26790 37745 30477	.62782 14288 75984
0.8925	0.26787 98665 24970	0.62787 50072 40098
26	.26785 59579 74478	.62792 85808 22557
27	.26783 20488 79528	.62798 21496 23252
28	.26780 81392 40646	.62803 57136 42073
29	.26778 42290 58361	.62808 92728 78912
0.8930	0.26776 03183 33197	0.62814 28273 33660
31	.26773 64070 65682	.62819 63770 06209
32	.26771 24952 56342	.62824 99218 96450
33	.26768 85829 05705	.62830 34620 04276
34	.26766 46700 14296	.62835 69973 29577
0.8935	0.26764 07565 82642	0.62841 05278 72245
36	.26761 68426 11270	.62846 40536 32174
37	.26759 29281 00706	.62851 75746 09254
38	.26756 90130 51477	.62857 10908 03378
39	.26754 50974 64108	.62862 46022 14439
0.8940	0.26752 11813 39128	0.62867 81088 42328
41	.26749 72646 77060	.62873 16106 86938
42	.26747 33474 78433	.62878 51077 48163
43	.26744 94297 43773	.62883 86000 25894
44	.26742 55114 73605	.62889 20875 20025
0.8945	0.26740 15926 68456	0.62894 55702 30448
46	.26737 76733 28852	.62899 90481 57056
47	.26735 37534 55319	.62905 25212 99744
48	.26732 98330 48384	.62910 59896 58403
49	.26730 59121 08572	.62915 94532 32928
0.8950	0.26728 19906 36410	0.62921 29120 23211

x	$\frac{1}{\sqrt{2\pi}} e^{-\frac{x^2}{2}}$	$\frac{1}{\sqrt{2\pi}} \int_{-x}^{x} e^{-\frac{\alpha^2}{2}} d\alpha$
0.8950	0.26728 19906 36410	0.62921 29120 23211
51	.26725 80686 32424	.62926 63660 29147
52	.26723 41460 97139	.62931 98152 50628
53	.26721 02230 31082	.62937 32596 87550
54	.26718 62994 34778	.62942 66993 39806
0.8955	0.26716 23753 08754	0.62948 01342 07289
56	.26713 84506 53536	.62953 35642 89894
57	.26711 45254 69649	.62958 69895 87515
58	.26709 05997 57618	.62964 04101 00046
59	.26706 66735 17971	.62969 38258 27383
0.8960	0.26704 27467 51233	0.62974 72367 69418
61	.26701 88194 57929	.62980 06429 26048
62	.26699 48916 38585	.62985 40442 97167
63	.26697 09632 93727	.62990 74408 82669
64	.26694 70344 23880	.62996 08326 82449
0.8965	0.26692 31050 29570	0.63001 42196 96403
66	.26689 91751 11323	.63006 76019 24426
67	.26687 52446 69664	.63012 09793 66413
68	.26685 13137 05119	.63017 43520 22259
69	.26682 73822 18213	.63022 77198 91860
0.8970	0.26680 34502 09472	0.63028 10829 75111
71	.26677 95176 79421	.63033 44412 71909
72	.26675 55846 28585	.63038 77947 82148
73	.26673 16510 57490	.63044 11435 05726
74	.26670 77169 66662	.63049 44874 42537
0.8975	0.26668 37823 56624	0.63054 78265 92478
76	.26665 98472 27904	.63060 11609 55445
77	.26663 59115 81025	.63065 44905 31334
78	.26661 19754 16513	.63070 78153 20043
79	.26658 80387 34894	.63076 11353 21467
0.8980	0.26656 41015 36693	0.63081 44505 35502
81	.26654 01638 22433	.63086 77609 62047
82	.26651 62255 92642	.63092 10666 00997
83	.26649 22868 47843	.63097 43674 52250
84	.26646 83475 88562	.63102 76635 15702
0.8985	0.26644 44078 15323	0.63108 09547 91251
86	.26642 04675 28652	.63113 42412 78794
87	.26639 65267 29074	.63118 75229 78228
88	.26637 25854 17113	.63124 07998 89451
89	.26634 86435 93294	.63129 40720 12361
0.8990	0.26632 47012 58143	0.63134 73393 46854
91	.26630 07584 12183	.63140 06018 92830
92	.26627 68150 55940	.63145 38596 50185
93	.26625 28711 89938	.63150 71126 18818
94	.26622 89268 14703	.63156 03607 98627
0.8995	0.26620 49819 30758	0.63161 36041 89510
96	.26618 10365 38628	.63166 68427 91366
97	.26615 70906 38838	.63172 00766 04092
98	.26613 31442 31913	.63177 33056 27587
99	.26610 91973 18377	.63182 65298 61751
0.9000	0.26608 52498 98755	0.63187 97493 06481

x	$\frac{1}{\sqrt{2\pi}} e^{-\frac{x^2}{2}}$	$\frac{1}{\sqrt{2\pi}} \int_{-x}^{x} e^{-\frac{\alpha^2}{2}} d\alpha$
0.9000	0.26608 52498 98755	0.63187 97493 06481
01	.26606 13019 73570	.63193 29639 61677
02	.26603 73535 43348	.63198 61738 27237
03	.26601 34046 08613	.63203 93789 03060
04	.26598 94551 69889	.63209 25791 89047
0.9005	0.26596 55052 27701	0.63214 57746 85095
06	.26594 15547 82573	.63219 89653 91104
07	.26591 76038 35028	.63225 21513 06974
08	.26589 36523 85592	.63230 53324 32605
09	.26586 97004 34789	.63235 85087 67895
0.9010	0.26584 57479 83143	0.63241 16803 12745
11	.26582 17950 31177	.63246 48470 67055
12	.26579 78415 79417	.63251 80090 30724
13	.26577 38876 28386	.63257 11662 03654
14	.26574 99331 78608	.63262 43185 85743
0.9015	0.26572 59782 30607	0.63267 74661 76892
16	.26570 20227 84907	.63273 06089 77002
17	.26567 80668 42033	.63278 37469 85973
18	.26565 41104 02508	.63283 68802 03705
19	.26563 01534 66856	.63289 00086 30100
0.9020	0.26560 61960 35600	0.63294 31322 65059
21	.26558 22381 09265	.63299 62511 08482
22	.26555 82796 88375	.63304 93651 60270
23	.26553 43207 73453	.63310 24744 20324
24	.26551 03613 65023	.63315 55788 88546
0.9025	0.26548 64014 63608	0.63320 86785 64837
26	.26546 24410 69733	.63326 17734 49099
27	.26543 84801 83921	.63331 48635 41232
28	.26541 45188 06695	.63336 79488 41140
29	.26539 05569 38580	.63342 10293 48722
0.9030	0.26536 65945 80098	0.63347 41050 63882
31	.26534 26317 31773	.63352 71759 86522
32	.26531 86683 94129	.63358 02421 16542
33	.26529 47045 67689	.63363 33034 53847
34	.26527 07402 52976	.63368 63599 98337
0.9035	0.26524 67754 50514	0.63373 94117 49915
36	.26522 28101 60827	.63379 24587 08485
37	.26519 88443 84437	.63384 55008 73947
38	.26517 48781 21867	.63389 85382 46206
39	.26515 09113 73642	.63395 15708 25164
0.9040	0.26512 69441 40283	0.63400 45986 10723
41	.26510 29764 22315	.63405 76216 02788
42	.26507 90082 20261	.63411 06398 01260
43	.26505 50395 34643	.63416 36532 06043
44	.26503 10703 65985	.63421 66618 17041
0.9045	0.26500 71007 14810	0.63426 96656 34158
46	.26498 31305 81640	.63432 26646 57295
47	.26495 91599 66999	.63437 56588 86358
48	.26493 51888 71410	.63442 86483 21250
49	.26491 12172 95395	.63448 16329 61875
0.9050	0.26488 72452 39478	0.63453 46128 08136

X	$\dfrac{1}{\sqrt{2\pi}}\,e^{-\frac{x^2}{2}}$	$\dfrac{1}{\sqrt{2\pi}}\displaystyle\int_{-x}^{x} e^{-\frac{\alpha^2}{2}}\,d\alpha$
0.9050	0.26488 72452 39478	0.63453 46128 08136
51	.26486 32727 04181	.63458 75878 59939
52	.26483 92996 90028	.63464 05581 17186
53	.26481 53261 97540	.63469 35235 79783
54	.26479 13522 27241	.63474 64842 47633
0.9055	0.26476 73777 79653	0.63479 94401 20642
56	.26474 34028 55299	.63485 23911 98713
57	.26471 94274 54702	.63490 53374 81752
58	.26469 54515 78384	.63495 82789 69663
59	.26467 14752 26868	.63501 12156 62352
0.9060	0.26464 74984 00676	0.63506 41475 59722
61	.26462 35211 00332	.63511 70746 61680
62	.26459 95433 26357	.63516 99969 68131
63	.26457 55650 79274	.63522 29144 78979
64	.26455 15863 59605	.63527 58271 94131
0.9065	0.26452 76071 67872	0.63532 87351 13492
66	.26450 36275 04599	.63538 16382 36967
67	.26447 96473 70307	.63543 45365 64462
68	.26445 56667 65519	.63548 74300 95884
69	.26443 16856 90757	.63554 03188 31137
0.9070	0.26440 77041 46543	0.63559 32027 70129
71	.26438 37221 33399	.63564 60819 12764
72	.26435 97396 51847	.63569 89562 58951
73	.26433 57567 02410	.63575 18258 08594
74	.26431 17732 85610	.63580 46905 61601
0.9075	0.26428 77894 01969	0.63585 75505 17877
76	.26426 38050 52008	.63591 04056 77330
77	.26423 98202 36249	.63596 32560 39867
78	.26421 58349 55216	.63601 61016 05394
79	.26419 18492 09429	.63606 89423 73818
0.9080	0.26416 78629 99410	0.63612 17783 45047
81	.26414 38763 25682	.63617 46095 18987
82	.26411 98891 88766	.63622 74358 95546
83	.26409 59015 89184	.63628 02574 74632
84	.26407 19135 27457	.63633 30742 56151
0.9085	0.26404 79250 04108	0.63638 58862 40012
86	.26402 39360 19658	.63643 86934 26122
87	.26399 99465 74629	.63649 14958 14389
88	.26397 59566 69541	.63654 42934 04721
89	.26395 19663 04918	.63659 70861 97026
0.9090	0.26392 79754 81280	0.63664 98741 91212
91	.26390 39841 99149	.63670 26573 87188
92	.26387 99924 59047	.63675 54357 84861
93	.26385 60002 61495	.63680 82093 84141
94	.26383 20076 07013	.63686 09781 84936
0.9095	0.26380 80144 96125	0.63691 37421 87153
96	.26378 40209 29350	.63696 65013 90704
97	.26376 00269 07211	.63701 92557 95495
98	.26373 60324 30228	.63707 20054 01436
99	.26371 20374 98924	.63712 47502 08437
0.9100	0.26368 80421 13818	0.63717 74902 16406

x	$\dfrac{1}{\sqrt{2\pi}} e^{-\frac{x^2}{2}}$	$\dfrac{1}{\sqrt{2\pi}} \displaystyle\int_{-x}^{x} e^{-\frac{\alpha^2}{2}} \, d\alpha$
0.9100	0.26368 80421 13818	0.63717 74902 16406
01	.26366 40462 75433	.63723 02254 25252
02	.26364 00499 84289	.63728 29558 34886
03	.26361 60532 40907	.63733 56814 45216
04	.26359 20560 45809	.63738 84022 56152
0.9105	0.26356 80583 99516	0.63744 11182 67604
06	.26354 40603 02549	.63749 38294 79482
07	.26352 00617 55428	.63754 65358 91695
08	.26349 60627 58674	.63759 92375 04154
09	.26347 20633 12809	.63765 19343 16768
0.9110	0.26344 80634 18353	0.63770 46263 29449
11	.26342 40630 75828	.63775 73135 42106
12	.26340 00622 85753	.63780 99959 54649
13	.26337 60610 48650	.63786 26735 66990
14	.26335 20593 65040	.63791 53463 79039
0.9115	0.26332 80572 35443	0.63796 80143 90707
16	.26330 40546 60380	.63802 06776 01904
17	.26328 00516 40371	.63807 33360 12541
18	.26325 60481 75937	.63812 59896 22530
19	.26323 20442 67599	.63817 86384 31782
0.9120	0.26320 80399 15877	0.63823 12824 40208
21	.26318 40351 21292	.63828 39216 47719
22	.26316 00298 84364	.63833 65560 54227
23	.26313 60242 05613	.63838 91856 59643
24	.26311 20180 85561	.63844 18104 63879
0.9125	0.26308 80115 24726	0.63849 44304 66848
26	.26306 40045 23631	.63854 70456 68460
27	.26303 99970 82794	.63859 96560 68628
28	.26301 59892 02737	.63865 22616 67264
29	.26299 19808 83979	.63870 48624 64280
0.9130	0.26296 79721 27040	0.63875 74584 59588
31	.26294 39629 32442	.63881 00496 53101
32	.26291 99533 00703	.63886 26360 44732
33	.26289 59432 32344	.63891 52176 34393
34	.26287 19327 27885	.63896 77944 21996
0.9135	0.26284 79217 87847	0.63902 03664 07455
36	.26282 39104 12748	.63907 29335 90682
37	.26279 98986 03109	.63912 54959 71591
38	.26277 58863 59451	.63917 80535 50094
39	.26275 18736 82292	.63923 06063 26106
0.9140	0.26272 78605 72152	0.63928 31542 99538
41	.26270 38470 29552	.63933 56974 70306
42	.26267 98330 55012	.63938 82358 38321
43	.26265 58186 49050	.63944 07694 03499
44	.26263 18038 12187	.63949 32981 65752
0.9145	0.26260 77885 44942	0.63954 58221 24995
46	.26258 37728 47835	.63959 83412 81142
47	.26255 97567 21386	.63965 08556 34106
48	.26253 57401 66114	.63970 33651 83802
49	.26251 17231 82538	.63975 58699 30144
0.9150	0.26248 77057 71179	0.63980 83698 73046

x	$\frac{1}{\sqrt{2\pi}} e^{-\frac{x^2}{2}}$	$\frac{1}{\sqrt{2\pi}} \int_{-x}^{x} e^{-\frac{\alpha^2}{2}} d\alpha$
0.9150	0.26248 77057 71179	0.63980 83698 73046
51	.26246 36879 32555	.63986 08650 12424
52	.26243 96696 67187	.63991 33553 48191
53	.26241 56509 75592	.63996 58408 80262
54	.26239 16318 58292	.64001 83216 08553
0.9155	0.26236 76123 15805	0.64007 07975 32977
56	.26234 35923 48650	.64012 32686 53451
57	.26231 95719 57347	.64017 57349 69888
58	.26229 55511 42415	.64022 81964 82205
59	.26227 15299 04373	.64028 06531 90317
0.9160	0.26224 75082 43740	0.64033 31050 94139
61	.26222 34861 61036	.64038 55521 93586
62	.26219 94636 56779	.64043 79944 88575
63	.26217 54407 31488	.64049 04319 79021
64	.26215 14173 85683	.64054 28646 64840
0.9165	0.26212 73936 19883	0.64059 52925 45947
66	.26210 33694 34606	.64064 77156 22260
67	.26207 93448 30371	.64070 01338 93693
68	.26205 53198 07697	.64075 25473 60164
69	.26203 12943 67104	.64080 49560 21588
0.9170	0.26200 72685 09109	0.64085 73598 77883
71	.26198 32422 34232	.64090 97589 28964
72	.26195 92155 42992	.64096 21531 74749
73	.26193 51884 35906	.64101 45426 15154
74	.26191 11609 13494	.64106 69272 50096
0.9175	0.26188 71329 76274	0.64111 93070 79491
76	.26186 31046 24766	.64117 16821 03258
77	.26183 90758 59487	.64122 40523 21314
78	.26181 50466 80955	.64127 64177 33575
79	.26179 10170 89691	.64132 87783 39959
0.9180	0.26176 69870 86211	0.64138 11341 40383
81	.26174 29566 71034	.64143 34851 34766
82	.26171 89258 44680	.64148 58313 23024
83	.26169 48946 07665	.64153 81727 05076
84	.26167 08629 60509	.64159 05092 80840
0.9185	0.26164 68309 03729	0.64164 28410 50233
86	.26162 27984 37845	.64169 51680 13174
87	.26159 87655 63373	.64174 74901 69581
88	.26157 47322 80833	.64179 98075 19372
89	.26155 06985 90742	.64185 21200 62466
0.9190	0.26152 66644 93618	0.64190 44277 98781
91	.26150 26299 89981	.64195 67307 28236
92	.26147 85950 80346	.64200 90288 50750
93	.26145 45597 65234	.64206 13221 66242
94	.26143 05240 45160	.64211 36106 74629
0.9195	0.26140 64879 20645	0.64216 58943 75833
96	.26138 24513 92204	.64221 81732 69771
97	.26135 84144 60357	.64227 04473 56363
98	.26133 43771 25621	.64232 27166 35528
99	.26131 03393 88514	.64237 49811 07186
0.9200	0.26128 63012 49553	0.64242 72407 71257

x	$\dfrac{1}{\sqrt{2\pi}} e^{-\frac{x^2}{2}}$	$\dfrac{1}{\sqrt{2\pi}} \displaystyle\int_{-x}^{x} e^{-\frac{\alpha^2}{2}}\, d\alpha$
0.9200	0.26128 63012 49553	0.64242 72407 71257
01	.26126 22627 09257	.64247 94956 27659
02	.26123 82237 68142	.64253 17456 76314
03	.26121 41844 26727	.64258 39909 17140
04	.26119 01446 85529	.64263 62313 50058
0.9205	0.26116 61045 45066	0.64268 84669 74987
06	.26114 20640 05855	.64274 06977 91849
07	.26111 80230 68413	.64279 29238 00563
08	.26109 39817 33259	.64284 51450 01050
09	.26106 99400 00910	.64289 73613 93230
0.9210	0.26104 58978 71882	0.64294 95729 77024
11	.26102 18553 46694	.64300 17797 52352
12	.26099 78124 25863	.64305 39817 19136
13	.26097 37691 09905	.64310 61788 77296
14	.26094 97253 99339	.64315 83712 26754
0.9215	0.26092 56812 94681	0.64321 05587 67430
16	.26090 16367 96449	.64326 27414 99245
17	.26087 75919 05159	.64331 49194 22122
18	.26085 35466 21329	.64336 70925 35981
19	.26082 95009 45476	.64341 92608 40745
0.9220	0.26080 54548 78117	0.64347 14243 36333
21	.26078 14084 19769	.64352 35830 22670
22	.26075 73615 70949	.64357 57368 99675
23	.26073 33143 32173	.64362 78859 67272
24	.26070 92667 03960	.64368 00302 25382
0.9225	0.26068 52186 86824	0.64373 21696 73928
26	.26066 11702 81284	.64378 43043 12831
27	.26063 71214 87856	.64383 64341 42014
28	.26061 30723 07057	.64388 85591 61400
29	.26058 90227 39403	.64394 06793 70911
0.9230	0.26056 49727 85412	0.64399 27947 70470
31	.26054 09224 45599	.64404 49053 60000
32	.26051 68717 20482	.64409 70111 39423
33	.26049 28206 10577	.64414 91121 08662
34	.26046 87691 16400	.64420 12082 67641
0.9235	0.26044 47172 38469	0.64425 32996 16283
36	.26042 06649 77299	.64430 53861 54511
37	.26039 66123 33406	.64435 74678 82249
38	.26037 25593 07308	.64440 95447 99419
39	.26034 85058 99521	.64446 16169 05946
0.9240	0.26032 44521 10560	0.64451 36842 01754
41	.26030 03979 40943	.64456 57466 86765
42	.26027 63433 91185	.64461 78043 60905
43	.26025 22884 61802	.64466 98572 24096
44	.26022 82331 53312	.64472 19052 76264
0.9245	0.26020 41774 66229	0.64477 39485 17332
46	.26018 01214 01070	.64482 59869 47225
47	.26015 60649 58352	.64487 80205 65868
48	.26013 20081 38589	.64493 00493 73184
49	.26010 79509 42298	.64498 20733 69098
0.9250	0.26008 38933 69996	0.64503 40925 53535

X	$\frac{1}{\sqrt{2\pi}} e^{-\frac{x^2}{2}}$	$\frac{1}{\sqrt{2\pi}} \int_{-x}^{x} e^{-\frac{\alpha^2}{2}} d\alpha$
0.9250	0.26008 38933 69996	0.64503 40925 53535
51	.26005 98354 22197	.64508 61069 26421
52	.26003 57770 99418	.64513 81164 87679
53	.26001 17184 02174	.64519 01212 37236
54	.25998 76593 30982	.64524 21211 75015
0.9255	0.25996 35998 86357	0.64529 41163 00943
56	.25993 95400 68815	.64534 61066 14945
57	.25991 54798 78872	.64539 80921 16946
58	.25989 14193 17042	.64545 00728 06872
59	.25986 73583 83843	.64550 20486 84648
0.9260	0.25984 32970 79789	0.64555 40197 50201
61	.25981 92354 05395	.64560 59860 03455
62	.25979 51733 61179	.64565 79474 44338
63	.25977 11109 47654	.64570 99040 72775
64	.25974 70481 65336	.64576 18558 88692
0.9265	0.25972 29850 14742	0.64581 38028 92017
66	.25969 89214 96385	.64586 57450 82674
67	.25967 48576 10782	.64591 76824 60591
68	.25965 07933 58447	.64596 96150 25694
69	.25962 67287 39896	.64602 15427 77910
0.9270	0.25960 26637 55645	0.64607 34657 17165
71	.25957 85984 06208	.64612 53838 43388
72	.25955 45326 92100	.64617 72971 56503
73	.25953 04666 13837	.64622 92056 56440
74	.25950 64001 71934	.64628 11093 43125
0.9275	0.25948 23333 66905	0.64633 30082 16485
76	.25945 82661 99266	.64638 49022 76447
77	.25943 41986 69531	.64643 67915 22940
78	.25941 01307 78216	.64648 86759 55891
79	.25938 60625 25836	.64654 05555 75227
0.9280	0.25936 19939 12904	0.64659 24303 80877
81	.25933 79249 39937	.64664 43003 72769
82	.25931 38556 07449	.64669 61655 50829
83	.25928 97859 15954	.64674 80259 14988
84	.25926 57158 65967	.64679 98814 65172
0.9285	0.25924 16454 58003	0.64685 17322 01310
86	.25921 75746 92577	.64690 35781 23331
87	.25919 35035 70203	.64695 54192 31163
88	.25916 94320 91395	.64700 72555 24736
89	.25914 53602 56669	.64705 90870 03976
0.9290	0.25912 12880 66538	0.64711 09136 68815
91	.25909 72155 21518	.64716 27355 19179
92	.25907 31426 22122	.64721 45525 54999
93	.25904 90693 68864	.64726 63647 76204
94	.25902 49957 62260	.64731 81721 82723
0.9295	0.25900 09218 02823	0.64736 99747 74486
96	.25897 68474 91068	.64742 17725 51421
97	.25895 27728 27509	.64747 35655 13459
98	.25892 86978 12660	.64752 53536 60529
99	.25890 46224 47035	.64757 71369 92561
0.9300	0.25888 05467 31149	0.64762 89155 09484

x	$\dfrac{1}{\sqrt{2\pi}}e^{-\frac{x^2}{2}}$	$\dfrac{1}{\sqrt{2\pi}}\displaystyle\int_{-x}^{x}e^{-\frac{\alpha^2}{2}}\,d\alpha$
0.9300	0.25888 05467 31149	0.64762 89155 09484
01	.25885 64706 65515	.64768 06892 11230
02	.25883 23942 50647	.64773 24580 97727
03	.25880 83174 87060	.64778 42221 68907
04	.25878 42403 75267	.64783 59814 24699
0.9305	0.25876 01629 15782	0.64788 77358 65034
06	.25873 60851 09119	.64793 94854 89842
07	.25871 20069 55793	.64799 12302 99054
08	.25868 79284 56316	.64804 29702 92601
09	.25866 38496 11202	.64809 47054 70414
0.9310	0.25863 97704 20966	0.64814 64358 32423
11	.25861 56908 86121	.64819 81613 78559
12	.25859 16110 07181	.64824 98821 08754
13	.25856 75307 84659	.64830 15980 22939
14	.25854 34502 19068	.64835 33091 21045
0.9315	0.25851 93693 10923	0.64840 50154 03004
16	.25849 52880 60737	.64845 67168 68747
17	.25847 12064 69023	.64850 84135 18205
18	.25844 71245 36294	.64856 01053 51312
19	.25842 30422 63065	.64861 17923 67997
0.9320	0.25839 89596 49848	0.64866 34745 68194
21	.25837 48766 97157	.64871 51519 51834
22	.25835 07934 05506	.64876 68245 18850
23	.25832 67097 75406	.64881 84922 69174
24	.25830 26258 07372	.64887 01552 02738
0.9325	0.25827 85415 01917	0.64892 18133 19475
26	.25825 44568 59553	.64897 34666 19316
27	.25823 03718 80794	.64902 51151 02196
28	.25820 62865 66153	.64907 67587 68046
29	.25818 22009 16143	.64912 83976 16800
0.9330	0.25815 81149 31277	0.64918 00316 48390
31	.25813 40286 12068	.64923 16608 62750
32	.25810 99419 59029	.64928 32852 59813
33	.25808 58549 72672	.64933 49048 39512
34	.25806 17676 53510	.64938 65196 01780
0.9335	0.25803 76800 02057	0.64943 81295 46551
36	.25801 35920 18825	.64948 97346 73759
37	.25798 95037 04326	.64954 13349 83336
38	.25796 54150 59074	.64959 29304 75218
39	.25794 13260 83581	.64964 45211 49338
0.9340	0.25791 72367 78359	0.64969 61070 05630
41	.25789 31471 43921	.64974 76880 44027
42	.25786 90571 80780	.64979 92642 64465
43	.25784 49668 89449	.64985 08356 66878
44	.25782 08762 70438	.64990 24022 51199
0.9345	0.25779 67853 24262	0.64995 39640 17364
46	.25777 26940 51432	.65000 55209 65307
47	.25774 86024 52461	.65005 70730 94963
48	.25772 45105 27860	.65010 86204 06266
49	.25770 04182 78143	.65016 01628 99152
0.9350	0.25767 63257 03821	0.65021 17005 73556

x	$\frac{1}{\sqrt{2\pi}} e^{-\frac{x^2}{2}}$	$\frac{1}{\sqrt{2\pi}} \int_{-x}^{x} e^{-\frac{\alpha^2}{2}} d\alpha$
0.9350	0.25767 63257 03821	0.65021 17005 73556
51	.25765 22328 05407	.65026 32334 29412
52	.25762 81395 83413	.65031 47614 66657
53	.25760 40460 38350	.65036 62846 85224
54	.25757 99521 70732	.65041 78030 85050
0.9355	0.25755 58579 81069	0.65046 93166 66071
56	.25753 17634 69874	.65052 08254 28221
57	.25750 76686 37659	.65057 23293 71438
58	.25748 35734 84936	.65062 38284 95655
59	.25745 94780 12216	.65067 53228 00810
0.9360	0.25743 53822 20012	0.65072 68122 86839
61	.25741 12861 08835	.65077 82969 53677
62	.25738 71896 79197	.65082 97768 01261
63	.25736 30929 31610	.65088 12518 29527
64	.25733 89958 66585	.65093 27220 38413
0.9365	0.25731 48984 84635	0.65098 41874 27853
66	.25729 08007 86270	.65103 56479 97785
67	.25726 67027 72002	.65108 71037 48146
68	.25724 26044 42343	.65113 85546 78873
69	.25721 85057 97804	.65119 00007 89902
0.9370	0.25719 44068 38897	0.65124 14420 81171
71	.25717 03075 66133	.65129 28785 52617
72	.25714 62079 80024	.65134 43102 04177
73	.25712 21080 81080	.65139 57370 35788
74	.25709 80078 69813	.65144 71590 47388
0.9375	0.25707 39073 46735	0.65149 85762 38915
76	.25704 98065 12356	.65154 99886 10306
77	.25702 57053 67188	.65160 13961 61499
78	.25700 16039 11742	.65165 27988 92433
79	.25697 75021 46529	.65170 41968 03044
0.9380	0.25695 34000 72059	0.65175 55898 93271
81	.25692 92976 88845	.65180 69781 63052
82	.25690 51949 97397	.65185 83616 12326
83	.25688 10919 98226	.65190 97402 41030
84	.25685 69886 91843	.65196 11140 49104
0.9385	0.25683 28850 78759	0.65201 24830 36487
86	.25680 87811 59484	.65206 38472 03115
87	.25678 46769 34530	.65211 52065 48930
88	.25676 05724 04407	.65216 65610 73869
89	.25673 64675 69626	.65221 79107 77871
0.9390	0.25671 23624 30697	0.65226 92556 60876
91	.25668 82569 88131	.65232 05957 22823
92	.25666 41512 42440	.65237 19309 63652
93	.25664 00451 94132	.65242 32613 83300
94	.25661 59388 43720	.65247 45869 81709
0.9395	0.25659 18321 91712	0.65252 59077 58818
96	.25656 77252 38621	.65257 72237 14566
97	.25654 36179 84956	.65262 85348 48893
98	.25651 95104 31227	.65267 98411 61740
99	.25649 54025 77945	.65273 11426 53046
0.9400	0.25647 12944 25620	0.65278 24393 22751

x	$\dfrac{1}{\sqrt{2\pi}}\,e^{-\frac{x^2}{2}}$	$\dfrac{1}{\sqrt{2\pi}}\displaystyle\int_{-x}^{x} e^{-\frac{\alpha^2}{2}}\,d\alpha$
0.9400	0.25647 12944 25620	0.65278 24393 22751
01	.25644 71859 74763	.65283 37311 70796
02	.25642 30772 25883	.65288 50181 97121
03	.25639 89681 79492	.65293 63004 01666
04	.25637 48588 36098	.65298 75777 84373
0.9405	0.25635 07491 96212	0.65303 88503 45181
06	.25632 66392 60344	.65309 01180 84032
07	.25630 25290 29004	.65314 13810 00865
08	.25627 84185 02702	.65319 26390 95624
09	.25625 43076 81949	.65324 38923 68247
0.9410	0.25623 01965 67253	0.65329 51408 18677
11	.25620 60851 59125	.65334 63844 46854
12	.25618 19734 58074	.65339 76232 52721
13	.25615 78614 64611	.65344 88572 36218
14	.25613 37491 79245	.65350 00863 97287
0.9415	0.25610 96366 02485	0.65355 13107 35870
16	.25608 55237 34842	.65360 25302 51909
17	.25606 14105 76825	.65365 37449 45345
18	.25603 72971 28944	.65370 49548 16120
19	.25601 31833 91708	.65375 61598 64177
0.9420	0.25598 90693 65626	0.65380 73600 89458
21	.25596 49550 51209	.65385 85554 91904
22	.25594 08404 48966	.65390 97460 71459
23	.25591 67255 59405	.65396 09318 28065
24	.25589 26103 83036	.65401 21127 61664
0.9425	0.25586 84949 20370	0.65406 32888 72199
26	.25584 43791 71914	.65411 44601 59613
27	.25582 02631 38178	.65416 56266 23848
28	.25579 61468 19671	.65421 67882 64849
29	.25577 20302 16903	.65426 79450 82557
0.9430	0.25574 79133 30383	0.65431 90970 76917
31	.25572 37961 60619	.65437 02442 47871
32	.25569 96787 08121	.65442 13865 95362
33	.25567 55609 73397	.65447 25241 19335
34	.25565 14429 56957	.65452 36568 19733
0.9435	0.25562 73246 59309	0.65457 47846 96499
36	.25560 32060 80963	.65462 59077 49578
37	.25557 90872 22427	.65467 70259 78913
38	.25555 49680 84211	.65472 81393 84448
39	.25553 08486 66821	.65477 92479 66128
0.9440	0.25550 67289 70769	0.65483 03517 23896
41	.25548 26089 96561	.65488 14506 57698
42	.25545 84887 44708	.65493 25447 67476
43	.25543 43682 15716	.65498 36340 53177
44	.25541 02474 10096	.65503 47185 14744
0.9445	0.25538 61263 28355	0.65508 57981 52123
46	.25536 20049 71002	.65513 68729 65257
47	.25533 78833 38545	.65518 79429 54093
48	.25531 37614 31493	.65523 90081 18574
49	.25528 96392 50355	.65529 00684 58647
0.9450	0.25526 55167 95637	0.65534 11239 74256

X	$\dfrac{1}{\sqrt{2\pi}}\, e^{-\frac{x^2}{2}}$	$\dfrac{1}{\sqrt{2\pi}}\displaystyle\int_{-x}^{x} e^{-\frac{\alpha^2}{2}}\, d\alpha$
0.9450	0.25526 55167 95637	0.65534 11239 74256
51	.25524 13940 67850	.65539 21746 65347
52	.25521 72710 67500	.65544 32205 31865
53	.25519 31477 95097	.65549 42615 73756
54	.25516 90242 51147	.65554 52977 90965
0.9455	0.25514 49004 36160	0.65559 63291 83438
56	.25512 07763 50644	.65564 73557 51122
57	.25509 66519 95106	.65569 83774 93961
58	.25507 25273 70055	.65574 93944 11902
59	.25504 84024 75998	.65580 04065 04891
0.9460	0.25502 42773 13444	0.65585 14137 72874
61	.25500 01518 82900	.65590 24162 15798
62	.25497 60261 84874	.65595 34138 33610
63	.25495 19002 19874	.65600 44066 26254
64	.25492 77739 88408	.65605 53945 93680
0.9465	0.25490 36474 90983	0.65610 63777 35832
66	.25487 95207 28107	.65615 73560 52658
67	.25485 53937 00288	.65620 83295 44106
68	.25483 12664 08033	.65625 92982 10121
69	.25480 71388 51850	.65631 02620 50651
0.9470	0.25478 30110 32246	0.65636 12210 65644
71	.25475 88829 49729	.65641 21752 55047
72	.25473 47546 04807	.65646 31246 18806
73	.25471 06259 97986	.65651 40691 56871
74	.25468 64971 29775	.65656 50088 69188
0.9475	0.25466 23680 00679	0.65661 59437 55706
76	.25463 82386 11208	.65666 68738 16371
77	.25461 41089 61867	.65671 77990 51133
78	.25458 99790 53164	.65676 87194 59939
79	.25456 58488 85606	.65681 96350 42737
0.9480	0.25454 17184 59701	0.65687 05457 99476
81	.25451 75877 75955	.65692 14517 30103
82	.25449 34568 34876	.65697 23528 34569
83	.25446 93256 36970	.65702 32491 12820
84	.25444 51941 82745	.65707 41405 64807
0.9485	0.25442 10624 72707	0.65712 50271 90476
86	.25439 69305 07363	.65717 59089 89779
87	.25437 27982 87220	.65722 67859 62662
88	.25434 86658 12785	.65727 76581 09077
89	.25432 45330 84564	.65732 85254 28970
0.9490	0.25430 04001 03065	0.65737 93879 22293
91	.25427 62668 68793	.65743 02455 88995
92	.25425 21333 82257	.65748 10984 29024
93	.25422 79996 43061	.65753 19464 42331
94	.25420 38656 54413	.65758 27896 28865
0.9495	0.25417 97314 14119	0.65763 36279 88576
96	.25415 55969 23586	.65768 44615 21414
97	.25413 14621 83320	.65773 52902 27329
98	.25410 73271 93828	.65778 61141 06271
99	.25408 31919 55615	.65783 69331 58190
0.9500	0.25405 90564 69189	0.65788 77473 83036

x	$\dfrac{1}{\sqrt{2\pi}}\, e^{-\frac{x^2}{2}}$	$\dfrac{1}{\sqrt{2\pi}} \displaystyle\int_{-x}^{x} e^{-\frac{\alpha^2}{2}}\, d\alpha$
0.9500	0.25405 90564 69189	0.65788 77473 83036
01	.25403 49207 35055	.65793 85567 80761
02	.25401 07847 53720	.65798 93613 51314
03	.25398 66485 25689	.65804 01610 94646
04	.25396 25120 51470	.65809 09560 10708
0.9505	0.25393 83753 31567	0.65814 17460 99450
06	.25391 42383 66488	.65819 25313 60824
07	.25389 01011 56738	.65824 33117 94780
08	.25386 59637 02822	.65829 40874 01270
09	.25384 18260 05248	.65834 48581 80245
0.9510	0.25381 76880 64521	0.65839 56241 31656
11	.25379 35498 81147	.65844 63852 55455
12	.25376 94114 55632	.65849 71415 51593
13	.25374 52727 88480	.65854 78930 20021
14	.25372 11338 80199	.65859 86396 60692
0.9515	0.25369 69947 31294	0.65864 93814 73557
16	.25367 28553 42271	.65870 01184 58569
17	.25364 87157 13634	.65875 08506 15678
18	.25362 45758 45890	.65880 15779 44838
19	.25360 04357 39545	.65885 23004 46001
0.9520	0.25357 62953 95103	0.65890 30181 19118
21	.25355 21548 13070	.65895 37309 64143
22	.25352 80139 93952	.65900 44389 81027
23	.25350 38729 38253	.65905 51421 69725
24	.25347 97316 46480	.65910 58405 30187
0.9525	0.25345 55901 19138	0.65915 65340 62367
26	.25343 14483 56731	.65920 72227 66219
27	.25340 73063 59765	.65925 79066 41695
28	.25338 31641 28745	.65930 85856 88747
29	.25335 90216 64177	.65935 92599 07330
0.9530	0.25333 48789 66565	0.65940 99292 97397
31	.25331 07360 36414	.65946 05938 58902
32	.25328 65928 74230	.65951 12535 91796
33	.25326 24494 80517	.65956 19084 96036
34	.25323 83058 55780	.65961 25585 71573
0.9535	0.25321 41620 00525	0.65966 32038 18363
36	.25319 00179 15255	.65971 38442 36358
37	.25316 58736 00476	.65976 44798 25514
38	.25314 17290 56693	.65981 51105 85783
39	.25311 75842 84410	.65986 57365 17121
0.9540	0.25309 34392 84131	0.65991 63576 19482
41	.25306 92940 56362	.65996 69738 92819
42	.25304 51486 01608	.66001 75853 37089
43	.25302 10029 20372	.66006 81919 52245
44	.25299 68570 13158	.66011 87937 38242
0.9545	0.25297 27108 80473	0.66016 93906 95035
46	.25294 85645 22820	.66021 99828 22579
47	.25292 44179 40702	.66027 05701 20829
48	.25290 02711 34626	.66032 11525 89741
49	.25287 61241 05095	.66037 17302 29268
0.9550	0.25285 19768 52613	0.66042 23030 39368

x	$\dfrac{1}{\sqrt{2\pi}} e^{-\frac{x^2}{2}}$	$\dfrac{1}{\sqrt{2\pi}} \displaystyle\int_{-x}^{x} e^{-\frac{\alpha^2}{2}} \, d\alpha$
0.9550	0.25285 19768 52613	0.66042 23030 39368
51	.25282 78293 77684	.66047 28710 19995
52	.25280 36816 80813	.66052 34341 71104
53	.25277 95337 62504	.66057 39924 92652
54	.25275 53856 23260	.66062 45459 84594
0.9555	0.25273 12372 63587	0.66067 50946 46887
56	.25270 70886 83987	.66072 56384 79485
57	.25268 29398 84965	.66077 61774 82346
58	.25265 87908 67025	.66082 67116 55425
59	.25263 46416 30671	.66087 72409 98678
0.9560	0.25261 04921 76406	0.66092 77655 12062
61	.25258 63425 04735	.66097 82851 95534
62	.25256 21926 16161	.66102 88000 49050
63	.25253 80425 11187	.66107 93100 72566
64	.25251 38921 90318	.66112 98152 66040
0.9565	0.25248 97416 54057	0.66118 03156 29428
66	.25246 55909 02907	.66123 08111 62687
67	.25244 14399 37373	.66128 13018 65775
68	.25241 72887 57957	.66133 17877 38648
69	.25239 31373 65164	.66138 22687 81264
0.9570	0.25236 89857 59496	0.66143 27449 93580
71	.25234 48339 41458	.66148 32163 75553
72	.25232 06819 11551	.66153 36829 27142
73	.25229 65296 70280	.66158 41446 48304
74	.25227 23772 18148	.66163 46015 38996
0.9575	0.25224 82245 55658	0.66168 50535 99177
76	.25222 40716 83313	.66173 55008 28804
77	.25219 99186 01617	.66178 59432 27836
78	.25217 57653 11072	.66183 63807 96231
79	.25215 16118 12182	.66188 68135 33947
0.9580	0.25212 74581 05449	0.66193 72414 40942
81	.25210 33041 91376	.66198 76645 17175
82	.25207 91500 70467	.66203 80827 62605
83	.25205 49957 43224	.66208 84961 77190
84	.25203 08412 10151	.66213 89047 60889
0.9585	0.25200 66864 71749	0.66218 93085 13660
86	.25198 25315 28522	.66223 97074 35464
87	.25195 83763 80972	.66229 01015 26258
88	.25193 42210 29602	.66234 04907 86002
89	.25191 00654 74915	.66239 08752 14656
0.9590	0.25188 59097 17413	0.66244 12548 12179
91	.25186 17537 57598	.66249 16295 78530
92	.25183 75975 95974	.66254 19995 13668
93	.25181 34412 33043	.66259 23646 17555
94	.25178 92846 69307	.66264 27248 90148
0.9595	0.25176 51279 05268	0.66269 30803 31409
96	.25174 09709 41429	.66274 34309 41297
97	.25171 68137 78293	.66279 37767 19772
98	.25169 26564 16360	.66284 41176 66795
99	.25166 84988 56134	.66289 44537 82326
0.9600	0.25164 43410 98117	0.66294 47850 66324

x	$\frac{1}{\sqrt{2\pi}} e^{-\frac{x^2}{2}}$	$\frac{1}{\sqrt{2\pi}} \int_{-x}^{x} e^{-\frac{\alpha^2}{2}} d\alpha$
0.9600	0.25164 43410 98117	0.66294 47850 66324
01	.25162 01831 42811	.66299 51115 18752
02	.25159 60249 90717	.66304 54331 39568
03	.25157 18666 42339	.66309 57499 28735
04	.25154 77080 98177	.66314 60618 86212
0.9605	0.25152 35493 58735	0.66319 63690 11961
06	.25149 93904 24513	.66324 66713 05943
07	.25147 52312 96014	.66329 69687 68118
08	.25145 10719 73739	.66334 72613 98448
09	.25142 69124 58190	.66339 75491 96895
0.9610	0.25140 27527 49870	0.66344 78321 63419
11	.25137 85928 49279	.66349 81102 97982
12	.25135 44327 56920	.66354 83836 00546
13	.25133 02724 73293	.66359 86520 71072
14	.25130 61119 98901	.66364 89157 09522
0.9615	0.25128 19513 34245	0.66369 91745 15859
16	.25125 77904 79827	.66374 94284 90043
17	.25123 36294 36147	.66379 96776 32038
18	.25120 94682 03708	.66384 99219 41805
19	.25118 53067 83011	.66390 01614 19307
0.9620	0.25116 11451 74556	0.66395 03960 64506
21	.25113 69833 78846	.66400 06258 77364
22	.25111 28213 96382	.66405 08508 57845
23	.25108 86592 27664	.66410 10710 05910
24	.25106 44968 73194	.66415 12863 21524
0.9625	0.25104 03343 33473	0.66420 14968 04647
26	.25101 61716 09001	.66425 17024 55245
27	.25099 20087 00281	.66430 19032 73279
28	.25096 78456 07813	.66435 20992 58713
29	.25094 36823 32098	.66440 22904 11510
0.9630	0.25091 95188 73637	0.66445 24767 31633
31	.25089 53552 32930	.66450 26582 19047
32	.25087 11914 10479	.66455 28348 73714
33	.25084 70274 06784	.66460 30066 95599
34	.25082 28632 22345	.66465 31736 84665
0.9635	0.25079 86988 57665	0.66470 33358 40876
36	.25077 45343 13242	.66475 34931 64196
37	.25075 03695 89579	.66480 36456 54589
38	.25072 62046 87175	.66485 37933 12020
39	.25070 20396 06530	.66490 39361 36452
0.9640	0.25067 78743 48146	0.66495 40741 27851
41	.25065 37089 12523	.66500 42072 86180
42	.25062 95433 00160	.66505 43356 11404
43	.25060 53775 11559	.66510 44591 03488
44	.25058 12115 47220	.66515 45777 62397
0.9645	0.25055 70454 07643	0.66520 46915 88095
46	.25053 28790 93328	.66525 48005 80548
47	.25050 87126 04775	.66530 49047 39721
48	.25048 45459 42484	.66535 50040 65579
49	.25046 03791 06957	.66540 50985 58086
0.9650	0.25043 62120 98691	0.66545 51882 17210

x	$\dfrac{1}{\sqrt{2\pi}}e^{-\frac{x^2}{2}}$	$\dfrac{1}{\sqrt{2\pi}}\displaystyle\int_{-x}^{x}e^{-\frac{\alpha^2}{2}}\,d\alpha$
0.9650	0.25043 62120 98691	0.66545 51882 17210
51	.25041 20449 18188	.66550 52730 42914
52	.25038 78775 65948	.66555 53530 35166
53	.25036 37100 42469	.66560 54281 93929
54	.25033 95423 48253	.66565 54985 19171
0.9655	0.25031 53744 83799	0.66570 55640 10857
56	.25029 12064 49607	.66575 56246 68953
57	.25026 70382 46176	.66580 56804 93426
58	.25024 28698 74007	.66585 57314 84241
59	.25021 87013 33598	.66590 57776 41364
0.9660	0.25019 45326 25450	0.66595 58189 64763
61	.25017 03637 50061	.66600 58554 54403
62	.25014 61947 07932	.66605 58871 10252
63	.25012 20254 99563	.66610 59139 32275
64	.25009 78561 25451	.66615 59359 20441
0.9665	0.25007 36865 86097	0.66620 59530 74714
66	.25004 95168 82000	.66625 59653 95064
67	.25002 53470 13660	.66630 59728 81456
68	.25000 11769 81575	.66635 59755 33859
69	.24997 70067 86245	.66640 59733 52238
0.9670	0.24995 28364 28169	0.66645 59663 36562
71	.24992 86659 07846	.66650 59544 86799
72	.24990 44952 25776	.66655 59378 02915
73	.24988 03243 82456	.66660 59162 84878
74	.24985 61533 78387	.66665 58899 32657
0.9675	0.24983 19822 14067	0.66670 58587 46219
76	.24980 78108 89995	.66675 58227 25532
77	.24978 36394 06670	.66680 57818 70564
78	.24975 94677 64590	.66685 57361 81284
79	.24973 52959 64255	.66690 56856 57659
0.9680	0.24971 11240 06164	0.66695 56302 99659
81	.24968 69518 90814	.66700 55701 07251
82	.24966 27796 18705	.66705 55050 80405
83	.24963 86071 90335	.66710 54352 19088
84	.24961 44346 06202	.66715 53605 23271
0.9685	0.24959 02618 66806	0.66720 52809 92921
86	.24956 60889 72645	.66725 51966 28007
87	.24954 19159 24217	.66730 51074 28499
88	.24951 77427 22020	.66735 50133 94367
89	.24949 35693 66553	.66740 49145 25578
0.9690	0.24946 93958 58314	0.66745 48108 22103
91	.24944 52221 97802	.66750 47022 83911
92	.24942 10483 85514	.66755 45889 10972
93	.24939 68744 21949	.66760 44707 03255
94	.24937 27003 07605	.66765 43476 60731
0.9695	0.24934 85260 42979	0.66770 42197 83368
96	.24932 43516 28571	.66775 40870 71138
97	.24930 01770 64877	.66780 39495 24010
98	.24927 60023 52397	.66785 38071 41954
99	.24925 18274 91627	.66790 36599 24941
0.9700	0.24922 76524 83066	0.66795 35078 72941

x	$\frac{1}{\sqrt{2\pi}} e^{-\frac{x^2}{2}}$	$\frac{1}{\sqrt{2\pi}} \int_{-x}^{x} e^{-\frac{\alpha^2}{2}} d\alpha$
0.9700	0.24922 76524 83066	0.66795 35078 72941
01	.24920 34773 27211	.66800 33509 85924
02	.24917 93020 24561	.66805 31892 63862
03	.24915 51265 75612	.66810 30227 06724
04	.24913 09509 80863	.66815 28513 14482
0.9705	0.24910 67752 40812	0.66820 26750 87107
06	.24908 25993 55955	.66825 24940 24569
07	.24905 84233 26791	.66830 23081 26840
08	.24903 42471 53816	.66835 21173 93890
09	.24901 00708 37529	.66840 19218 25692
0.9710	0.24898 58943 78427	0.66845 17214 22216
11	.24896 17177 77007	.66850 15161 83434
12	.24893 75410 33766	.66855 13061 09317
13	.24891 33641 49202	.66860 10911 99838
14	.24888 91871 23812	.66865 08714 54967
0.9715	0.24886 50099 58093	0.66870 06468 74678
16	.24884 08326 52543	.66875 04174 58941
17	.24881 66552 07658	.66880 01832 07730
18	.24879 24776 23935	.66884 99441 21015
19	.24876 82999 01873	.66889 97001 98770
0.9720	0.24874 41220 41966	0.66894 94514 40967
21	.24871 99440 44713	.66899 91978 47578
22	.24869 57659 10611	.66904 89394 18575
23	.24867 15876 40155	.66909 86761 53933
24	.24864 74092 33844	.66914 84080 53622
0.9725	0.24862 32306 92173	0.66919 81351 17617
26	.24859 90520 15640	.66924 78573 45890
27	.24857 48732 04740	.66929 75747 38415
28	.24855 06942 59972	.66934 72872 95163
29	.24852 65151 81831	.66939 69950 16110
0.9730	0.24850 23359 70813	0.66944 66979 01227
31	.24847 81566 27416	.66949 63959 50489
32	.24845 39771 52136	.66954 60891 63869
33	.24842 97975 45469	.66959 57775 41341
34	.24840 56178 07911	.66964 54610 82879
0.9735	0.24838 14379 39959	0.66969 51397 88456
36	.24835 72579 42110	.66974 48136 58046
37	.24833 30778 14858	.66979 44826 91624
38	.24830 88975 58701	.66984 41468 89163
39	.24828 47171 74135	.66989 38062 50639
0.9740	0.24826 05366 61656	0.66994 34607 76025
41	.24823 63560 21759	.66999 31104 65295
42	.24821 21752 54941	.67004 27553 18425
43	.24818 79943 61698	.67009 23953 35389
44	.24816 38133 42525	.67014 20305 16161
0.9745	0.24813 96321 97919	0.67019 16608 60717
46	.24811 54509 28375	.67024 12863 69032
47	.24809 12695 34389	.67029 09070 41080
48	.24806 70880 16457	.67034 05228 76837
49	.24804 29063 75074	.67039 01338 76279
0.9750	0.24801 87246 10737	0.67043 97400 39379

x	$\dfrac{1}{\sqrt{2\pi}} e^{-\frac{x^2}{2}}$	$\dfrac{1}{\sqrt{2\pi}} \displaystyle\int_{-x}^{x} e^{-\frac{\alpha^2}{2}} d\alpha$
0.9750	0.24801 87246 10737	0.67043 97400 39379
51	.24799 45427 23941	.67048 93413 66115
52	.24797 03607 15180	.67053 89378 56461
53	.24794 61785 84952	.67058 85295 10393
54	.24792 19963 33751	.67063 81163 27887
0.9755	0.24789 78139 62072	0.67068 76983 08918
56	.24787 36314 70412	.67073 72754 53463
57	.24784 94488 59265	.67078 68477 61498
58	.24782 52661 29126	.67083 64152 32999
59	.24780 10832 80492	.67088 59778 67942
0.9760	0.24777 69003 13857	0.67093 55356 66304
61	.24775 27172 29716	.67098 50886 28060
62	.24772 85340 28564	.67103 46367 53188
63	.24770 43507 10897	.67108 41800 41663
64	.24768 01672 77209	.67113 37184 93464
0.9765	0.24765 59837 27996	0.67118 32521 08567
66	.24763 18000 63752	.67123 27808 86948
67	.24760 76162 84973	.67128 23048 28585
68	.24758 34323 92152	.67133 18239 33454
69	.24755 92483 85785	.67138 13382 01534
0.9770	0.24753 50642 66367	0.67143 08476 32801
71	.24751 08800 34393	.67148 03522 27233
72	.24748 66956 90356	.67152 98519 84807
73	.24746 25112 34752	.67157 93469 05502
74	.24743 83266 68075	.67162 88369 89294
0.9775	0.24741 41419 90820	0.67167 83222 36161
76	.24738 99572 03481	.67172 78026 46083
77	.24736 57723 06552	.67177 72782 19036
78	.24734 15873 00528	.67182 67489 54998
79	.24731 74021 85904	.67187 62148 53948
0.9780	0.24729 32169 63174	0.67192 56759 15865
81	.24726 90316 32831	.67197 51321 40727
82	.24724 48461 95370	.67202 45835 28511
83	.24722 06606 51286	.67207 40300 79198
84	.24719 64750 01072	.67212 34717 92765
0.9785	0.24717 22892 45223	0.67217 29086 69191
86	.24714 81033 84231	.67222 23407 08456
87	.24712 39174 18593	.67227 17679 10538
88	.24709 97313 48801	.67232 11902 75416
89	.24707 55451 75349	.67237 06078 03070
0.9790	0.24705 13588 98731	0.67242 00204 93479
91	.24702 71725 19441	.67246 94283 46623
92	.24700 29860 37973	.67251 88313 62480
93	.24697 87994 54820	.67256 82295 41031
94	.24695 46127 70476	.67261 76228 82256
0.9795	0.24693 04259 85435	0.67266 70113 86133
96	.24690 62391 00190	.67271 63950 52643
97	.24688 20521 15235	.67276 57738 81766
98	.24685 78650 31063	.67281 51478 73483
99	.24683 36778 48168	.67286 45170 27772
0.9800	0.24680 94905 67043	0.67291 38813 44615

x	$\dfrac{1}{\sqrt{2\pi}} e^{-\frac{x^2}{2}}$	$\dfrac{1}{\sqrt{2\pi}} \displaystyle\int_{-x}^{x} e^{-\frac{\alpha^2}{2}} \, d\alpha$
0.9800	0.24680 94905 67043	0.67291 38813 44615
01	.24678 53031 88181	.67296 32408 23992
02	.24676 11157 12076	.67301 25954 65884
03	.24673 69281 39221	.67306 19452 70271
04	.24671 27404 70110	.67311 12902 37133
0.9805	0.24668 85527 05234	0.67316 06303 66452
06	.24666 43648 45088	.67320 99656 58209
07	.24664 01768 90165	.67325 92961 12384
08	.24661 59888 40958	.67330 86217 28959
09	.24659 18006 97959	.67335 79425 07914
0.9810	0.24656 76124 61661	0.67340 72584 49232
11	.24654 34241 32558	.67345 65695 52893
12	.24651 92357 11142	.67350 58758 18879
13	.24649 50471 97906	.67355 51772 47171
14	.24647 08585 93343	.67360 44738 37752
0.9815	0.24644 66698 97946	0.67365 37655 90602
16	.24642 24811 12206	.67370 30525 05705
17	.24639 82922 36618	.67375 23345 83041
18	.24637 41032 71673	.67380 16118 22594
19	.24634 99142 17864	.67385 08842 24344
0.9820	0.24632 57250 75683	0.67390 01517 88275
21	.24630 15358 45623	.67394 94145 14368
22	.24627 73465 28176	.67399 86724 02607
23	.24625 31571 23835	.67404 79254 52974
24	.24622 89676 33092	.67409 71736 65451
0.9825	0.24620 47780 56439	0.67414 64170 40021
26	.24618 05883 94368	.67419 56555 76668
27	.24615 63986 47371	.67424 48892 75374
28	.24613 22088 15942	.67429 41181 36121
29	.24610 80189 00570	.67434 33421 58894
0.9830	0.24608 38289 01750	0.67439 25613 43676
31	.24605 96388 19972	.67444 17756 90450
32	.24603 54486 55729	.67449 09851 99198
33	.24601 12584 09513	.67454 01898 69906
34	.24598 70680 81814	.67458 93897 02557
0.9835	0.24596 28776 73126	0.67463 85846 97134
36	.24593 86871 83940	.67468 77748 53621
37	.24591 44966 14747	.67473 69601 72002
38	.24589 03059 66040	.67478 61406 52261
39	.24586 61152 38309	.67483 53162 94383
0.9840	0.24584 19244 32047	0.67488 44870 98351
41	.24581 77335 47745	.67493 36530 64151
42	.24579 35425 85894	.67498 28141 91765
43	.24576 93515 46986	.67503 19704 81180
44	.24574 51604 31512	.67508 11219 32379
0.9845	0.24572 09692 39964	0.67513 02685 45347
46	.24569 67779 72833	.67517 94103 20070
47	.24567 25866 30609	.67522 85472 56532
48	.24564 83952 13785	.67527 76793 54717
49	.24562 42037 22852	.67532 68066 14612
0.9850	0.24560 00121 58300	0.67537 59290 36201

x	$\dfrac{1}{\sqrt{2\pi}}\,e^{-\frac{x^2}{2}}$	$\dfrac{1}{\sqrt{2\pi}}\displaystyle\int_{-x}^{x} e^{-\frac{\alpha^2}{2}}\,d\alpha$
0.9850	0.24560 00121 58300	0.67537 59290 36201
51	.24557 58205 20620	.67542 50466 19471
52	.24555 16288 10305	.67547 41593 64405
53	.24552 74370 27843	.67552 32672 70990
54	.24550 32451 73727	.67557 23703 39211
0.9855	0.24547 90532 48448	0.67562 14685 69055
56	.24545 48612 52496	.67567 05619 60506
57	.24543 06691 86362	.67571 96505 13551
58	.24540 64770 50536	.67576 87342 28176
59	.24538 22848 45510	.67581 78131 04367
0 9860	0.24535 80925 71774	0.67586 68871 42109
61	.24533 39002 29818	.67591 59563 41391
62	.24530 97078 20134	.67596 50207 02197
63	.24528 55153 43211	.67601 40802 24514
64	.24526 13227 99541	.67606 31349 08330
0.9865	0.24523 71301 89613	0.67611 21847 53630
66	.24521 29375 13918	.67616 12297 60401
67	.24518 87447 72946	.67621 02699 28631
68	.24516 45519 67188	.67625 93052 58306
69	.24514 03590 97133	.67630 83357 49413
0.9870	0.24511 61661 63272	0.67635 73614 01941
71	.24509 19731 66096	.67640 63822 15875
72	.24506 77801 06093	.67645 53981 91203
73	.24504 35869 83755	.67650 44093 27913
74	.24501 93937 99571	.67655 34156 25992
0.9875	0.24499 52005 54031	0.67660 24170 85429
76	.24497 10072 47625	.67665 14137 06210
77	.24494 68138 80843	.67670 04054 88324
78	.24492 26204 54174	.67674 93924 31758
79	.24489 84269 68109	.67679 83745 36501
0.9880	0.24487 42334 23137	0.67684 73518 02541
81	.24485 00398 19748	.67689 63242 29867
82	.24482 58461 58431	.67694 52918 18465
83	.24480 16524 39676	.67699 42545 68326
84	.24477 74586 63973	.67704 32124 79438
0.9885	0.24475 32648 31811	0.67709 21655 51788
86	.24472 90709 43679	.67714 11137 85367
87	.24470 48770 00067	.67719 00571 80162
88	.24468 06830 01464	.67723 89957 36163
89	.24465 64889 48359	.67728 79294 53359
0.9890	0.24463 22948 41243	0.67733 68583 31739
91	.24460 81006 80603	.67738 57823 71292
92	.24458 39064 66929	.67743 47015 72007
93	.24455 97122 00710	.67748 36159 33875
94	.24453 55178 82436	.67753 25254 56884
0.9895	0.24451 13235 12595	0.67758 14301 41025
96	.24448 71290 91676	.67763 03299 86286
97	.24446 29346 20168	.67767 92249 92658
98	.24443 87400 98560	.67772 81151 60131
99	.24441 45455 27341	.67777 70004 88694
0.9900	0.24439 03509 07000	0.67782 58809 78338

x	$\dfrac{1}{\sqrt{2\pi}}\,e^{-\frac{x^2}{2}}$	$\dfrac{1}{\sqrt{2\pi}}\displaystyle\int_{-x}^{x} e^{-\frac{\alpha^2}{2}}\,d\alpha$
0.9900	0.24439 03509 07000	0.67782 58809 78338
01	.24436 61562 38024	.67787 47566 29053
02	.24434 19615 20904	.67792 36274 40830
03	.24431 77667 56128	.67797 24934 13659
04	.24429 35719 44183	.67802 13545 47529
0.9905	0.24426 93770 85560	0.67807 02108 42433
06	.24424 51821 80746	.67811 90622 98361
07	.24422 09872 30229	.67816 79089 15302
08	.24419 67922 34499	.67821 67506 93250
09	.24417 25971 94043	.67826 55876 32193
0.9910	0.24414 84021 09349	0.67831 44197 32124
11	.24412 42069 80907	.67836 32469 93034
12	.24410 00118 09204	.67841 20694 14914
13	.24407 58165 94729	.67846 08869 97755
14	.24405 16213 37969	.67850 96997 41549
0.9915	0.24402 74260 39413	0.67855 85076 46287
16	.24400 32306 99548	.67860 73107 11962
17	.24397 90353 18863	.67865 61089 38564
18	.24395 48398 97845	.67870 49023 26087
19	.24393 06444 36983	.67875 36908 74521
0.9920	0.24390 64489 36765	0.67880 24745 83859
21	.24388 22533 97677	.67885 12534 54093
22	.24385 80578 20208	.67890 00274 85215
23	.24383 38622 04846	.67894 87966 77219
24	.24380 96665 52077	.67899 75610 30095
0.9925	0.24378 54708 62391	0.67904 63205 43837
26	.24376 12751 36274	.67909 50752 18437
27	.24373 70793 74213	.67914 38250 53889
28	.24371 28835 76697	.67919 25700 50185
29	.24368 86877 44213	.67924 13102 07317
0.9930	0.24366 44918 77248	0.67929 00455 25280
31	.24364 02959 76288	.67933 87760 04066
32	.24361 61000 41823	.67938 75016 43668
33	.24359 19040 74339	.67943 62224 44081
34	.24356 77080 74322	.67948 49384 05296
0.9935	0.24354 35120 42261	0.67953 36495 27308
36	.24351 93159 78642	.67958 23558 10111
37	.24349 51198 83952	.67963 10572 53698
38	.24347 09237 58678	.67967 97538 58062
39	.24344 67276 03308	.67972 84456 23199
0.9940	0.24342 25314 18328	0.67977 71325 49102
41	.24339 83352 04224	.67982 58146 35764
42	.24337 41389 61484	.67987 44918 83181
43	.24334 99426 90595	.67992 31642 91347
44	.24332 57463 92043	.67997 18318 60256
0.9945	0.24330 15500 66315	0.68002 04945 89902
46	.24327 73537 13897	.68006 91524 80281
47	.24325 31573 35276	.68011 78055 31386
48	.24322 89609 30939	.68016 64537 43213
49	.24320 47645 01372	.68021 50971 15757
0.9950	0.24318 05680 47061	0.68026 37356 49012

x	$\frac{1}{\sqrt{2\pi}} e^{-\frac{x^2}{2}}$	$\frac{1}{\sqrt{2\pi}} \int_{-x}^{x} e^{-\frac{\alpha^2}{2}} d\alpha$
0.9950	0.24318 05680 47061	0.68026 37356 49012
51	.24315 63715 68493	.68031 23693 42974
52	.24313 21750 66153	.68036 09981 97638
53	.24310 79785 40529	.68040 96222 12999
54	.24308 37819 92107	.68045 82413 89052
0.9955	0.24305 95854 21373	0.68050 68557 25794
56	.24303 53888 28812	.68055 54652 23220
57	.24301 11922 14911	.68060 40698 81324
58	.24298 69955 80156	.68065 26697 00104
59	.24296 27989 25033	.68070 12646 79555
0.9960	0.24293 86022 50028	0.68074 98548 19673
61	.24291 44055 55627	.68079 84401 20454
62	.24289 02088 42315	.68084 70205 81894
63	.24286 60121 10579	.68089 55962 03989
64	.24284 18153 60904	.68094 41669 86737
0.9965	0.24281 76185 93776	0.68099 27329 30133
66	.24279 34218 09680	.68104 12940 34173
67	.24276 92250 09103	.68108 98502 98855
68	.24274 50281 92529	.68113 84017 24176
69	.24272 08313 60444	.68118 69483 10131
0.9970	0.24269 66345 13334	0.68123 54900 56719
71	.24267 24376 51684	.68128 40269 63936
72	.24264 82407 75979	.68133 25590 31779
73	.24262 40438 86705	.68138 10862 60245
74	.24259 98469 84347	.68142 96086 49332
0.9975	0.24257 56500 69391	0.68147 81261 99038
76	.24255 14531 42320	.68152 66389 09359
77	.24252 72562 03621	.68157 51467 80294
78	.24250 30592 53779	.68162 36498 11840
79	.24247 88622 93278	.68167 21480 03995
0.9980	0.24245 46653 22604	0.68172 06413 56757
81	.24243 04683 42242	.68176 91298 70123
82	.24240 62713 52675	.68181 76135 44093
83	.24238 20743 54390	.68186 60923 78664
84	.24235 78773 47871	.68191 45663 73834
0.9985	0.24233 36803 33603	0.68196 30355 29603
86	.24230 94833 12070	.68201 14998 45967
87	.24228 52862 83757	.68205 99593 22927
88	.24226 10892 49149	.68210 84139 60480
89	.24223 68922 08731	.68215 68637 58626
0.9990	0.24221 26951 62985	0.68220 53087 17363
91	.24218 84981 12398	.68225 37488 36691
92	.24216 43010 57454	.68230 21841 16608
93	.24214 01039 98637	.68235 06145 57114
94	.24211 59069 36430	.68239 90401 58207
0.9995	0.24209 17098 71320	0.68244 74609 19888
96	.24206 75128 03788	.68249 58768 42156
97	.24204 33157 34321	.68254 42879 25010
98	.24201 91186 63402	.68259 26941 68449
99	.24199 49215 91515	.68264 10955 72475
1.0000	0.24197 07245 19143	0.68268 94921 37086

x	$\dfrac{1}{\sqrt{2\pi}}\,e^{-\frac{x^2}{2}}$	$\dfrac{1}{\sqrt{2\pi}}\displaystyle\int_{-x}^{x} e^{-\frac{\alpha^2}{2}}\,d\alpha$
1.000	0.24197 07245 19143	0.68268 94921 37086
01	.24172 87538 75261	.68317 31916 15440
02	.24148 67837 15037	.68365 64071 52909
03	.24124 48145 21686	.68413 91387 50945
04	.24100 28467 77934	.68462 13864 11963
1.005	0.24076 08809 66021	0.68510 31501 39344
06	.24051 89175 67694	.68558 44299 37436
07	.24027 69570 64212	.68606 52258 11545
08	.24003 49999 36339	.68654 55377 67943
09	.23979 30466 64348	.68702 53658 13861
1.010	0.23955 10977 28013	0.68750 47099 57491
11	.23930 91536 06614	.68798 35702 07983
12	.23906 72147 78931	.68846 19465 75446
13	.23882 52817 23245	.68893 98390 70947
14	.23858 33549 17336	.68941 72477 06506
1.015	0.23834 14348 38481	0.68989 41724 95101
16	.23809 95219 63454	.69037 06134 50662
17	.23785 76167 68523	.69084 65705 88075
18	.23761 57197 29450	.69132 20439 23174
19	.23737 38313 21487	.69179 70334 72747
1.020	0.23713 19520 19380	0.69227 15392 54530
21	.23689 00822 97360	.69274 55612 87211
22	.23664 82226 29150	.69321 90995 90422
23	.23640 63734 87956	.69369 21541 84745
24	.23616 45353 46472	.69416 47250 91707
1.025	0.23592 27086 76873	0.69463 68123 33779
26	.23568 08939 50817	.69510 84159 34377
27	.23543 90916 39445	.69557 95359 17859
28	.23519 73022 13376	.69605 01723 09525
29	.23495 55261 42707	.69652 03251 35616
1.030	0.23471 37638 97012	0.69698 99944 23313
31	.23447 20159 45341	.69745 91802 00734
32	.23423 02827 56219	.69792 78824 96936
33	.23398 85647 97644	.69839 61013 41912
34	.23374 68625 37082	.69886 38367 66592
1.035	0.23350 51764 41475	0.69933 10888 02837
36	.23326 35069 77229	.69979 78574 83445
37	.23302 18546 10221	.70026 41428 42144
38	.23278 02198 05793	.70072 99449 13594
39	.23253 86030 28751	.70119 52637 33386
1.040	0.23229 70047 43366	0.70166 00993 38037
41	.23205 54254 13372	.70212 44517 64996
42	.23181 38655 01964	.70258 83210 52636
43	.23157 23254 71794	.70305 17072 40258
44	.23133 08057 84977	.70351 46103 68086
1.045	0.23108 93069 03081	0.70397 70304 77268
46	.23084 78292 87134	.70443 89676 09875
47	.23060 63733 97615	.70490 04218 08901
48	.23036 49396 94459	.70536 13931 18257
49	.23012 35286 37053	.70582 18815 82776
1.050	0.22988 21406 84233	0.70628 18872 48208

X	$\dfrac{1}{\sqrt{2\pi}} e^{-\frac{x^2}{2}}$	$\dfrac{1}{\sqrt{2\pi}} \displaystyle\int_{-x}^{x} e^{-\frac{\alpha^2}{2}} d\alpha$
1.050	0.22988 21406 84233	0.70628 18872 48208
51	.22964 07762 94287	.70674 14101 61221
52	.22939 94359 24949	.70720 04503 69399
53	.22915 81200 33402	.70765 90079 21240
54	.22891 68290 76275	.70811 70828 66156
1.055	0.22867 55635 09641	0.70857 46752 54472
56	.22843 43237 89016	.70903 17851 37425
57	.22819 31103 69359	.70948 84125 67162
58	.22795 19237 05068	.70994 45575 96739
59	.22771 07642 49985	.71040 02202 80122
1.060	0.22746 96324 57386	0.71085 54006 72181
61	.22722 85287 79986	.71131 00988 28695
62	.22698 74536 69938	.71176 43148 06346
63	.22674 64075 78826	.71221 80486 62720
64	.22650 53909 57671	.71267 13004 56308
1.065	0.22626 44042 56924	0.71312 40702 46498
66	.22602 34479 26470	.71357 63580 93582
67	.22578 25224 15621	.71402 81640 58750
68	.22554 16281 73120	.71447 94882 04090
69	.22530 07656 47137	.71493 03305 92587
1.070	0.22505 99352 85270	0.71538 06912 88122
71	.22481 91375 34538	.71583 05703 55469
72	.22457 83728 41390	.71627 99678 60298
73	.22433 76416 51693	.71672 88838 69170
74	.22409 69444 10739	.71717 73184 49537
1.075	0.22385 62815 63239	0.71762 52716 69742
76	.22361 56535 53325	.71807 27435 99015
77	.22337 50608 24545	.71851 97343 07476
78	.22313 45038 19867	.71896 62438 66130
79	.22289 39829 81673	.71941 22723 46867
1.080	0.22265 34987 51761	0.71985 78198 22462
81	.22241 30515 71342	.72030 28863 66573
82	.22217 26418 81041	.72074 74720 53741
83	.22193 22701 20892	.72119 15769 59384
84	.22169 19367 30342	.72163 52011 59804
1.085	0.22145 16421 48247	0.72207 83447 32178
86	.22121 13868 12870	.72252 10077 54561
87	.22097 11711 61881	.72296 31903 05886
88	.22073 09956 32357	.72340 48924 65957
89	.22049 08606 60779	.72384 61143 15454
1.090	0.22025 07666 83033	0.72428 68559 35929
91	.22001 07141 34407	.72472 71174 09805
92	.21977 07034 49589	.72516 68988 20376
93	.21953 07350 62669	.72560 62002 51802
94	.21929 08094 07138	.72604 50217 89114
1.095	0.21905 09269 15882	0.72648 33635 18207
96	.21881 10880 21186	.72692 12255 25842
97	.21857 12931 54732	.72735 86078 99644
98	.21833 15427 47596	.72779 55107 28101
99	.21809 18372 30248	.72823 19341 00561
1.100	0.21785 21770 32551	0.72866 78781 07235

x	$\dfrac{1}{\sqrt{2\pi}}e^{-\frac{x^2}{2}}$	$\dfrac{1}{\sqrt{2\pi}}\displaystyle\int_{-x}^{x}e^{-\frac{\alpha^2}{2}}\,d\alpha$
1.100	0.21785 21770 32551	0.72866 78781 07235
01	.21761 25625 83760	.72910 33428 39190
02	.21737 29943 12522	.72953 83283 88355
03	.21713 34726 46872	.72997 28348 47511
04	.21689 39980 14235	.73040 68623 10298
1.105	0.21665 45708 41425	0.73084 04108 71208
06	.21641 51915 54640	.73127 34806 25587
07	.21617 58605 79465	.73170 60716 69634
08	.21593 65783 40871	.73213 81841 00396
09	.21569 73452 63210	.73256 98180 15772
1.110	0.21545 81617 70220	0.73300 09735 14506
11	.21521 90282 85017	.73343 16506 96191
12	.21497 99452 30100	.73386 18496 61266
13	.21474 09130 27348	.73429 15705 11013
14	.21450 19320 98016	.73472 08133 47557
1.115	0.21426 30028 62741	0.73514 95782 73868
16	.21402 41257 41532	.73557 78653 93751
17	.21378 53011 53777	.73600 56748 11856
18	.21354 65295 18237	.73643 30066 33668
19	.21330 78112 53048	.73685 98609 65509
1.120	0.21306 91467 75718	0.73728 62379 14539
21	.21283 05365 03126	.73771 21375 88749
22	.21259 19808 51523	.73813 75600 96965
23	.21235 34802 36530	.73856 25055 48846
24	.21211 50350 73136	.73898 69740 54879
1.125	0.21187 66457 75699	0.73941 09657 26382
26	.21163 83127 57944	.73983 44806 75502
27	.21140 00364 32960	.74025 75190 15209
28	.21116 18172 13203	.74068 00808 59304
29	.21092 36555 10494	.74110 21663 22407
1.130	0.21068 55517 36015	0.74152 37755 19964
31	.21044 75063 00313	.74194 49085 68243
32	.21020 95196 13293	.74236 55655 84331
33	.20997 15920 84224	.74278 57466 86135
34	.20973 37241 21732	.74320 54519 92379
1.135	0.20949 59161 33804	0.74362 46816 22605
36	.20925 81685 27783	.74404 34356 97169
37	.20902 04817 10369	.74446 17143 37242
38	.20878 28560 87618	.74487 95176 64807
39	.20854 52920 64943	.74529 68458 02659
1.140	0.20830 77900 47108	0.74571 36988 74403
41	.20807 03504 38234	.74613 00770 04454
42	.20783 29736 41791	.74654 59803 18031
43	.20759 56600 60602	.74696 14089 41164
44	.20735 84100 96842	.74737 63630 00685
1.145	0.20712 12241 52033	0.74779 08426 24231
46	.20688 41026 27049	.74820 48479 40240
47	.20664 70459 22110	.74861 83790 77953
48	.20641 00544 36784	.74903 14361 67408
49	.20617 31285 69986	.74944 40193 39445
1.150	0.20593 62687 19975	0.74985 61287 25699

x	$\frac{1}{\sqrt{2\pi}} e^{-\frac{x^2}{2}}$	$\frac{1}{\sqrt{2\pi}} \int_{-x}^{x} e^{-\frac{\alpha^2}{2}} d\alpha$
1.150	0.20593 62687 19975	0.74985 61287 25699
51	.20569 94752 84356	.75026 77644 58602
52	.20546 27486 60077	.75067 89266 71378
53	.20522 60892 43430	.75108 96154 98047
54	.20498 94974 30050	.75149 98310 73420
1.155	0.20475 29736 14910	0.75190 95735 33099
56	.20451 65181 92328	.75231 88430 13475
57	.20428 01315 55958	.75272 76396 51726
58	.20404 38140 98795	.75313 59635 85818
59	.20380 75662 13172	.75354 38149 54502
1.160	0.20357 13882 90759	0.75395 11938 97313
61	.20333 52807 22563	.75435 81005 54568
62	.20309 92438 98925	.75476 45350 67367
63	.20286 32782 09523	.75517 04975 77587
64	.20262 73840 43369	.75557 59882 27887
1.165	0.20239 15617 88807	0.75598 10071 61701
66	.20215 58118 33516	.75638 55545 23242
67	.20192 01345 64503	.75678 96304 57493
68	.20168 45303 68111	.75719 32351 10215
69	.20144 89996 30009	.75759 63686 27938
1.170	0.20121 35427 35197	0.75799 90311 57964
71	.20097 81600 68006	.75840 12228 48364
72	.20074 28520 12092	.75880 29438 47976
73	.20050 76189 50439	.75920 41943 06408
74	.20027 24612 65359	.75960 49743 74029
1.175	0.20003 73793 38488	0.76000 52842 01975
76	.19980 23735 50788	.76040 51239 42143
77	.19956 74442 82546	.76080 44937 47191
78	.19933 25919 13371	.76120 33937 70539
79	.19909 78168 22196	.76160 18241 66363
1.180	0.19886 31193 87276	0.76199 97850 89599
81	.19862 84999 86187	.76239 72766 95935
82	.19839 39589 95828	.76279 42991 41817
83	.19815 94967 92414	.76319 08525 84443
84	.19792 51137 51482	.76358 69371 81762
1.185	0.19769 08102 47888	0.76398 25530 92474
86	.19745 65866 55805	.76437 77004 76028
87	.19722 24433 48724	.76477 23794 92620
88	.19698 83806 99450	.76516 65903 03195
89	.19675 43990 80109	.76556 03330 69438
1.190	0.19652 04988 62137	0.76595 36079 53783
91	.19628 66804 16287	.76634 64151 19401
92	.19605 29441 12626	.76673 87547 30209
93	.19581 92903 20534	.76713 06269 50860
94	.19558 57194 08704	.76752 20319 46745
1.195	0.19535 22317 45140	0.76791 29698 83993
96	.19511 88276 97157	.76830 34409 29469
97	.19488 55076 31382	.76869 34452 50770
98	.19465 22719 13751	.76908 29830 16227
99	.19441 91209 09510	.76947 20543 94901
1.200	0.19418 60549 83213	0.76986 06595 56583

x	$\frac{1}{\sqrt{2\pi}} e^{-\frac{x^2}{2}}$	$\frac{1}{\sqrt{2\pi}} \int_{-x}^{x} e^{-\frac{\alpha^2}{2}} d\alpha$
1.200	0.19418 60549 83213	0.76986 06595 56583
01	.19395 30744 98722	.77024 87986 71795
02	.19372 01798 19208	.77063 64719 11782
03	.19348 73713 07147	.77102 36794 48517
04	.19325 46493 24322	.77141 04214 54696
1.205	0.19302 20142 31821	0.77179 66981 03741
06	.19278 94663 90038	.77218 25095 69791
07	.19255 70061 58672	.77256 78560 27708
08	.19232 46338 96722	.77295 27376 53072
09	.19209 23499 62496	.77333 71546 22180
1.210	0.19186 01547 13599	0.77372 11071 12045
11	.19162 80485 06942	.77410 45953 00396
12	.19139 60316 98736	.77448 76193 65672
13	.19116 41046 44492	.77487 01794 87027
14	.19093 22676 99023	.77525 22758 44323
1.215	0.19070 05212 16439	0.77563 39086 18132
16	.19046 88655 50153	.77601 50779 89733
17	.19023 73010 52874	.77639 57841 41111
18	.19000 58280 76609	.77677 60272 54958
19	.18977 44469 72664	.77715 58075 14666
1.220	0.18954 31580 91640	0.77753 51251 04331
21	.18931 19617 83436	.77791 39802 08748
22	.18908 08583 97246	.77829 23730 13413
23	.18884 98482 81559	.77867 03037 04517
24	.18861 89317 84160	.77904 77724 68951
1.225	0.18838 81092 52126	0.77942 47794 94298
26	.18815 73810 31831	.77980 13249 68834
27	.18792 67474 68940	.78017 74090 81530
28	.18769 62089 08411	.78055 30320 22045
29	.18746 57656 94493	.78092 81939 80728
1.230	0.18723 54181 70730	0.78130 28951 48616
31	.18700 51666 79953	.78167 71357 17433
32	.18677 50115 64286	.78205 09158 79586
33	.18654 49531 65145	.78242 42358 28168
34	.18631 49918 23231	.78279 70957 56951
1.235	0.18608 51278 78537	0.78316 94958 60392
36	.18585 53616 70346	.78354 14363 33623
37	.18562 56935 37226	.78391 29173 72457
38	.18539 61238 17035	.78428 39391 73381
39	.18516 66528 46918	.78465 45019 33558
1.240	0.18493 72809 63305	0.78502 46058 50826
41	.18470 80085 01916	.78539 42511 23693
42	.18447 88357 97752	.78576 34379 51339
43	.18424 97631 85105	.78613 21665 33612
44	.18402 07909 97546	.78650 04370 71029
1.245	0.18379 19195 67936	0.78686 82497 64774
46	.18356 31492 28417	.78723 56048 16694
47	.18333 44803 10415	.78760 25024 29302
48	.18310 59131 44640	.78796 89428 05771
49	.18287 74480 61084	.78833 49261 49935
1.250	0.18264 90853 89022	0.78870 04526 66289

x	$\frac{1}{\sqrt{2\pi}}e^{-\frac{x^2}{2}}$	$\frac{1}{\sqrt{2\pi}}\int_{-x}^{x}e^{-\frac{\alpha^2}{2}}d\alpha$
1.250	0.18264 90853 89022	0.78870 04526 66289
51	.18242 08254 57011	.78906 55225 59985
52	.18219 26685 92888	.78943 01360 36829
53	.18196 46151 23774	.78979 42933 03286
54	.18173 66653 76068	.79015 79945 66472
1.255	0.18150 88196 75451	0.79052 12400 34155
56	.18128 10783 46883	.79088 40299 14755
57	.18105 34417 14603	.79124 63644 17340
58	.18082 59101 02132	.79160 82437 51627
59	.18059 84838 32265	.79196 96681 27977
1.260	0.18037 11632 27080	0.79233 06377 57399
61	.18014 39486 07931	.79269 11528 51543
62	.17991 68402 95448	.79305 12136 22702
63	.17968 98386 09541	.79341 08202 83809
64	.17946 29438 69395	.79376 99730 48437
1.265	0.17923 61563 93472	0.79412 86721 30796
66	.17900 94764 99511	.79448 69177 45733
67	.17878 29045 04526	.79484 47101 08727
68	.17855 64407 24806	.79520 20494 35894
69	.17833 00854 75915	.79555 89359 43980
1.270	0.17810 38390 72694	0.79591 53698 50362
71	.17787 77018 29254	.79627 13513 73044
72	.17765 16740 58985	.79662 68807 30661
73	.17742 57560 74548	.79698 19581 42471
74	.17719 99481 87876	.79733 65838 28358
1.275	0.17697 42507 10180	0.79769 07580 08828
76	.17674 86639 51938	.79804 44809 05011
77	.17652 31882 22904	.79839 77527 38655
78	.17629 78238 32104	.79875 05737 32128
79	.17607 25710 87834	.79910 29441 08415
1.280	0.17584 74302 97662	0.79945 48640 91116
81	.17562 24017 68430	.79980 63339 04446
82	.17539 74858 06247	.80015 73537 73234
83	.17517 26827 16495	.80050 79239 22920
84	.17494 79928 03825	.80085 80445 79552
1.285	0.17472 34163 72160	0.80120 77159 69789
86	.17449 89537 24691	.80155 69383 20896
87	.17427 46051 63879	.80190 57118 60745
88	.17405 03709 91454	.80225 40368 17811
89	.17382 62515 08416	.80260 19134 21171
1.290	0.17360 22470 15033	0.80294 93419 00504
91	.17337 83578 10841	.80329 63224 86090
92	.17315 45841 94645	.80364 28554 08806
93	.17293 09264 64518	.80398 89409 00126
94	.17270 73849 17799	.80433 45791 92120
1.295	0.17248 39598 51097	0.80467 97705 17451
96	.17226 06515 60288	.80502 45151 09375
97	.17203 74603 40512	.80536 88132 01739
98	.17181 43864 86178	.80571 26650 28981
99	.17159 14302 90963	.80605 60708 26124
1.300	0.17136 85920 47807	0.80639 90308 28779

x	$\frac{1}{\sqrt{2\pi}} e^{-\frac{x^2}{2}}$	$\frac{1}{\sqrt{2\pi}} \int_{-x}^{x} e^{-\frac{\alpha^2}{2}} d\alpha$
1.300	0.17136 85920 47807	0.80639 90308 28779
01	.17114 58720 48919	.80674 15452 73144
02	.17092 32705 85772	.80708 36143 95999
03	.17070 07879 49104	.80742 52384 34705
04	.17047 84244 28922	.80776 64176 27206
1.305	0.17025 61803 14495	0.80810 71522 12025
06	.17003 40558 94357	.80844 74424 28260
07	.16981 20514 56309	.80878 72885 15590
08	.16959 01672 87416	.80912 66907 14265
09	.16936 84036 74006	.80946 56492 65110
1.310	0.16914 67609 01672	0.80980 41644 09522
11	.16892 52392 55273	.81014 22363 89468
12	.16870 38390 18930	.81047 98654 47483
13	.16848 25604 76027	.81081 70518 26672
14	.16826 14039 09213	.81115 37957 70705
1.315	0.16804 03696 00401	0.81149 00975 23814
16	.16781 94578 30766	.81182 59573 30799
17	.16759 86688 80747	.81216 13754 37017
18	.16737 80030 30045	.81249 63520 88388
19	.16715 74605 57625	.81283 08875 31390
1.320	0.16693 70417 41714	0.81316 49820 13056
21	.16671 67468 59801	.81349 86357 80979
22	.16649 65761 88638	.81383 18490 83303
23	.16627 65300 04240	.81416 46221 68725
24	.16605 66085 81883	.81449 69552 86494
1.325	0.16583 68121 96105	0.81482 88486 86410
26	.16561 71411 20707	.81516 03026 18819
27	.16539 75956 28750	.81549 13173 34615
28	.16517 81759 92559	.81582 18930 85238
29	.16495 88824 83719	.81615 20301 22670
1.330	0.16473 97153 73077	0.81648 17286 99438
31	.16452 06749 30740	.81681 09890 68608
32	.16430 17614 26078	.81713 98114 83786
33	.16408 29751 27721	.81746 81961 99117
34	.16386 43163 03561	.81779 61434 69280
1.335	0.16364 57852 20751	0.81812 36535 49492
36	.16342 73821 45703	.81845 07266 95502
37	.16320 91073 44092	.81877 73631 63590
38	.16299 09610 80854	.81910 35632 10570
39	.16277 29436 20182	.81942 93270 93782
1.340	0.16255 50552 25534	0.81975 46550 71095
41	.16233 72961 59627	.82007 95474 00904
42	.16211 96666 84436	.82040 40043 42127
43	.16190 21670 61201	.82072 80261 54209
44	.16168 47975 50419	.82105 16130 97114
1.345	0.16146 75584 11849	0.82137 47654 31326
46	.16125 04499 04508	.82169 74834 17849
47	.16103 34722 86675	.82201 97673 18204
48	.16081 66258 15891	.82234 16173 94427
49	.16059 99107 48952	.82266 30339 09070
1.350	0.16038 33273 41920	0.82298 40171 25196

X	$\frac{1}{\sqrt{2\pi}}e^{-\frac{x^2}{2}}$	$\frac{1}{\sqrt{2\pi}}\int_{-x}^{x}e^{-\frac{\alpha^2}{2}}\,d\alpha$
1.350	0.16038 33273 41920	0.82298 40171 25196
51	.16016 68758 50112	.82330 45673 06381
52	.15995 05565 28109	.82362 46847 16710
53	.15973 43696 29750	.82394 43696 20776
54	.15951 83154 08134	.82426 36222 83680
1.355	0.15930 23941 15621	0.82458 24429 71028
56	.15908 66060 03831	.82490 08319 48929
57	.15887 09513 23642	.82521 87894 83997
58	.15865 54303 25195	.82553 63158 43345
59	.15844 00432 57889	.82585 34112 94586
1.360	0.15822 47903 70383	0.82617 00761 05830
61	.15800 96719 10598	.82648 63105 45686
62	.15779 46881 25712	.82680 21148 83256
63	.15757 98392 62167	.82711 74893 88136
64	.15736 51255 65660	.82743 24343 30416
1.365	0.15715 05472 81153	.82774 69499 80673
66	.15693 61046 52866	.82806 10366 09978
67	.15672 17979 24279	.82837 46944 89885
68	.15650 76273 38131	.82868 79238 92437
69	.15629 35931 36425	.82900 07250 90160
1.370	0.15607 96955 60421	0.82931 30983 56066
71	.15586 59348 50640	.82962 50439 63646
72	.15565 23112 46864	.82993 65621 86873
73	.15543 88249 88136	.83024 76533 00197
74	.15522 54763 12758	.83055 83175 78547
1.375	0.15501 22654 58293	0.83086 85552 97329
76	.15479 91926 61566	.83117 83667 32419
77	.15458 62581 58660	.83148 77521 60171
78	.15437 34621 84922	.83179 67118 57407
79	.15416 08049 74957	.83210 52461 01420
1.380	0.15394 82867 62634	0.83241 33551 69971
81	.15373 59077 81079	.83272 10393 41291
82	.15352 36682 62682	.83302 82988 94071
83	.15331 15684 39095	.83333 51341 07471
84	.15309 96085 41227	.83364 15452 61111
1.385	0.15288 77887 99254	0.83394 75326 35073
86	.15267 61094 42608	.83425 30965 09899
87	.15246 45706 99988	.83455 82371 66587
88	.15225 31727 99350	.83486 29548 86593
89	.15204 19159 67914	.83516 72499 51830
1.390	0.15183 08004 32162	0.83547 11226 44662
91	.15161 98264 17837	.83577 45732 47906
92	.15140 89941 49946	.83607 76020 44831
93	.15119 83038 52757	.83638 02093 19153
94	.15098 77557 49800	.83668 23953 55038
1.395	0.15077 73500 63868	0.83698 41604 37097
96	.15056 70870 17017	.83728 55048 50387
97	.15035 69668 30566	.83758 64288 80406
98	.15014 69897 25097	.83788 69328 13096
99	.14993 71559 20454	.83818 70169 34840
1.400	0.14972 74656 35745	0.83848 66815 32458

x	$\dfrac{1}{\sqrt{2\pi}}e^{-\frac{x^2}{2}}$	$\dfrac{1}{\sqrt{2\pi}}\displaystyle\int_{-x}^{x}e^{-\frac{\alpha^2}{2}}\,d\alpha$
1.400	0.14972 74656 35745	0.83848 66815 32458
01	.14951 79190 89341	.83878 59268 93208
02	.14930 85164 98879	.83908 47533 04786
03	.14909 92580 81256	.83938 31610 55319
04	.14889 01440 52634	.83968 11504 33370
1.405	0.14868 11746 28442	0.83997 87217 27933
06	.14847 23500 23369	.84027 58752 28430
07	.14826 36704 51372	.84057 26112 24715
08	.14805 51361 25670	.84086 89300 07067
09	.14784 67472 58748	.84116 48318 66190
1.410	0.14763 85040 62356	0.84146 03170 93215
11	.14743 04067 47508	.84175 53859 79694
12	.14722 24555 24485	.84205 00388 17600
13	.14701 46506 02833	.84234 42758 99326
14	.14680 69921 91363	.84263 80975 17685
1.415	0.14659 94804 98153	0.84293 15039 65904
16	.14639 21157 30546	.84322 44955 37628
17	.14618 48980 95152	.84351 70725 26914
18	.14597 78277 97847	.84380 92352 28234
19	.14577 09050 43776	.84410 09839 36468
1.420	0.14556 41300 37348	0.84439 23189 46907
21	.14535 75029 82240	.84468 32405 55251
22	.14515 10240 81398	.84497 37490 57606
23	.14494 46935 37035	.84526 38447 50481
24	.14473 85115 50630	.84555 35279 30792
1.425	0.14453 24783 22933	0.84584 27988 95856
26	.14432 65940 53960	.84613 16579 43390
27	.14412 08589 42998	.84642 01053 71511
28	.14391 52731 88600	.84670 81414 78733
29	.14370 98369 88590	.84699 57665 63968
1.430	0.14350 45505 40062	0.84728 29809 26522
31	.14329 94140 39378	.84756 97848 66094
32	.14309 44276 82171	.84785 61786 82775
33	.14288 95916 63343	.84814 21626 77048
34	.14268 49061 77067	.84842 77371 49783
1.435	0.14248 03714 16786	0.84871 29024 02240
36	.14227 59875 75217	.84899 76587 36063
37	.14207 17548 44344	.84928 20064 53282
38	.14186 76734 15426	.84956 59458 56308
39	.14166 37434 78990	.84984 94772 47938
1.440	0.14145 99652 24839	0.85013 26009 31346
41	.14125 63388 42046	.85041 53172 10085
42	.14105 28645 18957	.85069 76263 88087
43	.14084 95424 43192	.85097 95287 69659
44	.14064 63728 01642	.85126 10246 59483
1.445	0.14044 33557 80475	0.85154 21143 62613
46	.14024 04915 65129	.85182 27981 84475
47	.14003 77803 40319	.85210 30764 30867
48	.13983 52222 90033	.85238 29494 07953
49	.13963 28175 97534	.85266 24174 22266
1.450	0.13943 05664 45360	0.85294 14807 80703

x	$\frac{1}{\sqrt{2\pi}} e^{-\frac{x^2}{2}}$	$\frac{1}{\sqrt{2\pi}} \int_{-x}^{x} e^{-\frac{\alpha^2}{2}} d\alpha$
1.450	0.13943 05664 45360	0.85294 14807 80703
51	.13922 84690 15326	.85322 01397 90529
52	.13902 65254 88520	.85349 83947 59367
53	.13882 47360 45309	.85377 62459 95205
54	.13862 31008 65333	.85405 36938 06390
1.455	0.13842 16201 27511	0.85433 07385 01628
56	.13822 02940 10040	.85460 73803 89980
57	.13801 91226 90391	.85488 36197 80867
58	.13781 81063 45316	.85515 94569 84058
59	.13761 72451 50844	.85543 48923 09682
1.460	0.13741 65392 82282	0.85570 99260 68212
61	.13721 59889 14215	.85598 45585 70478
62	.13701 55942 20509	.85625 87901 27652
63	.13681 53553 74309	.85653 26210 51258
64	.13661 52725 48039	.85680 60516 53163
1.465	0.13641 53459 13403	0.85707 90822 45578
66	.13621 55756 41388	.85735 17131 41058
67	.13601 59619 02259	.85762 39446 52499
68	.13581 65048 65563	.85789 57770 93135
69	.13561 72047 00130	.85816 72107 76542
1.470	0.13541 80615 74071	0.85843 82460 16629
71	.13521 90756 54781	.85870 88831 27643
72	.13502 02471 08934	.85897 91224 24164
73	.13482 15761 02492	.85924 89642 21105
74	.13462 30628 00698	.85951 84088 33710
1.475	0.13442 47073 68079	0.85978 74565 77554
76	.13422 65099 68447	.86005 61077 68538
77	.13402 84707 64899	.86032 43627 22892
78	.13383 05899 19816	.86059 22217 57170
79	.13363 28675 94866	.86085 96851 88251
1.480	0.13343 53039 51002	0.86112 67533 33337
81	.13323 78991 48465	.86139 34265 09949
82	.13304 06533 46781	.86165 97050 35931
83	.13284 35667 04765	.86192 55892 29443
84	.13264 66393 80517	.86219 10794 08962
1.485	0.13244 98715 31428	0.86245 61758 93282
86	.13225 32633 14176	.86272 08790 01509
87	.13205 68148 84729	.86298 51890 53064
88	.13186 05263 98343	.86324 91063 67677
89	.13166 43980 09565	.86351 26312 65389
1.490	0.13146 84298 72231	0.86377 57640 66549
91	.13127 26221 39470	.86403 85050 91814
92	.13107 69749 63699	.86430 08546 62145
93	.13088 14884 96630	.86456 28130 98808
94	.13068 61628 89265	.86482 43807 23371
1.495	0.13049 09982 91897	0.86508 55578 57705
96	.13029 59948 54117	.86534 63448 23979
97	.13010 11527 24803	.86560 67419 44660
98	.12990 64720 52133	.86586 67495 42516
99	.12971 19529 83574	.86612 63679 40605
1.500	0.12951 75956 65892	0.86638 55974 62284

x	$\dfrac{1}{\sqrt{2\pi}}\, e^{-\frac{x^2}{2}}$	$\dfrac{1}{\sqrt{2\pi}}\displaystyle\int_{-x}^{x} e^{-\frac{\alpha^2}{2}}\, d\alpha$
1.500	0.12951 75956 65892	0.86638 55974 62284
01	.12932 34002 45145	.86664 44384 31200
02	.12912 93668 66690	.86690 28911 71293
03	.12893 54956 75178	.86716 09560 06791
04	.12874 17868 14556	.86741 86332 62214
1.505	0.12854 82404 28071	0.86767 59232 62366
06	.12835 48566 58265	.86793 28263 32337
07	.12816 16356 46980	.86818 93427 97504
08	.12796 85775 35355	.86844 54729 83525
09	.12777 56824 63829	.86870 12172 16339
1.510	0.12758 29505 72142	0.86895 65758 22167
11	.12739 03819 99331	.86921 15491 27507
12	.12719 79768 83736	.86946 61374 59136
13	.12700 57353 62998	.86972 03411 44105
14	.12681 36575 74059	.86997 41605 09742
1.515	0.12662 17436 53163	0.87022 75958 83647
16	.12642 99937 35856	.87048 06475 93691
17	.12623 84079 56990	.87073 33159 68016
18	.12604 69864 50717	.87098 56013 35034
19	.12585 57293 50495	.87123 75040 23423
1.520	0.12566 46367 89088	0.87148 90243 62128
21	.12547 37088 98563	.87174 01626 80360
22	.12528 29458 10294	.87199 09193 07591
23	.12509 23476 54961	.87224 12945 73556
24	.12490 19145 62551	.87249 12888 08253
1.525	0.12471 16466 62357	0.87274 09023 41935
26	.12452 15440 82983	.87299 01355 05116
27	.12433 16069 52338	.87323 89886 28566
28	.12414 18353 97642	.87348 74620 43309
29	.12395 22295 45424	.87373 55560 80625
1.530	0.12376 27895 21523	0.87398 32710 72043
31	.12357 35154 51090	.87423 06073 49346
32	.12338 44074 58584	.87447 75652 44566
33	.12319 54656 67779	.87472 41450 89982
34	.12300 66902 01761	.87497 03472 18120
1.535	0.12281 80811 82925	0.87521 61719 61754
36	.12262 96387 32985	.87546 16196 53898
37	.12244 13629 72965	.87570 66906 27812
38	.12225 32540 23205	.87595 13852 16997
39	.12206 53120 03361	.87619 57037 55192
1.540	0.12187 75370 32402	0.87643 96465 76376
41	.12168 99292 28616	.87668 32140 14766
42	.12150 24887 09607	.87692 64064 04814
43	.12131 52155 92295	.87716 92240 81206
44	.12112 81099 92922	.87741 16673 78862
1.545	0.12094 11720 27043	0.87765 37366 32933
46	.12075 44018 09537	.87789 54321 78802
47	.12056 77994 54600	.87813 67543 52080
48	.12038 13650 75750	.87837 77034 88605
49	.12019 50987 85826	.87861 82799 24442
1.550	0.12000 90006 96986	0.87885 84839 95882

x	$\dfrac{1}{\sqrt{2\pi}}e^{-\frac{x^2}{2}}$	$\dfrac{1}{\sqrt{2\pi}}\displaystyle\int_{-x}^{x}e^{-\frac{\alpha^2}{2}}\,d\alpha$
1.550	0.12000 90006 96986	0.87885 84839 95882
51	.11982 30709 20713	.87909 83160 39438
52	.11963 73095 67812	.87933 77763 91847
53	.11945 17167 48411	.87957 68653 90065
54	.11926 62925 71963	.87981 55833 71269
1.555	0.11908 10371 47244	0.88005 39306 72854
56	.11889 59505 82356	.88029 19076 32432
57	.11871 10329 84728	.88052 95145 87829
58	.11852 62844 61115	.88076 67518 77087
59	.11834 17051 17596	.88100 36198 38460
1.560	0.11815 72950 59582	0.88124 01188 10414
61	.11797 30543 91811	.88147 62491 31625
62	.11778 89832 18348	.88171 20111 40977
63	.11760 50816 42590	.88194 74051 77563
64	.11742 13497 67264	.88218 24315 80681
1.565	0.11723 77876 94426	0.88241 70906 89834
66	.11705 43955 25465	.88265 13828 44728
67	.11687 11733 61103	.88288 53083 85272
68	.11668 81213 01392	.88311 88676 51576
69	.11650 52394 45719	.88335 20609 83947
1.570	0.11632 25278 92807	0.88358 48887 22894
71	.11613 99867 40710	.88381 73512 09119
72	.11595 76160 86821	.88404 94487 83522
73	.11577 54160 27865	.88428 11817 87196
74	.11559 33866 59908	.88451 25505 61428
1.575	0.11541 15280 78350	0.88474 35554 47694
76	.11522 98403 77931	.88497 41967 87662
77	.11504 83236 52728	.88520 44749 23189
78	.11486 69779 96159	.88543 43901 96319
79	.11468 58035 00981	.88566 39429 49281
1.580	0.11450 48002 59292	0.88589 31335 24492
81	.11432 39683 62532	.88612 19622 64548
82	.11414 33079 01481	.88635 04295 12232
83	.11396 28189 66263	.88657 85356 10505
84	.11378 25016 46347	.88680 62809 02507
1.585	0.11360 23560 30542	0.88703 36657 31560
86	.11342 23822 07006	.88726 06904 41158
87	.11324 25802 63240	.88748 73553 74974
88	.11306 29502 86091	.88771 36608 76855
89	.11288 34923 61754	.88793 96072 90820
1.590	0.11270 42065 75771	0.88816 51949 61061
91	.11252 50930 13031	.88839 04242 31939
92	.11234 61517 57774	.88861 52954 47985
93	.11216 73828 93589	.88883 98089 53897
94	.11198 87865 03413	.88906 39650 94542
1.595	0.11181 03626 69538	0.88928 77642 14949
96	.11163 21114 73603	.88951 12066 60312
97	.11145 40329 96604	.88973 42927 75989
98	.11127 61273 18887	.88995 70229 07498
99	.11109 83945 20152	.89017 93974 00517
1.600	0.11092 08346 79456	0.89040 14166 00884

x	$\dfrac{1}{\sqrt{2\pi}}\,e^{-\frac{x^2}{2}}$	$\dfrac{1}{\sqrt{2\pi}}\displaystyle\int_{-x}^{x} e^{-\frac{\alpha^2}{2}}\,d\alpha$
1.600	0.11092 08346 79456	0.89040 14166 00884
01	.11074 34478 75207	.89062 30808 54593
02	.11056 62341 85174	.89084 43905 07794
03	.11038 91936 86479	.89106 53459 06794
04	.11021 23264 55602	.89128 59473 98052
1.605	0.11003 56325 68382	0.89150 61953 28179
06	.10985 91121 00016	.89172 60900 43938
07	.10968 27651 25062	.89194 56318 92242
08	.10950 65917 17437	.89216 48212 20150
09	.10933 05919 50418	.89238 36583 74872
1.610	0.10915 47658 96647	0.89260 21437 03761
11	.10897 91136 28126	.89282 02775 54315
12	.10880 36352 16220	.89303 80602 74178
13	.10862 83307 31660	.89325 54922 11132
14	.10845 32002 44539	.89347 25737 13102
1.615	0.10827 82438 24318	0.89368 93051 28154
16	.10810 34615 39823	.89390 56868 04490
17	.10792 88534 59247	.89412 17190 90450
18	.10775 44196 50150	.89433 74023 34508
19	.10758 01601 79463	.89455 27368 85276
1.620	0.10740 60751 13484	0.89476 77230 91496
21	.10723 21645 17880	.89498 23613 02043
22	.10705 84284 57692	.89519 66518 65924
23	.10688 48669 97329	.89541 05951 32274
24	.10671 14802 00575	.89562 41914 50356
1.625	0.10653 82681 30585	0.89583 74411 69561
26	.10636 52308 49889	.89605 03446 39405
27	.10619 23684 20392	.89626 29022 09528
28	.10601 96809 03372	.89647 51142 29695
29	.10584 71683 59485	.89668 69810 49790
1.630	0.10567 48308 48764	0.89689 85030 19821
31	.10550 26684 30618	.89710 96804 89914
32	.10533 06811 63836	.89732 05138 10311
33	.10515 88691 06585	.89753 10033 31375
34	.10498 72323 16413	.89774 11494 03582
1.635	0.10481 57708 50248	0.89795 09523 77524
36	.10464 44847 64399	.89816 04126 03904
37	.10447 33741 14560	.89836 95304 33539
38	.10430 24389 55804	.89857 83062 17356
39	.10413 16793 42591	.89878 67403 06392
1.640	0.10396 10953 28764	0.89899 48330 51793
41	.10379 06869 67553	.89920 25848 04809
42	.10362 04543 11573	.89940 99959 16800
43	.10345 03974 12826	.89961 70667 39227
44	.10328 05163 22703	.89982 37976 23657
1.645	0.10311 08110 91981	0.90003 01889 21757
46	.10294 12817 70831	.90023 62409 85298
47	.10277 19284 08810	.90044 19541 66147
48	.10260 27510 54867	.90064 73288 16272
49	.10243 37497 57346	.90085 23652 87737
1.650	0.10226 49245 63978	0.90105 70639 32704

x	$\frac{1}{\sqrt{2\pi}} e^{-\frac{x^2}{2}}$	$\frac{1}{\sqrt{2\pi}} \int_{-x}^{x} e^{-\frac{\alpha^2}{2}} \, d\alpha$
1.650	0.10226 49245 63978	0.90105 70639 32704
51	.10209 62755 21893	.90126 14251 03427
52	.10192 78026 77611	.90146 54491 52257
53	.10175 95060 77051	.90166 91364 31634
54	.10159 13857 65524	.90187 24872 94091
1.655	0.10142 34417 87741	0.90207 55020 92251
56	.10125 56741 87809	.90227 81811 78827
57	.10108 80830 09233	.90248 05249 06617
58	.10092 06682 94918	.90268 25336 28507
59	.10075 34300 87168	.90288 42076 97468
1.660	0.10058 63684 27691	0.90308 55474 66554
61	.10041 94833 57591	.90328 65532 88905
62	.10025 27749 17380	.90348 72255 17738
63	.10008 62431 46971	.90368 75645 06354
64	.09991 98880 85680	.90388 75706 08132
1.665	0.09975 37097 72230	0.90408 72441 76529
66	.09958 77082 44749	.90428 65855 65078
67	.09942 18835 40771	.90448 55951 27390
68	.09925 62356 97239	.90468 42732 17148
69	.09909 07647 50504	.90488 26201 88110
1.670	0.09892 54707 36324	0.90508 06363 94105
71	.09876 03536 89869	.90527 83221 89034
72	.09859 54136 45721	.90547 56779 26866
73	.09843 06506 37871	.90567 27039 61641
74	.09826 60646 99724	.90586 94006 47464
1.675	0.09810 16558 64098	0.90606 57683 38508
76	.09793 74241 63226	.90626 18073 89011
77	.09777 33696 28754	.90645 75181 53272
78	.09760 94922 91748	.90665 29009 85657
79	.09744 57921 82686	.90684 79562 40591
1.680	0.09728 22693 31467	0.90704 26842 72560
81	.09711 89237 67408	.90723 70854 36109
82	.09695 57555 19243	.90743 11600 85840
83	.09679 27646 15130	.90762 49085 76415
84	.09662 99510 82645	.90781 83312 62548
1.685	0.09646 73149 48787	0.90801 14284 99011
86	.09630 48562 39979	.90820 42006 40627
87	.09614 25749 82065	.90839 66480 42272
88	.09598 04712 00317	.90858 87710 58873
89	.09581 85449 19429	.90878 05700 45407
1.690	0.09565 67961 63524	0.90897 20453 56900
91	.09549 52249 56151	.90916 31973 48427
92	.09533 38313 20286	.90935 40263 75106
93	.09517 26152 78336	.90954 45327 92104
94	.09501 15768 52137	.90973 47169 54630
1.695	0.09485 07160 62955	0.90992 45792 17937
96	.09469 00329 31489	.91011 41199 37320
97	.09452 95274 77867	.91030 33394 68115
98	.09436 91997 21656	.91049 22381 65697
99	.09420 90496 81851	.91068 08163 85479
1.700	0.09404 90773 76887	0.91086 90744 82914

x	$\dfrac{1}{\sqrt{2\pi}}\,e^{-\frac{x^2}{2}}$	$\dfrac{1}{\sqrt{2\pi}}\displaystyle\int_{-x}^{x} e^{-\frac{\alpha^2}{2}}\,d\alpha$
1.700	0.09404 90773 76887	0.91086 90744 82914
01	.09388 92828 24632	.91105 70128 13489
02	.09372 96660 42392	.91124 46317 32726
03	.09357 02270 46911	.91143 19315 96183
04	.09341 09658 54371	.91161 89127 59449
1.705	0.09325 18824 80394	0.91180 55755 78146
06	.09309 29769 40041	.91199 19204 07926
07	.09293 42492 47816	.91217 79476 04471
08	.09277 56994 17664	.91236 36575 23492
09	.09261 73274 62975	.91254 90505 20726
1.710	0.09245 91333 96581	0.91273 41269 51936
11	.09230 11172 30759	.91291 88871 72912
12	.09214 32789 77232	.91310 33315 39467
13	.09198 56186 47172	.91328 74604 07437
14	.09182 81362 51194	.91347 12741 32679
1.715	0.09167 08317 99366	0.91365 47730 71071
16	.09151 37053 01203	.91383 79575 78512
17	.09135 67567 65670	.91402 08280 10918
18	.09119 99862 01184	.91420 33847 24222
19	.09104 33936 15614	.91438 56280 74375
1.720	0.09088 69790 16283	0.91456 75584 17342
21	.09073 07424 09966	.91474 91761 09102
22	.09057 46838 02894	.91493 04815 05648
23	.09041 88032 00754	.91511 14749 62984
24	.09026 31006 08688	.91529 21568 37125
1.725	0.09010 75760 31298	0.91547 25274 84095
26	.08995 22294 72643	.91565 25872 59929
27	.08979 70609 36241	.91583 23365 20667
28	.08964 20704 25072	.91601 17756 22357
29	.08948 72579 41576	.91619 09049 21053
1.730	0.08933 26234 87655	0.91636 97247 72810
31	.08917 81670 64675	.91654 82355 33691
32	.08902 38886 73464	.91672 64375 59757
33	.08886 97883 14319	.91690 43312 07072
34	.08871 58659 86998	.91708 19168 31702
1.735	0.08856 21216 90729	0.91725 91947 89708
36	.08840 85554 24208	.91743 61654 37151
37	.08825 51671 85596	.91761 28291 30090
38	.08810 19569 72527	.91778 91862 24577
39	.08794 89247 82106	.91796 52370 76662
1.740	0.08779 60706 10906	0.91814 09820 42385
41	.08764 33944 54974	.91831 64214 77782
42	.08749 08963 09833	.91849 15557 38879
43	.08733 85761 70475	.91866 63851 81692
44	.08718 64340 31372	.91884 09101 62228
1.745	0.08703 44698 86468	0.91901 51310 36480
46	.08688 26837 29188	.91918 90481 60432
47	.08673 10755 52433	.91936 26618 90051
48	.08657 96453 48581	.91953 59725 81290
49	.08642 83931 09494	.91970 89805 90088
1.750	0.08627 73188 26512	0.91988 16862 72366

x	$\dfrac{1}{\sqrt{2\pi}} e^{-\frac{x^2}{2}}$	$\dfrac{1}{\sqrt{2\pi}} \displaystyle\int_{-x}^{x} e^{-\frac{\alpha^2}{2}} \, d\alpha$
1.750	0.08627 73188 26512	0.91988 16862 72366
51	.08612 64224 90456	.92005 40899 84026
52	.08597 57040 91632	.92022 61920 80952
53	.08582 51636 19829	.92039 79929 19010
54	.08567 48010 64320	.92056 94928 54043
1.755	0.08552 46164 13863	0.92074 06922 41871
56	.08537 46096 56703	.92091 15914 38294
57	.08522 47807 80574	.92108 21907 99085
58	.08507 51297 72695	.92125 24906 79995
59	.08492 56566 19778	.92142 24914 36746
1.760	0.08477 63613 08022	0.92159 21934 25035
61	.08462 72438 23120	.92176 15970 00529
62	.08447 83041 50254	.92193 07025 18869
63	.08432 95422 74102	.92209 95103 35661
64	.08418 09581 78835	.92226 80208 06486
1.765	0.08403 25518 48118	0.92243 62342 86886
66	.08388 43232 65114	.92260 41511 32377
67	.08373 62724 12482	.92277 17716 98434
68	.08358 83992 72377	.92293 90963 40501
69	.08344 07038 26456	.92310 61254 13986
1.770	0.08329 31860 55874	0.92327 28592 74258
71	.08314 58459 41288	.92343 92982 76647
72	.08299 86834 62853	.92360 54427 76447
73	.08285 16986 00233	.92377 12931 28909
74	.08270 48913 32589	.92393 68496 89244
1.775	0.08255 82616 38592	0.92410 21128 12622
76	.08241 18094 96414	.92426 70828 54167
77	.08226 55348 83738	.92443 17601 68960
78	.08211 94377 77752	.92459 61451 12039
79	.08197 35181 55151	.92476 02380 38394
1.780	0.08182 77759 92143	0.92492 40393 02966
81	.08168 22112 64443	.92508 75492 60652
82	.08153 68239 47280	.92525 07682 66298
83	.08139 16140 15394	.92541 36966 74698
84	.08124 65814 43038	.92557 63348 40599
1.785	0.08110 17262 03980	0.92573 86831 18693
86	.08095 70482 71503	.92590 07418 63619
87	.08081 25476 18407	.92606 25114 29965
88	.08066 82242 17007	.92622 39921 72261
89	.08052 40780 39138	.92638 51844 44982
1.790	0.08038 01090 56154	0.92654 60886 02547
91	.08023 63172 38929	.92670 67049 99317
92	.08009 27025 57856	.92686 70339 89594
93	.07994 92649 82854	.92702 70759 27619
94	.07980 60044 83362	.92718 68311 67576
1.795	0.07966 29210 28343	0.92734 63000 63583
96	.07952 00145 86287	.92750 54829 69698
97	.07937 72851 25208	.92766 43802 39915
98	.07923 47326 12649	.92782 29922 28164
99	.07909 23570 15678	.92798 13192 88309
1.800	0.07895 01583 00894	0.92813 93617 74148

x	$\frac{1}{\sqrt{2\pi}} e^{-\frac{x^2}{2}}$	$\frac{1}{\sqrt{2\pi}} \int_{-x}^{x} e^{-\frac{\alpha^2}{2}} d\alpha$
1.800	0.07895 01583 00894	0.92813 93617 74148
01	.07880 81364 34426	.92829 71200 39412
02	.07866 62913 81932	.92845 45944 37762
03	.07852 46231 08604	.92861 17853 22792
04	.07838 31315 79166	.92876 86930 48026
1.805	0.07824 18167 57875	0.92892 53179 66914
06	.07810 06786 08524	.92908 16604 32839
07	.07795 97170 94440	.92923 77207 99105
08	.07781 89321 78489	.92939 34994 18948
09	.07767 83238 23073	.92954 89966 45526
1.810	0.07753 78919 90134	0.92970 42128 31922
11	.07739 76366 41153	.92985 91483 31143
12	.07725 75577 37151	.93001 38034 96117
13	.07711 76552 38691	.93016 81786 79695
14	.07697 79291 05881	.93032 22742 34649
1.815	0.07683 83792 98369	0.93047 60905 13669
16	.07669 90057 75350	.93062 96278 69365
17	.07655 98084 95564	.93078 28866 54266
18	.07642 07874 17297	.93093 58672 20815
19	.07628 19424 98384	.93108 85699 21375
1.820	0.07614 32736 96207	0.93124 09951 08220
21	.07600 47809 67699	.93139 31431 33542
22	.07586 64642 69342	.93154 50143 49444
23	.07572 83235 57172	.93169 66091 07943
24	.07559 03587 86774	.93184 79277 60967
1.825	0.07545 25699 13290	0.93199 89706 60355
26	.07531 49568 91415	.93214 97381 57855
27	.07517 75196 75399	.93230 02306 05125
28	.07504 02582 19050	.93245 04483 53730
29	.07490 31724 75731	.93260 03917 55143
1.830	0.07476 62623 98368	0.93275 00611 60743
31	.07462 95279 39441	.93289 94569 21815
32	.07449 29690 50995	.93304 85793 89548
33	.07435 65856 84633	.93319 74289 15034
34	.07422 03777 91524	.93334 60058 49269
1.835	0.07408 43453 22398	0.93349 43105 43150
36	.07394 84882 27550	.93364 23433 47475
37	.07381 28064 56841	.93379 01046 12942
38	.07367 72999 59698	.93393 75946 90151
39	.07354 19686 85116	.93408 48139 29596
1.840	0.07340 68125 81657	0.93423 17626 81672
41	.07327 18315 97454	.93437 84412 96669
42	.07313 70256 80211	.93452 48501 24773
43	.07300 23947 77202	.93467 09895 16066
44	.07286 79388 35274	.93481 68598 20523
1.845	0.07273 36578 00847	0.93496 24613 88012
46	.07259 95516 19916	.93510 77945 68295
47	.07246 56202 38052	.93525 28597 11025
48	.07233 18636 00402	.93539 76571 65744
49	.07219 82816 51689	.93554 21872 81886
1.850	0.07206 48743 36218	.0.93568 64504 08773

x	$\dfrac{1}{\sqrt{2\pi}}e^{-\frac{x^2}{2}}$	$\dfrac{1}{\sqrt{2\pi}}\displaystyle\int_{-x}^{x}e^{-\frac{\alpha^2}{2}}\,d\alpha$
1.850	0.07206 48743 36218	0.93568 64504 08773
51	.07193 16415 97870	.93583 04468 95615
52	.07179 85833 80107	.93597 41770 91511
53	.07166 56996 25975	.93611 76413 45445
54	.07153 29902 78099	.93626 08400 06286
1.855	0.07140 04552 78691	0.93640 37734 22789
56	.07126 80945 69544	.93654 64419 43594
57	.07113 59080 92040	.93668 88459 17222
58	.07100 38957 87144	.93683 09856 92077
59	.07087 20575 95411	.93697 28616 16446
1.860	0.07074 03934 56983	0.93711 44740 38495
61	.07060 89033 11593	.93725 58233 06269
62	.07047 75870 98564	.93739 69097 67696
63	.07034 64447 56808	.93753 77337 70578
64	.07021 54762 24834	.93767 82956 62596
1.865	0.07008 46814 40741	0.93781 85957 91309
66	.06995 40603 42224	.93795 86345 04150
67	.06982 36128 66574	.93809 84121 48427
68	.06969 33389 50676	.93823 79290 71322
69	.06956 32385 31015	.93837 71856 19893
1.870	0.06943 33115 43674	0.93851 61821 41068
71	.06930 35579 24336	.93865 49189 81647
72	.06917 39776 08282	.93879 33964 88301
73	.06904 45705 30399	.93893 16150 07572
74	.06891 53366 25172	.93906 95748 85871
1.875	0.06878 62758 26692	0.93920 72764 69477
76	.06865 73880 68654	.93934 47201 04538
77	.06852 86732 84360	.93948 19061 37068
78	.06840 01314 06715	.93961 88349 12947
79	.06827 17623 68236	.93975 55067 77921
1.880	0.06814 35661 01045	0.93989 19220 77600
81	.06801 55425 36875	.94002 80811 57460
82	.06788 76916 07071	.94016 39843 62838
83	.06776 00132 42586	.94029 96320 38932
84	.06763 25073 73990	.94043 50245 30805
1.885	0.06750 51739 31464	0.94057 01621 83379
86	.06737 80128 44803	.94070 50453 41435
87	.06725 10240 43420	.94083 96743 49615
88	.06712 42074 56343	.94097 40495 52418
89	.06699 75630 12217	.94110 81712 94202
1.890	0.06687 10906 39307	0.94124 20399 19181
91	.06674 47902 65498	.94137 56557 71425
92	.06661 86618 18295	.94150 90191 94861
93	.06649 27052 24824	.94164 21305 33268
94	.06636 69204 11834	.94177 49901 30281
1.895	0.06624 13073 05699	0.94190 75983 29386
96	.06611 58658 32416	.94203 99554 73925
97	.06599 05959 17608	.94217 20619 07088
98	.06586 54974 86525	.94230 39179 71918
99	.06574 05704 64046	.94243 55240 11307
1.900	0.06561 58147 74677	0.94256 68803 67996

x	$\frac{1}{\sqrt{2\pi}} e^{-\frac{x^2}{2}}$	$\frac{1}{\sqrt{2\pi}} \int_{-x}^{x} e^{-\frac{\alpha^2}{2}} d\alpha$
1.900	0.06561 58147 74677	0.94256 68803 67996
01	.06549 12303 42553	.94269 79873 84577
02	.06536 68170 91442	.94282 88454 03487
03	.06524 25749 44742	.94295 94547 67012
04	.06511 85038 25485	.94308 98158 17285
1.905	0.06499 46036 56335	0.94321 99288 96281
06	.06487 08743 59593	.94334 97943 45825
07	.06474 73158 57194	.94347 94125 07582
08	.06462 39280 70711	.94360 87837 23064
09	.06450 07109 21353	.94373 79083 33623
1.910	0.06437 76643 29969	0.94386 67866 80455
11	.06425 47882 17049	.94399 54191 04596
12	.06413 20825 02720	.94412 38059 46922
13	.06400 95471 06756	.94425 19475 48152
14	.06388 71819 48569	.94437 98442 48841
1.915	0.06376 49869 47217	0.94450 74963 89384
16	.06364 29620 21402	.94463 49043 10014
17	.06352 11070 89474	.94476 20683 50799
18	.06339 94220 69428	.94488 89888 51646
19	.06327 79068 78905	.94501 56661 52296
1.920	0.06315 65614 35199	0.94514 21005 92326
21	.06303 53856 55250	.94526 82925 11146
22	.06291 43794 55651	.94539 42422 48001
23	.06279 35427 52646	.94551 99501 41967
24	.06267 28754 62132	.94564 54165 31953
1.925	0.06255 23774 99660	0.94577 06417 56701
26	.06243 20487 80436	.94589 56261 54781
27	.06231 18892 19321	.94602 03700 64595
28	.06219 18987 30834	.94614 48738 24373
29	.06207 20772 29150	.94626 91377 72176
1.930	0.06195 24246 28105	0.94639 31622 45890
31	.06183 29408 41194	.94651 69475 83231
32	.06171 36257 81572	.94664 04941 21740
33	.06159 44793 62057	.94676 38021 98784
34	.06147 55014 95129	.94688 68721 51556
1.935	0.06135 66920 92932	0.94700 97043 17074
36	.06123 80510 67277	.94713 22990 32179
37	.06111 95783 29636	.94725 46566 33535
38	.06100 12737 91153	.94737 67774 57630
39	.06088 31373 62636	.94749 86618 40773
1.940	0.06076 51689 54565	0.94762 03101 19095
41	.06064 73684 77087	.94774 17226 28545
42	.06052 97358 40022	.94786 28997 04897
43	.06041 22709 52860	.94798 38416 83739
44	.06029 49737 24766	.94810 45489 00481
1.945	0.06017 78440 64576	0.94822 50216 90350
46	.06006 08818 80805	.94834 52603 88390
47	.05994 40870 81638	.94846 52653 29463
48	.05982 74595 74943	.94858 50368 48245
49	.05971 09992 68262	.94870 45752 79229
1.950	0.05959 47060 68816	0.94882 38809 56723

x	$\frac{1}{\sqrt{2\pi}} e^{-\frac{x^2}{2}}$	$\frac{1}{\sqrt{2\pi}} \int_{-x}^{x} e^{-\frac{\alpha^2}{2}} d\alpha$
1.950	0.05959 47060 68816	0.94882 38809 56723
51	.05947 85798 83507	.94894 29542 14847
52	.05936 26206 18918	.94906 17953 87537
53	.05924 68281 81313	.94918 04048 08541
54	.05913 12024 76638	.94929 87828 11418
1.955	0.05901 57434 10525	0.94941 69297 29540
56	.05890 04508 88289	.94953 48458 96089
57	.05878 53248 14932	.94965 25316 44059
58	.05867 03650 95141	.94976 99873 06251
59	.05855 55716 33293	.94988 72132 15278
1.960	0.05844 09443 33451	0.95000 42097 03559
61	.05832 64830 99372	.95012 09771 03322
62	.05821 21878 34499	.95023 75157 46603
63	.05809 80584 41970	.95035 38259 65242
64	.05798 40948 24615	.95046 99080 90887
1.965	0.05787 02968 84956	0.95058 57624 54992
66	.05775 66645 25212	.95070 13893 88814
67	.05764 31976 47297	.95081 67892 23414
68	.05752 98961 52821	.95093 19622 89659
69	.05741 67599 43092	.95104 69089 18215
1.970	0.05730 37889 19117	0.95116 16294 39555
71	.05719 09829 81603	.95127 61241 83950
72	.05707 83420 30956	.95139 03934 81473
73	.05696 58659 67286	.95150 44376 61998
74	.05685 35546 90404	.95161 82570 55200
1.975	0.05674 14080 99824	0.95173 18519 90550
76	.05662 94260 94767	.95184 52227 97323
77	.05651 76085 74157	.95195 83698 04586
78	.05640 59554 36626	.95207 12933 41208
79	.05629 44665 80514	.95218 39937 35853
1.980	0.05618 31419 03868	0.95229 64713 16983
81	.05607 19813 04446	.95240 87264 12854
82	.05596 09846 79714	.95252 07593 51517
83	.05585 01519 26854	.95263 25704 60820
84	.05573 94829 42755	.95274 41600 68404
1.985	0.05562 89776 24024	0.95285 55285 01702
86	.05551 86358 66980	.95296 66760 87941
87	.05540 84575 67658	.95307 76031 54141
88	.05529 84426 21810	.95318 83100 27114
89	.05518 85909 24903	.95329 87970 33461
1.990	0.05507 89023 72126	0.95340 90644 99576
91	.05496 93768 58384	.95351 91127 51642
92	.05486 00142 78305	.95362 89421 15632
93	.05475 08145 26236	.95373 85529 17308
94	.05464 17774 96247	.95384 79454 82219
1.995	0.05453 29030 82132	0.95395 71201 35703
96	.05442 41911 77409	.95406 60772 02887
97	.05431 56416 75321	.95417 48170 08681
98	.05420 72544 68836	.95428 33398 77785
99	.05409 90294 50650	.95439 16461 34682
2.000	0.05399 09665 13188	0.95449 97361 03642

x	$\dfrac{1}{\sqrt{2\pi}}e^{-\frac{x^2}{2}}$	$\dfrac{1}{\sqrt{2\pi}}\displaystyle\int_{-x}^{x}e^{-\frac{\alpha^2}{2}}\,d\alpha$
2.000	0.05399 09665 13188	0.95449 97361 03642
01	.05388 30655 48603	.95460 76101 08717
02	.05377 53264 48779	.95471 52684 73746
03	.05366 77491 05329	.95482 27115 22350
04	.05356 03334 09600	.95492 99395 77932
2.005	0.05345 30792 52672	0.95503 69529 63681
06	.05334 59865 25357	.95514 37520 02563
07	.05323 90551 18204	.95525 03370 17329
08	.05313 22849 21497	.95535 67083 30509
09	.05302 56758 25256	.95546 28662 64415
2.010	0.05291 92277 19240	0.95556 88111 41137
11	.05281 29404 92947	.95567 45432 82545
12	.05270 68140 35613	.95578 00630 10288
13	.05260 08482 36217	.95588 53706 45793
14	.05249 50429 83478	.95599 04665 10264
2.015	0.05238 93981 65858	0.95609 53509 24684
16	.05228 39136 71562	.95620 00242 09810
17	.05217 85893 88542	.95630 44866 86177
18	.05207 34252 04492	.95640 87386 74097
19	.05196 84210 06855	.95651 27804 93653
2.020	0.05186 35766 82821	0.95661 66124 64706
21	.05175 88921 19327	.95672 02349 06891
22	.05165 43672 03062	.95682 36481 39615
23	.05155 00018 20462	.95692 68524 82059
24	.05144 57958 57718	.95702 98482 53177
2.025	0.05134 17492 00769	0.95713 26357 71694
26	.05123 78617 35312	.95723 52153 56108
27	.05113 41333 46793	.95733 75873 24687
28	.05103 05639 20418	.95743 97519 95470
29	.05092 71533 41145	.95754 17096 86266
2.030	0.05082 39014 93691	0.95764 34607 14655
31	.05072 08082 62532	.95774 50053 97985
32	.05061 78735 31900	.95784 63440 53373
33	.05051 50971 85789	.95794 74769 97703
34	.05041 24791 07954	.95804 84045 47628
2.035	0.05031 00191 81911	0.95814 91270 19569
36	.05020 77172 90937	.95824 96447 29712
37	.05010 55733 18077	.95834 99579 94011
38	.05000 35871 46136	.95845 00671 28185
39	.04990 17586 57688	.95854 99724 47718
2.040	0.04980 00877 35071	0.95864 96742 67860
41	.04969 85742 60392	.95874 91729 03624
42	.04959 72181 15526	.95884 84686 69788
43	.04949 60191 82118	.95894 75618 80894
44	.04939 49773 41582	.95904 64528 51245
2.045	0.04929 40924 75103	0.95914 51418 94909
46	.04919 33644 63640	.95924 36293 25715
47	.04909 27931 87924	.95934 19154 57254
48	.04899 23785 28459	.95944 00006 02878
49	.04889 21203 65527	.95953 78850 75699
2.050	0.04879 20185 79183	0.95963 55691 88591

x	$\frac{1}{\sqrt{2\pi}} e^{-\frac{x^2}{2}}$	$\frac{1}{\sqrt{2\pi}} \int_{-x}^{x} e^{-\frac{\alpha^2}{2}} d\alpha$
2.050	0.04879 20185 79183	0.95963 55691 88591
51	.04869 20730 49260	.95973 30532 54187
52	.04859 22836 55368	.95983 03375 84879
53	.04849 26502 76898	.95992 74224 92819
54	.04839 31727 93017	.96002 43082 89916
2.055	0.04829 38510 82677	0.96012 09952 87840
56	.04819 46850 24608	.96021 74837 98015
57	.04809 56744 97325	.96031 37741 31625
58	.04799 68193 79123	.96040 98665 99611
59	.04789 81195 48085	.96050 57615 12667
2.060	0.04779 95748 82077	0.96060 14591 81246
61	.04770 11852 58753	.96069 69599 15557
62	.04760 29505 55552	.96079 22640 25561
63	.04750 48706 49702	.96088 73718 20977
64	.04740 69454 18222	.96098 22836 11276
2.065	0.04730 91747 37917	0.96107 69997 05684
66	.04721 15584 85385	.96117 15204 13180
67	.04711 40965 37017	.96126 58460 42495
68	.04701 67887 68994	.96135 99769 02115
69	.04691 96350 57293	.96145 39133 00275
2.070	0.04682 26352 77683	0.96154 76555 44965
71	.04672 57893 05731	.96164 12039 43925
72	.04662 90970 16799	.96173 45588 04644
73	.04653 25582 86046	.96182 77204 34364
74	.04643 61729 88431	.96192 06891 40077
2.075	0.04633 99409 98709	0.96201 34652 28523
76	.04624 38621 91439	.96210 60490 06193
77	.04614 79364 40977	.96219 84407 79327
78	.04605 21636 21483	.96229 06408 53911
79	.04595 65436 06920	.96238 26495 35682
2.080	0.04586 10762 71055	0.96247 44671 30124
81	.04576 57614 87457	.96256 60939 42468
82	.04567 05991 29504	.96265 75302 77691
83	.04557 55890 70377	.96274 87764 40519
84	.04548 07311 83068	.96283 98327 35421
2.085	0.04538 60253 40374	0.96293 06994 66614
86	.04529 14714 14903	.96302 13769 38060
87	.04519 70692 79072	.96311 18654 53467
88	.04510 28188 05110	.96320 21653 16285
89	.04500 87198 65057	.96329 22768 29710
2.090	0.04491 47723 30767	0.96338 22002 96682
91	.04482 09760 73906	.96347 19360 19885
92	.04472 73309 65956	.96356 14843 01744
93	.04463 38368 78213	.96365 08454 44429
94	.04454 04936 81791	.96374 00197 49851
2.095	0.04444 73012 47620	0.96382 90075 19664
96	.04435 42594 46449	.96391 78090 55263
97	.04426 13681 48846	.96400 64246 57785
98	.04416 86272 25199	.96409 48546 28108
99	.04407 60365 45716	.96418 30992 66849
2.100	0.04398 35959 80427	0.96427 11588 74367

x	$\dfrac{1}{\sqrt{2\pi}}\,e^{-\frac{x^2}{2}}$	$\dfrac{1}{\sqrt{2\pi}}\displaystyle\int_{-x}^{x} e^{-\frac{\alpha^2}{2}}\,d\alpha$
2.100	0.04398 35959 80427	0.96427 11588 74367
01	.04389 13053 99186	.96435 90337 50760
02	.04379 91646 71669	.96444 67241 95866
03	.04370 71736 67378	.96453 42305 09262
04	.04361 53322 55637	.96462 15529 90264
2.105	0.04352 36403 05601	0.96470 86919 37926
06	.04343 20976 86249	.96479 56476 51040
07	.04334 07042 66387	.96488 24204 28137
08	.04324 94599 14654	.96496 90105 67485
09	.04315 83644 99514	.96505 54183 67087
2.110	0.04306 74178 89266	0.96514 16441 24686
11	.04297 66199 52036	.96522 76881 37759
12	.04288 59705 55787	.96531 35507 03521
13	.04279 54695 68312	.96539 92321 18922
14	.04270 51168 57240	.96548 47326 80645
2.115	0.04261 49122 90034	0.96557 00526 85113
16	.04252 48557 33993	.96565 51924 28480
17	.04243 49470 56252	.96574 01522 06635
18	.04234 51861 23787	.96582 49323 15202
19	.04225 55728 03409	.96590 95330 49538
2.120	0.04216 61069 61770	0.96599 39547 04734
21	.04207 67884 65362	.96607 81975 75615
22	.04198 76171 80518	.96616 22619 56737
23	.04189 85929 73414	.96624 61481 42389
24	.04180 97157 10066	.96632 98564 26593
2.125	0.04172 09852 56339	0.96641 33871 03102
26	.04163 24014 77937	.96649 67404 65402
27	.04154 39642 40413	.96657 99168 06708
28	.04145 56734 09165	.96666 29164 19968
29	.04136 75288 49440	.96674 57395 97859
2.130	0.04127 95304 26330	0.96682 83866 32790
31	.04119 16780 04780	.96691 08578 16899
32	.04110 39714 49580	.96699 31534 42053
33	.04101 64106 25375	.96707 52737 99851
34	.04092 89953 96659	.96715 72191 81618
2.135	0.04084 17256 27780	0.96723 89898 78411
36	.04075 46011 82938	.96732 05861 81012
37	.04066 76219 26187	.96740 20083 79935
38	.04058 07877 21437	.96748 32567 65418
39	.04049 40984 32455	.96756 43316 27431
2.140	0.04040 75539 22860	0.96764 52332 55668
41	.04032 11540 56134	.96772 59619 39551
42	.04023 48986 95614	.96780 65179 68230
43	.04014 87877 04498	.96788 69016 30580
44	.04006 28209 45842	.96796 71132 15203
2.145	0.03997 69982 82565	0.96804 71530 10427
46	.03989 13195 77447	.96812 70213 04305
47	.03980 57846 93130	.96820 67183 84617
48	.03972 03934 92121	.96828 62445 38867
49	.03963 51458 36789	.96836 56000 54283
2.150	0.03955 00415 89370	0.96844 47852 17819

x	$\frac{1}{\sqrt{2\pi}} e^{-\frac{x^2}{2}}$	$\frac{1}{\sqrt{2\pi}} \int_{-x}^{x} e^{-\frac{\alpha^2}{2}} d\alpha$
2.150	0.03955 00415 89370	0.96844 47852 17819
51	.03946 50806 11966	.96852 38003 16153
52	.03938 02627 66545	.96860 26456 35688
53	.03929 55879 14942	.96868 13214 62549
54	.03921 10559 18863	.96875 98280 82585
2.155	0.03912 66666 39880	0.96883 81657 81369
56	.03904 24199 39438	.96891 63348 44197
57	.03895 83156 78851	.96899 43355 56087
58	.03887 43537 19307	.96907 21682 01780
59	.03879 05339 21864	.96914 98330 65739
2.160	0.03870 68561 47456	0.96922 73304 32149
61	.03862 33202 56889	.96930 46605 84918
62	.03853 99261 10845	.96938 18238 07673
63	.03845 66735 69884	.96945 88203 83765
64	.03837 35624 94440	.96953 56505 96263
2.165	0.03829 05927 44825	0.96961 23147 27959
66	.03820 77641 81232	.96968 88130 61366
67	.03812 50766 63729	.96976 51458 78715
68	.03804 25300 52268	.96984 13134 61958
69	.03796 01242 06680	.96991 73160 92768
2.170	0.03787 78589 86677	0.96999 31540 52536
71	.03779 57342 51857	.97006 88276 22372
72	.03771 37498 61696	.97014 43370 83106
73	.03763 19056 75559	.97021 96827 15288
74	.03755 02015 52694	.97029 48647 99184
2.175	0.03746 86373 52234	0.97036 98836 14780
76	.03738 72129 33200	.97044 47394 41780
77	.03730 59281 54499	.97051 94325 59607
78	.03722 47828 74928	.97059 39632 47398
79	.03714 37769 53173	.97066 83317 84011
2.180	0.03706 29102 47806	0.97074 25384 48021
81	.03698 21826 17296	.97081 65835 17719
82	.03690 15939 19997	.97089 04672 71113
83	.03682 11440 14161	.97096 41899 85927
84	.03674 08327 57928	.97103 77519 39603
2.185	0.03666 06600 09335	0.97111 11534 09297
86	.03658 06256 26313	.97118 43946 71884
87	.03650 07294 66688	.97125 74760 03951
88	.03642 09713 88183	.97133 03976 81804
89	.03634 13512 48416	.97140 31599 81463
2.190	0.03626 18689 04906	0.97147 57631 78662
91	.03618 25242 15068	.97154 82075 48852
92	.03610 33170 36218	.97162 04933 67197
93	.03602 42472 25570	.97169 26209 08576
94	.03594 53146 40242	.97176 45904 47582
2.195	0.03586 65191 37252	0.97183 64022 58525
96	.03578 78605 73520	.97190 80566 15424
97	.03570 93388 05872	.97197 95537 92016
98	.03563 09536 91034	.97205 08940 61750
99	.03555 27050 85641	.97212 20776 97787
2.200	0.03547 45928 46231	0.97219 31049 73003

226

x	$\frac{1}{\sqrt{2\pi}} e^{-\frac{x^2}{2}}$	$\frac{1}{\sqrt{2\pi}} \int_{-x}^{x} e^{-\frac{\alpha^2}{2}} d\alpha$
2.200	0.03547 45928 46231	0.97219 31049 73003
01	.03539 66168 29251	.97226 39761 59986
02	.03531 87768 91051	.97233 46915 31039
03	.03524 10728 87894	.97240 52513 58174
04	.03516 35046 75949	.97247 56559 13118
2.205	0.03508 60721 11294	0.97254 59054 67309
06	.03500 87750 49919	.97261 60002 91899
07	.03493 16133 47726	.97268 59406 57749
08	.03485 45868 60525	.97275 57268 35433
09	.03477 76954 44044	.97282 53590 95238
2.210	0.03470 09389 53919	0.97289 48377 07160
11	.03462 43172 45704	.97296 41629 40908
12	.03454 78301 74867	.97303 33350 65901
13	.03447 14775 96791	.97310 23543 51269
14	.03439 52593 66776	.97317 12210 65854
2.215	0.03431 91753 40040	0.97323 99354 78205
16	.03424 32253 71718	.97330 84978 56586
17	.03416 74093 16864	.97337 69084 68968
18	.03409 17270 30452	.97344 51675 83033
19	.03401 61783 67375	.97351 32754 66172
2.220	0.03394 07631 82449	0.97358 12323 85487
21	.03386 54813 30411	.97364 90386 07790
22	.03379 03326 65920	.97371 66943 99601
23	.03371 53170 43559	.97378 42000 27149
24	.03364 04343 17834	.97385 15557 56373
2.225	0.03356 56843 43178	0.97391 87618 52921
26	.03349 10669 73947	.97398 58185 82149
27	.03341 65820 64425	.97405 27262 09123
28	.03334 22294 68823	.97411 94849 98616
29	.03326 80090 41280	.97418 60952 15110
2.230	0.03319 39206 35861	0.97425 25571 22796
31	.03311 99641 06564	.97431 88709 85571
32	.03304 61393 07315	.97438 50370 67042
33	.03297 24460 91970	.97445 10556 30523
34	.03289 88843 14320	.97451 69269 39035
2.235	0.03282 54538 28083	0.97458 26512 55308
36	.03275 21544 86915	.97464 82288 41778
37	.03267 89861 44403	.97471 36599 60588
38	.03260 59486 54068	.97477 89448 73590
39	.03253 30418 69369	.97484 40838 42341
2.240	0.03246 02656 43697	0.97490 90771 28107
41	.03238 76198 30384	.97497 39249 91858
42	.03231 51042 82696	.97503 86276 94272
43	.03224 27188 53839	.97510 31854 95734
44	.03217 04633 96956	.97516 75986 56335
2.245	0.03209 83377 65131	0.97523 18674 35872
46	.03202 63418 11389	.97529 59920 93848
47	.03195 44753 88693	.97535 99728 89472
48	.03188 27383 49951	.97542 38100 81659
49	.03181 11305 48012	.97548 75039 29030
2.250	0.03173 96518 35667	0.97555 10546 89911

x	$\dfrac{1}{\sqrt{2\pi}}\,e^{-\frac{x^2}{2}}$	$\dfrac{1}{\sqrt{2\pi}}\displaystyle\int_{-x}^{x} e^{-\frac{\alpha^2}{2}}\,d\alpha$
2.250	0.03173 96518 35667	0.97555 10546 89911
51	.03166 83020 65654	.97561 44626 22334
52	.03159 70810 90652	.97567 77279 84037
53	.03152 59887 63288	.97574 08510 32462
54	.03145 50249 36133	.97580 38320 24757
2.255	0.03138 41894 61707	0.97586 66712 17775
56	.03131 34821 92474	.97592 93688 68073
57	.03124 29029 80850	.97599 19252 31916
58	.03117 24516 79198	.97605 43405 65270
59	.03110 21281 39830	.97611 66151 23808
2.260	0.03103 19322 15008	0.97617 87491 62906
61	.03096 18637 56948	.97624 07429 37646
62	.03089 19226 17813	.97630 25967 02813
63	.03082 21086 49723	.97636 43107 12898
64	.03075 24217 04747	.97642 58852 22094
2.265	0.03068 28616 34911	0.97648 73204 84300
66	.03061 34282 92193	.97654 86167 53118
67	.03054 41215 28528	.97660 97742 81855
68	.03047 49411 95805	.97667 07933 23520
69	.03040 58871 45872	.97673 16741 30827
2.270	0.03033 69592 30532	0.97679 24169 56193
71	.03026 81573 01546	.97685 30220 51740
72	.03019 94812 10635	.97691 34896 69291
73	.03013 09308 09478	.97697 38200 60375
74	.03006 25059 49715	.97703 40134 76223
2.275	0.02999 42064 82945	0.97709 40701 67770
76	.02992 60322 60731	.97715 39903 85651
77	.02985 79831 34596	.97721 37743 80210
78	.02979 00589 56026	.97727 34224 01488
79	.02972 22595 76469	.97733 29346 99233
2.280	0.02965 45848 47341	0.97739 23115 22894
81	.02958 70346 20019	.97745 15531 21624
82	.02951 96087 45847	.97751 06597 44277
83	.02945 23070 76134	.97756 96316 39410
84	.02938 51294 62157	.97762 84690 55285
2.285	0.02931 80757 55160	0.97768 71722 39864
86	.02925 11458 06355	.97774 57414 40811
87	.02918 43394 66922	.97780 41769 05495
88	.02911 76565 88012	.97786 24788 80986
89	.02905 10970 20744	.97792 06476 14055
2.290	0.02898 46606 16209	0.97797 86833 51177
91	.02891 83472 25471	.97803 65863 38529
92	.02885 21566 99562	.97809 43568 21989
93	.02878 60888 89491	.97815 19950 47138
94	.02872 01436 46238	.97820 95012 59258
2.295	0.02865 43208 20756	0.97826 68757 03335
96	.02858 86202 63976	.97832 41186 24054
97	.02852 30418 26802	.97838 12302 65804
98	.02845 75853 60113	.97843 82108 72675
99	.02839 22507 14768	.97849 50606 88458
2.300	0.02832 70377 41601	0.97855 17799 56648

x	$\dfrac{1}{\sqrt{2\pi}} e^{-\frac{x^2}{2}}$	$\dfrac{1}{\sqrt{2\pi}} \displaystyle\int_{-x}^{x} e^{-\frac{\alpha^2}{2}}\, d\alpha$
2.300	0.02832 70377 41601	0.97855 17799 56648
01	.02826 19462 91424	.97860 83689 20440
02	.02819 69762 15028	.97866 48278 22730
03	.02813 21273 63183	.97872 11569 06116
04	.02806 73995 86640	.97877 73564 12900
2.305	0.02800 27927 36129	0.97883 34265 85080
06	.02793 83066 62361	.97888 93676 64362
07	.02787 39412 16030	.97894 51798 92148
08	.02780 96962 47812	.97900 08635 09545
09	.02774 55716 08367	.97905 64187 57359
2.310	0.02768 15671 48337	0.97911 18458 76098
11	.02761 76827 18348	.97916 71451 05972
12	.02755 39181 69014	.97922 23166 86892
13	.02749 02733 50932	.97927 73608 58469
14	.02742 67481 14685	.97933 22778 60017
2.315	0.02736 33423 10845	0.97938 70679 30549
16	.02730 00557 89970	.97944 17313 08782
17	.02723 68884 02606	.97949 62682 33131
18	.02717 38399 99289	.97955 06789 41715
19	.02711 09104 30542	.97960 49636 72352
2.320	0.02704 80995 46882	0.97965 91226 62561
21	.02698 54071 98812	.97971 31561 49563
22	.02692 28332 36829	.97976 70643 70280
23	.02686 03775 11421	.97982 08475 61335
24	.02679 80398 73070	.97987 45059 59050
2.325	0.02673 58201 72248	0.97992 80397 99452
26	.02667 37182 59424	.97998 14493 18265
27	.02661 17339 85058	.98003 47347 50915
28	.02654 98671 99609	.98008 78963 32531
29	.02648 81177 53527	.98014 09342 97940
2.330	0.02642 64854 97262	0.98019 38488 81671
31	.02636 49702 81258	.98024 66403 17956
32	.02630 35719 55958	.98029 93088 40724
33	.02624 22903 71802	.98035 18546 83607
34	.02618 11253 79229	.98040 42780 79939
2.335	0.02612 00768 28677	0.98045 65792 62752
36	.02605 91445 70585	.98050 87584 64782
37	.02599 83284 55390	.98056 08159 18463
38	.02593 76283 33531	.98061 27518 55932
39	.02587 70440 55449	.98066 45665 09026
2.340	0.02581 65754 71588	0.98071 62601 09283
41	.02575 62224 32391	.98076 78328 87942
42	.02569 59847 88309	.98081 92850 75943
43	.02563 58623 89795	.98087 06169 03926
44	.02557 58550 87304	.98092 18286 02233
2.345	0.02551 59627 31300	0.98097 29204 00906
46	.02545 61851 72251	.98102 38925 29689
47	.02539 65222 60631	.98107 47452 18027
48	.02533 69738 46921	.98112 54786 95064
49	.02527 75397 81610	.98117 60931 89647
2.350	0.02521 82199 15194	0.98122 65889 30323

x	$\dfrac{1}{\sqrt{2\pi}}\,e^{-\frac{x^2}{2}}$	$\dfrac{1}{\sqrt{2\pi}}\displaystyle\int_{-x}^{x} e^{-\frac{\alpha^2}{2}}\,d\alpha$
2.350	0.02521 82199 15194	0.98122 65889 30323
51	.02515 90140 98179	.98127 69661 45340
52	.02509 99221 81078	.98132 72250 62649
53	.02504 09440 14415	.98137 73659 09898
54	.02498 20794 48726	.98142 73889 14440
2.355	0.02492 33283 34554	0.98147 72943 03328
56	.02486 46905 22458	.98152 70823 03313
57	.02480 61658 63004	.98157 67531 40853
58	.02474 77542 06775	.98162 63070 42101
59	.02468 94554 04365	.98167 57442 32916
2.360	0.02463 12693 06382	0.98172 50649 38855
61	.02457 31957 63449	.98177 42693 85178
62	.02451 52346 26202	.98182 33577 96846
63	.02445 73857 45295	.98187 23303 98520
64	.02439 96489 71396	.98192 11874 14565
2.365	0.02434 20241 55190	0.98196 99290 69044
66	.02428 45111 47379	.98201 85555 85724
67	.02422 71097 98683	.98206 70671 88073
68	.02416 98199 59841	.98211 54640 99259
69	.02411 26414 81609	.98216 37465 42153
2.370	0.02405 55742 14763	0.98221 19147 39326
71	.02399 86180 10099	.98225 99689 13053
72	.02394 17727 18435	.98230 79092 85309
73	.02388 50381 90606	.98235 57360 77770
74	.02382 84142 77472	.98240 34495 11814
2.375	0.02377 19008 29914	0.98245 10498 08523
76	.02371 54976 98835	.98249 85371 88678
77	.02365 92047 35162	.98254 59118 72764
78	.02360 30217 89845	.98259 31740 80965
79	.02354 69487 13858	.98264 03240 33169
2.380	0.02349 09853 58201	0.98268 73619 48967
81	.02343 51315 73899	.98273 42880 47650
82	.02337 93872 12001	.98278 11025 48211
83	.02332 37521 23584	.98282 78056 69347
84	.02326 82261 59752	.98287 43976 29455
2.385	0.02321 28091 71636	0.98292 08786 46636
86	.02315 75010 10395	.98296 72489 38693
87	.02310 23015 27215	.98301 35087 23130
88	.02304 72105 73314	.98305 96582 17154
89	.02299 22279 99937	.98310 56976 37677
2.390	0.02293 73536 58361	0.98315 16272 01309
91	.02288 25873 99891	.98319 74471 24365
92	.02282 79290 75866	.98324 31576 22864
93	.02277 33785 37654	.98328 87589 12526
94	.02271 89356 36657	.98333 42512 08773
2.395	0.02266 46002 24309	0.98337 96347 26732
96	.02261 03721 52077	.98342 49096 81231
97	.02255 62512 71462	.98347 00762 86801
98	.02250 22374 33999	.98351 51347 57678
99	.02244 83304 91258	.98356 00853 07800
2.400	0.02239 45302 94843	0.98360 49281 50808

x	$\frac{1}{\sqrt{2\pi}} e^{-\frac{x^2}{2}}$	$\frac{1}{\sqrt{2\pi}} \int_{-x}^{x} e^{-\frac{\alpha^2}{2}} d\alpha$
2.400	0.02239 45302 94843	0.98360 49281 50808
01	.02234 08366 96395	.98364 96635 00045
02	.02228 72495 47592	.98369 42915 68560
03	.02223 37687 00146	.98373 88125 69103
04	.02218 03940 05809	.98378 32267 14129
2.405	0.02212 71253 16369	0.98382 75342 15796
06	.02207 39624 83652	.98387 17352 85966
07	.02202 09053 59526	.98391 58301 36203
08	.02196 79537 95893	.98395 98189 77777
09	.02191 51076 44700	.98400 37020 21662
2.410	0.02186 23667 57929	0.98404 74794 78533
11	.02180 97309 87608	.98409 11515 58771
12	.02175 72001 85803	.98413 47184 72462
13	.02170 47742 04622	.98417 81804 29395
14	.02165 24528 96215	.98422 15376 39062
2.415	0.02160 02361 12777	0.98426 47903 10663
16	.02154 81237 06543	.98430 79386 53098
17	.02149 61155 29794	.98435 09828 74975
18	.02144 42114 34855	.98439 39231 84605
19	.02139 24112 74093	.98443 67597 90004
2.420	0.02134 07148 99923	0.98447 94928 98893
21	.02128 91221 64805	.98452 21227 18697
22	.02123 76329 21244	.98456 46494 56546
23	.02118 62470 21793	.98460 70733 19278
24	.02113 49643 19050	.98464 93945 13431
2.425	0.02108 37846 65664	0.98469 16132 45253
26	.02103 27079 14328	.98473 37297 20695
27	.02098 17339 17786	.98477 57441 45414
28	.02093 08625 28830	.98481 76567 24771
29	.02088 00936 00302	.98485 94676 63836
2.430	0.02082 94269 85092	0.98490 11771 67382
31	.02077 88625 36143	.98494 27854 39887
32	.02072 84001 06447	.98498 42926 85539
33	.02067 80395 49049	.98502 56991 08228
34	.02062 77807 17042	.98506 70049 11552
2.435	0.02057 76234 63576	0.98510 82102 98815
36	.02052 75676 41850	.98514 93154 73028
37	.02047 76131 05118	.98519 03206 36906
38	.02042 77597 06687	.98523 12259 92874
39	.02037 80072 99918	.98527 20317 43060
2.440	0.02032 83557 38226	0.98531 27380 89303
41	.02027 88048 75081	.98535 33452 33146
42	.02022 93545 64010	.98539 38533 75838
43	.02018 00046 58594	.98543 42627 18339
44	.02013 07550 12470	.98547 45734 61312
2.445	0.02008 16054 79334	0.98551 47858 05131
46	.02003 25559 12937	.98555 48999 49874
47	.01998 36061 67087	.98559 49160 95330
48	.01993 47560 95654	.98563 48344 40992
49	.01988 60055 52561	.98567 46551 86064
2.450	0.01983 73543 91795	0.98571 43785 29457

x	$\frac{1}{\sqrt{2\pi}} e^{-\frac{x^2}{2}}$	$\frac{1}{\sqrt{2\pi}} \int_{-x}^{x} e^{-\frac{\alpha^2}{2}} d\alpha$
2.450	0.01983 73543 91795	0.98571 43785 29457
51	.01978 88024 67400	.98575 40046 69789
52	.01974 03496 33478	.98579 35338 05387
53	.01969 19957 44195	.98583 29661 34286
54	.01964 37406 53776	.98587 23018 54230
2.455	0.01959 55842 16505	0.98591 15411 62670
56	.01954 75262 86732	.98595 06842 56767
57	.01949 95667 18865	.98598 97313 33392
58	.01945 17053 67377	.98602 86825 89120
59	.01940 39420 86801	.98606 75382 20242
2.460	0.01935 62767 31737	0.98610 62984 22751
61	.01930 87091 56846	.98614 49633 92355
62	.01926 12392 16853	.98618 35333 24469
63	.01921 38667 66549	.98622 20084 14216
64	.01916 65916 60790	.98626 03888 56431
2.465	0.01911 94137 54496	0.98629 86748 45659
66	.01907 23329 02654	.98633 68665 76152
67	.01902 53489 60316	.98637 49642 41876
68	.01897 84617 82601	.98641 29680 36503
69	.01893 16712 24697	.98645 08781 53419
2.470	0.01888 49771 41856	0.98648 86947 85719
71	.01883 83793 89401	.98652 64181 26207
72	.01879 18778 22722	.98656 40483 67400
73	.01874 54722 97277	.98660 15857 01525
74	.01869 91626 68594	.98663 90303 20520
2.475	0.01865 29487 92270	0.98667 63824 16035
76	.01860 68305 23973	.98671 36421 79428
77	.01856 08077 19439	.98675 08098 01773
78	.01851 48802 34478	.98678 78854 73852
79	.01846 90479 24969	.98682 48693 86161
2.480	0.01842 33106 46862	0.98686 17617 28906
81	.01837 76682 56180	.98689 85626 92007
82	.01833 21206 09019	.98693 52724 65094
83	.01828 66675 61545	.98697 18912 37509
84	.01824 13089 70001	.98700 84191 98310
2.485	0.01819 60446 90699	0.98704 48565 36264
86	.01815 08745 80030	.98708 12034 39852
87	.01810 57984 94454	.98711 74600 97268
88	.01806 08162 90510	.98715 36266 96418
89	.01801 59278 24809	.98718 97034 24922
2.490	0.01797 11329 5404C	0.98722 56904 70114
91	.01792 64315 34965	.98726 15880 19039
92	.01788 18234 24425	.98729 73962 58459
93	.01783 73084 79336	.98733 31153 74847
94	.01779 28865 56691	.98736 87455 54391
2.495	0.01774 85575 13561	0.98740 42869 82994
96	.01770 43212 07094	.98743 97398 46270
97	.01766 01774 94517	.98747 51043 29551
98	.01761 61262 33135	.98751 03806 17882
99	.01757 21672 80331	.98754 55688 96023
2.500	0.01752 83004 93569	0.98758 06693 48448

x	$\dfrac{1}{\sqrt{2\pi}}\,e^{-\frac{x^2}{2}}$	$\dfrac{1}{\sqrt{2\pi}}\displaystyle\int_{-x}^{x} e^{-\frac{\alpha^2}{2}}\,d\alpha$
2.500	0.01752 83004 93569	0.98758 06693 48448
01	.01748 45257 30391	.98761 56821 59346
02	.01744 08428 48419	.98765 06075 12623
03	.01739 72517 05358	.98768 54455 91899
04	.01735 37521 58990	.98772 01965 80509
2.505	0.01731 03440 67181	0.98775 48606 61505
06	.01726 70272 87876	.98778 94380 17653
07	.01722 38016 79104	.98782 39288 31437
08	.01718 06670 98974	.98785 83332 85055
09	.01713 76234 05680	.98789 26515 60424
2.510	0.01709 46704 57497	0.98792 68838 39175
11	.01705 18081 12784	.98796 10303 02656
12	.01700 90362 29983	.98799 50911 31934
13	.01696 63546 67620	.98802 90665 07790
14	.01692 37632 84308	.98806 29566 10724
2.515	0.01688 12619 38739	0.98809 67616 20952
16	.01683 88504 89697	.98813 04817 18410
17	.01679 65287 96045	.98816 41170 82748
18	.01675 42967 16736	.98819 76678 93337
19	.01671 21541 10806	.98823 11343 29264
2.520	0.01667 01008 37381	0.98826 45165 69335
21	.01662 81367 55671	.98829 78147 92074
22	.01658 62617 24973	.98833 10291 75725
23	.01654 44756 04673	.98836 41598 98248
24	.01650 27782 54244	.98839 72071 37323
2.525	0.01646 11695 33247	0.98843 01710 70351
26	.01641 96493 01332	.98846 30518 74449
27	.01637 82174 18238	.98849 58497 26456
28	.01633 68737 43791	.98852 85648 02928
29	.01629 56181 37910	.98856 11972 80143
2.530	0.01625 44504 60600	0.98859 37473 34099
31	.01621 33705 71960	.98862 62151 40511
32	.01617 23783 32176	.98865 86008 74819
33	.01613 14736 01527	.98869 09047 12180
34	.01609 06562 40383	.98872 31268 27471
2.535	0.01604 99261 09203	0.98875 52673 95294
36	.01600 92830 68542	.98878 73265 89969
37	.01596 87269 79043	.98881 93045 85536
38	.01592 82577 01445	.98885 12015 55759
39	.01588 78750 96576	.98888 30176 74124
2.540	0.01584 75790 25361	0.98891 47531 13835
41	.01580 73693 48815	.98894 64080 47821
42	.01576 72459 28049	.98897 79826 48734
43	.01572 72086 24267	.98900 94770 88945
44	.01568 72572 98768	.98904 08915 40550
2.545	0.01564 73918 12945	0.98907 22261 75366
46	.01560 76120 28285	.98910 34811 64936
47	.01556 79178 06374	.98913 46566 80521
48	.01552 83090 08889	.98916 57528 93111
49	.01548 87854 97606	.98919 67699 73414
2.550	0.01544 93471 34395	0.98922 77080 91867

x	$\frac{1}{\sqrt{2\pi}} e^{-\frac{x^2}{2}}$	$\frac{1}{\sqrt{2\pi}} \int_{-x}^{x} e^{-\frac{\alpha^2}{2}} d\alpha$
2.550	0.01544 93471 34395	0.98922 77080 91867
51	.01540 99937 81225	.98925 85674 18625
52	.01537 07253 00161	.98928 93481 23573
53	.01533 15415 53364	.98932 00503 76316
54	.01529 24424 03092	.98935 06743 46184
2.555	0.01525 34277 11704	0.98938 12202 02234
56	.01521 44973 41653	.98941 16881 13245
57	.01517 56511 55494	.98944 20782 47723
58	.01513 68890 15878	.98947 23907 73898
59	.01509 82107 85556	.98950 26258 59726
2.560	0.01505 96163 27377	0.98953 27836 72888
61	.01502 11055 04293	.98956 28643 80792
62	.01498 26781 79351	.98959 28681 50571
63	.01494 43342 15702	.98962 27951 49084
64	.01490 60734 76595	.98965 26455 42917
2.565	0.01486 78958 25381	0.98968 24194 98382
66	.01482 98011 25511	.98971 21171 81519
67	.01479 17892 40539	.98974 17387 58094
68	.01475 38600 34119	.98977 12843 93600
69	.01471 60133 70006	.98980 07542 53259
2.570	0.01467 82491 12060	0.98983 01485 02018
71	.01464 05671 24241	.98985 94673 04554
72	.01460 29672 70612	.98988 87108 25271
73	.01456 54494 15340	.98991 78792 28302
74	.01452 80134 22695	.98994 69726 77507
2.575	0.01449 06591 57048	0.98997 59913 36477
76	.01445 33864 82879	.99000 49353 68530
77	.01441 61952 64766	.99003 38049 36713
78	.01437 90853 67397	.99006 26002 03803
79	.01434 20566 55559	.99009 13213 32306
2.580	0.01430 51089 94150	0.99011 99684 84459
81	.01426 82422 48167	.99014 85418 22226
82	.01423 14562 82717	.99017 70415 07305
83	.01419 47509 63011	.99020 54677 01121
84	.01415 81261 54366	.99023 38205 64831
2.585	0.01412 15817 22204	0.99026 21002 59323
86	.01408 51175 32056	.99029 03069 45215
87	.01404 87334 49558	.99031 84407 82856
88	.01401 24293 40454	.99034 65019 32328
89	.01397 62050 70594	.99037 44905 53444
2.590	0.01394 00605 05936	0.99040 24068 05748
91	.01390 39955 12546	.99043 02508 48515
92	.01386 80099 56599	.99045 80228 40756
93	.01383 21037 04377	.99048 57229 41211
94	.01379 62766 22270	.99051 33513 08354
2.595	0.01376 05285 76779	0.99054 09081 00391
96	.01372 48594 34511	.99056 83934 75263
97	.01368 92690 62185	.99059 58075 90642
98	.01365 37573 26629	.99062 31506 03936
99	.01361 83240 94780	.99065 04226 72285
2.600	0.01358 29692 33686	0.99067 76239 52562

x	$\dfrac{1}{\sqrt{2\pi}}\, e^{-\frac{x^2}{2}}$	$\dfrac{1}{\sqrt{2\pi}}\displaystyle\int_{-x}^{x} e^{-\frac{\alpha^2}{2}}\, d\alpha$
2.600	0.01358 29692 33686	0.99067 76239 52562
01	.01354 76926 10503	.99070 47546 01378
02	.01351 24940 92500	.99073 18147 75075
03	.01347 73735 47057	.99075 88046 29730
04	.01344 23308 41663	.99078 57243 21156
2.605	0.01340 73658 43919	0.99081 25740 04902
06	.01337 24784 21539	.99083 93538 36249
07	.01333 76684 42346	.99086 60639 70216
08	.01330 29357 74278	.99089 27045 61559
09	.01326 82802 85383	.99091 92757 64766
2.610	0.01323 37018 43821	0.99094 57777 34065
11	.01319 92003 17868	.99097 22106 23419
12	.01316 47755 75909	.99099 85745 86526
13	.01313 04274 86445	.99102 48697 76824
14	.01309 61559 18088	.99105 10963 47486
2.615	0.01306 19607 39566	0.99107 72544 51423
16	.01302 78418 19720	.99110 33442 41283
17	.01299 37990 27503	.99112 93658 69454
18	.01295 98322 31985	.99115 53194 88058
19	.01292 59413 02350	.99118 12052 48959
2.620	0.01289 21261 07895	0.99120 70233 03757
21	.01285 83865 18035	.99123 27738 03793
22	.01282 47224 02296	.99125 84569 00146
23	.01279 11336 30324	.99128 40727 43632
24	.01275 76200 71878	.99130 96214 84809
2.625	0.01272 41815 96831	0.99133 51032 73975
26	.01269 08180 75177	.99136 05182 61165
27	.01265 75293 77023	.99138 58665 96158
28	.01262 43153 72591	.99141 11484 28469
29	.01259 11759 32224	.99143 63639 07358
2.630	0.01255 81109 26378	0.99146 15131 81821
31	.01252 51202 25629	.99148 65964 00600
32	.01249 22037 00668	.99151 16137 12174
33	.01245 93612 22305	.99153 65652 64767
34	.01242 65926 61467	.99156 14512 06342
2.635	0.01239 38978 89199	0.99158 62716 84605
36	.01236 12767 76665	.99161 10268 47005
37	.01232 87291 95146	.99163 57168 40733
38	.01229 62550 16043	.99166 03418 12721
39	.01226 38541 10874	.99168 49019 09646
2.640	0.01223 15263 51278	0.99170 93972 77928
41	.01219 92716 09012	.99173 38280 63729
42	.01216 70897 55951	.99175 81944 12957
43	.01213 49806 64093	.99178 24964 71261
44	.01210 29442 05553	.99180 67343 84035
2.645	0.01207 09802 52566	0.99183 09082 96420
46	.01203 90886 77489	.99185 50183 53298
47	.01200 72693 52797	.99187 90646 99297
48	.01197 55221 51087	.99190 30474 78791
49	.01194 38469 45077	.99192 69668 35898
2.650	0.01191 22436 07605	0.99195 08229 14483

x	$\dfrac{1}{\sqrt{2\pi}}\,e^{-\frac{x^2}{2}}$	$\dfrac{1}{\sqrt{2\pi}}\displaystyle\int_{-x}^{x} e^{-\frac{\alpha^2}{2}}\,d\alpha$
2.650	0.01191 22436 07605	0.99195 08229 14483
51	.01188 07120 11630	.99197 46158 58156
52	.01184 92520 30233	.99199 83458 10273
53	.01181 78635 36616	.99202 20129 13936
54	.01178 65464 04103	.99204 56173 11993
2.655	0.01175 53005 06139	0.99206 91591 47042
56	.01172 41257 16291	.99209 26385 61423
57	.01169 30219 08251	.99211 60556 97228
58	.01166 19889 55829	.99213 94106 96294
59	.01163 10267 32960	.99216 27037 00205
2.660	0.01160 01351 13703	0.99218 59348 50294
61	.01156 93139 72236	.99220 91042 87645
62	.01153 85631 82864	.99223 22121 53085
63	.01150 78826 20013	.99225 52585 87194
64	.01147 72721 58234	.99227 82437 30299
2.665	0.01144 67316 72199	0.99230 11677 22477
66	.01141 62610 36707	.99232 40307 03555
67	.01138 58601 26679	.99234 68328 13108
68	.01135 55288 17161	.99236 95741 90462
69	.01132 52669 83322	.99239 22549 74693
2.670	0.01129 50745 00456	0.99241 48753 04629
71	.01126 49512 43983	.99243 74353 18846
72	.01123 48970 89446	.99245 99351 55673
73	.01120 49119 12514	.99248 23749 53189
74	.01117 49955 88981	.99250 47548 49225
2.675	0.01114 51479 94765	0.99252 70749 81364
76	.01111 53690 05911	.99254 93354 86941
77	.01108 56584 98589	.99257 15365 03042
78	.01105 60163 49096	.99259 36781 66507
79	.01102 64424 33852	.99261 57606 13928
2.680	0.01099 69366 29406	0.99263 77839 81650
81	.01096 74988 12431	.99265 97484 05771
82	.01093 81288 59728	.99268 16540 22143
83	.01090 88266 48224	.99270 35009 66371
84	.01087 95920 54973	.99272 52893 73814
2.685	0.01085 04249 57154	0.99274 70193 79587
86	.01082 13252 32076	.99276 86911 18558
87	.01079 22927 57174	.99279 03047 25349
88	.01076 33274 10008	.99281 18603 34339
89	.01073 44290 68268	.99283 33580 79660
2.690	0.01070 55976 09772	0.99285 47980 95201
91	.01067 68329 12464	.99287 61805 14606
92	.01064 81348 54416	.99289 75054 71277
93	.01061 95033 13829	.99291 87730 98369
94	.01059 09381 69032	.99293 99835 28796
2.695	0.01056 24392 98482	0.99296 11368 95228
96	.01053 40065 80763	.99298 22333 30092
97	.01050 56398 94591	.99300 32729 65572
98	.01047 73391 18807	.99302 42559 33610
99	.01044 91041 32385	.99304 51823 65907
2.700	0.01042 09348 14423	0.99306 60523 93919

236

x	$\frac{1}{\sqrt{2\pi}} e^{-\frac{x^2}{2}}$	$\frac{1}{\sqrt{2\pi}} \int_{-x}^{x} e^{-\frac{\alpha^2}{2}} d\alpha$
2.700	0.01042 09348 14423	0.99306 60523 93919
01	.01039 28310 44151	.99308 68661 48863
02	.01036 47927 00930	.99310 76237 61713
03	.01033 68196 64247	.99312 83253 63204
04	.01030 89118 13719	.99314 89710 83828
2.705	0.01028 10690 29096	0.99316 95610 53836
06	.01025 32911 90253	.99319 00954 03241
07	.01022 55781 77198	.99321 05742 61814
08	.01019 79298 70069	.99323 09977 59087
09	.01017 03461 49133	.99325 13660 24352
2.710	0.01014 28268 94787	0.99327 16791 86662
11	.01011 53719 87561	.99329 19373 74829
12	.01008 79813 08112	.99331 21407 17430
13	.01006 06547 37230	.99333 22893 42801
14	.01003 33921 55836	.99335 23833 79039
2.715	0.01000 61934 44981	0.99337 24229 54005
16	.00997 90584 85846	.99339 24081 95320
17	.00995 19871 59745	.99341 23392 30370
18	.00992 49793 48123	.99343 22161 86302
19	.00989 80349 32556	.99345 20391 90027
2.720	0.00987 11537 94751	0.99347 18083 68217
21	.00984 43358 16548	.99349 15238 47312
22	.00981 75808 79916	.99351 11857 53511
23	.00979 08888 66960	.99353 07942 12781
24	.00976 42596 59914	.99355 03493 50850
2.725	0.00973 76931 41144	0.99356 98512 93213
26	.00971 11891 93150	.99358 93001 65128
27	.00968 47476 98562	.99360 86960 91621
28	.00965 83685 40145	.99362 80391 97480
29	.00963 20516 00795	.99364 73296 07261
2.730	0.00960 57967 63540	0.99366 65674 45284
31	.00957 96039 11542	.99368 57528 35638
32	.00955 34729 28095	.99370 48859 02176
33	.00952 74036 96627	.99372 39667 68519
34	.00950 13961 00698	.99374 29955 58053
2.735	0.00947 54500 24002	0.99376 19723 93934
36	.00944 95653 50365	.99378 08973 99085
37	.00942 37419 63747	.99379 97706 96194
38	.00939 79797 48242	.99381 85924 07720
39	.00937 22785 88077	.99383 73626 55890
2.740	0.00934 66383 67612	0.99385 60815 62699
41	.00932 10589 71343	.99387 47492 49910
42	.00929 55402 83896	.99389 33658 39057
43	.00927 00821 90036	.99391 19314 51442
44	.00924 46845 74656	.99393 04462 08136
2.745	0.00921 93473 22789	0.99394 89102 29982
46	.00919 40703 19598	.99396 73236 37593
47	.00916 88534 50382	.99398 56865 51350
48	.00914 36966 00575	.99400 39990 91407
49	.00911 85996 55744	.99402 22613 77689
2.750	0.00909 35625 01591	0.99404 04735 29891

x	$\dfrac{1}{\sqrt{2\pi}}\,e^{-\frac{x^2}{2}}$	$\dfrac{1}{\sqrt{2\pi}}\displaystyle\int_{-x}^{x} e^{-\frac{\alpha^2}{2}}\,d\alpha$
2.750	0.00909 35625 01591	0.99404 04735 29891
51	.00906 85850 23953	.99405 86356 67480
52	.00904 36671 08802	.99407 67479 09695
53	.00901 88086 42244	.99409 48103 75547
54	.00899 40095 10521	.99411 28231 83821
2.755	0.00896 92696 00008	0.99413 07864 53070
56	.00894 45887 97218	.99414 87003 01626
57	.00891 99669 88796	.99416 65648 47589
58	.00889 54040 61525	.99418 43802 08835
59	.00887 08999 02321	.99420 21465 03014
2.760	0.00884 64543 98237	0.99421 98638 47548
61	.00882 20674 36461	.99423 75323 59635
62	.00879 77389 04317	.99425 51521 56247
63	.00877 34686 89263	.99427 27233 54130
64	.00874 92566 78894	.99429 02460 69807
2.765	0.00872 51027 60941	0.99430 77204 19574
66	.00870 10068 23271	.99432 51465 19504
67	.00867 69687 53885	.99434 25244 85446
68	.00865 29884 40922	.99435 98544 33024
69	.00862 90657 72657	.99437 71364 77639
2.770	0.00860 52006 37500	0.99439 43707 34470
71	.00858 13929 23997	.99441 15573 18470
72	.00855 76425 20832	.99442 86963 44373
73	.00853 39493 16824	.99444 57879 26687
74	.00851 03132 00929	.99446 28321 79699
2.775	0.00848 67340 62239	0.99447 98292 17475
76	.00846 32117 89982	.99449 67791 53859
77	.00843 97462 73525	.99451 36821 02472
78	.00841 63374 02369	.99453 05381 76716
79	.00839 29850 66153	.99454 73474 89772
2.780	0.00836 96891 54653	0.99456 41101 54597
81	.00834 64495 57781	.99458 08262 83933
82	.00832 32661 65585	.99459 74959 90298
83	.00830 01388 68253	.99461 41193 85992
84	.00827 70675 56108	.99463 06965 83095
2.785	0.00825 40521 19611	0.99464 72276 93467
86	.00823 10924 49358	.99466 37128 28751
87	.00820 81884 36084	.99468 01521 00369
88	.00818 53399 70662	.99469 65456 19527
89	.00816 25469 44100	.99471 28934 97211
2.790	0.00813 98092 47546	0.99472 91958 44190
91	.00811 71267 72283	.99474 54527 71015
92	.00809 44994 09733	.99476 16643 88021
93	.00807 19270 51455	.99477 78308 05324
94	.00804 94095 89146	.99479 39521 32824
2.795	0.00802 69469 14639	0.99481 00284 80206
96	.00800 45389 19906	.99482 60599 56936
97	.00798 21854 97058	.99484 20466 72267
98	.00795 98865 38341	.99485 79887 35234
99	.00793 76419 36141	.99487 38862 54658
2.800	0.00791 54515 82980	0.99488 97393 39144

x	$\frac{1}{\sqrt{2\pi}} e^{-\frac{x^2}{2}}$	$\frac{1}{\sqrt{2\pi}} \int_{-x}^{x} e^{-\frac{\alpha^2}{2}} d\alpha$
2.800	0.00791 54515 82980	0.99488 97393 39144
01	.00789 33153 71519	.99490 55480 97084
02	.00787 12331 94558	.99492 13126 36653
03	.00784 92049 45032	.99493 70330 65814
04	.00782 72305 16017	.99495 27094 92314
2.805	0.00780 53098 00726	0.99496 83420 23687
06	.00778 34426 92509	.99498 39307 67255
07	.00776 16290 84855	.99499 94758 30124
08	.00773 98688 71392	.99501 49773 19190
09	.00771 81619 45885	.99503 04353 41135
2.810	0.00769 65082 02237	0.99504 58500 02428
11	.00767 49075 34492	.99506 12214 09328
12	.00765 33598 36828	.99507 65496 67880
13	.00763 18650 03565	.99509 18348 83918
14	.00761 04229 29160	.99510 70771 63066
2.815	0.00758 90335 08208	0.99512 22766 10737
16	.00756 76966 35443	.99513 74333 32131
17	.00754 64122 05738	.99515 25474 32241
18	.00752 51801 14103	.99516 76190 15846
19	.00750 40002 55688	.99518 26481 87519
2.820	0.00748 28725 25781	0.99519 76350 51621
21	.00746 17968 19808	.99521 25797 12305
22	.00744 07730 33335	.99522 74822 73514
23	.00741 98010 62065	.99524 23428 38982
24	.00739 88808 01842	.99525 71615 12236
2.825	0.00737 80121 48647	0.99527 19383 96594
26	.00735 71949 98599	.99528 66735 95166
27	.00733 64292 47957	.99530 13672 10855
28	.00731 57147 93120	.99531 60193 46355
29	.00729 50515 30623	.99533 06301 04155
2.830	0.00727 44393 57141	0.99534 51995 86537
31	.00725 38781 69489	.99535 97278 95574
32	.00723 33678 64620	.99537 42151 33137
33	.00721 29083 39624	.99538 86614 00886
34	.00719 24994 91734	.99540 30668 00280
2.835	0.00717 21412 18318	0.99541 74314 32569
36	.00715 18334 16886	.99543 17553 98801
37	.00713 15759 85083	.99544 60387 99817
38	.00711 13688 20698	.99546 02817 36253
39	.00709 12118 21655	.99547 44843 08543
2.840	0.00707 11048 86019	0.99548 86466 16915
41	.00705 10479 11994	.99550 27687 61395
42	.00703 10407 97921	.99551 68508 41803
43	.00701 10834 42282	.99553 08929 57759
44	.00699 11757 43698	.99554 48952 08677
2.845	0.00697 13176 00928	0.99555 88576 93771
46	.00695 15089 12871	.99557 27805 12051
47	.00693 17495 78565	.99558 66637 62325
48	.00691 20394 97187	.99560 05075 43200
49	.00689 23785 68051	.99561 43119 53082
2.850	0.00687 27666 90614	0.99562 80770 90174

x	$\dfrac{1}{\sqrt{2\pi}}e^{-\frac{x^2}{2}}$	$\dfrac{1}{\sqrt{2\pi}}\displaystyle\int_{-x}^{x}e^{-\frac{\alpha^2}{2}}\,d\alpha$
2.850	0.00687 27666 90614	0.99562 80770 90174
51	.00685 32037 64469	.99564 18030 52478
52	.00683 36896 89350	.99565 54899 37799
53	.00681 42243 65128	.99566 91378 43736
54	.00679 48076 91816	.99568 27468 67693
2.855	0.00677 54395 69564	0.99569 63171 06871
56	.00675 61198 98660	.99570 98486 58272
57	.00673 68485 79535	.99572 33416 18700
58	.00671 76255 12756	.99573 67960 84759
59	.00669 84505 99030	.99575 02121 52853
2.860	0.00667 93237 39203	0.99576 35899 19191
61	.00666 02448 34260	.99577 69294 79780
62	.00664 12137 85326	.99579 02309 30432
63	.00662 22304 93664	.99580 34943 66759
64	.00660 32948 60676	.99581 67198 84179
2.865	0.00658 44067 87905	0.99582 99075 77909
66	.00656 55661 77032	.99584 30575 42972
67	.00654 67729 29875	.99585 61698 74193
68	.00652 80269 48395	.99586 92446 66202
69	.00650 93281 34688	.99588 22820 13432
2.870	0.00649 06763 90993	0.99589 52820 10120
71	.00647 20716 19686	.99590 82447 50311
72	.00645 35137 23281	.99592 11703 27849
73	.00643 50026 04434	.99593 40588 36389
74	.00641 65381 65937	.99594 69103 69387
2.875	0.00639 81203 10724	0.99595 97250 20108
76	.00637 97489 41864	.99597 25028 81621
77	.00636 14239 62570	.99598 52440 46802
78	.00634 31452 76190	.99599 79486 08333
79	.00632 49127 86213	.99601 06166 58704
2.880	0.00630 67263 96266	0.99602 32482 90211
81	.00628 85860 10116	.99603 58435 94958
82	.00627 04915 31667	.99604 84026 64857
83	.00625 24428 64965	.99606 09255 91626
84	.00623 44399 14192	.99607 34124 66794
2.885	0.00621 64825 83670	0.99608 58633 81697
86	.00619 85707 77861	.99609 82784 27479
87	.00618 07044 01364	.99611 06576 95094
88	.00616 28833 58917	.99612 30012 75307
89	.00614 51075 55398	.99613 53092 58689
2.890	0.00612 73768 95824	0.99614 75817 35624
91	.00610 96912 85348	.99615 98187 96305
92	.00609 20506 29266	.99617 20205 30735
93	.00607 44548 33009	.99618 41870 28729
94	.00605 69038 02149	.99619 63183 79911
2.895	0.00603 93974 42396	0.99620 84146 73718
96	.00602 19356 59597	.99622 04759 99398
97	.00600 45183 59741	.99623 25024 46012
98	.00598 71454 48952	.99624 44941 02430
99	.00596 98168 33496	.99625 64510 57338
2.900	0.00595 25324 19776	0.99626 83733 99232

x	$\dfrac{1}{\sqrt{2\pi}}\,e^{-\frac{x^2}{2}}$	$\dfrac{1}{\sqrt{2\pi}}\displaystyle\int_{-x}^{x} e^{-\frac{\alpha^2}{2}}\,d\alpha$
2.900	0.00595 25324 19776	0.99626 83733 99232
01	.00593 52921 14332	.99628 02612 16422
02	.00591 80958 23845	.99629 21145 97033
03	.00590 09434 55133	.99630 39336 28999
04	.00588 38349 15153	.99631 57184 00072
2.905	0.00586 67701 11001	0.99632 74689 97817
06	.00584 97489 49909	.99633 91855 09612
07	.00583 27713 39251	.99635 08680 22650
08	.00581 58371 86536	.99636 25166 23941
09	.00579 89463 99413	.99637 41314 00307
2.910	0.00578 20988 85669	0.99638 57124 38387
11	.00576 52945 53230	.99639 72598 24637
12	.00574 85333 10158	.99640 87736 45326
13	.00573 18150 64655	.99642 02539 86542
14	.00571 51397 25061	.99643 17009 34189
2.915	0.00569 85071 99853	0.99644 31145 73986
16	.00568 19173 97647	.99645 44949 91470
17	.00566 53702 27198	.99646 58422 71997
18	.00564 88655 97395	.99647 71565 00739
19	.00563 24034 17271	.99648 84377 62687
2.920	0.00561 59835 95991	0.99649 96861 42648
21	.00559 96060 42862	.99651 09017 25250
22	.00558 32706 67326	.99652 20845 94938
23	.00556 69773 78965	.99653 32348 35977
24	.00555 07260 87498	.99654 43525 32451
2.925	0.00553 45167 02780	0.99655 54377 68265
26	.00551 83491 34807	.99656 64906 27140
27	.00550 22232 93710	.99657 75111 92622
28	.00548 61390 89759	.99658 84995 48073
29	.00547 00964 33359	.99659 94557 76679
2.930	0.00545 40952 35057	0.99661 03799 61445
31	.00543 81354 05532	.99662 12721 85199
32	.00542 22168 55605	.99663 21325 30587
33	.00540 63394 96233	.99664 29610 80081
34	.00539 05032 38508	.99665 37579 15973
2.935	0.00537 47079 93662	0.99666 45231 20377
36	.00535 89536 73064	.99667 52567 75231
37	.00534 32401 88219	.99668 59589 62294
38	.00532 75674 50769	.99669 66297 63149
39	.00531 19353 72494	.99670 72692 59203
2.940	0.00529 63438 65311	0.99671 78775 31686
41	.00528 07928 41273	.99672 84546 61653
42	.00526 52822 12572	.99673 90007 29981
43	.00524 98118 91533	.99674 95158 17375
44	.00523 43817 90622	.99676 00000 04361
2.945	0.00521 89918 22440	0.99677 04533 71292
46	.00520 36418 99723	.99678 08759 98348
47	.00518 83319 35347	.99679 12679 65530
48	.00517 30618 42323	.99680 16293 52670
49	.00515 78315 33797	.99681 19602 39422
2.950	0.00514 26409 23054	0.99682 22607 05270

x	$\dfrac{1}{\sqrt{2\pi}}\,e^{-\frac{x^2}{2}}$	$\dfrac{1}{\sqrt{2\pi}}\displaystyle\int_{-x}^{x}e^{-\frac{\alpha^2}{2}}\,d\alpha$
2.950	0.00514 26409 23054	0.99682 22607 05270
51	.00512 74899 23514	.99683 25308 29522
52	.00511 23784 48734	.99684 27706 91314
53	.00509 73064 12406	.99685 29803 69609
54	.00508 22737 28361	.99686 31599 43199
2.955	0.00506 72803 10564	0.99687 33094 90700
56	.00505 23260 73116	.99688 34290 90561
57	.00503 74109 30255	.99689 35188 21056
58	.00502 25347 96355	.99690 35787 60288
59	.00500 76975 85925	.99691 36089 86190
2.960	0.00499 28992 13612	0.99692 36095 76524
61	.00497 81395 94197	.99693 35806 08880
62	.00496 34186 42597	.99694 35221 60679
63	.00494 87362 73865	.99695 34343 09172
64	.00493 40924 03191	.99696 33171 31440
2.965	0.00491 94869 45897	0.99697 31707 04394
66	.00490 49198 17444	.99698 29951 04776
67	.00489 03909 33427	.99699 27904 09160
68	.00487 59002 09578	.99700 25566 93950
69	.00486 14475 61761	.99701 22940 35382
2.970	0.00484 70329 05979	0.99702 20025 09525
71	.00483 26561 58368	.99703 16821 92278
72	.00481 83172 35199	.99704 13331 59375
73	.00480 40160 52880	.99705 09554 86380
74	.00478 97525 27952	.99706 05492 48691
2.975	0.00477 55265 77092	0.99707 01145 21541
76	.00476 13381 17111	.99707 96513 79994
77	.00474 71870 64956	.99708 91598 98948
78	.00473 30733 37709	.99709 86401 53137
79	.00471 89968 52585	.99710 80922 17127
2.980	0.00470 49575 26934	0.99711 75161 65320
81	.00469 09552 78242	.99712 69120 71953
82	.00467 69900 24127	.99713 62800 11096
83	.00466 30616 82345	.99714 56200 56657
84	.00464 91701 70782	.99715 49322 82379
2.985	0.00463 53154 07462	0.99716 42167 61839
86	.00462 14973 10541	.99717 34735 68453
87	.00460 77157 98309	.99718 27027 75471
88	.00459 39707 89192	.99719 19044 55982
89	.00458 02622 01748	.99720 10786 82909
2.990	0.00456 65899 54670	0.99721 02255 29015
91	.00455 29539 66784	.99721 93450 66901
92	.00453 93541 57050	.99722 84373 69001
93	.00452 57904 44562	.99723 75025 07594
94	.00451 22627 48547	.99724 65405 54791
2.995	0.00449 87709 88366	0.99725 55515 82545
96	.00448 53150 83513	.99726 45356 62648
97	.00447 18949 53617	.99727 34928 66729
98	.00445 85105 18437	.99728 24232 66259
99	.00444 51616 97869	.99729 13269 32546
3.000	0.00443 18484 11938	0.99730 02039 36740

242

x	$\frac{1}{\sqrt{2\pi}} e^{-\frac{x^2}{2}}$	$\frac{1}{\sqrt{2\pi}} \int_{-x}^{x} e^{-\frac{\alpha^2}{2}} d\alpha$
3.000	0.00443 18484 11938	0.99730 02039 36740
01	.00441 85705 80806	.99730 90543 49830
02	.00440 53281 24765	.99731 78782 42646
03	.00439 21209 64242	.99732 66756 85859
04	.00437 89490 19796	.99733 54467 49981
3.005	0.00436 58122 12117	0.99734 41915 05363
06	.00435 27104 62031	.99735 29100 22201
07	.00433 96436 90494	.99736 16023 70530
08	.00432 66118 18595	.99737 02686 20229
09	.00431 36147 67556	.99737 89088 41019
3.010	0.00430 06524 58730	0.99738 75231 02461
11	.00428 77248 13605	.99739 61114 73963
12	.00427 48317 53798	.99740 46740 24772
13	.00426 19732 01059	.99741 32108 23983
14	.00424 91490 77271	.99742 17219 40529
3.015	0.00423 63593 04448	0.99743 02074 43192
16	.00422 36038 04736	.99743 86674 00596
17	.00421 08825 00412	.99744 71018 81208
18	.00419 81953 13887	.99745 55109 53343
19	.00418 55421 67700	.99746 38946 85157
3.020	0.00417 29229 84524	0.99747 22531 44655
21	.00416 03376 87163	.99748 05863 99686
22	.00414 77861 98552	.99748 88945 17943
23	.00413 52684 41756	.99749 71775 66968
24	.00412 27843 39974	.99750 54356 14147
3.025	0.00411 03338 16533	0.99751 36687 26713
26	.00409 79167 94892	.99752 18769 71748
27	.00408 55331 98642	.99753 00604 16177
28	.00407 31829 51503	.99753 82191 26775
29	.00406 08659 77326	.99754 63531 70165
3.030	0.00404 85822 00094	0.99755 44626 12815
31	.00403 63315 43920	.99756 25475 21046
32	.00402 41139 33045	.99757 06079 61021
33	.00401 19292 91842	.99757 86439 98758
34	.00399 97775 44816	.99758 66557 00118
3.035	0.00398 76586 16600	0.99759 46431 30816
36	.00397 55724 31956	.99760 26063 56414
37	.00396 35189 15779	.99761 05454 42323
38	.00395 14979 93091	.99761 84604 53806
39	.00393 95095 89046	.99762 63514 55974
3.040	0.00392 75536 28925	0.99763 42185 13791
41	.00391 56300 38141	.99764 20616 92070
42	.00390 37387 42235	.99764 98810 55474
43	.00389 18796 66878	.99765 76766 68519
44	.00388 00527 37870	.99766 54485 95572
3.045	0.00386 82578 81141	0.99767 31969 00852
46	.00385 64950 22749	.99768 09216 48429
47	.00384 47640 88880	.99768 86229 02226
48	.00383 30650 05851	.99769 63007 26018
49	.00382 13977 00107	.99770 39551 83434
3.050	0.00380 97620 98222	0.99771 15863 37955

x	$\frac{1}{\sqrt{2\pi}} e^{-\frac{x^2}{2}}$	$\frac{1}{\sqrt{2\pi}} \int_{-x}^{x} e^{-\frac{\alpha^2}{2}} d\alpha$
3.050	0.00380 97620 98222	0.99771 15863 37955
51	.00379 81581 26897	.99771 91942 52914
52	.00378 65857 12963	.99772 67789 91500
53	.00377 50447 83379	.99773 43406 16755
54	.00376 35352 65233	.99774 18791 91575
3.055	0.00375 20570 85739	0.99774 93947 78709
56	.00374 06101 72242	.99775 68874 40762
57	.00372 91944 52212	.99776 43572 40193
58	.00371 78098 53248	.99777 18042 39318
59	.00370 64563 03079	.99777 92285 00306
3.060	0.00369 51337 29559	0.99778 66300 85182
61	.00368 38420 60670	.99779 40090 55827
62	.00367 25812 24521	.99780 13654 73979
63	.00366 13511 49351	.99780 86994 01232
64	.00365 01517 63523	.99781 60108 99036
3.065	0.00363 89829 95529	0.99782 33000 28698
66	.00362 78447 73988	.99783 05668 51383
67	.00361 67370 27645	.99783 78114 28111
68	.00360 56596 85372	.99784 50338 19763
69	.00359 46126 76170	.99785 22340 87075
3.070	0.00358 35959 29162	0.99785 94122 90642
71	.00357 26093 73603	.99786 65684 90919
72	.00356 16529 38870	.99787 37027 48217
73	.00355 07265 54469	.99788 08151 22708
74	.00353 98301 50031	.99788 79056 74422
3.075	0.00352 89636 55314	0.99789 49744 63248
76	.00351 81270 00200	.99790 20215 48936
77	.00350 73201 14699	.99790 90469 91095
78	.00349 65429 28947	.99791 60508 49195
79	.00348 57953 73203	.99792 30331 82564
3.080	0.00347 50773 77855	0.99792 99940 50394
81	.00346 43888 73414	.99793 69335 11736
82	.00345 37297 90517	.99794 38516 25502
83	.00344 31000 59927	.99795 07484 50466
84	.00343 24996 12531	.99795 76240 45264
3.085	0.00342 19283 79342	0.99796 44784 68393
86	.00341 13862 91497	.99797 13117 78212
87	.00340 08732 80259	.99797 81240 32943
88	.00339 03892 77014	.99798 49152 90671
89	.00337 99342 13275	.99799 16856 09344
3.090	0.00336 95080 20677	0.99799 84350 46772
91	.00335 91106 30982	.99800 51636 60629
92	.00334 87419 76072	.99801 18715 08452
93	.00333 84019 87959	.99801 85586 47644
94	.00332 80905 98773	.99802 52251 35470
3.095	0.00331 78077 40773	0.99803 18710 29060
96	.00330 75533 46339	.99803 84963 85409
97	.00329 73273 47974	.99804 51012 61376
98	.00328 71296 78308	.99805 16857 13687
99	.00327 69602 70092	.99805 82497 98930
3.100	0.00326 68190 56200	0.99806 47935 73563

244

x	$\frac{1}{\sqrt{2\pi}} e^{-\frac{x^2}{2}}$	$\frac{1}{\sqrt{2\pi}} \int_{-x}^{x} e^{-\frac{\alpha^2}{2}} d\alpha$
3.100	0.00326 68190 56200	0.99806 47935 73563
01	.00325 67059 69630	.99807 13170 93907
02	.00324 66209 43504	.99807 78204 16149
03	.00323 65639 11065	.99808 43035 96343
04	.00322 65348 05681	.99809 07666 90411
3.105	0.00321 65335 60842	0.99809 72097 54140
06	.00320 65601 10160	.99810 36328 43184
07	.00319 66143 87370	.99811 00360 13066
08	.00318 66963 26330	.99811 64193 19175
09	.00317 68058 61019	.99812 27828 16768
3.110	0.00316 69429 25540	0.99812 91265 60972
11	.00315 71074 54117	.99813 54506 06780
12	.00314 72993 81096	.99814 17550 09054
13	.00313 75186 40946	.99814 80398 22526
14	.00312 77651 68255	.99815 43051 01796
3.115	0.00311 80388 97735	0.99816 05509 01334
16	.00310 83397 64220	.99816 67772 75478
17	.00309 86677 02663	.99817 29842 78439
18	.00308 90226 48140	.99817 91719 64294
19	.00307 94045 35848	.99818 53403 86993
3.120	0.00306 98133 01105	0.99819 14896 00355
21	.00306 02488 79349	.99819 76196 58072
22	.00305 07112 06140	.99820 37306 13705
23	.00304 12002 17158	.99820 98225 20686
24	.00303 17158 48204	.99821 58954 32320
3.125	0.00302 22580 35199	0.99822 19494 01783
26	.00301 28267 14184	.99822 79844 82123
27	.00300 34218 21322	.99823 40007 26259
28	.00299 40432 92894	.99823 99981 86984
29	.00298 46910 65303	.99824 59769 16964
3.130	0.00297 53650 75068	0.99825 19369 68737
31	.00296 60652 58833	.99825 78783 94714
32	.00295 67915 53358	.99826 38012 47179
33	.00294 75438 95523	.99826 97055 78292
34	.00293 83222 22328	.99827 55914 40085
3.135	0.00292 91264 70893	0.99828 14588 84463
36	.00291 99565 78455	.99828 73079 63207
37	.00291 08124 82372	.99829 31387 27974
38	.00290 16941 20119	.99829 89512 30293
39	.00289 26014 29292	.99830 47455 21569
3.140	0.00288 35343 47603	0.99831 05216 53083
41	.00287 44928 12886	.99831 62796 75991
42	.00286 54767 63089	.99832 20196 41324
43	.00285 64861 36283	.99832 77415 99992
44	.00284 75208 70652	.99833 34456 02777
3.145	0.00283 85809 04502	0.99833 91317 00341
46	.00282 96661 76256	.99834 47999 43220
47	.00282 07766 24454	.99835 04503 81830
48	.00281 19121 87754	.99835 60830 66461
49	.00280 30728 04932	.99836 16980 47283
3.150	0.00279 42584 14879	0.99836 72953 74343

x	$\dfrac{1}{\sqrt{2\pi}} e^{-\frac{x^2}{2}}$	$\dfrac{1}{\sqrt{2\pi}} \displaystyle\int_{-x}^{x} e^{-\frac{\alpha^2}{2}} \, d\alpha$
3.150	0.00279 42584 14879	0.99836 72953 74343
51	.00278 54689 56608	.99837 28750 97564
52	.00277 67043 69244	.99837 84372 66750
53	.00276 79645 92031	.99838 39819 31581
54	.00275 92495 64333	.99838 95091 41618
3.155	0.00275 05592 25625	0.99839 50189 46298
56	.00274 18935 15503	.99840 05113 94939
57	.00273 32523 73678	.99840 59865 36739
58	.00272 46357 39978	.99841 14444 20773
59	.00271 60435 54345	.99841 68850 95997
3.160	0.00270 74757 56841	0.99842 23086 11249
61	.00269 89322 87640	.99842 77150 15244
62	.00269 04130 87035	.99843 31043 56578
63	.00268 19180 95433	.99843 84766 83731
64	.00267 34472 53357	.99844 38320 45060
3.165	0.00266 50005 01446	0.99844 91704 88805
66	.00265 65777 80453	.99845 44920 63086
67	.00264 81790 31249	.99845 97968 15908
68	.00263 98041 94816	.99846 50847 95153
69	.00263 14532 12256	.99847 03560 48589
3.170	0.00262 31260 24781	0.99847 56106 23866
71	.00261 48225 73721	.99848 08485 68513
72	.00260 65428 00519	.99848 60699 29946
73	.00259 82866 46733	.99849 12747 55461
74	.00259 00540 54035	.99849 64630 92240
3.175	0.00258 18449 64212	0.99850 16349 87346
76	.00257 36593 19165	.99850 67904 87727
77	.00256 54970 60907	.99851 19296 40214
78	.00255 73581 31568	.99851 70524 91523
79	.00254 92424 73389	.99852 21590 88254
3.180	0.00254 11500 28727	0.99852 72494 76892
81	.00253 30807 40049	.99853 23237 03806
82	.00252 50345 49938	.99853 73818 15251
83	.00251 70114 01090	.99854 24238 57367
84	.00250 90112 36314	.99854 74498 76178
3.185	0.00250 10339 98530	0.99855 24599 17597
86	.00249 30796 30773	.99855 74540 27419
87	.00248 51480 76190	.99856 24322 51329
88	.00247 72392 78041	.99856 73946 34895
89	.00246 93531 79696	.99857 23412 23574
3.190	0.00246 14897 24641	0.99857 72720 62709
91	.00245 36488 56470	.99858 21871 97531
92	.00244 58305 18893	.99858 70866 73156
93	.00243 80346 55730	.99859 19705 34589
94	.00243 02612 10911	.99859 68388 26724
3.195	0.00242 25101 28481	0.99860 16915 94341
96	.00241 47813 52594	.99860 65288 82109
97	.00240 70748 27516	.99861 13507 34585
98	.00239 93904 97624	.99861 61571 96216
99	.00239 17283 07407	.99862 09483 11336
3.200	0.00238 40882 01465	0.99862 57241 24168

x	$\dfrac{1}{\sqrt{2\pi}}\,e^{-\frac{x^2}{2}}$	$\dfrac{1}{\sqrt{2\pi}}\displaystyle\int_{-x}^{x} e^{-\frac{\alpha^2}{2}}\,d\alpha$
3.200	0.00238 40882 01465	0.99862 57241 24168
01	.00237 64701 24506	.99863 04846 78827
02	.00236 88740 21353	.99863 52300 19316
03	.00236 12998 36936	.99863 99601 89525
04	.00235 37475 16297	.99864 46752 33239
3.205	0.00234 62170 04587	0.99864 93751 94130
06	.00233 87082 47070	.99865 40601 15760
07	.00233 12211 89116	.99865 87300 41584
08	.00232 37557 76208	.99866 33850 14947
09	.00231 63119 53938	.99866 80250 79083
3.210	0.00230 88896 68006	0.99867 26502 77120
11	.00230 14888 64224	.99867 72606 52076
12	.00229 41094 88512	.99868 18562 46862
13	.00228 67514 86898	.99868 64371 04280
14	.00227 94148 05521	.99869 10032 67023
3.215	0.00227 20993 90629	0.99869 55547 77680
16	.00226 48051 88576	.99870 00916 78728
17	.00225 75321 45829	.99870 46140 12540
18	.00225 02802 08959	.99870 91218 21382
19	.00224 30493 24649	.99871 36151 47411
3.220	0.00223 58394 39689	0.99871 80940 32680
21	.00222 86505 00975	.99872 25585 19134
22	.00222 14824 55515	.99872 70086 48613
23	.00221 43352 50421	.99873 14444 62850
24	.00220 72088 32915	.99873 58660 03473
3.225	0.00220 01031 50327	0.99874 02733 12005
26	.00219 30181 50092	.99874 46664 29862
27	.00218 59537 79755	.99874 90453 98358
28	.00217 89099 86966	.99875 34102 58700
29	.00217 18867 19483	.99875 77610 51990
3.230	0.00216 48839 25171	0.99876 20978 19226
31	.00215 79015 52001	.99876 64206 01304
32	.00215 09395 48053	.99877 07294 39014
33	.00214 39978 61509	.99877 50243 73041
34	.00213 70764 40661	.99877 93054 43970
3.235	0.00213 01752 33907	0.99878 35726 92280
36	.00212 32941 89750	.99878 78261 58348
37	.00211 64332 56799	.99879 20658 82447
38	.00210 95923 83768	.99879 62919 04748
39	.00210 27715 19479	.99880 05042 65321
3.240	0.00209 59706 12858	0.99880 47030 04131
41	.00208 91896 12936	.99880 88881 61043
42	.00208 24284 68850	.99881 30597 75820
43	.00207 56871 29842	.99881 72178 88122
44	.00206 89655 45259	.99882 13625 37509
3.245	0.00206 22636 64552	0.99882 54937 63439
46	.00205 55814 37279	.99882 96116 05270
47	.00204 89188 13099	.99883 37161 02257
48	.00204 22757 41779	.99883 78072 93557
49	.00203 56521 73188	.99884 18852 18226
3.250	0.00202 90480 57300	0.99884 59499 15218

x	$\dfrac{1}{\sqrt{2\pi}}e^{-\frac{x^2}{2}}$	$\dfrac{1}{\sqrt{2\pi}}\displaystyle\int_{-x}^{x}e^{-\frac{\alpha^2}{2}}\,d\alpha$
3.250	0.00202 90480 57300	0.99884 59499 15218
51	.00202 24633 44192	.99885 00014 23390
52	.00201 58979 84047	.99885 40397 81497
53	.00200 93519 27150	.99885 80650 28195
54	.00200 28251 23889	.99886 20772 02042
3.255	0.00199 63175 24758	0.99886 60763 41494
56	.00198 98290 80352	.99887 00624 84910
57	.00198 33597 41370	.99887 40356 70552
58	.00197 69094 58615	.99887 79959 36580
59	.00197 04781 82990	.99888 19433 21058
3.260	0.00196 40658 65504	0.99888 58778 61951
61	.00195 76724 57268	.99888 97995 97126
62	.00195 12979 09493	.99889 37085 64353
63	.00194 49421 73495	.99889 76048 01305
64	.00193 86052 00691	.99890 14883 45556
3.265	0.00193 22869 42602	0.99890 53592 34584
66	.00192 59873 50847	.99890 92175 05771
67	.00191 97063 77150	.99891 30631 96400
68	.00191 34439 73337	.99891 68963 43659
69	.00190 72000 91333	.99892 07169 84641
3.270	0.00190 09746 83166	0.99892 45251 56341
71	.00189 47677 00965	.99892 83208 95658
72	.00188 85790 96960	.99893 21042 39397
73	.00188 24088 23482	.99893 58752 24266
74	.00187 62568 32962	.99893 96338 86879
3.275	0.00187 01230 77934	0.99894 33802 63755
76	.00186 40075 11029	.99894 71143 91316
77	.00185 79100 84983	.99895 08363 05893
78	.00185 18307 52627	.99895 45460 43719
79	.00184 57694 66896	.99895 82436 40934
3.280	0.00183 97261 80824	0.99896 19291 33586
81	.00183 37008 47545	.99896 56025 57626
82	.00182 76934 20290	.99896 92639 48914
83	.00182 17038 52395	.99897 29133 43214
84	.00181 57320 97290	.99897 65507 76198
3.285	0.00180 97781 08507	0.99898 01762 83447
86	.00180 38418 39677	.99898 37899 00446
87	.00179 79232 44529	.99898 73916 62588
88	.00179 20222 76893	.99899 09816 05175
89	.00178 61388 90695	.99899 45597 63417
3.290	0.00178 02730 39962	0.99899 81261 72429
91	.00177 44246 78817	.99900 16808 67236
92	.00176 85937 61483	.99900 52238 82773
93	.00176 27802 42281	.99900 87552 53881
94	.00175 69840 75630	.99901 22750 15311
3.295	0.00175 12052 16046	0.99901 57832 01721
96	.00174 54436 18144	.99901 92798 47682
97	.00173 96992 36636	.99902 27649 87672
98	.00173 39720 26330	.99902 62386 56076
99	.00172 82619 42135	.99902 97008 87194
3.300	0.00172 25689 39054	0.99903 31517 15232

x	$\dfrac{1}{\sqrt{2\pi}}\,e^{-\frac{x^2}{2}}$	$\dfrac{1}{\sqrt{2\pi}}\displaystyle\int_{-x}^{x} e^{-\frac{\alpha^2}{2}}\,d\alpha$
3.300	0.00172 25689 39054	0.99903 31517 15232
01	.00171 68929 72187	.99903 65911 74308
02	.00171 12339 96733	.99904 00192 98449
03	.00170 55919 67987	.99904 34361 21593
04	.00169 99668 41339	.99904 68416 77589
3.305	0.00169 43585 72278	0.99905 02360 00197
06	.00168 87671 16387	.99905 36191 23087
07	.00168 31924 29347	.99905 69910 79841
08	.00167 76344 66934	.99906 03519 03954
09	.00167 20931 85021	.99906 37016 28829
3.310	0.00166 65685 39575	0.99906 70402 87785
11	.00166 10604 86659	.99907 03679 14049
12	.00165 55689 82434	.99907 36845 40764
13	.00165 00939 83154	.99907 69902 00982
14	.00164 46354 45168	.99908 02849 27671
3.315	0.00163 91933 24921	0.99908 35687 53708
16	.00163 37675 78952	.99908 68417 11887
17	.00162 83581 63898	.99909 01038 34911
18	.00162 29650 36485	.99909 33551 55401
19	.00161 75881 53539	.99909 65957 05887
3.320	0.00161 22274 71977	0.99909 98255 18816
21	.00160 68829 48812	.99910 30446 26547
22	.00160 15545 41149	.99910 62530 61355
23	.00159 62422 06189	.99910 94508 55427
24	.00159 09459 01227	.99911 26380 40866
3.325	0.00158 56655 83649	0.99911 58146 49690
26	.00158 04012 10938	.99911 89807 13831
27	.00157 51527 40668	.99912 21362 65135
28	.00156 99201 30507	.99912 52813 35367
29	.00156 47033 38215	.99912 84159 56203
3.330	0.00155 95023 21648	0.99913 15401 59237
31	.00155 43170 38751	.99913 46539 75978
32	.00154 91474 47564	.99913 77574 37853
33	.00154 39935 06220	.99914 08505 76202
34	.00153 88551 72942	.99914 39334 22283
3.335	0.00153 37324 06047	0.99914 70060 07271
36	.00152 86251 63945	.99915 00683 62257
37	.00152 35334 05136	.99915 31205 18249
38	.00151 84570 88212	.99915 61625 06172
39	.00151 33961 71858	.99915 91943 56869
3.340	0.00150 83506 14850	0.99916 22161 01099
41	.00150 33203 76055	.99916 52277 69541
42	.00149 83054 14432	.99916 82293 92788
43	.00149 33056 89030	.99917 12210 01356
44	.00148 83211 58991	.99917 42026 25675
3.345	0.00148 33517 83545	0.99917 71742 96095
46	.00147 83975 22015	.99918 01360 42885
47	.00147 34583 33813	.99918 30878 96232
48	.00146 85341 78444	.99918 60298 86242
49	.00146 36250 15501	.99918 89620 42940
3.350	0.00145 87308 04667	0.99919 18843 96272

x	$\frac{1}{\sqrt{2\pi}}e^{-\frac{x^2}{2}}$	$\frac{1}{\sqrt{2\pi}}\int_{-x}^{x}e^{-\frac{\alpha^2}{2}}d\alpha$
3.350	0.00145 87308 04667	0.99919 18843 96272
51	.00145 38515 05716	.99919 47969 76100
52	.00144 89870 78512	.99919 76998 12209
53	.00144 41374 83008	.99920 05929 34302
54	.00143 93026 79246	.99920 34763 72003
3.355	0.00143 44826 27361	0.99920 63501 54854
56	.00142 96772 87572	.99920 92143 12320
57	.00142 48866 20192	.99921 20688 73786
58	.00142 01105 85619	.99921 49138 68556
59	.00141 53491 44343	.99921 77493 25857
3.360	0.00141 06022 56941	0.99922 05752 74836
61	.00140 58698 84080	.99922 33917 44561
62	.00140 11519 86514	.99922 61987 64022
63	.00139 64485 25085	.99922 89963 62131
64	.00139 17594 60726	.99923 17845 67721
3.365	0.00138 70847 54454	0.99923 45634 09546
66	.00138 24243 67378	.99923 73329 16285
67	.00137 77782 60693	.99924 00931 16536
68	.00137 31463 95680	.99924 28440 38822
69	.00136 85287 33709	.99924 55857 11587
3.370	0.00136 39252 36239	0.99924 83181 63200
71	.00135 93358 64813	.99925 10414 21950
72	.00135 47605 81063	.99925 37555 16051
73	.00135 01993 46708	.99925 64604 73640
74	.00134 56521 23553	.99925 91563 22778
3.375	0.00134 11188 73490	0.99926 18430 91450
76	.00133 65995 58498	.99926 45208 07563
77	.00133 20941 40641	.99926 71894 98949
78	.00132 76025 82070	.99926 98491 93365
79	.00132 31248 45023	.99927 24999 18491
3.380	0.00131 86608 91823	0.99927 51417 01934
81	.00131 42106 84878	.99927 77745 71223
82	.00130 97741 86684	.99928 03985 53813
83	.00130 53513 59820	.99928 30136 77084
84	.00130 09421 66953	.99928 56199 68341
3.385	0.00129 65465 70832	0.99928 82174 54816
86	.00129 21645 34295	.99929 08061 63664
87	.00128 77960 20261	.99929 33861 21968
88	.00128 34409 91736	.99929 59573 56736
89	.00127 90994 11811	.99929 85198 94901
3.390	0.00127 47712 43662	0.99930 10737 63324
91	.00127 04564 50547	.99930 36189 88792
92	.00126 61549 95809	.99930 61555 98018
93	.00126 18668 42878	.99930 86836 17643
94	.00125 75919 55265	.99931 12030 74234
3.395	0.00125 33302 96565	0.99931 37139 94284
96	.00124 90818 30458	.99931 62164 04215
97	.00124 48465 20708	.99931 87103 30376
98	.00124 06243 31159	.99932 11957 99045
99	.00123 64152 25744	.99932 36728 36424
3.400	0.00123 22191 68473	0.99932 61414 68646

X	$\dfrac{1}{\sqrt{2\pi}}\,e^{-\frac{x^2}{2}}$	$\dfrac{1}{\sqrt{2\pi}}\displaystyle\int_{-x}^{x} e^{-\frac{\alpha^2}{2}}\,d\alpha$
3.400	0.00123 22191 68473	0.99932 61414 68646
01	.00122 80361 23444	.99932 86017 21772
02	.00122 38660 54835	.99933 10536 21791
03	.00121 97089 26908	.99933 34971 94619
04	.00121 55647 04007	.99933 59324 66102
3.405	0.00121 14333 50559	0.99933 83594 62015
06	.00120 73148 31073	.99934 07782 08060
07	.00120 32091 10140	.99934 31887 29871
08	.00119 91161 52435	.99934 55910 53010
09	.00119 50359 22711	.99934 79852 02966
3.410	0.00119 09683 85806	0.99935 03712 05162
11	.00118 69135 06639	.99935 27490 84948
12	.00118 28712 50211	.99935 51188 67604
13	.00117 88415 81602	.99935 74805 78341
14	.00117 48244 65976	.99935 98342 42299
3.415	0.00117 08198 68577	0.99936 21798 84550
16	.00116 68277 54729	.99936 45175 30096
17	.00116 28480 89838	.99936 68472 03868
18	.00115 88808 39392	.99936 91689 30731
19	.00115 49259 68956	.99937 14827 35479
3.420	0.00115 09834 44178	0.99937 37886 42838
21	.00114 70532 30787	.99937 60866 77464
22	.00114 31352 94589	.99937 83768 63946
23	.00113 92296 01473	.99938 06592 26804
24	.00113 53361 17407	.99938 29337 90491
3.425	0.00113 14548 08437	0.99938 52005 79390
26	.00112 75856 40691	.99938 74596 17819
27	.00112 37285 80376	.99938 97109 30025
28	.00111 98835 93777	.99939 19545 40189
29	.00111 60506 47258	.99939 41904 72426
3.430	0.00111 22297 07266	0.99939 64187 50783
31	.00110 84207 40321	.99939 86393 99238
32	.00110 46237 13026	.99940 08524 41704
33	.00110 08385 92061	.99940 30579 02027
34	.00109 70653 44185	.99940 52558 03987
3.435	0.00109 33039 36236	0.99940 74461 71297
36	.00108 95543 35128	.99940 96290 27604
37	.00108 58165 07856	.99941 18043 96487
38	.00108 20904 21490	.99941 39723 01462
39	.00107 83760 43180	.99941 61327 65978
3.440	0.00107 46733 40154	0.99941 82858 13419
41	.00107 09822 79715	.99942 04314 67101
42	.00106 73028 29245	.99942 25697 50277
43	.00106 36349 56204	.99942 47006 86136
44	.00105 99786 28128	.99942 68242 97799
3.445	0.00105 63338 12631	0.99942 89406 08323
46	.00105 27004 77402	.99943 10496 40703
47	.00104 90785 90209	.99943 31514 17865
48	.00104 54681 18895	.99943 52459 62674
49	.00104 18690 31380	.99943 73332 97930
3.450	0.00103 82812 95661	0.99943 94134 46368

x	$\dfrac{1}{\sqrt{2\pi}}e^{-\frac{x^2}{2}}$	$\dfrac{1}{\sqrt{2\pi}}\displaystyle\int_{-x}^{x}e^{-\frac{\alpha^2}{2}}\,d\alpha$
3.450	0.00103 82812 95661	0.99943 94134 46368
51	.00103 47048 79811	.99944 14864 30659
52	.00103 11397 51976	.99944 35522 73412
53	.00102 75858 80384	.99944 56109 97171
54	.00102 40432 33333	.99944 76626 24417
3.455	0.00102 05117 79199	0.99944 97071 77566
56	.00101 69914 86435	.99945 17446 78974
57	.00101 34823 23566	.99945 37751 50932
58	.00100 99842 59196	.99945 57986 15668
59	.00100 64972 62001	.99945 78150 95347
3.460	0.00100 30213 00734	0.99945 98246 12073
61	.00099 95563 44222	.99946 18271 87886
62	.00099 61023 61366	.99946 38228 44766
63	.00099 26593 21143	.99946 58116 04627
64	.00098 92271 92604	.99946 77934 89325
3.465	0.00098 58059 44873	0.99946 97685 20651
66	.00098 23955 47151	.99947 17367 20338
67	.00097 89959 68711	.99947 36981 10053
68	.00097 56071 78899	.99947 56527 11405
69	.00097 22291 47137	.99947 76005 45940
3.470	0.00096 88618 42920	0.99947 95416 35145
71	.00096 55052 35815	.99948 14760 00443
72	.00096 21592 95466	.99948 34036 63199
73	.00095 88239 91585	.99948 53246 44716
74	.00095 54992 93962	.99948 72389 66237
3.475	0.00095 21851 72456	0.99948 91466 48943
76	.00094 88815 97003	.99949 10477 13957
77	.00094 55885 37608	.99949 29421 82342
78	.00094 23059 64351	.99949 48300 75098
79	.00093 90338 47383	.99949 67114 13170
3.480	0.00093 57721 56927	0.99949 85862 17439
81	.00093 25208 63281	.99950 04545 08729
82	.00092 92799 36812	.99950 23163 07803
83	.00092 60493 47960	.99950 41716 35368
84	.00092 28290 67237	.99950 60205 12067
3.485	0.00091 96190 65226	0.99950 78629 58489
86	.00091 64193 12582	.99950 96989 95161
87	.00091 32297 80032	.99951 15286 42553
88	.00091 00504 38374	.99951 33519 21075
89	.00090 68812 58476	.99951 51688 51081
3.490	0.00090 37222 11278	0.99951 69794 52864
91	.00090 05732 67790	.99951 87837 46662
92	.00089 74343 99094	.99952 05817 52652
93	.00089 43055 76342	.99952 23734 90956
94	.00089 11867 70757	.99952 41589 81635
3.495	0.00088 80779 53631	0.99952 59382 44698
96	.00088 49790 96327	.99952 77113 00090
97	.00088 18901 70279	.99952 94781 67704
98	.00087 88111 46989	.99953 12388 67373
99	.00087 57419 98030	.99953 29934 18875
3.500	0.00087 26826 95046	0.99953 47418 41929

x	$\frac{1}{\sqrt{2\pi}} e^{-\frac{x^2}{2}}$	$\frac{1}{\sqrt{2\pi}} \int_{-x}^{x} e^{-\frac{\alpha^2}{2}} \, d\alpha$
3.500	0.00087 26826 95046	0.99953 47418 41929
01	.00086 96332 09747	.99953 64841 56200
02	.00086 65935 13917	.99953 82203 81294
03	.00086 35635 79404	.99953 99505 36763
04	.00086 05433 78131	.99954 16746 42101
3.505	0.00085 75328 82085	0.99954 33927 16746
06	.00085 45320 63325	.99954 51047 80081
07	.00085 15408 93977	.99954 68108 51432
08	.00084 85593 46238	.99954 85109 50071
09	.00084 55873 92370	.99955 02050 95213
3.510	0.00084 26250 04707	0.99955 18933 06018
11	.00083 96721 55649	.99955 35756 01591
12	.00083 67288 17664	.99955 52520 00981
13	.00083 37949 63290	.99955 69225 23184
14	.00083 08705 65132	.99955 85871 87138
3.515	0.00082 79555 95861	0.99956 02460 11730
16	.00082 50500 28217	.99956 18990 15790
17	.00082 21538 35009	.99956 35462 18093
18	.00081 92669 89111	.99956 51876 37361
19	.00081 63894 63466	.99956 68232 92263
3.520	0.00081 35212 31082	0.99956 84532 01411
21	.00081 06622 65036	.99957 00773 83365
22	.00080 78125 38470	.99957 16958 56630
23	.00080 49720 24596	.99957 33086 39660
24	.00080 21406 96688	.99957 49157 50853
3.525	0.00079 93185 28091	0.99957 65172 08553
26	.00079 65054 92213	.99957 81130 31054
27	.00079 37015 62529	.99957 97032 36593
28	.00079 09067 12582	.99958 12878 43357
29	.00078 81209 15979	.99958 28668 69479
3.530	0.00078 53441 46392	0.99958 44403 33039
31	.00078 25763 77562	.99958 60082 52065
32	.00077 98175 83293	.99958 75706 44532
33	.00077 70677 37455	.99958 91275 28364
34	.00077 43268 13983	.99959 06789 21430
3.535	0.00077 15947 86878	0.99959 22248 41550
36	.00076 88716 30206	.99959 37653 06491
37	.00076 61573 18097	.99959 53003 33968
38	.00076 34518 24747	.99959 68299 41643
39	.00076 07551 24416	.99959 83541 47129
3.540	0.00075 80671 91429	0.99959 98729 67985
41	.00075 53880 00174	.99960 13864 21722
42	.00075 27175 25107	.99960 28945 25797
43	.00075 00557 40743	.99960 43972 97616
44	.00074 74026 21666	.99960 58947 54537
3.545	0.00074 47581 42520	0.99960 73869 13863
46	.00074 21222 78016	.99960 88737 92850
47	.00073 94950 02926	.99961 03554 08701
48	.00073 68762 92088	.99961 18317 78571
49	.00073 42661 20401	.99961 33029 19562
3.550	0.00073 16644 62830	0.99961 47688 48729

x	$\frac{1}{\sqrt{2\pi}} e^{-\frac{x^2}{2}}$	$\frac{1}{\sqrt{2\pi}} \int_{-x}^{x} e^{-\frac{\alpha^2}{2}} d\alpha$
3.550	0.00073 16644 62830	0.99961 47688 48729
51	.00072 90712 94401	.99961 62295 83073
52	.00072 64865 90205	.99961 76851 39549
53	.00072 39103 25393	.99961 91355 35060
54	.00072 13424 75181	.99962 05807 86460
3.555	0.00071 87830 14849	0.99962 20209 10554
56	.00071 62319 19737	.99962 34559 24097
57	.00071 36891 65247	.99962 48858 43794
58	.00071 11547 26847	.99962 63106 86302
59	.00070 86285 80064	.99962 77304 68229
3.560	0.00070 61107 00488	0.99962 91452 06133
61	.00070 36010 63771	.99963 05549 16526
62	.00070 10996 45627	.99963 19596 15868
63	.00069 86064 21831	.99963 33593 20571
64	.00069 61213 68221	.99963 47540 47002
3.565	0.00069 36444 60695	0.99963 61438 11475
66	.00069 11756 75213	.99963 75286 30259
67	.00068 87149 87796	.99963 89085 19574
68	.00068 62623 74528	.99964 02834 95593
69	.00068 38178 11550	.99964 16535 74439
3.570	0.00068 13812 75067	0.99964 30187 72190
71	.00067 89527 41344	.99964 43791 04875
72	.00067 65321 86707	.99964 57345 88475
73	.00067 41195 87541	.99964 70852 38925
74	.00067 17149 20293	.99964 84310 72113
3.575	0.00066 93181 61470	0.99964 97721 03879
76	.00066 69292 87638	.99965 11083 50016
77	.00066 45482 75423	.99965 24398 26270
78	.00066 21751 01514	.99965 37665 48343
79	.00065 98097 42656	.99965 50885 31887
3.580	0.00065 74521 75655	0.99965 64057 92508
81	.00065 51023 77376	.99965 77183 45768
82	.00065 27603 24746	.99965 90262 07181
83	.00065 04259 94748	.99966 03293 92216
84	.00064 80993 64425	.99966 16279 16294
3.585	0.00064 57804 10881	0.99966 29217 94791
86	.00064 34691 11276	.99966 42110 43040
87	.00064 11654 42832	.99966 54956 76324
88	.00063 88693 82826	.99966 67757 09883
89	.00063 65809 08596	.99966 80511 58912
3.590	0.00063 42999 97539	0.99966 93220 38560
91	.00063 20266 27108	.99967 05883 63930
92	.00062 97607 74817	.99967 18501 50080
93	.00062 75024 18235	.99967 31074 12026
94	.00062 52515 34992	.99967 43601 64735
3.595	0.00062 30081 02773	0.99967 56084 23133
96	.00062 07720 99324	.99967 68522 02099
97	.00061 85435 02445	.99967 80915 16468
98	.00061 63222 89997	.99967 93263 81032
99	.00061 41084 39895	.99968 05568 10536
3.600	0.00061 19019 30114	0.99968 17828 19685

x	$\dfrac{1}{\sqrt{2\pi}}\,e^{-\frac{x^2}{2}}$	$\dfrac{1}{\sqrt{2\pi}}\displaystyle\int_{-x}^{x} e^{-\frac{\alpha^2}{2}}\,d\alpha$
3.600	0.00061 19019 30114	0.99968 17828 19685
01	.00060 97027 38685	.99968 30044 23136
02	.00060 75108 43695	.99968 42216 35504
03	.00060 53262 23291	.99968 54344 71360
04	.00060 31488 55674	.99968 66429 45232
3.605	0.00060 09787 19102	0.99968 78470 71604
06	.00059 88157 91890	.99968 90468 64915
07	.00059 66600 52410	.99969 02423 39563
08	.00059 45114 79091	.99969 14335 09902
09	.00059 23700 50415	.99969 26203 90243
3.610	0.00059 02357 44923	0.99969 38029 94852
11	.00058 81085 41211	.99969 49813 37957
12	.00058 59884 17931	.99969 61554 33738
13	.00058 38753 53792	.99969 73252 96335
14	.00058 17693 27555	.99969 84909 39845
3.615	0.00057 96703 18041	0.99969 96523 78323
16	.00057 75783 04123	.99970 08096 25781
17	.00057 54932 64731	.99970 19626 96189
18	.00057 34151 78850	.99970 31116 03475
19	.00057 13440 25520	.99970 42563 61526
3.620	0.00056 92797 83834	0.99970 53969 84185
21	.00056 72224 32944	.99970 65334 85255
22	.00056 51719 52052	.99970 76658 78497
23	.00056 31283 20418	.99970 87941 77629
24	.00056 10915 17356	.99970 99183 96331
3.625	0.00055 90615 22232	0.99971 10385 48238
26	.00055 70383 14469	.99971 21546 46945
27	.00055 50218 73543	.99971 32667 06007
28	.00055 30121 78984	.99971 43747 38936
29	.00055 10092 10376	.99971 54787 59207
3.630	0.00054 90129 47357	0.99971 65787 80248
31	.00054 70233 69618	.99971 76748 15453
32	.00054 50404 56904	.99971 87668 78170
33	.00054 30641 89014	.99971 98549 81710
34	.00054 10945 45800	.99972 09391 39343
3.635	0.00053 91315 07166	0.99972 20193 64297
36	.00053 71750 53071	.99972 30956 69761
37	.00053 52251 63526	.99972 41680 68885
38	.00053 32818 18595	.99972 52365 74778
39	.00053 13449 98395	.99972 63012 00509
3.640	0.00052 94146 83095	0.99972 73619 59108
41	.00052 74908 52918	.99972 84188 63565
42	.00052 55734 88138	.99972 94719 26830
43	.00052 36625 69081	.99973 05211 61815
44	.00052 17580 76128	.99973 15665 81391
3.645	0.00051 98599 89708	0.99973 26081 98390
46	.00051 79682 90306	.99973 36460 25608
47	.00051 60829 58455	.99973 46800 75797
48	.00051 42039 74744	.99973 57103 61673
49	.00051 23313 19810	.99973 67368 95915
3.650	0.00051 04649 74344	0.99973 77596 91159

x	$\frac{1}{\sqrt{2\pi}} e^{-\frac{x^2}{2}}$	$\frac{1}{\sqrt{2\pi}} \int_{-x}^{x} e^{-\frac{\alpha^2}{2}} d\alpha$
3.650	0.00051 04649 74344	0.99973 77596 91159
51	.00050 86049 19087	.99973 87787 60006
52	.00050 67511 34831	.99973 97941 15016
53	.00050 49036 02421	.99974 08057 68713
54	.00050 30623 02752	.99974 18137 33581
3.655	0.00050 12272 16770	0.99974 28180 22066
56	.00049 93983 25472	.99974 38186 46578
57	.00049 75756 09905	.99974 48156 19485
58	.00049 57590 51169	.99974 58089 53122
59	.00049 39486 30411	.99974 67986 59782
3.660	0.00049 21443 28833	0.99974 77847 51723
61	.00049 03461 27683	.99974 87672 41164
62	.00048 85540 08261	.99974 97461 40288
63	.00048 67679 51918	.99975 07214 61239
64	.00048 49879 40054	.99975 16932 16126
3.665	0.00048 32139 54118	0.99975 26614 17017
66	.00048 14459 75612	.99975 36260 75947
67	.00047 96839 86083	.99975 45872 04912
68	.00047 79279 67132	.99975 55448 15872
69	.00047 61779 00407	.99975 64989 20749
3.670	0.00047 44337 67607	0.99975 74495 31429
71	.00047 26955 50477	.99975 83966 59763
72	.00047 09632 30815	.99975 93403 17563
73	.00046 92367 90467	.99976 02805 16606
74	.00046 75162 11325	.99976 12172 68632
3.675	0.00046 58014 75335	0.99976 21505 85346
76	.00046 40925 64487	.99976 30804 78417
77	.00046 23894 60823	.99976 40069 59476
78	.00046 06921 46430	.99976 49300 40120
79	.00045 90006 03447	.99976 58497 31909
3.680	0.00045 73148 14060	0.99976 67660 46369
81	.00045 56347 60502	.99976 76789 94989
82	.00045 39604 25055	.99976 85885 89223
83	.00045 22917 90050	.99976 94948 40490
84	.00045 06288 37863	.99977 03977 60172
3.685	0.00044 89715 50922	0.99977 12973 59618
86	.00044 73199 11699	.99977 21936 50141
87	.00044 56739 02715	.99977 30866 43018
88	.00044 40335 06538	.99977 39763 49494
89	.00044 23987 05783	.99977 48627 80775
3.690	0.00044 07694 83115	0.99977 57459 48036
91	.00043 91458 21243	.99977 66258 62415
92	.00043 75277 02923	.99977 75025 35016
93	.00043 59151 10960	.99977 83759 76910
94	.00043 43080 28205	.99977 92461 99133
3.695	0.00043 27064 37555	0.99978 01132 12685
96	.00043 11103 21954	.99978 09770 28533
97	.00042 95196 64393	.99978 18376 57611
98	.00042 79344 47909	.99978 26951 10818
99	.00042 63546 55585	.99978 35493 99019
3.700	0.00042 47802 70551	0.99978 44005 33045

x	$\dfrac{1}{\sqrt{2\pi}}\,e^{-\frac{x^2}{2}}$	$\dfrac{1}{\sqrt{2\pi}}\displaystyle\int_{-x}^{x} e^{-\frac{\alpha^2}{2}}\,d\alpha$
3.700	0.00042 47802 70551	0.99978 44005 33045
01	.00042 32112 75982	.99978 52485 23695
02	.00042 16476 55101	.99978 60933 81732
03	.00042 00893 91174	.99978 69351 17886
04	.00041 85364 67515	.99978 77737 42856
3.705	0.00041 69888 67483	0.99978 86092 67306
06	.00041 54465 74483	.99978 94417 01864
07	.00041 39095 71964	.99979 02710 57131
08	.00041 23778 43422	.99979 10973 43668
09	.00041 08513 72398	.99979 19205 72009
3.710	0.00040 93301 42478	0.99979 27407 52652
11	.00040 78141 37292	.99979 35578 96062
12	.00040 63033 40517	.99979 43720 12673
13	.00040 47977 35873	.99979 51831 12886
14	.00040 32973 07127	.99979 59912 07067
3.715	0.00040 18020 38087	0.99979 67963 05554
16	.00040 03119 12609	.99979 75984 18649
17	.00039 88269 14593	.99979 83975 56623
18	.00039 73470 27981	.99979 91937 29715
19	.00039 58722 36763	.99979 99869 48132
3.720	0.00039 44025 24969	0.99980 07772 22048
21	.00039 29378 76676	.99980 15645 61607
22	.00039 14782 76005	.99980 23489 76920
23	.00039 00237 07119	.99980 31304 78066
24	.00038 85741 54225	.99980 39090 75092
3.725	0.00038 71296 01576	0.99980 46847 78016
26	.00038 56900 33465	.99980 54575 96822
27	.00038 42554 34233	.99980 62275 41463
28	.00038 28257 88260	.99980 69946 21861
29	.00038 14010 79971	.99980 77588 47907
3.730	0.00037 99812 93835	0.99980 85202 29462
31	.00037 85664 14363	.99980 92787 76354
32	.00037 71564 26110	.99981 00344 98380
33	.00037 57513 13672	.99981 07874 05309
34	.00037 43510 61689	.99981 15375 06875
3.735	0.00037 29556 54844	0.99981 22848 12786
36	.00037 15650 77863	.99981 30293 32715
37	.00037 01793 15512	.99981 37710 76307
38	.00036 87983 52603	.99981 45100 53176
39	.00036 74221 73986	.99981 52462 72907
3.740	0.00036 60507 64557	0.99981 59797 45052
41	.00036 46841 09253	.99981 67104 79134
42	.00036 33221 93052	.99981 74384 84648
43	.00036 19650 00974	.99981 81637 71056
44	.00036 06125 18082	.99981 88863 47792
3.745	0.00035 92647 29480	0.99981 96062 24258
46	.00035 79216 20314	.99982 03234 09829
47	.00035 65831 75770	.99982 10379 13849
48	.00035 52493 81078	.99982 17497 45632
49	.00035 39202 21506	.99982 24589 14463
3.750	0.00035 25956 82367	0.99982 31654 29598

x	$\frac{1}{\sqrt{2\pi}}e^{-\frac{x^2}{2}}$	$\frac{1}{\sqrt{2\pi}}\int_{-x}^{x}e^{-\frac{\alpha^2}{2}}d\alpha$
3.750	0.00035 25956 82367	0.99982 31654 29598
51	.00035 12757 49013	.99982 38693 00263
52	.00034 99604 06836	.99982 45705 35655
53	.00034 86496 41272	.99982 52691 44942
54	.00034 73434 37794	.99982 59651 37262
3.755	0.00034 60417 81919	0.99982 66585 21725
56	.00034 47446 59204	.99982 73493 07411
57	.00034 34520 55245	.99982 80375 03374
58	.00034 21639 55680	.99982 87231 18635
59	.00034 08803 46187	.99982 94061 62190
3.760	0.00033 96012 12484	0.99983 00866 43004
61	.00033 83265 40329	.99983 07645 70014
62	.00033 70563 15520	.99983 14399 52130
63	.00033 57905 23897	.99983 21127 98232
64	.00033 45291 51337	.99983 27831 17172
3.765	0.00033 32721 83758	0.99983 34509 17774
66	.00033 20196 07119	.99983 41162 08834
67	.00033 07714 07416	.99983 47789 99120
68	.00032 95275 70688	.99983 54392 97372
69	.00032 82880 83009	.99983 60971 12302
3.770	0.00032 70529 30496	0.99983 67524 52595
71	.00032 58220 99305	.99983 74053 26905
72	.00032 45955 75628	.99983 80557 43864
73	.00032 33733 45700	.99983 87037 12070
74	.00032 21553 95792	.99983 93492 40100
3.775	0.00032 09417 12216	0.99983 99923 36498
76	.00031 97322 81321	.99984 06330 09784
77	.00031 85270 89497	.99984 12712 68449
78	.00031 73261 23169	.99984 19071 20959
79	.00031 61293 68805	.99984 25405 75750
3.780	0.00031 49368 12908	0.99984 31716 41233
81	.00031 37484 42020	.99984 38003 25791
82	.00031 25642 42722	.99984 44266 37782
83	.00031 13842 01634	.99984 50505 85534
84	.00031 02083 05411	.99984 56721 77352
3.785	0.00030 90365 40750	0.99984 62914 21510
86	.00030 78688 94382	.99984 69083 26260
87	.00030 67053 53078	.99984 75228 99825
88	.00030 55459 03647	.99984 81351 50400
89	.00030 43905 32933	.99984 87450 86158
3.790	0.00030 32392 27822	0.99984 93527 15243
91	.00030 20919 75233	.99984 99580 45771
92	.00030 09487 62125	.99985 05610 85837
93	.00029 98095 75492	.99985 11618 43504
94	.00029 86744 02369	.99985 17603 26814
3.795	0.00029 75432 29823	0.99985 23565 43781
96	.00029 64160 44963	.99985 29505 02392
97	.00029 52928 34931	.99985 35422 10610
98	.00029 41735 86907	.99985 41316 76373
99	.00029 30582 88110	.99985 47189 07591
3.800	0.00029 19469 25791	0.99985 53039 12150

x	$\dfrac{1}{\sqrt{2\pi}}e^{-\frac{x^2}{2}}$	$\dfrac{1}{\sqrt{2\pi}}\displaystyle\int_{-x}^{x}e^{-\frac{\alpha^2}{2}}\,d\alpha$
3.800	0.00029 19469 25791	0.99985 53039 12150
01	.00029 08394 87243	.99985 58866 97910
02	.00028 97359 59791	.99985 64672 72706
03	.00028 86363 30799	.99985 70456 44348
04	.00028 75405 87665	.99985 76218 20620
3.805	0.00028 64487 17825	0.99985 81958 09281
06	.00028 53607 08752	.99985 87676 18065
07	.00028 42765 47952	.99985 93372 54681
08	.00028 31962 22970	.99985 99047 26814
09	.00028 21197 21384	.99986 04700 42122
3.810	0.00028 10470 30810	0.99986 10332 08240
11	.00027 99781 38899	.99986 15942 32778
12	.00027 89130 33337	.99986 21531 23320
13	.00027 78517 01846	.99986 27098 87427
14	.00027 67941 32183	.99986 32645 32635
3.815	0.00027 57403 12142	0.99986 38170 66456
16	.00027 46902 29550	.99986 43674 96376
17	.00027 36438 72271	.99986 49158 29858
18	.00027 26012 28201	.99986 54620 74340
19	.00027 15622 85276	.99986 60062 37238
3.820	0.00027 05270 31462	0.99986 65483 25941
21	.00026 94954 54762	.99986 70883 47815
22	.00026 84675 43215	.99986 76263 10203
23	.00026 74432 84891	.99986 81622 20423
24	.00026 64226 67900	.99986 86960 85770
3.825	0.00026 54056 80380	0.99986 92279 13515
26	.00026 43923 10509	.99986 97577 10904
27	.00026 33825 46496	.99987 02854 85161
28	.00026 23763 76585	.99987 08112 43486
29	.00026 13737 89055	.99987 13349 93055
3.830	0.00026 03747 72218	0.99987 18567 41022
31	.00025 93793 14421	.99987 23764 94517
32	.00025 83874 04044	.99987 28942 60645
33	.00025 73990 29500	.99987 34100 46490
34	.00025 64141 79238	.99987 39238 59112
3.835	0.00025 54328 41740	0.99987 44357 05549
36	.00025 44550 05520	.99987 49455 92814
37	.00025 34806 59126	.99987 54535 27898
38	.00025 25097 91141	.99987 59595 17769
39	.00025 15423 90180	.99987 64635 69373
3.840	0.00025 05784 44891	0.99987 69656 89633
41	.00024 96179 43956	.99987 74658 85449
42	.00024 86608 76089	.99987 79641 63698
43	.00024 77072 30039	.99987 84605 31235
44	.00024 67569 94585	.99987 89549 94892
3.845	0.00024 58101 58541	0.99987 94475 61479
46	.00024 48667 10753	.99987 99382 37785
47	.00024 39266 40100	.99988 04270 30574
48	.00024 29899 35493	.99988 09139 46589
49	.00024 20565 85876	.99988 13989 92552
3.850	0.00024 11265 80226	0.99988 18821 75162

x	$\frac{1}{\sqrt{2\pi}} e^{-\frac{x^2}{2}}$	$\frac{1}{\sqrt{2\pi}} \int_{-x}^{x} e^{-\frac{\alpha^2}{2}} d\alpha$
3.850	0.00024 11265 80226	0.99988 18821 75162
51	.00024 01999 07550	.99988 23635 01095
52	.00023 92765 56890	.99988 28429 77007
53	.00023 83565 17319	.99988 33206 09530
54	.00023 74397 77942	.99988 37964 05276
3.855	0.00023 65263 27895	0.99988 42703 70835
56	.00023 56161 56349	.99988 47425 12774
57	.00023 47092 52503	.99988 52128 37639
58	.00023 38056 05591	.99988 56813 51955
59	.00023 29052 04877	.99988 61480 62225
3.860	0.00023 20080 39657	0.99988 66129 74931
61	.00023 11140 99259	.99988 70760 96534
62	.00023 02233 73041	.99988 75374 33471
63	.00022 93358 50394	.99988 79969 92162
64	.00022 84515 20740	.99988 84547 79002
3.865	0.00022 75703 73531	0.99988 89108 00366
66	.00022 66923 98252	.99988 93650 62610
67	.00022 58175 84418	.99988 98175 72067
68	.00022 49459 21575	.99989 02683 35049
69	.00022 40773 99300	.99989 07173 57847
3.870	0.00022 32120 07200	0.99989 11646 46733
71	.00022 23497 34915	.99989 16102 07956
72	.00022 14905 72114	.99989 20540 47745
73	.00022 06345 08496	.99989 24961 72310
74	.00021 97815 33793	.99989 29365 87839
3.875	0.00021 89316 37765	0.99989 33753 00498
76	.00021 80848 10202	.99989 38123 16435
77	.00021 72410 40928	.99989 42476 41777
78	.00021 64003 19793	.99989 46812 82631
79	.00021 55626 36680	.99989 51132 45082
3.880	0.00021 47279 81500	0.99989 55435 35196
81	.00021 38963 44196	.99989 59721 59020
82	.00021 30677 14739	.99989 63991 22578
83	.00021 22420 83131	.99989 68244 31877
84	.00021 14194 39404	.99989 72480 92903
3.885	0.00021 05997 73618	0.99989 76701 11620
86	.00020 97830 75864	.99989 80904 93976
87	.00020 89693 36264	.99989 85092 45896
88	.00020 81585 44966	.99989 89263 73287
89	.00020 73506 92149	.99989 93418 82035
3.390	0.00020 65457 68023	0.99989 97557 78008
91	.00020 57437 62825	.99990 01680 67053
92	.00020 49446 66821	.99990 05787 54998
93	.00020 41484 70309	.99990 09878 47653
94	.00020 33551 63611	.99990 13953 50806
3.895	0.00020 25647 37084	0.99990 18012 70228
96	.00020 17771 81109	.99990 22056 11668
97	.00020 09924 86097	.99990 26083 80859
98	.00020 02106 42490	.99990 30095 83514
99	.00019 94316 40756	.99990 34092 25324
3.900	0.00019 86554 71393	0.99990 38073 11965

x	$\frac{1}{\sqrt{2\pi}} e^{-\frac{x^2}{2}}$	$\frac{1}{\sqrt{2\pi}} \int_{-x}^{x} e^{-\frac{\alpha^2}{2}} \, d\alpha$
3.900	0.00019 86554 71393	0.99990 38073 11965
01	.00019 78821 24926	.99990 42038 49091
02	.00019 71115 91910	.99990 45988 42340
03	.00019 63438 62928	.99990 49922 97328
04	.00019 55789 28591	.99990 53842 19655
3.905	0.00019 48167 79538	0.99990 57746 14900
06	.00019 40574 06437	.99990 61634 88624
07	.00019 33007 99982	.99990 65508 46370
08	.00019 25469 50898	.99990 69366 93662
09	.00019 17958 49936	.99990 73210 36005
3.910	0.00019 10474 87875	0.99990 77038 78888
11	.00019 03018 55521	.99990 80852 27777
12	.00018 95589 43710	.99990 84650 88123
13	.00018 88187 43304	.99990 88434 65359
14	.00018 80812 45193	.99990 92203 64898
3.915	0.00018 73464 40294	0.99990 95957 92135
16	.00018 66143 19552	.99990 99697 52449
17	.00018 58848 73938	.99991 03422 51197
18	.00018 51580 94454	.99991 07132 93722
19	.00018 44339 72124	.99991 10828 85346
3.920	0.00018 37124 98002	0.99991 14510 31376
21	.00018 29936 63171	.99991 18177 37098
22	.00018 22774 58736	.99991 21830 07782
23	.00018 15638 75834	.99991 25468 48681
24	.00018 08529 05625	.99991 29092 65027
3.925	0.00018 01445 39298	0.99991 32702 62039
26	.00017 94387 68067	.99991 36298 44915
27	.00017 87355 83176	.99991 39880 18835
28	.00017 80349 75891	.99991 43447 88966
29	.00017 73369 37508	.99991 47001 60452
3.930	0.00017 66414 59348	0.99991 50541 38422
31	.00017 59485 32758	.99991 54067 27990
32	.00017 52581 49112	.99991 57579 34249
33	.00017 45702 99811	.99991 61077 62276
34	.00017 38849 76280	.99991 64562 17132
3.935	0.00017 32021 69973	0.99991 68033 03859
36	.00017 25218 72366	.99991 71490 27484
37	.00017 18440 74966	.99991 74933 93016
38	.00017 11687 69301	.99991 78364 05445
39	.00017 04959 46928	.99991 81780 69748
3.940	0.00016 98255 99429	0.99991 85183 90883
41	.00016 91577 18412	.99991 88573 73790
42	.00016 84922 95508	.99991 91950 23395
43	.00016 78293 22378	.99991 95313 44606
44	.00016 71687 90704	.99991 98663 42312
3.945	0.00016 65106 92197	0.99992 02000 21390
46	.00016 58550 18592	.99992 05323 86698
47	.00016 52017 61648	.99992 08634 43076
48	.00016 45509 13151	.99992 11931 95350
49	.00016 39024 64912	.99992 15216 48329
3.950	0.00016 32564 08766	0.99992 18488 06804

x	$\frac{1}{\sqrt{2\pi}} e^{-\frac{x^2}{2}}$	$\frac{1}{\sqrt{2\pi}} \int_{-x}^{x} e^{-\frac{\alpha^2}{2}} d\alpha$
3.950	0.00016 32564 08766	0.99992 18488 06804
51	.00016 26127 36574	.99992 21746 75553
52	.00016 19714 40221	.99992 24992 59335
53	.00016 13325 11618	.99992 28225 62893
54	.00016 06959 42700	.99992 31445 90954
3.955	0.00016 00617 25427	0.99992 34653 48231
56	.00015 94298 51784	.99992 37848 39418
57	.00015 88003 13781	.99992 41030 69195
58	.00015 81731 03450	.99992 44200 42225
59	.00015 75482 12851	.99992 47357 63156
3.960	0.00015 69256 34066	0.99992 50502 36618
61	.00015 63053 59202	.99992 53634 67228
62	.00015 56873 80391	.99992 56754 59585
63	.00015 50716 89789	.99992 59862 18275
64	.00015 44582 79575	.99992 62957 47865
3.965	0.00015 38471 41954	0.99992 66040 52908
66	.00015 32382 69153	.99992 69111 37942
67	.00015 26316 53424	.99992 72170 07490
68	.00015 20272 87044	.99992 75216 66056
69	.00015 14251 62311	.99992 78251 18132
3.970	0.00015 08252 71551	0.99992 81273 68194
71	.00015 02276 07108	.99992 84284 20703
72	.00014 96321 61356	.99992 87282 80102
73	.00014 90389 26687	.99992 90269 50822
74	.00014 84478 95521	.99992 93244 37278
3.975	0.00014 78590 60298	0.99992 96207 43868
76	.00014 72724 13484	.99992 99158 74978
77	.00014 66879 47566	.99993 02098 34976
78	.00014 61056 55056	.99993 05026 28217
79	.00014 55255 28490	.99993 07942 59040
3.980	0.00014 49475 60424	0.99993 10847 31770
81	.00014 43717 43440	.99993 13740 50716
82	.00014 37980 70141	.99993 16622 20173
83	.00014 32265 33155	.99993 19492 44421
84	.00014 26571 25132	.99993 22351 27725
3.985	0.00014 20898 38744	0.99993 25198 74336
86	.00014 15246 66686	.99993 28034 88489
87	.00014 09616 01677	.99993 30859 74407
88	.00014 04006 36458	.99993 33673 36296
89	.00013 98417 63792	.99993 36475 78348
3.990	0.00013 92849 76466	0.99993 39267 04741
91	.00013 87302 67287	.99993 42047 19639
92	.00013 81776 29086	.99993 44816 27191
93	.00013 76270 54718	.99993 47574 31531
94	.00013 70785 37056	.99993 50321 36781
3.995	0.00013 65320 69000	0.99993 53057 47046
96	.00013 59876 43469	.99993 55782 66419
97	.00013 54452 53404	.99993 58496 98977
98	.00013 49048 91771	.99993 61200 48785
99	.00013 43665 51555	.99993 63893 19892
4.000	0.00013 38302 25765	0.99993 66575 16334

X	$\dfrac{1}{\sqrt{2\pi}}\, e^{-\frac{x^2}{2}}$	$\dfrac{1}{\sqrt{2\pi}}\displaystyle\int_{-x}^{x} e^{-\frac{\alpha^2}{2}}\, d\alpha$
4.000	0.00013 38302 25765	0.99993 66575 16334
01	.00013 32959 07430	.99993 69246 42133
02	.00013 27635 89601	.99993 71907 01297
03	.00013 22332 65353	.99993 74556 97820
04	.00013 17049 27781	.99993 77196 35683
4.005	0.00013 11785 70001	0.99993 79825 18851
06	.00013 06541 85151	.99993 82443 51278
07	.00013 01317 66393	.99993 85051 36903
08	.00012 96113 06906	.99993 87648 79650
09	.00012 90927 99894	.99993 90235 83432
4.010	0.00012 85762 38582	0.99993 92812 52147
11	.00012 80616 16213	.99993 95378 89679
12	.00012 75489 26055	.99993 97934 99900
13	.00012 70381 61397	.99994 00480 86667
14	.00012 65293 15545	.99994 03016 53825
4.015	0.00012 60223 81831	0.99994 05542 05204
16	.00012 55173 53606	.99994 08057 44622
17	.00012 50142 24241	.99994 10562 75884
18	.00012 45129 87130	.99994 13058 02781
19	.00012 40136 35685	.99994 15543 29090
4.020	0.00012 35161 63341	0.99994 18018 58576
21	.00012 30205 63553	.99994 20483 94991
22	.00012 25268 29798	.99994 22939 42074
23	.00012 20349 55570	.99994 25385 03550
24	.00012 15449 34387	.99994 27820 83132
4.025	0.00012 10567 59787	0.99994 30246 84519
26	.00012 05704 25327	.99994 32663 11398
27	.00012 00859 24585	.99994 35069 67443
28	.00011 96032 51160	.99994 37466 56314
29	.00011 91223 98670	.99994 39853 81661
4.030	0.00011 86433 60755	0.99994 42231 47119
31	.00011 81661 31072	.99994 44599 56310
32	.00011 76907 03302	.99994 46958 12844
33	.00011 72170 71144	.99994 49307 20320
34	.00011 67452 28316	.99994 51646 82322
4.035	0.00011 62751 68558	0.99994 53977 02422
36	.00011 58068 85629	.99994 56297 84181
37	.00011 53403 73307	.99994 58609 31145
38	.00011 48756 25391	.99994 60911 46850
39	.00011 44126 35699	.99994 63204 34819
4.040	0.00011 39513 98069	0.99994 65487 98561
41	.00011 34919 06358	.99994 67762 41575
42	.00011 30341 54444	.99994 70027 67346
43	.00011 25781 36222	.99994 72283 79349
44	.00011 21238 45610	.99994 74530 81043
4.045	0.00011 16712 76541	0.99994 76768 75879
46	.00011 12204 22970	.99994 78997 67293
47	.00011 07712 78873	.99994 81217 58710
48	.00011 03238 38240	.99994 83428 53544
49	.00010 98780 95085	.99994 85630 55195
4.050	0.00010 94340 43440	0.99994 87823 67052

x	$\dfrac{1}{\sqrt{2\pi}}\,e^{-\frac{x^2}{2}}$	$\dfrac{1}{\sqrt{2\pi}}\displaystyle\int_{-x}^{x} e^{-\frac{\alpha^2}{2}}\,d\alpha$
4.050	0.00010 94340 43440	0.99994 87823 67052
51	.00010 89916 77354	.99994 90007 92492
52	.00010 85509 90896	.99994 92183 34881
53	.00010 81119 78156	.99994 94349 97572
54	.00010 76746 33240	.99994 96507 83906
4.055	0.00010 72389 50275	0.99994 98656 97213
56	.00010 68049 23405	.99995 00797 40811
57	.00010 63725 46794	.99995 02929 18006
58	.00010 59418 14624	.99995 05052 32094
59	.00010 55127 21096	.99995 07166 86357
4.060	0.00010 50852 60430	0.99995 09272 84067
61	.00010 46594 26864	.99995 11370 28484
62	.00010 42352 14654	.99995 13459 22856
63	.00010 38126 18075	.99995 15539 70419
64	.00010 33916 31420	.99995 17611 74401
4.065	0.00010 29722 49002	0.99995 19675 38015
66	.00010 25544 65149	.99995 21730 64463
67	.00010 21382 74210	.99995 23777 56937
68	.00010 17236 70552	.99995 25816 18618
69	.00010 13106 48558	.99995 27846 52674
4.070	0.00010 08992 02631	0.99995 29868 62263
71	.00010 04893 27191	.99995 31882 50531
72	.00010 00810 16678	.99995 33888 20615
73	.00009 96742 65547	.99995 35885 75638
74	.00009 92690 68272	.99995 37875 18713
4.075	0.00009 88654 19345	0.99995 39856 52943
76	.00009 84633 13277	.99995 41829 81419
77	.00009 80627 44594	.99995 43795 07221
78	.00009 76637 07842	.99995 45752 33419
79	.00009 72661 97584	.99995 47701 63070
4.080	0.00009 68702 08399	0.99995 49642 99223
81	.00009 64757 34885	.99995 51576 44914
82	.00009 60827 71659	.99995 53502 03169
83	.00009 56913 13351	.99995 55419 77004
84	.00009 53013 54613	.99995 57329 69422
4.085	0.00009 49128 90112	0.99995 59231 83419
86	.00009 45259 14532	.99995 61126 21976
87	.00009 41404 22575	.99995 63012 88066
88	.00009 37564 08961	.99995 64891 84651
89	.00009 33738 68424	.99995 66763 14684
4.090	0.00009 29927 95718	0.99995 68626 81104
91	.00009 26131 85614	.99995 70482 86842
92	.00009 22350 32899	.99995 72331 34818
93	.00009 18583 32376	.99995 74172 27941
94	.00009 14830 78867	.99995 76005 69112
4.095	0.00009 11092 67208	0.99995 77831 61218
96	.00009 07368 92256	.99995 79650 07139
97	.00009 03659 48880	.99995 81461 09741
98	.00008 99964 31969	.99995 83264 71885
99	.00008 96283 36428	.99995 85060 96417
4.100	0.00008 92616 57177	0.99995 86849 86175

x	$\dfrac{1}{\sqrt{2\pi}}\, e^{-\frac{x^2}{2}}$	$\dfrac{1}{\sqrt{2\pi}} \displaystyle\int_{-x}^{x} e^{-\frac{\alpha^2}{2}}\, d\alpha$
4.100	0.00008 92616 57177	0.99995 86849 86175
01	.00008 88963 89154	.99995 88631 43986
02	.00008 85325 27314	.99995 90405 72669
03	.00008 81700 66627	.99995 92172 75030
04	.00008 78090 02079	.99995 93932 53866
4.105	0.00008 74493 28675	0.99995 95685 11966
06	.00008 70910 41433	.99995 97430 52105
07	.00008 67341 35390	.99995 99168 77052
08	.00008 63786 05599	.99996 00899 89564
09	.00008 60244 47126	.99996 02623 92389
4.110	0.00008 56716 55056	0.99996 04340 88264
11	.00008 53202 24491	.99996 06050 79917
12	.00008 49701 50545	.99996 07753 70066
13	.00008 46214 28353	.99996 09449 61420
14	.00008 42740 53061	.99996 11138 56677
4.115	0.00008 39280 19835	0.99996 12820 58527
16	.00008 35833 23854	.99996 14495 69648
17	.00008 32399 60314	.99996 16163 92711
18	.00008 28979 24427	.99996 17825 30374
19	.00008 25572 11420	.99996 19479 85290
4.120	0.00008 22178 16536	0.99996 21127 60099
21	.00008 18797 35034	.99996 22768 57432
22	.00008 15429 62187	.99996 24402 79911
23	.00008 12074 93286	.99996 26030 30150
24	.00008 08733 23635	.99996 27651 10751
4.125	0.00008 05404 48556	0.99996 29265 24308
26	.00008 02088 63383	.99996 30872 73405
27	.00007 98785 63468	.99996 32473 60618
28	.00007 95495 44178	.99996 34067 88513
29	.00007 92218 00894	.99996 35655 59645
4.130	0.00007 88953 29014	0.99996 37236 76564
31	.00007 85701 23950	.99996 38811 41806
32	.00007 82461 81128	.99996 40379 57901
33	.00007 79234 95992	.99996 41941 27369
34	.00007 76020 63999	.99996 43496 52720
4.135	0.00007 72818 80621	0.99996 45045 36457
36	.00007 69629 41344	.99996 46587 81072
37	.00007 66452 41673	.99996 48123 89049
38	.00007 63287 77123	.99996 49653 62862
39	.00007 60135 43227	.99996 51177 04978
4.140	0.00007 56995 35530	0.99996 52694 17853
41	.00007 53867 49595	.99996 54205 03935
42	.00007 50751 80998	.99996 55709 65663
43	.00007 47648 25329	.99996 57208 05467
44	.00007 44556 78193	.99996 58700 25770
4.145	0.00007 41477 35210	0.99996 60186 28983
46	.00007 38409 92015	.99996 61666 17510
47	.00007 35354 44256	.99996 63139 93748
48	.00007 32310 87597	.99996 64607 60082
49	.00007 29279 17715	.99996 66069 18889
4.150	0.00007 26259 30302	0.99996 67524 72541

x	$\dfrac{1}{\sqrt{2\pi}}e^{-\frac{x^2}{2}}$	$\dfrac{1}{\sqrt{2\pi}}\displaystyle\int_{-x}^{x}e^{-\frac{\alpha^2}{2}}\,d\alpha$
4.150	0.00007 26259 30302	0.99996 67524 72541
51	.00007 23251 21065	.99996 68974 23396
52	.00007 20254 85723	.99996 70417 73808
53	.00007 17270 20012	.99996 71855 26119
54	.00007 14297 19680	.99996 73286 82665
4.155	0.00007 11335 80491	0.99996 74712 45772
56	.00007 08385 98221	.99996 76132 17758
57	.00007 05447 68662	.99996 77546 00933
58	.00007 02520 87618	.99996 78953 97598
59	.00006 99605 50910	.99996 80356 10046
4.160	0.00006 96701 54369	0.99996 81752 40562
61	.00006 93808 93843	.99996 83142 91421
62	.00006 90927 65193	.99996 84527 64892
63	.00006 88057 64293	.99996 85906 63234
64	.00006 85198 87031	.99996 87279 88698
4.165	0.00006 82351 29310	0.99996 88647 43528
66	.00006 79514 87045	.99996 90009 29959
67	.00006 76689 56166	.99996 91365 50217
68	.00006 73875 32614	.99996 92716 06522
69	.00006 71072 12348	.99996 94061 01083
4.170	0.00006 68279 91337	0.99996 95400 36104
71	.00006 65498 65564	.99996 96734 13779
72	.00006 62728 31026	.99996 98062 36294
73	.00006 59968 83734	.99996 99385 05828
74	.00006 57220 19711	.99997 00702 24551
4.175	0.00006 54482 34995	0.99997 02013 94626
76	.00006 51755 25635	.99997 03320 18208
77	.00006 49038 87695	.99997 04620 97443
78	.00006 46333 17251	.99997 05916 34470
79	.00006 43638 10394	.99997 07206 31421
4.180	0.00006 40953 63227	0.99997 08490 90418
81	.00006 38279 71865	.99997 09770 13578
82	.00006 35616 32438	.99997 11044 03007
83	.00006 32963 41088	.99997 12312 60806
84	.00006 30320 93969	.99997 13575 89068
4.185	0.00006 27688 87250	0.99997 14833 89876
86	.00006 25067 17112	.99997 16086 65308
87	.00006 22455 79748	.99997 17334 17433
88	.00006 19854 71365	.99997 18576 48313
89	.00006 17263 88182	.99997 19813 60002
4.190	0.00006 14683 26431	0.99997 21045 54546
91	.00006 12112 82357	.99997 22272 33986
92	.00006 09552 52217	.99997 23494 00352
93	.00006 07002 32281	.99997 24710 55668
94	.00006 04462 18832	.99997 25922 01952
4.195	0.00006 01932 08164	0.99997 27128 41212
96	.00005 99411 96586	.99997 28329 75450
97	.00005 96901 80418	.99997 29526 06662
98	.00005 94401 55992	.99997 30717 36833
99	.00005 91911 19652	.99997 31903 67945
4.200	0.00005 89430 67757	0.99997 33085 01968

x	$\dfrac{1}{\sqrt{2\pi}} e^{-\frac{x^2}{2}}$	$\dfrac{1}{\sqrt{2\pi}} \displaystyle\int_{-x}^{x} e^{-\frac{\alpha^2}{2}}\, d\alpha$
4.200	0.00005 89430 67757	0.99997 33085 01968
01	.00005 86959 96675	.99997 34261 40869
02	.00005 84499 02788	.99997 35432 86606
03	.00005 82047 82492	.99997 36599 41130
04	.00005 79606 32191	.99997 37761 06383
4.205	0.00005 77174 48304	0.99997 38917 84303
06	.00005 74752 27263	.99997 40069 76818
07	.00005 72339 65509	.99997 41216 85851
08	.00005 69936 59497	.99997 42359 13317
09	.00005 67543 05695	.99997 43496 61124
4.210	0.00005 65159 00580	0.99997 44629 31173
11	.00005 62784 40644	.99997 45757 25357
12	.00005 60419 22389	.99997 46880 45563
13	.00005 58063 42330	.99997 47998 93672
14	.00005 55716 96993	.99997 49112 71555
4.215	0.00005 53379 82916	0.99997 50221 81080
16	.00005 51051 96649	.99997 51326 24106
17	.00005 48733 34754	.99997 52426 02483
18	.00005 46423 93803	.99997 53521 18059
19	.00005 44123 70383	.99997 54611 72670
4.220	0.00005 41832 61090	0.99997 55697 68149
21	.00005 39550 62531	.99997 56779 06322
22	.00005 37277 71327	.99997 57855 89005
23	.00005 35013 84109	.99997 58928 18010
24	.00005 32758 97519	.99997 59995 95141
4.225	0.00005 30513 08213	0.99997 61059 22198
26	.00005 28276 12856	.99997 62118 00970
27	.00005 26048 08124	.99997 63172 33243
28	.00005 23828 90706	.99997 64222 20794
29	.00005 21618 57302	.99997 65267 65395
4.230	0.00005 19417 04622	0.99997 66308 68811
31	.00005 17224 29390	.99997 67345 32799
32	.00005 15040 28338	.99997 68377 59111
33	.00005 12864 98211	.99997 69405 49493
34	.00005 10698 35764	.99997 70429 05682
4.235	0.00005 08540 37765	0.99997 71448 29412
36	.00005 06391 00992	.99997 72463 22407
37	.00005 04250 22233	.99997 73473 86388
38	.00005 02117 98289	.99997 74480 23066
39	.00004 99994 25970	.99997 75482 34149
4.240	0.00004 97879 02098	0.99997 76480 21336
41	.00004 95772 23506	.99997 77473 86321
42	.00004 93673 87038	.99997 78463 30791
43	.00004 91583 89548	.99997 79448 56428
44	.00004 89502 27901	.99997 80429 64907
4.245	0.00004 87428 98974	0.99997 81406 57895
46	.00004 85363 99653	.99997 82379 37056
47	.00004 83307 26836	.99997 83348 04045
48	.00004 81258 77430	.99997 84312 60512
49	.00004 79218 48356	.99997 85273 08101
4.250	0.00004 77186 36541	0.99997 86229 48450

x	$\dfrac{1}{\sqrt{2\pi}}e^{-\frac{x^2}{2}}$	$\dfrac{1}{\sqrt{2\pi}}\displaystyle\int_{-x}^{x}e^{-\frac{\alpha^2}{2}}\,d\alpha$
4.250	0.00004 77186 36541	0.99997 86229 48450
51	.00004 75162 38927	.99997 87181 83190
52	.00004 73146 52463	.99997 88130 13947
53	.00004 71138 74111	.99997 89074 42339
54	.00004 69139 00842	.99997 90014 69980
4.255	0.00004 67147 29638	0.99997 90950 98477
56	.00004 65163 57492	.99997 91883 29431
57	.00004 63187 81406	.99997 92811 64438
58	.00004 61219 98393	.99997 93736 05085
59	.00004 59260 05477	.99997 94656 52958
4.260	0.00004 57307 99692	0.99997 95573 09632
61	.00004 55363 78080	.99997 96485 76679
62	.00004 53427 37697	.99997 97394 55365
63	.00004 51498 75607	.99997 98299 48149
64	.00004 49577 88884	.99997 99200 55685
4.265	0.00004 47664 74614	0.99998 00097 79820
66	.00004 45759 29889	.99998 00991 22096
67	.00004 43861 51816	.99998 01880 84050
68	.00004 41971 37510	.99998 02766 67212
69	.00004 40088 84094	.99998 03648 73107
4.270	0.00004 38213 88704	0.99998 04527 03254
71	.00004 36346 48484	.99998 05401 59166
72	.00004 34486 60590	.99998 06272 42350
73	.00004 32634 22185	.99998 07139 54308
74	.00004 30789 30443	.99998 08002 96536
4.275	0.00004 28951 82550	0.99998 08862 70525
76	.00004 27121 75699	.99998 09718 77760
77	.00004 25299 07093	.99998 10571 19720
78	.00004 23483 73946	.99998 11419 97879
79	.00004 21675 73482	.99998 12265 13705
4.280	0.00004 19875 02932	0.99998 13106 68660
81	.00004 18081 59539	.99998 13944 64201
82	.00004 16295 40555	.99998 14779 01781
83	.00004 14516 43242	.99998 15609 82844
84	.00004 12744 64871	.99998 16437 08833
4.285	0.00004 10980 02722	0.99998 17260 81181
86	.00004 09222 54086	.99998 18081 01320
87	.00004 07472 16262	.99998 18897 70672
88	.00004 05728 86558	.99998 19710 90657
89	.00004 03992 62294	.99998 20520 62688
4.290	0.00004 02263 40797	0.99998 21326 88174
91	.00004 00541 19404	.99998 22129 68518
92	.00003 98825 95462	.99998 22929 05117
93	.00003 97117 66325	.99998 23724 99363
94	.00003 95416 29359	.99998 24517 52644
4.295	0.00003 93721 81938	0.99998 25306 66340
96	.00003 92034 21445	.99998 26092 41829
97	.00003 90353 45273	.99998 26874 80482
98	.00003 88679 50824	.99998 27653 83665
99	.00003 87012 35507	.99998 28429 52738
4.300	0.00003 85351 96742	0.99998 29201 89058

x	$\dfrac{1}{\sqrt{2\pi}}\,e^{-\frac{x^2}{2}}$	$\dfrac{1}{\sqrt{2\pi}}\displaystyle\int_{-x}^{x} e^{-\frac{\alpha^2}{2}}\,d\alpha$
4.300	0.00003 85351 96742	0.99998 29201 89058
01	.00003 83698 31959	.99998 29970 93975
02	.00003 82051 38595	.99998 30736 68833
03	.00003 80411 14097	.99998 31499 14975
04	.00003 78777 55920	.99998 32258 33734
4.305	0.00003 77150 61530	0.99998 33014 26441
06	.00003 75530 28400	.99998 33766 94421
07	.00003 73916 54012	.99998 34516 38994
08	.00003 72309 35858	.99998 35262 61475
09	.00003 70708 71437	.99998 36005 63173
4.310	0.00003 69114 58259	0.99998 36745 45394
11	.00003 67526 93841	.99998 37482 09439
12	.00003 65945 75709	.99998 38215 56601
13	.00003 64371 01400	.99998 38945 88171
14	.00003 62802 68455	.99998 39673 05434
4.315	0.00003 61240 74429	0.99998 40397 09670
16	.00003 59685 16881	.99998 41118 02156
17	.00003 58135 93383	.99998 41835 84161
18	.00003 56593 01510	.99998 42550 56951
19	.00003 55056 38852	.99998 43262 21786
4.320	0.00003 53526 03002	0.99998 43970 79924
21	.00003 52001 91564	.99998 44676 32614
22	.00003 50484 02152	.99998 45378 81105
23	.00003 48972 32384.	.99998 46078 26636
24	.00003 47466 79892	.99998 46774 70446
4.325	0.00003 45967 42311	0.99998 47468 13766
26	.00003 44474 17287	.99998 48158 57823
27	.00003 42987 02476	.99998 48846 03842
28	.00003 41505 95538	.99998 49530 53039
29	.00003 40030 94146	.99998 50212 06628
4.330	0.00003 38561 95977	0.99998 50890 65817
31	.00003 37098 98719	.99998 51566 31812
32	.00003 35642 00067	.99998 52239 05811
33	.00003 34190 97725	.99998 52908 89010
34	.00003 32745 89405	.99998 53575 82598
4.335	0.00003 31306 72826	0.99998 54239 87762
36	.00003 29873 45716	.99998 54901 05682
37	.00003 28446 05810	.99998 55559 37536
38	.00003 27024 50854	.99998 56214 84496
39	.00003 25608 78599	.99998 56867 47728
4.340	0.00003 24198 86804	0.99998 57517 28397
41	.00003 22794 73239	.99998 58164 27661
42	.00003 21396 35677	.99998 58808 46674
43	.00003 20003 71905	.99998 59449 86586
44	.00003 18616 79712	.99998 60088 48543
4.345	0.00003 17235 56899	0.99998 60724 33685
46	.00003 15860 01273	.99998 61357 43148
47	.00003 14490 10649	.99998 61987 78066
48	.00003 13125 82850	.99998 62615 39566
49	.00003 11767 15707	.99998 63240 28771
4.350	0.00003 10414 07058	0.99998 63862 46801

x	$\dfrac{1}{\sqrt{2\pi}}e^{-\frac{x^2}{2}}$	$\dfrac{1}{\sqrt{2\pi}}\displaystyle\int_{-x}^{x}e^{-\frac{\alpha^2}{2}}\,d\alpha$
4.350	0.00003 10414 07058	0.99998 63862 46801
51	.00003 09066 54749	.99998 64481 94771
52	.00003 07724 56634	.99998 65098 73790
53	.00003 06388 10575	.99998 65712 84965
54	.00003 05057 14440	.99998 66324 29399
4.355	0.00003 03731 66107	0.99998 66933 08188
56	.00003 02411 63459	.99998 67539 22427
57	.00003 01097 04389	.99998 68142 73204
58	.00002 99787 86796	.99998 68743 61605
59	.00002 98484 08587	.99998 69341 88711
4.360	0.00002 97185 67676	0.99998 69937 55598
61	.00002 95892 61986	.99998 70530 63339
62	.00002 94604 89444	.99998 71121 13001
63	.00002 93322 47989	.99998 71709 05650
64	.00002 92045 35564	.99998 72294 42346
4.365	0.00002 90773 50121	0.99998 72877 24144
66	.00002 89506 89619	.99998 73457 52096
67	.00002 88245 52023	.99998 74035 27251
68	.00002 86989 35307	.99998 74610 50652
69	.00002 85738 37452	.99998 75183 23338
4.370	0.00002 84492 56446	0.99998 75753 46346
71	.00002 83251 90284	.99998 76321 20707
72	.00002 82016 36968	.99998 76886 47449
73	.00002 80785 94508	.99998 77449 27596
74	.00002 79560 60920	.99998 78009 62167
4.375	0.00002 78340 34229	0.99998 78567 52177
76	.00002 77125 12466	.99998 79122 98640
77	.00002 75914 93667	.99998 79676 02563
78	.00002 74709 75880	.99998 80226 64949
79	.00002 73509 57154	.99998 80774 86799
4.380	0.00002 72314 35551	0.99998 81320 69109
81	.00002 71124 09135	.99998 81864 12871
82	.00002 69938 75981	.99998 82405 19074
83	.00002 68758 34168	.99998 82943 88703
84	.00002 67582 81782	.99998 83480 22737
4.385	0.00002 66412 16919	0.99998 84014 22155
86	.00002 65246 37678	.99998 84545 87929
87	.00002 64085 42167	.99998 85075 21028
88	.00002 62929 28502	.99998 85602 22418
89	.00002 61777 94802	.99998 86126 93062
4.390	0.00002 60631 39196	0.99998 86649 33916
91	.00002 59489 59819	.99998 87169 45936
92	.00002 58352 54812	.99998 87687 30072
93	.00002 57220 22325	.99998 88202 87270
94	.00002 56092 60510	.99998 88716 18475
4.395	0.00002 54969 67532	0.99998 89227 24625
96	.00002 53851 41556	.99998 89736 06656
97	.00002 52737 80760	.99998 90242 65501
98	.00002 51628 83323	.99998 90747 02088
99	.00002 50524 47435	.99998 91249 17342
4.400	0.00002 49424 71290	0.99998 91749 12185

270

x	$\frac{1}{\sqrt{2\pi}}e^{-\frac{x^2}{2}}$	$\frac{1}{\sqrt{2\pi}}\int_{-x}^{x}e^{-\frac{\alpha^2}{2}}d\alpha$
4.400	0.00002 49424 71290	0.99998 91749 12185
01	.00002 48329 53089	.99998 92246 87533
02	.00002 47238 91041	.99998 92742 44301
03	.00002 46152 83358	.99998 93235 83400
04	.00002 45071 28263	.99998 93727 05736
4.405	0.00002 43994 23983	0.99998 94216 12213
06	.00002 42921 68750	.99998 94703 03732
07	.00002 41853 60806	.99998 95187 81187
08	.00002 40789 98397	.99998 95670 45472
09	.00002 39730 79775	.99998 96150 97476
4.410	0.00002 38676 03200	0.99998 96629 38086
11	.00002 37625 66938	.99998 97105 68182
12	.00002 36579 69260	.99998 97579 88646
13	.00002 35538 08444	.99998 98052 00351
14	.00002 34500 82776	.99998 98522 04170
4.415	0.00002 33467 90545	0.99998 98990 00971
16	.00002 32439 30048	.99998 99455 91620
17	.00002 31414 99590	.99998 99919 76978
18	.00002 30394 97478	.99999 00381 57903
19	.00002 29379 22030	.99999 00841 35252
4.420	0.00002 28367 71565	0.99999 01299 09875
21	.00002 27360 44413	.99999 01754 82620
22	.00002 26357 38906	.99999 02208 54334
23	.00002 25358 53385	.99999 02660 25856
24	.00002 24363 86197	.99999 03109 98026
4.425	0.00002 23373 35692	0.99999 03557 71679
26	.00002 22387 00230	.99999 04003 47646
27	.00002 21404 78173	.99999 04447 26755
28	.00002 20426 67894	.99999 04889 09833
29	.00002 19452 67766	.99999 05328 97700
4.430	0.00002 18482 76173	0.99999 05766 91176
31	.00002 17516 91503	.99999 06202 91076
32	.00002 16555 12149	.99999 06636 98212
33	.00002 15597 36511	.99999 07069 13394
34	.00002 14643 62994	.99999 07499 37427
4.435	0.00002 13693 90011	0.99999 07927 71113
36	.00002 12748 15978	.99999 08354 15253
37	.00002 11806 39319	.99999 08778 70642
38	.00002 10868 58462	.99999 09201 38074
39	.00002 09934 71843	.99999 09622 18338
4.440	0.00002 09004 77900	0.99999 10041 12223
41	.00002 08078 75082	.99999 10458 20511
42	.00002 07156 61839	.99999 10873 43983
43	.00002 06238 36629	.99999 11286 83417
44	.00002 05323 97915	.99999 11698 39587
4.445	0.00002 04413 44167	0.99999 12108 13265
46	.00002 03506 73858	.99999 12516 05219
47	.00002 02603 85469	.99999 12922 16215
48	.00002 01704 77486	.99999 13326 47015
49	.00002 00809 48400	.99999 13728 98378
4.450	0.00001 99917 96707	0.99999 14129 71060

X	$\frac{1}{\sqrt{2\pi}} e^{-\frac{x^2}{2}}$	$\frac{1}{\sqrt{2\pi}} \int_{-x}^{x} e^{-\frac{\alpha^2}{2}} d\alpha$
4.450	0.00001 99917 96707	0.99999 14129 71060
51	.00001 99030 20911	14528 65815
52	.00001 98146 19518	14925 83393
53	.00001 97265 91044	15321 24542
54	.00001 96389 34006	15714 90005
4.455	0.00001 95516 46929	0.99999 16106 80524
56	.00001 94647 28342	16496 96838
57	.00001 93781 76782	16885 39683
58	.00001 92919 90789	17272 09789
59	.00001 92061 68909	17657 07888
4.460	0.00001 91207 09693	0.99999 18040 34707
61	.00001 90356 11698	18421 90968
62	.00001 89508 73487	18801 77393
63	.00001 88664 93627	19179 94701
64	.00001 87824 70690	19556 43606
4.465	0.00001 86988 03255	0.99999 19931 24821
66	.00001 86154 89905	20304 39055
67	.00001 85325 29230	20675 87015
68	.00001 84499 19822	21045 69406
69	.00001 83676 60280	21413 86928
4.470	0.00001 82857 49210	0.99999 21780 40279
71	.00001 82041 85219	22145 30156
72	.00001 81229 66924	22508 57251
73	.00001 80420 92944	22870 22253
74	.00001 79615 61903	23230 25851
4.475	0.00001 78813 72432	0.99999 23588 68729
76	.00001 78015 23166	23945 51568
77	.00001 77220 12745	24300 75047
78	.00001 76428 39813	24654 39844
79	.00001 75640 03022	25006 46631
4.480	0.00001 74855 01027	0.99999 25356 96079
81	.00001 74073 32487	25705 88857
82	.00001 73294 96069	26053 25630
83	.00001 72519 90442	26399 07062
84	.00001 71748 14282	26743 33812
4.485	0.00001 70979 66268	0.99999 27086 06538
86	.00001 70214 45087	27427 25895
87	.00001 69452 49427	27766 92535
88	.00001 68693 77984	28105 07109
89	.00001 67938 29458	28441 70262
4.490	0.00001 67186 02552	0.99999 28776 82641
91	.00001 66436 95977	29110 44886
92	.00001 65691 08447	29442 57637
93	.00001 64948 38681	29773 21532
94	.00001 64208 85402	30102 37203
4.495	0.00001 63472 47340	0.99999 30430 05283
96	.00001 62739 23227	30756 26402
97	.00001 62009 11803	31081 01185
98	.00001 61282 11808	31404 30257
99	.00001 60558 21992	31726 14239
4.500	0.00001 59837 41107	0.99999 32046 53751

x	$\dfrac{1}{\sqrt{2\pi}}\,e^{-\frac{x^2}{2}}$	$\dfrac{1}{\sqrt{2\pi}}\displaystyle\int_{-x}^{x} e^{-\frac{\alpha^2}{2}}\,d\alpha$
4.500	0.00001 59837 41107	0.99999 32046 53751
01	.00001 59119 67909	32365 49408
02	.00001 58405 01160	32683 01826
03	.00001 57693 39626	32999 11616
04	.00001 56984 82078	33313 79388
4.505	0.00001 56279 27292	0.99999 33627 05747
06	.00001 55576 74047	33938 91298
07	.00001 54877 21129	34249 36643
08	.00001 54180 67326	34558 42382
09	.00001 53487 11433	34866 09111
4.510	0.00001 52796 52247	0.99999 35172 37425
11	.00001 52108 88571	35477 27917
12	.00001 51424 19213	35780 81176
13	.00001 50742 42985	36082 97789
14	.00001 50063 58702	36383 78342
4.515	0.00001 49387 65186	0.99999 36683 23418
16	.00001 48714 61262	36981 33596
17	.00001 48044 45759	37278 09455
18	.00001 47377 17511	37573 51571
19	.00001 46712 75357	37867 60516
4.520	0.00001 46051 18139	0.99999 38160 36862
21	.00001 45392 44705	38451 81178
22	.00001 44736 53906	38741 94029
23	.00001 44083 44599	39030 75981
24	.00001 43433 15642	39318 27595
4.525	0.00001 42785 65901	0.99999 39604 49430
26	.00001 42140 94244	39889 42044
27	.00001 41498 99545	40173 05991
28	.00001 40859 80680	40455 41826
29	.00001 40223 36532	40736 50097
4.530	0.00001 39589 65985	0.99999 41016 31354
31	.00001 38958 67931	41294 86143
32	.00001 38330 41262	41572 15007
33	.00001 37704 84878	41848 18488
34	.00001 37081 97681	42122 97126
4.535	0.00001 36461 78578	0.99999 42396 51458
36	.00001 35844 26479	42668 82018
37	.00001 35229 40300	42939 89341
38	.00001 34617 18959	43209 73956
39	.00001 34007 61380	43478 36392
4.540	0.00001 33400 66490	0.99999 43745 77177
41	.00001 32796 33221	44011 96833
42	.00001 32194 60507	44276 95883
43	.00001 31595 47289	44540 74848
44	.00001 30998 92509	44803 34245
4.545	0.00001 30404 95116	0.99999 45064 74589
46	.00001 29813 54060	45324 96396
47	.00001 29224 68297	45584 00176
48	.00001 28638 36787	45841 86439
49	.00001 28054 58493	46098 55692
4.550	0.00001 27473 32382	0.99999 46354 08441

x	$\dfrac{1}{\sqrt{2\pi}}e^{-\frac{x^2}{2}}$	$\dfrac{1}{\sqrt{2\pi}}\displaystyle\int_{-x}^{x}e^{-\frac{\alpha^2}{2}}\,d\alpha$
4.550	0.00001 27473 32382	0.99999 46354 08441
51	.00001 26894 57426	46608 45189
52	.00001 26318 32599	46861 66437
53	.00001 25744 56882	47113 72685
54	.00001 25173 29257	47364 64430
4.555	0.00001 24604 48710	0.99999 47614 42167
56	.00001 24038 14233	47863 06389
57	.00001 23474 24820	48110 57587
58	.00001 22912 79470	48356 96251
59	.00001 22353 77185	48602 22867
4.560	0.00001 21797 16970	0.99999 48846 37921
61	.00001 21242 97837	49089 41896
62	.00001 20691 18797	49331 35273
63	.00001 20141 78870	49572 18530
64	.00001 19594 77075	49811 92147
4.565	0.00001 19050 12439	0.99999 50050 56597
66	.00001 18507 83988	50288 12354
67	.00001 17967 90757	50524 59890
68	.00001 17430 31781	50759 99673
69	.00001 16895 06099	50994 32172
4.570	0.00001 16362 12756	0.99999 51227 57852
71	.00001 15831 50798	51459 77178
72	.00001 15303 19276	51690 90609
73	.00001 14777 17244	51920 98608
74	.00001 14253 43760	52150 01631
4.575	0.00001 13731 97887	0.99999 52378 00134
76	.00001 13212 78689	52604 94573
77	.00001 12695 85235	52830 85400
78	.00001 12181 16597	53055 73064
79	.00001 11668 71852	53279 58015
4.580	0.00001 11158 50078	0.99999 53502 40700
81	.00001 10650 50360	53724 21564
82	.00001 10144 71783	53945 01049
83	.00001 09641 13438	54164 79598
84	.00001 09139 74418	54383 57649
4.585	0.00001 08640 53820	0.99999 54601 35641
86	.00001 08143 50745	54818 14009
87	.00001 07648 64297	55033 93188
88	.00001 07155 93583	55248 73610
89	.00001 06665 37714	55462 55706
4.590	0.00001 06176 95805	0.99999 55675 39904
91	.00001 05690 66973	55887 26631
92	.00001 05206 50340	56098 16313
93	.00001 04724 45029	56308 09373
94	.00001 04244 50170	56517 06234
4.595	0.00001 03766 64892	0.99999 56725 07314
96	.00001 03290 88331	56932 13032
97	.00001 02817 19625	57138 23806
98	.00001 02345 57915	57343 40049
99	.00001 01876 02346	57547 62175
4.600	0.00001 01408 52065	0.99999 57750 90595

x	$\dfrac{1}{\sqrt{2\pi}}\,e^{-\frac{x^2}{2}}$	$\dfrac{1}{\sqrt{2\pi}}\displaystyle\int_{-x}^{x} e^{-\frac{\alpha^2}{2}}\,d\alpha$
4.600	0.00001 01408 52065	0.99999 57750 90595
01	.00001 00943 06225	57953 25719
02	.00001 00479 63978	58154 67956
03	.00001 00018 24484	58355 17710
04	.00000 99558 86903	58554 75388
4.605	0.00000 99101 50399	0.99999 58753 41392
06	.00000 98646 14141	58951 16123
07	.00000 98192 77298	59147 99982
08	.00000 97741 39045	59343 93365
09	.00000 97291 98559	59538 96670
4.610	0.00000 96844 55020	0.99999 59733 10290
11	.00000 96399 07612	59926 34620
12	.00000 95955 55521	60118 70051
13	.00000 95513 97938	60310 16972
14	.00000 95074 34056	60500 75772
4.615	0.00000 94636 63069	0.99999 60690 46837
16	.00000 94200 84179	60879 30552
17	.00000 93766 96587	61067 27301
18	.00000 93334 99499	61254 37466
19	.00000 92904 92122	61440 61426
4.620	0.00000 92476 73670	0.99999 61625 99560
21	.00000 92050 43356	61810 52246
22	.00000 91626 00399	61994 19858
23	.00000 91203 44019	62177 02772
24	.00000 90782 73440	62359 01358
4.625	0.00000 90363 87889	0.99999 62540 15989
26	.00000 89946 86596	62720 47033
27	.00000 89531 68793	62899 94858
28	.00000 89118 33718	63078 59830
29	.00000 88706 80607	63256 42314
4.630	0.00000 88297 08704	0.99999 63433 42673
31	.00000 87889 17254	63609 61269
32	.00000 87483 05503	63784 98462
33	.00000 87078 72702	63959 54610
34	.00000 86676 18106	64133 30071
4.635	0.00000 86275 40970	0.99999 64306 25201
36	.00000 85876 40555	64478 40353
37	.00000 85479 16121	64649 75880
38	.00000 85083 66936	64820 32134
39	.00000 84689 92266	64990 09465
4.640	0.00000 84297 91383	0.99999 65159 08219
41	.00000 83907 63561	65327 28745
42	.00000 83519 08075	65494 71388
43	.00000 83132 24206	65661 36492
44	.00000 82747 11236	65827 24399
4.645	0.00000 82363 68451	0.99999 65992 35451
46	.00000 81981 95137	66156 69986
47	.00000 81601 90585	66320 28344
48	.00000 81223 54090	66483 10860
49	.00000 80846 84948	66645 17872
4.650	0.00000 80471 82456	0.99999 66806 49711

x	$\frac{1}{\sqrt{2\pi}} e^{-\frac{x^2}{2}}$	$\frac{1}{\sqrt{2\pi}} \int_{-x}^{x} e^{-\frac{\alpha^2}{2}} d\alpha$
4.650	0.00000 80471 82456	0.99999 66806 49711
51	80098 45919	66967 06712
52	79726 74638	67126 89205
53	79356 67923	67285 97520
54	78988 25083	67444 31986
4.655	0.00000 78621 45431	0.99999 67601 92929
56	78256 28281	67758 80676
57	77892 72953	67914 95550
58	77530 78767	68070 37875
59	77170 45046	68225 07972
4.660	0.00000 76811 71117	0.99999 68379 06162
61	76454 56308	68532 32763
62	76098 99951	68684 88093
63	75745 01380	68836 72468
64	75392 59931	68987 86203
4.665	0.00000 75041 74943	0.99999 69138 29612
66	74692 45759	69288 03007
67	74344 71724	69437 06699
68	73998 52183	69585 40997
69	73653 86487	69733 06210
4.670	0.00000 73310 73989	0.99999 69880 02645
71	72969 14042	70026 30607
72	72629 06004	70171 90402
73	72290 49235	70316 82332
74	71953 43098	70461 06700
4.675	0.00000 71617 86956	0.99999 70604 63805
76	71283 80179	70747 53947
77	70951 22135	70889 77425
78	70620 12198	71031 34534
79	70290 49741	71172 25572
4.680	0.00000 69962 34143	0.99999 71312 50831
81	69635 64783	71452 10606
82	69310 41044	71591 05187
83	68986 62310	71729 34867
84	68664 27969	71866 99933
4.685	0.00000 68343 37410	0.99999 72004 00674
86	68023 90025	72140 37378
87	67705 85209	72276 10329
88	67389 22359	72411 19813
89	67074 00874	72545 66113
4.690	0.00000 66760 20155	0.99999 72679 49511
91	66447 79606	72812 70287
92	66136 78635	72945 28722
93	65827 16649	73077 25094
94	65518 93060	73208 59681
4.695	0.00000 65212 07282	0.99999 73339 32759
96	64906 58730	73469 44602
97	64602 46822	73598 95485
98	64299 70978	73727 85680
99	63998 30622	73856 15459
4.700	0.00000 63698 25179	0.99999 73983 85092

x	$\dfrac{1}{\sqrt{2\pi}}\,e^{-\frac{x^2}{2}}$	$\dfrac{1}{\sqrt{2\pi}}\displaystyle\int_{-x}^{x} e^{-\frac{\alpha^2}{2}}\,d\alpha$
4.700	0.00000 63698 25179	0.99999 73983 85092
01	63399 54075	74110 94949
02	63102 16741	74237 44998
03	62806 12608	74363 35805
04	62511 41110	74488 67537
4.705	0.00000 62218 01685	0.99999 74613 40457
06	61925 93770	74737 54831
07	61635 16806	74861 10920
08	61345 70237	74984 08985
09	61057 53508	75106 49287
4.710	0.00000 60770 66067	0.99999 75228 32085
11	60485 07363	75349 57637
12	60200 76848	75470 26200
13	59917 73977	75590 38030
14	59635 98206	75709 93381
4.715	0.00000 59355 48993	0.99999 75828 92507
16	59076 25800	75947 35661
17	58798 28088	76065 23094
18	58521 55324	76182 55056
19	58246 06973	76299 31798
4.720	0.00000 57971 82506	0.99999 76415 53567
21	57698 81394	76531 20610
22	57427 03111	76646 33174
23	57156 47132	76760 91504
24	56887 12935	76874 95844
4.725	0.00000 56618 99999	0.99999 76988 46437
26	56352 07807	77101 43525
27	56086 35843	77213 87348
28	55821 83593	77325 78148
29	55558 50545	77437 16162
4.730	0.00000 55296 36189	0.99999 77548 01629
31	55035 40018	77658 34786
32	54775 61525	77768 15868
33	54517 00208	77877 45110
34	54259 55564	77986 22746
4.735	0.00000 54003 27094	0.99999 78094 49010
36	53748 14301	78202 24132
37	53494 16688	78309 48344
38	53241 33763	78416 21875
39	52989 65033	78522 44955
4.740	0.00000 52739 10010	0.99999 78628 17811
41	52489 68204	78733 40670
42	52241 39132	78838 13759
43	51994 22308	78942 37302
44	51748 17251	79046 11523
4.745	0.00000 51503 23482	0.99999 79149 36645
46	51259 40522	79252 12890
47	51016 67896	79354 40480
48	50775 05130	79456 19635
49	50534 51751	79557 50574
4.750	0.00000 50295 07289	0.99999 79658 33515

x	$\frac{1}{\sqrt{2\pi}} e^{-\frac{x^2}{2}}$	$\frac{1}{\sqrt{2\pi}} \int_{-x}^{x} e^{-\frac{\alpha^2}{2}} d\alpha$
4.750	0.00000 50295 07289	0.99999 79658 33515
51	50056 71276	79758 68675
52	49819 43245	79858 56272
53	49583 22732	79957 96520
54	49348 09275	80056 89634
4.755	0.00000 49114 02413	0.99999 80155 35828
56	48881 01686	80253 35315
57	48649 06637	80350 88305
58	48418 16812	80447 95011
59	48188 31758	80544 55643
4.760	0.00000 47959 51022	0.99999 80640 70408
61	47731 74154	80736 39516
62	47505 00708	80831 63173
63	47279 30237	80926 41587
64	47054 62297	81020 74963
4.765	0.00000 46830 96445	0.99999 81114 63505
66	46608 32241	81208 07416
67	46386 69246	81301 06901
68	46166 07023	81393 62161
69	45946 45137	81485 73396
4.770	0.00000 45727 83154	0.99999 81577 40808
71	45510 20642	81668 64595
72	45293 57172	81759 44956
73	45077 92315	81849 82089
74	44863 25645	81939 76191
4.775	0.00000 44649 56736	0.99999 82029 27457
76	44436 85167	82118 36083
77	44225 10515	82207 02262
78	44014 32362	82295 26189
79	43804 50289	82383 08056
4.780	0.00000 43595 63880	0.99999 82470 48054
81	43387 72720	82557 46375
82	43180 76398	82644 03208
83	42974 74501	82730 18743
84	42769 66620	82815 93169
4.785	0.00000 42565 52349	0.99999 82901 26672
86	42362 31279	82986 19440
87	42160 03008	83070 71659
88	41958 67133	83154 83514
89	41758 23251	83238 55189
4.790	0.00000 41558 70965	0.99999 83321 86868
91	41360 09875	83404 78734
92	41162 39586	83487 30968
93	40965 59703	83569 43752
94	40769 69834	83651 17267
4.795	0.00000 40574 69587	0.99999 83732 51692
96	40380 58571	83813 47205
97	40187 36400	83894 03985
98	39995 02685	83974 22209
99	39803 57044	84054 02054
4.800	0.00000 39612 99091	0.99999 84133 43696

278

x	$\frac{1}{\sqrt{2\pi}} e^{-\frac{x^2}{2}}$	$\frac{1}{\sqrt{2\pi}} \int_{-x}^{x} e^{-\frac{\alpha^2}{2}} d\alpha$
4.800	0.00000 39612 99091	0.99999 84133 43696
01	39423 28445	84212 47309
02	39234 44727	84291 13068
03	39046 47556	84369 41146
04	38859 36557	84447 31715
4.805	0.00000 38673 11353	0.99999 84524 84949
06	38487 71570	84602 01018
07	38303 16837	84678 80092
08	38119 46781	84755 22342
09	37936 61034	84831 27935
4.810	0.00000 37754 59227	0.99999 84906 97042
11	37573 40994	84982 29828
12	37393 05970	85057 26461
13	37213 53792	85131 87107
14	37034 84098	85206 11931
4.815	0.00000 36856 96528	0.99999 85280 01098
16	36679 90721	85353 54772
17	36503 66322	85426 73115
18	36328 22974	85499 56291
19	36153 60322	85572 04461
4.820	0.00000 35979 78014	0.99999 85644 17786
21	35806 75697	85715 96427
22	35634 53022	85787 40542
23	35463 09640	85858 50291
24	35292 45204	85929 25833
4.825	0.00000 35122 59367	0.99999 85999 67325
26	34953 51786	86069 74923
27	34785 22118	86139 48784
28	34617 70020	86208 89063
29	34450 95153	86277 95915
4.830	0.00000 34284 97178	0.99999 86346 69495
31	34119 75758	86415 09955
32	33955 30557	86483 17449
33	33791 61240	86550 92128
34	33628 67474	86618 34144
4.835	0.00000 33466 48927	0.99999 86685 43648
36	33305 05268	86752 20790
37	33144 36170	86818 65719
38	32984 41304	86884 78584
39	32825 20344	86950 59533
4.840	0.00000 32666 72964	0.99999 87016 08714
41	32508 98842	87081 26274
42	32351 97654	87146 12358
43	32195 69081	87210 67113
44	32040 12802	87274 90683
4.845	0.00000 31885 28499	0.99999 87338 83212
46	31731 15855	87402 44845
47	31577 74555	87465 75723
48	31425 04284	87528 75990
49	31273 04729	87591 45787
4.850	0.00000 31121 75579	0.99999 87653 85256

x	$\frac{1}{\sqrt{2\pi}} e^{-\frac{x^2}{2}}$	$\frac{1}{\sqrt{2\pi}} \int_{-x}^{x} e^{-\frac{\alpha^2}{2}} d\alpha$
4.850	0.00000 31121 75579	0.99999 87653 85256
51	30971 16523	87715 94536
52	30821 27252	87777 73769
53	30672 07458	87839 23092
54	30523 56834	87900 42645
4.855	0.00000 30375 75076	0.99999 87961 32565
56	30228 61879	88021 92991
57	30082 16941	88082 24058
58	29936 39960	88142 25904
59	29791 30635	88201 98663
4.860	0.00000 29646 88669	0.99999 88261 42471
61	29503 13762	88320 57462
62	29360 05620	88379 43771
63	29217 63945	88438 01529
64	29075 88446	88496 30871
4.865	0.00000 28934 78828	0.99999 88554 31927
66	28794 34800	88612 04830
67	28654 56072	88669 49710
68	28515 42354	88726 66697
69	28376 93359	88783 55922
4.870	0.00000 28239 08801	0.99999 88840 17514
71	28101 88393	88896 51600
72	27965 31851	88952 58310
73	27829 38892	89008 37770
74	27694 09235	89063 90107
4.875	0.00000 27559 42598	0.99999 89119 15449
76	27425 38701	89174 13920
77	27291 97268	89228 85645
78	27159 18019	89283 30750
79	27027 00680	89337 49359
4.880	0.00000 26895 44974	0.99999 89391 41594
81	26764 50629	89445 07579
82	26634 17373	89498 47437
83	26504 44932	89551 61289
84	26375 33037	89604 49257
4.885	0.00000 26246 81420	0.99999 89657 11462
86	26118 89811	89709 48023
87	25991 57944	89761 59061
88	25864 85553	89813 44694
89	25738 72373	89865 05043
4.890	0.00000 25613 18141	0.99999 89916 40223
91	25488 22594	89967 50354
92	25363 85471	90018 35553
93	25240 06512	90068 95935
94	25116 85457	90119 31617
4.895	0.00000 24994 22049	0.99999 90169 42715
96	24872 16030	90219 29344
97	24750 67145	90268 91617
98	24629 75138	90318 29650
99	24509 39756	90367 43556
4.900	0.00000 24389 60746	0.99999 90416 33447

x	$\dfrac{1}{\sqrt{2\pi}}e^{-\frac{x^2}{2}}$	$\dfrac{1}{\sqrt{2\pi}}\displaystyle\int_{-x}^{x}e^{-\frac{\alpha^2}{2}}\,d\alpha$
4.900	0.00000 24389 60746	0.99999 90416 33447
01	24270 37857	90464 99436
02	24151 70837	90513 41635
03	24033 59439	90561 60157
04	23916 03412	90609 55110
4.905	0.00000 23799 02510	0.99999 90657 26607
06	23682 56487	90704 74757
07	23566 65096	90751 99669
08	23451 28094	90799 01453
09	23336 45238	90845 80218
4.910	0.00000 23222 16285	0.99999 90892 36070
11	23108 40994	90938 69119
12	22995 19124	90984 79470
13	22882 50438	91030 67231
14	22770 34696	91076 32507
4.915	0.00000 22658 71662	0.99999 91121 75405
16	22547 61099	91166 96029
17	22437 02773	91211 94484
18	22326 96449	91256 70874
19	22217 41893	91301 25304
4.920	0.00000 22108 38875	0.99999 91345 57876
21	21999 87162	91389 68694
22	21891 86524	91433 57859
23	21784 36733	91477 25474
24	21677 37560	91520 71640
4.925	0.00000 21570 88778	0.99999 91563 96458
26	21464 90161	91607 00028
27	21359 41482	91649 82452
28	21254 42519	91692 43827
29	21149 93046	91734 84255
4.930	0.00000 21045 92843	0.99999 91777 03832
31	20942 41687	91819 02659
32	20839 39358	91860 80832
33	20736 85636	91902 38449
34	20634 80303	91943 75606
4.935	0.00000 20533 23140	0.99999 91984 92402
36	20432 13932	92025 88931
37	20331 52461	92066 65289
38	20231 38513	92107 21572
39	20131 71873	92147 57875
4.940	0.00000 20032 52330	0.99999 92187 74291
41	19933 79670	92227 70916
42	19835 53682	92267 47841
43	19737 74155	92307 05161
44	19640 40881	92346 42969
4.945	0.00000 19543 53650	0.99999 92385 61355
46	19447 12254	92424 60414
47	19351 16487	92463 40235
48	19255 66143	92502 00910
49	19160 61016	92540 42530
4.950	0.00000 19066 00903	0.99999 92578 65184

x	$\dfrac{1}{\sqrt{2\pi}}\,e^{-\frac{x^2}{2}}$	$\dfrac{1}{\sqrt{2\pi}}\displaystyle\int_{-x}^{x} e^{-\frac{\alpha^2}{2}}\,d\alpha$
4.950	0.00000 19066 00903	0.99999 92578 65184
51	18971 85600	92616 68963
52	18878 14904	92654 53956
53	18784 88614	92692 20252
54	18692 06529	92729 67940
4.955	0.00000 18599 68449	0.99999 92766 97108
56	18507 74175	92804 07843
57	18416 23510	92841 00234
58	18325 16254	92877 74366
59	18234 52213	92914 30327
4.960	0.00000 18144 31190	0.99999 92950 68204
61	18054 52991	92986 88081
62	17965 17421	93022 90044
63	17876 24288	93058 74179
64	17787 73398	93094 40569
4.965	0.00000 17699 64562	0.99999 93129 89300
66	17611 97587	93165 20455
67	17524 72284	93200 34118
68	17437 88464	93235 30372
69	17351 45939	93270 09300
4.970	0.00000 17265 44522	0.99999 93304 70983
71	17179 84025	93339 15505
72	17094 64263	93373 42947
73	17009 85051	93407 53389
74	16925 46204	93441 46914
4.975	0.00000 16841 47540	0.99999 93475 23601
76	16757 88875	93508 83531
77	16674 70029	93542 26783
78	16591 90818	93575 53437
79	16509 51065	93608 63573
4.980	0.00000 16427 50588	0.99999 93641 57268
81	16345 89209	93674 34601
82	16264 66751	93706 95650
83	16183 83036	93739 40494
84	16103 37887	93771 69208
4.985	0.00000 16023 31129	0.99999 93803 81871
86	15943 62588	93835 78558
87	15864 32088	93867 59347
88	15785 39456	93899 24312
89	15706 84521	93930 73530
4.990	0.00000 15628 67109	0.99999 93962 07075
91	15550 87050	93993 25023
92	15473 44173	94024 27448
93	15396 38309	94055 14424
94	15319 69289	94085 86026
4.995	0.00000 15243 36944	0.99999 94116 42326
96	15167 41107	94146 83398
97	15091 81611	94177 09315
98	15016 58291	94207 20148
99	14941 70980	94237 15972
5.000	0.00000 14867 19515	0.99999 94266 96856

x	$\dfrac{1}{\sqrt{2\pi}}\,e^{-\frac{x^2}{2}}$	$\dfrac{1}{\sqrt{2\pi}}\displaystyle\int_{-x}^{x} e^{-\frac{\alpha^2}{2}}\,d\alpha$
5.000	0.00000 14867 19515	0.99999 94266 96856
01	14793 03731	94296 62874
02	14719 23465	94326 14095
03	14645 78554	94355 50591
04	14572 68838	94384 72433
5.005	0.00000 14499 94154	0.99999 94413 79690
06	14427 54343	94442 72432
07	14355 49244	94471 50730
08	14283 78700	94500 14652
09	14212 42551	94528 64268
5.010	0.00000 14141 40640	0.99999 94556 99645
11	14070 72809	94585 20853
12	14000 38904	94613 27959
13	13930 38768	94641 21031
14	13860 72246	94669 00137
5.015	0.00000 13791 39184	0.99999 94696 65343
16	13722 39429	94724 16716
17	13653 72827	94751 54322
18	13585 39227	94778 78229
19	13517 38477	94805 88501
5.020	0.00000 13449 70426	0.99999 94832 85205
21	13382 34924	94859 68405
22	13315 31821	94886 38166
23	13248 60969	94912 94553
24	13182 22219	94939 37631
5.025	0.00000 13116 15423	0.99999 94965 67464
26	13050 40435	94991 84114
27	12984 97108	95017 87646
28	12919 85296	95043 78124
29	12855 04855	95069 55609
5.030	0.00000 12790 55640	0.99999 95095 20164
31	12726 37508	95120 71852
32	12662 50314	95146 10735
33	12598 93917	95171 36874
34	12535 68175	95196 50331
5.035	0.00000 12472 72946	0.99999 95221 51167
36	12410 08090	95246 39443
37	12347 73466	95271 15219
38	12285 68935	95295 78557
39	12223 94359	95320 29515
5.040	0.00000 12162 49599	0.99999 95344 68154
41	12101 34517	95368 94533
42	12040 48977	95393 08712
43	11979 92842	95417 10749
44	11919 65976	95441 00703
5.045	0.00000 11859 68244	0.99999 95464 78632
46	11799 99512	95488 44595
47	11740 59645	95511 98649
48	11681 48509	95535 40853
49	11622 65973	95558 71262
5.050	0.00000 11564 11904	0.99999 95581 89935

x	$\dfrac{1}{\sqrt{2\pi}}e^{-\frac{x^2}{2}}$	$\dfrac{1}{\sqrt{2\pi}}\displaystyle\int_{-x}^{x}e^{-\frac{\alpha^2}{2}}\,d\alpha$
5.050	0.00000 11564 11904	0.99999 95581 89935
51	11505 86169	95604 96929
52	11447 88638	95627 92299
53	11390 19181	95650 76102
54	11332 77667	95673 48394
5.055	0.00000 11275 63968	0.99999 95696 09231
56	11218 77953	95718 58669
57	11162 19495	95740 96761
58	11105 88466	95763 23565
59	11049 84740	95785 39134
5.060	0.00000 10994 08189	0.99999 95807 43522
61	10938 58687	95829 36784
62	10883 36109	95851 18975
63	10828 40331	95872 90147
64	10773 71227	95894 50354
5.065	0.00000 10719 28674	0.99999 95915 99649
66	10665 12548	95937 38086
67	10611 22728	95958 65717
68	10557 59090	95979 82594
69	10504 21513	96000 88771
5.070	0.00000 10451 09876	0.99999 96021 84298
71	10398 24059	96042 69227
72	10345 63941	96063 43611
73	10293 29403	96084 07500
74	10241 20325	96104 60946
5.075	0.00000 10189 36590	0.99999 96125 03998
76	10137 78080	96145 36709
77	10086 44676	96165 59128
78	10035 36263	96185 71304
79	09984 52723	96205 73289
5.080	0.00000 09933 93941	0.99999 96225 65132
81	09883 59802	96245 46881
82	09833 50191	96265 18587
83	09783 64993	96284 80298
84	09734 04094	96304 32063
5.085	0.00000 09684 67382	0.99999 96323 73931
86	09635 54744	96343 05949
87	09586 66066	96362 28166
88	09538 01238	96381 40629
89	09489 60148	96400 43387
5.090	0.00000 09441 42685	0.99999 96419 36486
91	09393 48738	96438 19973
92	09345 78199	96456 93896
93	09298 30958	96475 58301
94	09251 06905	96494 13235
5.095	0.00000 09204 05933	0.99999 96512 58744
96	09157 27933	96530 94874
97	09110 72798	96549 21671
98	09064 40421	96567 39181
99	09018 30696	96585 47448
5.100	0.00000 08972 43516	0.99999 96603 46519

x	$\dfrac{1}{\sqrt{2\pi}}\,e^{-\frac{x^2}{2}}$	$\dfrac{1}{\sqrt{2\pi}}\displaystyle\int_{-x}^{x} e^{-\frac{\alpha^2}{2}}\,d\alpha$
5.100	0.00000 08972 43516	0.99999 96603 46519
01	08926 78777	96621 36437
02	08881 36372	96639 17249
03	08836 16198	96656 88997
04	08791 18151	96674 51728
5.105	0.00000 08746 42126	0.99999 96692 05485
06	08701 88020	96709 50311
07	08657 55732	96726 86251
08	08613 45157	96744 13349
09	08569 56196	96761 31646
5.110	0.00000 08525 88745	0.99999 96778 41188
11	08482 42705	96795 42016
12	08439 17975	96812 34173
13	08396 14455	96829 17702
14	08353 32044	96845 92645
5.115	0.00000 08310 70645	0.99999 96862 59044
16	08268 30159	96879 16941
17	08226 10487	96895 66378
18	08184 11531	96912 07397
19	08142 33194	96928 40038
5.120	0.00000 08100 75379	0.99999 96944 64343
21	08059 37990	96960 80353
22	08018 20930	96976 88109
23	07977 24104	96992 87651
24	07936 47417	97008 79019
5.125	0.00000 07895 90774	0.99999 97024 62254
26	07855 54080	97040 37395
27	07815 37242	97056 04483
28	07775 40166	97071 63557
29	07735 62759	97087 14657
5.130	0.00000 07696 04929	0.99999 97102 57821
31	07656 66582	97117 93090
32	07617 47628	97133 20501
33	07578 47974	97148 40093
34	07539 67530	97163 51905
5.135	0.00000 07501 06205	0.99999 97178 55976
36	07462 63910	97193 52343
37	07424 40553	97208 41044
38	07386 36046	97223 22118
39	07348 50299	97237 95601
5.140	0.00000 07310 83225	0.99999 97252 61531
41	07273 34734	97267 19946
42	07236 04740	97281 70883
43	07198 93154	97296 14377
44	07161 99890	97310 50467
5.145	0.00000 07125 24861	0.99999 97324 79189
46	07088 67980	97339 00579
47	07052 29163	97353 14673
48	07016 08323	97367 21508
49	06980 05375	97381 21118
5.150	0.00000 06944 20235	0.99999 97395 13541

x	$\frac{1}{\sqrt{2\pi}} e^{-\frac{x^2}{2}}$	$\frac{1}{\sqrt{2\pi}} \int_{-x}^{x} e^{-\frac{\alpha^2}{2}} d\alpha$
5.150	0.00000 06944 20235	0.99999 97395 13541
51	06908 52819	97408 98811
52	06873 03042	97422 76964
53	06837 70821	97436 48035
54	06802 56072	97450 12059
5.155	0.00000 06767 58713	0.99999 97463 69071
56	06732 78662	97477 19105
57	06698 15837	97490 62197
58	06663 70155	97503 98380
59	06629 41535	97517 27689
5.160	0.00000 06595 29897	0.99999 97530 50158
61	06561 35160	97543 65820
62	06527 57243	97556 74709
63	06493 96067	97569 76860
64	06460 51553	97582 72305
5.165	0.00000 06427 23621	0.99999 97595 61077
66	06394 12192	97608 43210
67	06361 17188	97621 18737
68	06328 38531	97633 87690
69	06295 76143	97646 50102
5.170	0.00000 06263 29947	0.99999 97659 06005
71	06230 99866	97671 55432
72	06198 85822	97683 98415
73	06166 87741	97696 34986
74	06135 05546	97708 65177
5.175	0.00000 06103 39161	0.99999 97720 89019
76	06071 88510	97733 06544
77	06040 53520	97745 17784
78	06009 34116	97757 22769
79	05978 30222	97769 21530
5.180	0.00000 05947 41765	0.99999 97781 14100
81	05916 68673	97793 00508
82	05886 10870	97804 80785
83	05855 68285	97816 54961
84	05825 40845	97828 23068
5.185	0.00000 05795 28478	0.99999 97839 85135
86	05765 31111	97851 41192
87	05735 48673	97862 91269
88	05705 81093	97874 35396
89	05676 28300	97885 73603
5.190	0.00000 05646 90223	0.99999 97897 05919
91	05617 66792	97908 32374
92	05588 57937	97919 52996
93	05559 63588	97930 67815
94	05530 83676	97941 76860
5.195	0.00000 05502 18132	0.99999 97952 80160
96	05473 66887	97963 77742
97	05445 29873	97974 69637
98	05417 07021	97985 55871
99	05388 98264	97996 36474
5.200	0.00000 05361 03534	0.99999 98007 11474

x	$\dfrac{1}{\sqrt{2\pi}}e^{-\frac{x^2}{2}}$	$\dfrac{1}{\sqrt{2\pi}}\displaystyle\int_{-x}^{x}e^{-\frac{\alpha^2}{2}}\,d\alpha$
5.200	0.00000 05361 03534	0.99999 98007 11474
01	05333 22765	98017 80898
02	05305 55889	98028 44774
03	05278 02839	98039 03130
04	05250 63550	98049 55995
5.205	0.00000 05223 37956	0.99999 98060 03394
06	05196 25990	98070 45355
07	05169 27588	98080 81907
08	05142 42685	98091 13075
09	05115 71215	98101 38886
5.210	0.00000 05089 13115	0.99999 98111 59369
11	05062 68319	98121 74548
12	05036 36765	98131 84451
13	05010 18388	98141 89104
14	04984 13126	98151 88533
5.215	0.00000 04958 20915	0.99999 98161 82765
16	04932 41693	98171 71825
17	04906 75397	98181 55740
18	04881 21965	98191 34535
19	04855 81336	98201 08237
5.220	0.00000 04830 53447	0.99999 98210 76869
21	04805 38237	98220 40459
22	04780 35646	98229 99031
23	04755 45613	98239 52610
24	04730 68077	98249 01221
5.225	0.00000 04706 02978	0.99999 98258 44890
26	04681 50256	98267 83642
27	04657 09851	98277 17500
28	04632 81705	98286 46489
29	04608 65758	98295 70635
5.230	0.00000 04584 61952	0.99999 98304 89960
31	04560 70227	98314 04490
32	04536 90526	98323 14249
33	04513 22790	98332 19261
34	04489 66962	98341 19548
5.235	0.00000 04466 22985	0.99999 98350 15136
36	04442 90800	98359 06048
37	04419 70352	98367 92307
38	04396 61584	98376 73937
39	04373 64439	98385 50961
5.240	0.00000 04350 78861	0.99999 98394 23403
41	04328 04794	93402 91285
42	04305 42182	98411 54630
43	04282 90971	98420 13461
44	04260 51105	98428 67801
5.245	0.00000 04238 22529	0.99999 98437 17673
46	04216 05188	98445 63099
47	04193 99029	98454 04101
48	04172 03997	98462 40702
49	04150 20038	98470 72924
5.250	0.00000 04128 47099	0.99999 98479 00790

x	$\frac{1}{\sqrt{2\pi}} e^{-\frac{x^2}{2}}$	$\frac{1}{\sqrt{2\pi}} \int_{-x}^{x} e^{-\frac{\alpha^2}{2}} d\alpha$
5.250	0.00000 04128 47099	0.99999 98479 00790
51	04106 85126	98487 24320
52	04085 34066	98495 43537
53	04063 93866	98503 58464
54	04042 64475	98511 69120
5.255	0.00000 04021 45838	0.99999 98519 75529
56	04000 37904	98527 77711
57	03979 40622	98535 75687
58	03958 53940	98543 69480
59	03937 77805	98551 59110
5.260	0.00000 03917 12168	0.99999 98559 44598
61	03896 56976	98567 25966
62	03876 12180	98575 03233
63	03855 77729	98582 76421
64	03835 53572	98590 45551
5.265	0.00000 03815 39660	0.99999 98598 10643
66	03795 35943	98605 71716
67	03775 42371	98613 28793
68	03755 58895	98620 81893
69	03735 85466	98628 31035
5.270	0.00000 03716 22035	0.99999 98635 76241
71	03696 68554	98643 17530
72	03677 24973	98650 54922
73	03657 91246	98657 88437
74	03638 67323	98665 18094
5.275	0.00000 03619 53157	0.99999 98672 43912
76	03600 48701	98679 65913
77	03581 53908	98686 84114
78	03562 68729	98693 98535
79	03543 93119	98701 09195
5.280	0.00000 03525 27031	0.99999 98708 16113
81	03506 70419	98715 19309
82	03488 23235	98722 18801
83	03469 85435	98729 14609
84	03451 56972	98736 06749
5.285	0.00000 03433 37801	0.99999 98742 95243
86	03415 27876	98749 80107
87	03397 27153	98756 61360
88	03379 35586	98763 39021
89	03361 53131	98770 13109
5.290	0.00000 03343 79744	0.99999 98776 83640
91	03326 15379	98783 50634
92	03308 59993	98790 14108
93	03291 13542	98796 74080
94	03273 75982	98803 30568
5.295	0.00000 03256 47271	0.99999 98809 83589
96	03239 27363	98816 33163
97	03222 16218	98822 79305
98	03205 13791	98829 22033
99	03188 20039	98835 61366
5.300	0.00000 03171 34922	0.99999 98841 97319

x	$\frac{1}{\sqrt{2\pi}} e^{-\frac{x^2}{2}}$	$\frac{1}{\sqrt{2\pi}} \int_{-x}^{x} e^{-\frac{\alpha^2}{2}} d\alpha$
5.300	0.00000 03171 34922	0.99999 98841 97319
01	03154 58395	98848 29911
02	03137 90418	98854 59158
03	03121 30948	98860 85078
04	03104 79943	98867 07688
5.305	0.00000 03088 37363	0.99999 98873 27004
06	03072 03165	98879 43043
07	03055 77309	98885 55822
08	03039 59754	98891 65358
09	03023 50459	98897 71667
5.310	0.00000 03007 49383	0.99999 98903 74765
11	02991 56487	98909 74670
12	02975 71730	98915 71396
13	02959 95071	98921 64962
14	02944 26473	98927 55382
5.315	0.00000 02928 65894	0.99999 98933 42673
16	02913 13295	98939 26851
17	02897 68638	98945 07932
18	02882 31882	98950 85931
19	02867 02991	98956 60864
5.320	0.00000 02851 81923	0.99999 98962 32748
21	02836 68642	98968 01597
22	02821 63109	98973 67428
23	02806 65285	98979 30255
24	02791 75134	98984 90094
5.325	0.00000 02776 92616	0.99999 98990 46960
26	02762 17695	98996 00869
27	02747 50333	99001 51836
28	02732 90492	99006 99876
29	02718 38137	99012 45003
5.330	0.00000 02703 93229	0.99999 99017 87233
31	02689 55733	99023 26581
32	02675 25611	99028 63061
33	02661 02828	99033 96688
34	02646 87346	99039 27477
5.335	0.00000 02632 79131	0.99999 99044 55443
36	02618 78146	99049 80599
37	02604 84356	99055 02960
38	02590 97724	99060 22541
39	02577 18216	99065 39356
5.340	0.00000 02563 45797	0.99999 99070 53418
41	02549 80432	99075 64744
42	02536 22085	99080 73345
43	02522 70722	99085 79237
44	02509 26308	99090 82432
5.345	0.00000 02495 88810	0.99999 99095 82946
46	02482 58193	99100 80792
47	02469 34422	99105 75984
48	02456 17465	99110 68534
49	02443 07286	99115 58458
5.350	0.00000 02430 03854	0.99999 99120 45768

x	$\frac{1}{\sqrt{2\pi}}e^{-\frac{x^2}{2}}$	$\frac{1}{\sqrt{2\pi}}\int_{-x}^{x}e^{-\frac{\alpha^2}{2}}d\alpha$
5.350	0.00000 02430 03854	0.99999 99120 45768
51	02417 07134	99125 30478
52	02404 17093	99130 12601
53	02391 33699	99134 92151
54	02378 56917	99139 69140
5.355	0.00000 02365 86716	0.99999 99144 43583
56	02353 23062	99149 15492
57	02340 65924	99153 84879
58	02328 15269	99158 51760
59	02315 71065	99163 16145
5.360	0.00000 02303 33280	0.99999 99167 78048
61	02291 01882	99172 37482
62	02278 76839	99176 94460
63	02266 58120	99181 48994
64	02254 45694	99186 01097
5.365	0.00000 02242 39528	0.99999 99190 50781
66	02230 39593	99194 98059
67	02218 45857	99199 42943
68	02206 58290	99203 85446
69	02194 76860	99208 25580
5.370	0.00000 02183 01537	0.99999 99212 63358
71	02171 32291	99216 98791
72	02159 69092	99221 31891
73	02148 11909	99225 62671
74	02136 60713	99229 91143
5.375	0.00000 02125 15474	0.99999 99234 17318
76	02113 76162	99238 41209
77	02102 42748	99242 62826
78	02091 15202	99246 82183
79	02079 93495	99250 99291
5.380	0.00000 02068 77598	0.99999 99255 14161
81	02057 67482	99259 26805
82	02046 63119	99263 37235
83	02035 64479	99267 45462
84	02024 71534	99271 51497
5.385	0.00000 02013 84256	0.99999 99275 55352
86	02003 02616	99279 57038
87	01992 26587	99283 56566
88	01981 56140	99287 53948
89	01970 91247	99291 49194
5.390	0.00000 01960 31881	0.99999 99295 42316
91	01949 78014	99299 33325
92	01939 29619	99303 22232
93	01928 86668	99307 09047
94	01918 49134	99310 93782
5.395	0.00000 01908 16990	0.99999 99314 76447
96	01897 90210	99318 57054
97	01887 68766	99322 35612
98	01877 52631	99326 12132
99	01867 41779	99329 86626
5.400	0.00000 01857 36184	0.99999 99333 59103

x	$\dfrac{1}{\sqrt{2\pi}}e^{-\frac{x^2}{2}}$	$\dfrac{1}{\sqrt{2\pi}}\displaystyle\int_{-x}^{x}e^{-\frac{\alpha^2}{2}}\,d\alpha$
5.400	0.00000 01857 36184	0.99999 99333 59103
01	01847 35820	99337 29574
02	01837 40659	99340 98050
03	01827 50677	99344 64540
04	01817 65847	99348 29056
5.405	0.00000 01807 86143	0.99999 99351 91607
06	01798 11540	99355 52204
07	01788 42012	99359 10857
08	01778 77534	99362 67575
09	01769 18081	99366 22370
5.410	0.00000 01759 63626	0.99999 99369 75251
11	01750 14146	99373 26228
12	01740 69615	99376 75311
13	01731 30008	99380 22510
14	01721 95301	99383 67834
5.415	0.00000 01712 65469	0.99999 99387 11294
16	01703 40488	99390 52899
17	01694 20333	99393 92659
18	01685 04980	99397 30584
19	01675 94405	99400 66682
5.420	0.00000 01666 88584	0.99999 99404 00965
21	01657 87493	99407 33440
22	01648 91108	99410 64118
23	01639 99406	99413 93007
24	01631 12362	99417 20118
5.425	0.00000 01622 29955	0.99999 99420 45460
26	01613 52160	99423 69041
27	01604 78954	99426 90872
28	01596 10313	99430 10960
29	01587 46216	99433 29316
5.430	0.00000 01578 86639	0.99999 99436 45948
31	01570 31560	99439 60865
32	01561 80955	99442 74077
33	01553 34803	99445 85592
34	01544 93080	99448 95419
5.435	0.00000 01536 55764	0.99999 99452 03568
36	01528 22834	99455 10045
37	01519 94267	99458 14862
38	01511 70041	99461 18025
39	01503 50134	99464 19545
5.440	0.00000 01495 34525	0.99999 99467 19429
41	01487 23192	99470 17686
42	01479 16112	99473 14324
43	01471 13266	99476 09353
44	01463 14630	99479 02780
5.445	0.00000 01455 20185	0.99999 99481 94614
46	01447 29908	99484 84864
47	01439 43780	99487 73537
48	01431 61778	99490 60642
49	01423 83882	99493 46187
5.450	0.00000 01416 10071	0.99999 99496 30180

x	$\dfrac{1}{\sqrt{2\pi}}\,e^{-\frac{x^2}{2}}$	$\dfrac{1}{\sqrt{2\pi}}\displaystyle\int_{-x}^{x}e^{-\frac{\alpha^2}{2}}\,d\alpha$
5.450	0.00000 01416 10071	0.99999 99496 30180
51	01408 40325	99499 12630
52	01400 74623	99501 93544
53	01393 12945	99504 72931
54	01385 55269	99507 50798
5.455	0.00000 01378 01577	0.99999 99510 27155
56	01370 51848	99513 02007
57	01363 06061	99515 75365
58	01355 64197	99518 47234
59	01348 26235	99521 17624
5.460	0.00000 01340 92157	0.99999 99523 86542
61	01333 61942	99526 53995
62	01326 35572	99529 19992
63	01319 13025	99531 84540
64	01311 94283	99534 47647
5.465	0.00000 01304 79327	0.99999 99537 09320
66	01297 68138	99539 69566
67	01290 60696	99542 28395
68	01283 56982	99544 85812
69	01276 56978	99547 41825
5.470	0.00000 01269 60664	0.99999 99549 96442
71	01262 68022	99552 49670
72	01255 79033	99555 01517
73	01248 93679	99557 51989
74	01242 11940	99560 01094
5.475	0.00000 01235 33800	0.99999 99562 48839
76	01228 59239	99564 95231
77	01221 88240	99567 40278
78	01215 20783	99569 83987
79	01208 56852	99572 26364
5.480	0.00000 01201 96428	0.99999 99574 67416
81	01195 39493	99577 07152
82	01188 86030	99579 45577
83	01182 36021	99581 82698
84	01175 89448	99584 18523
5.485	0.00000 01169 46294	0.99999 99586 53058
86	01163 06541	99588 86311
87	01156 70173	99591 18287
88	01150 37171	99593 48993
89	01144 07519	99595 78438
5.490	0.00000 01137 81200	0.99999 99598 06626
91	01131 58196	99600 33565
92	01125 38491	99602 59261
93	01119 22068	99604 83721
94	01113 08909	99607 06951
5.495	0.00000 01106 99000	0.99999 99609 28959
96	01100 92322	99611 49749
97	01094 88859	99613 69330
98	01088 88596	99615 87707
99	01082 91515	99618 04886
5.500	0.00000 01076 97600	0.99999 99620 20875

x	$\dfrac{1}{\sqrt{2\pi}}\,e^{-\frac{x^2}{2}}$	$\dfrac{1}{\sqrt{2\pi}}\displaystyle\int_{-x}^{x} e^{-\frac{\alpha^2}{2}}\,d\alpha$
5.500	0.00000 01076 97600	0.99999 99620 20875
01	01071 06836	99622 35679
02	01065 19206	99624 49305
03	01059 34693	99626 61758
04	01053 53283	99628 73045
5.505	0.00000 01047 74959	0.99999 99630 83173
06	01041 99706	99632 92147
07	01036 27507	99634 99974
08	01030 58347	99637 06659
09	01024 92211	99639 12209
5.510	0.00000 01019 29083	0.99999 99641 16630
11	01013 68947	99643 19928
12	01008 11789	99645 22108
13	01002 57593	99647 23177
14	00997 06344	99649 23140
5.515	0.00000 00991 58026	0.99999 99651 22004
16	00986 12626	99653 19774
17	00980 70127	99655 16457
18	00975 30515	99657 12057
19	00969 93775	99659 06581
5.520	0.00000 00964 59893	0.99999 99661 00034
21	00959 28853	99662 92422
22	00954 00642	99664 83751
23	00948 75244	99666 74026
24	00943 52645	99668 63254
5.525	0.00000 00938 32831	0.99999 99670 51439
26	00933 15787	99672 38587
27	00928 01500	99674 24704
28	00922 89955	99676 09795
29	00917 81138	99677 93866
5.530	0.00000 00912 75034	0.99999 99679 76921
31	00907 71631	99681 58967
32	00902 70914	99683 40010
33	00897 72869	99685 20053
34	00892 77483	99686 99103
5.535	0.00000 00887 84741	0.99999 99688 77165
36	00882 94631	99690 54244
37	00878 07139	99692 30345
38	00873 22250	99694 05474
39	00868 39953	99695 79636
5.540	0.00000 00863 60233	0.99999 99697 52835
41	00858 83077	99699 25078
42	00854 08472	99700 96369
43	00849 36405	99702 66714
44	00844 66863	99704 36117
5.545	0.00000 00839 99832	0.99999 99706 04583
46	00835 35301	99707 72118
47	00830 73255	99709 38726
48	00826 13682	99711 04412
49	00821 56569	99712 69182
5.550	0.00000 00817 01904	0.99999 99714 33040

x	$\dfrac{1}{\sqrt{2\pi}}e^{-\frac{x^2}{2}}$	$\dfrac{1}{\sqrt{2\pi}}\displaystyle\int_{-x}^{x} e^{-\frac{\alpha^2}{2}}\,d\alpha$
5.550	0.00000 00817 01904	0.99999 99714 33040
51	00812 49674	99715 95991
52	00807 99866	99717 58041
53	00803 52468	99719 19192
54	00799 07467	99720 79452
5.555	0.00000 00794 64851	0.99999 99722 38824
56	00790 24608	99723 97313
57	00785 86726	99725 54924
58	00781 51192	99727 11661
59	00777 17993	99728 67530
5.560	0.00000 00772 87119	0.99999 99730 22535
61	00768 58556	99731 76680
62	00764 32294	99733 29971
63	00760 08320	99734 82411
64	00755 86622	99736 34006
5.565	0.00000 00751 67188	0.99999 99737 84759
66	00747 50007	99739 34676
67	00743 35067	99740 83760
68	00739 22356	99742 32018
69	00735 11864	99743 79451
5.570	0.00000 00731 03577	0.99999 99745 26066
71	00726 97486	99746 71867
72	00722 93578	99748 16858
73	00718 91843	99749 61043
74	00714 92268	99751 04427
5.575	0.00000 00710 94843	0.99999 99752 47013
76	00706 99557	99753 88807
77	00703 06398	99755 29813
78	00699 15356	99756 70034
79	00695 26419	99758 09476
5.580	0.00000 00691 39576	0.99999 99759 48142
81	00687 54817	99760 86036
82	00683 72131	99762 23162
83	00679 91507	99763 59525
84	00676 12935	99764 95130
5.585	0.00000 00672 36402	0.99999 99766 29979
86	00668 61900	99767 64077
87	00664 89418	99768 97428
88	00661 18944	99770 30036
89	00657 50469	99771 61905
5.590	0.00000 00653 83982	0.99999 99772 93039
91	00650 19473	99774 23442
92	00646 56931	99775 53118
93	00642 96346	99776 82071
94	00639 37708	99778 10305
5.595	0.00000 00635 81008	0.99999 99779 37823
96	00632 26234	99780 64630
97	00628 73376	99781 90729
98	00625 22426	99783 16125
99	00621 73372	99784 40820
5.600	0.00000 00618 26205	0.99999 99785 64819

x	$\dfrac{1}{\sqrt{2\pi}}\,e^{-\frac{x^2}{2}}$	$\dfrac{1}{\sqrt{2\pi}}\displaystyle\int_{-x}^{x} e^{-\frac{\alpha^2}{2}}\,d\alpha$
5.600	0.00000 00618 26205	0.99999 99785 64819
01	00614 80915	99786 88126
02	00611 37493	99788 10744
03	00607 95927	99789 32677
04	00604 56210	99790 53929
5.605	0.00000 00601 18331	0.99999 99791 74504
06	00597 82280	99792 94404
07	00594 48049	99794 13634
08	00591 15627	99795 32197
09	00587 85005	99796 50098
5.610	0.00000 00584 56174	0.99999 99797 67338
11	00581 29124	99798 83923
12	00578 03845	99799 99856
13	00574 80330	99801 15140
14	00571 58568	99802 29779
5.615	0.00000 00568 38551	0.99999 99803 43775
16	00565 20268	99804 57134
17	00562 03712	99805 69858
18	00558 88873	99806 81950
19	00555 75742	99807 93414
5.620	0.00000 00552 64310	0.99999 99809 04254
21	00549 54568	99810 14473
22	00546 46507	99811 24073
23	00543 40120	99812 33060
24	00540 35395	99813 41435
5.625	0.00000 00537 32327	0.99999 99814 49203
26	00534 30904	99815 56365
27	00531 31119	99816 62927
28	00528 32963	99817 68891
29	00525 36428	99818 74260
5.630	0.00000 00522 41506	0.99999 99819 79038
31	00519 48186	99820 83227
32	00516 56462	99821 86832
33	00513 66325	99822 89854
34	00510 77766	99823 92298
5.635	0.00000 00507 90778	0.99999 99824 94166
36	00505 05352	99825 95462
37	00502 21479	99826 96189
38	00499 39152	99827 96349
39	00496 58362	99828 95946
5.640	0.00000 00493 79102	0.99999 99829 94984
41	00491 01363	99830 93464
42	00488 25138	99831 91390
43	00485 50418	99832 88765
44	00482 77195	99833 85593
5.645	0.00000 00480 05462	0.99999 99834 81875
46	00477 35211	99835 77616
47	00474 66434	99836 72817
48	00471 99123	99837 67482
49	00469 33270	99838 61614
5.650	0.00000 00466 68868	0.99999 99839 55216

x	$\dfrac{1}{\sqrt{2\pi}}\,e^{-\frac{x^2}{2}}$	$\dfrac{1}{\sqrt{2\pi}}\displaystyle\int_{-x}^{x} e^{-\frac{\alpha^2}{2}}\,d\alpha$
5.650	0.00000 00466 68868	0.99999 99839 55216
51	00464 05909	99840 48291
52	00461 44386	99841 40841
53	00458 84291	99842 32869
54	00456 25616	99843 24379
5.655	0.00000 00453 68354	0.99999 99844 15373
56	00451 12497	99845 05853
57	00448 58039	99845 95824
58	00446 04971	99846 85286
59	00443 53286	99847 74244
5.660	0.00000 00441 02978	0.99999 99848 62700
61	00438 54038	99849 50657
62	00436 06460	99850 38118
63	00433 60236	99851 25084
64	00431 15360	99852 11559
5.665	0.00000 00428 71823	0.99999 99852 97546
66	00426 29619	99853 83048
67	00423 88742	99854 68066
68	00421 49183	99855 52603
69	00419 10936	99856 36663
5.670	0.00000 00416 73995	0.99999 99857 20248
71	00414 38351	99858 03360
72	00412 03999	99858 86002
73	00409 70931	99859 68177
74	00407 39140	99860 49887
5.675	0.00000 00405 08621	0.99999 99861 31134
76	00402 79365	99862 11922
77	00400 51367	99862 92253
78	00398 24620	99863 72129
79	00395 99116	99864 51552
5.680	0.00000 00393 74851	0.99999 99865 30526
81	00391 51816	99866 09052
82	00389 30006	99866 87134
83	00387 09413	99867 64773
84	00384 90032	99868 41972
5.685	0.00000 00382 71856	0.99999 99869 18734
86	00380 54879	99869 95061
87	00378 39094	99870 70954
88	00376 24495	99871 46418
89	00374 11076	99872 21453
5.690	0.00000 00371 98830	0.99999 99872 96063
91	00369 87751	99873 70249
92	00367 77833	99874 44015
93	00365 69070	99875 17361
94	00363 61456	99875 90292
5.695	0.00000 00361 54984	0.99999 99876 62808
96	00359 49648	99877 34912
97	00357 45443	99878 06607
98	00355 42363	99878 77895
99	00353 40401	99879 48777
5.700	0.00000 00351 39551	0.99999 99880 19257

x	$\dfrac{1}{\sqrt{2\pi}}\,e^{-\frac{x^2}{2}}$	$\dfrac{1}{\sqrt{2\pi}}\displaystyle\int_{-x}^{x} e^{-\frac{\alpha^2}{2}}\,d\alpha$
5.700	0.00000 00351 39551	0.99999 99880 19257
01	00349 39808	99880 89336
02	00347 41165	99881 59017
03	00345 43618	99882 28302
04	00343 47159	99882 97192
5.705	0.00000 00341 51783	0.99999 99883 65691
06	00339 57485	99884 33800
07	00337 64259	99885 01522
08	00335 72098	99885 68858
09	00333 80998	99886 35811
5.710	0.00000 00331 90952	0.99999 99887 02383
11	00330 01955	99887 68575
12	00328 14002	99888 34391
13	00326 27086	99888 99832
14	00324 41203	99889 64900
5.715	0.00000 00322 56346	0.99999 99890 29598
16	00320 72511	99890 93926
17	00318 89691	99891 57888
18	00317 07882	99892 21486
19	00315 27078	99892 84720
5.720	0.00000 00313 47274	0.99999 99893 47595
21	00311 68464	99894 10110
22	00309 90642	99894 72269
23	00308 13805	99895 34073
24	00306 37946	99895 95525
5.725	0.00000 00304 63060	0.99999 99896 56626
26	00302 89142	99897 17378
27	00301 16187	99897 77783
28	00299 44190	99898 37843
29	00297 73145	99898 97561
5.730	0.00000 00296 03047	0.99999 99899 56937
31	00294 33892	99900 15973
32	00292 65674	99900 74673
33	00290 98389	99901 33037
34	00289 32031	99901 91067
5.735	0.00000 00287 66595	0.99999 99902 48765
36	00286 02076	99903 06134
37	00284 38470	99903 63174
38	00282 75771	99904 19888
39	00281 13976	99904 76278
5.740	0.00000 00279 53078	0.99999 99905 32345
41	00277 93073	99905 88091
42	00276 33956	99906 43518
43	00274 75723	99906 98627
44	00273 18368	99907 53421
5.745	0.00000 00271 61888	0.99999 99908 07901
46	00270 06277	99908 62069
47	00268 51530	99909 15927
48	00266 97644	99909 69476
49	00265 44612	99910 22718
5.750	0.00000 00263 92432	0.99999 99910 75655

x	$\frac{1}{\sqrt{2\pi}}e^{-\frac{x^2}{2}}$	$\frac{1}{\sqrt{2\pi}}\int_{-x}^{x}e^{-\frac{\alpha^2}{2}}d\alpha$
5.750	0.00000 00263 92432	0.99999 99910 75655
51	00262 41098	99911 28288
52	00260 90605	99911 80620
53	00259 40950	99912 32651
54	00257 92127	99912 84384
5.755	0.00000 00256 44133	0.99999 99913 35821
56	00254 96962	99913 86961
57	00253 50610	99914 37809
58	00252 05074	99914 88364
59	00250 60347	99915 38630
5.760	0.00000 00249 16427	0.99999 99915 88606
61	00247 73309	99916 38296
62	00246 30987	99916 87700
63	00244 89460	99917 36820
64	00243 48721	99917 85659
5.765	0.00000 00242 08766	0.99999 99918 34216
66	00240 69592	99918 82494
67	00239 31194	99919 30495
68	00237 93568	99919 78219
69	00236 56710	99920 25670
5.770	0.00000 00235 20616	0.99999 99920 72847
71	00233 85281	99921 19753
72	00232 50702	99921 66388
73	00231 16873	99922 12756
74	00229 83793	99922 58856
5.775	0.00000 00228 51455	0.99999 99923 04691
76	00227 19857	99923 50263
77	00225 88994	99923 95571
78	00224 58863	99924 40619
79	00223 29458	99924 85407
5.780	0.00000 00222 00777	0.99999 99925 29937
81	00220 72816	99925 74211
82	00219 45570	99926 18229
83	00218 19036	99926 61994
84	00216 93210	99927 05506
5.785	0.00000 00215 68088	0.99999 99927 48767
86	00214 43666	99927 91779
87	00213 19940	99928 34542
88	00211 96908	99928 77059
89	00210 74564	99929 19330
5.790	0.00000 00209 52905	0.99999 99929 61358
91	00208 31928	99930 03142
92	00207 11628	99930 44686
93	00205 92003	99930 85989
94	00204 73048	99931 27054
5.795	0.00000 00203 54760	0.99999 99931 67882
96	00202 37135	99932 08474
97	00201 20170	99932 48831
98	00200 03861	99932 88955
99	00198 88204	99933 28847
5.800	0.00000 00197 73196	0.99999 99933 68508

X	$\frac{1}{\sqrt{2\pi}} e^{-\frac{x^2}{2}}$	$\frac{1}{\sqrt{2\pi}} \int_{-x}^{x} e^{-\frac{\alpha^2}{2}} d\alpha$
5.800	0.00000 00197 73196	0.99999 99933 68508
01	00196 58834	99934 07940
02	00195 45113	99934 47144
03	00194 32031	99934 86121
04	00193 19584	99935 24872
5.805	0.00000 00192 07768	0.99999 99935 63400
06	00190 96581	99936 01704
07	00189 86018	99936 39786
08	00188 76076	99936 77648
09	00187 66752	99937 15291
5.810	0.00000 00186 58043	0.99999 99937 52716
11	00185 49945	99937 89924
12	00184 42454	99938 26916
13	00183 35568	99938 63694
14	00182 29284	99939 00259
5.815	0.00000 00181 23597	0.99999 99939 36611
16	00180 18505	99939 72753
17	00179 14005	99940 08686
18	00178 10093	99940 44410
19	00177 06766	99940 79927
5.820	0.00000 00176 04020	0.99999 99941 15237
21	00175 01854	99941 50343
22	00174 00263	99941 85245
23	00172 99244	99942 19944
24	00171 98795	99942 54442
5.825	0.00000 00170 98911	0.99999 99942 88740
26	00169 99591	99943 22838
27	00169 00831	99943 56739
28	00168 02628	99943 90442
29	00167 04979	99944 23950
5.830	0.00000 00166 07880	0.99999 99944 57262
31	00165 11330	99944 90382
32	00164 15324	99945 23308
33	00163 19861	99945 56043
34	00162 24936	99945 88588
5.835	0.00000 00161 30547	0.99999 99946 20943
36	00160 36691	99946 53110
37	00159 43366	99946 85090
38	00158 50567	99947 16884
39	00157 58294	99947 48493
5.840	0.00000 00156 66541	0.99999 99947 79918
41	00155 75307	99948 11160
42	00154 84590	99948 42219
43	00153 94385	99948 73098
44	00153 04690	99949 03797
5.845	0.00000 00152 15502	0.99999 99949 34317
46	00151 26820	99949 64660
47	00150 38639	99949 94825
48	00149 50957	99950 24814
49	00148 63771	99950 54629
5.850	0.00000 00147 77080	0.99999 99950 84270

x	$\frac{1}{\sqrt{2\pi}} e^{-\frac{x^2}{2}}$	$\frac{1}{\sqrt{2\pi}} \int_{-x}^{x} e^{-\frac{\alpha^2}{2}} d\alpha$
5.850	0.00000 00147 77080	0.99999 99950 84270
51	00146 90879	99951 13738
52	00146 05166	99951 43034
53	00145 19939	99951 72159
54	00144 35195	99952 01114
5.855	0.00000 00143 50931	0.99999 99952 29900
56	00142 67144	99952 58518
57	00141 83833	99952 86969
58	00141 00994	99953 15253
59	00140 18625	99953 43373
5.860	0.00000 00139 36723	0.99999 99953 71328
61	00138 55286	99953 99120
62	00137 74311	99954 26750
63	00136 93795	99954 54218
64	00136 13736	99954 81525
5.865	0.00000 00135 34132	0.99999 99955 08673
66	00134 54980	99955 35662
67	00133 76278	99955 62493
68	00132 98022	99955 89167
69	00132 20211	99956 15686
5.870	0.00000 00131 42842	0.99999 99956 42049
71	00130 65913	99956 68257
72	00129 89422	99956 94313
73	00129 13365	99957 20215
74	00128 37740	99957 45966
5.875	0.00000 00127 62546	0.99999 99957 71567
76	00126 87780	99957 97017
77	00126 13439	99958 22318
78	00125 39521	99958 47471
79	00124 66023	99958 72476
5.880	0.00000 00123 92944	0.99999 99958 97335
81	00123 20281	99959 22048
82	00122 48032	99959 46617
83	00121 76195	99959 71041
84	00121 04767	99959 95322
5.885	0.00000 00120 33745	0.99999 99960 19460
86	00119 63129	99960 43457
87	00118 92915	99960 67313
88	00118 23101	99960 91029
89	00117 53685	99961 14606
5.890	0.00000 00116 84665	0.99999 99961 38044
91	00116 16039	99961 61344
92	00115 47804	99961 84508
93	00114 79959	99962 07536
94	00114 12501	99962 30428
5.895	0.00000 00113 45428	0.99999 99962 53186
96	00112 78737	99962 75810
97	00112 12428	99962 98301
98	00111 46497	99963 20660
99	00110 80943	99963 42888
5.900	0.00000 00110 15764	0.99999 99963 64984

x	$\dfrac{1}{\sqrt{2\pi}}\, e^{-\frac{x^2}{2}}$	$\dfrac{1}{\sqrt{2\pi}}\displaystyle\int_{-x}^{x} e^{-\frac{\alpha^2}{2}}\, d\alpha$
5.900	0.00000 00110 15764	0.99999 99963 64984
01	00109 50956	99963 86951
02	00108 86520	99964 08788
03	00108 22451	99964 30497
04	00107 58749	99964 52078
5.905	0.00000 00106 95411	0.99999 99964 73532
06	00106 32436	99964 94860
07	00105 69820	99965 16062
08	00105 07563	99965 37140
09	00104 45662	99965 58093
5.910	0.00000 00103 84116	0.99999 99965 78923
11	00103 22921	99965 99630
12	00102 62077	99966 20215
13	00102 01582	99966 40678
14	00101 41433	99966 61021
5.915	0.00000 00100 81628	0.99999 99966 81244
16	00100 22167	99967 01348
17	00099 63046	99967 21333
18	00099 04263	99967 41200
19	00098 45818	99967 60950
5.920	0.00000 00097 87708	0.99999 99967 80584
21	00097 29931	99968 00101
22	00096 72485	99968 19504
23	00096 15369	99968 38792
24	00095 58581	99968 57965
5.925	0.00000 00095 02119	0.99999 99968 77026
26	00094 45980	99968 95974
27	00093 90164	99969 14810
28	00093 34669	99969 33535
29	00092 79492	99969 52149
5.930	0.00000 00092 24632	0.99999 99969 70653
31	00091 70087	99969 89048
32	00091 15856	99970 07334
33	00090 61936	99970 25511
34	00090 08326	99970 43582
5.935	0.00000 00089 55025	0.99999 99970 61545
36	00089 02030	99970 79402
37	00088 49339	99970 97153
38	00087 96952	99971 14800
39	00087 44866	99971 32341
5.940	0.00000 00086 93080	0.99999 99971 49779
41	00086 41592	99971 67114
42	00085 90400	99971 84346
43	00085 39503	99972 01476
44	00084 88899	99972 18504
5.945	0.00000 00084 38586	0.99999 99972 35431
46	00083 88564	99972 52259
47	00083 38829	99972 68986
48	00082 89381	99972 85614
49	00082 40218	99973 02144
5.950	0.00000 00081 91338	0.99999 99973 18575

x	$\frac{1}{\sqrt{2\pi}} e^{-\frac{x^2}{2}}$	$\frac{1}{\sqrt{2\pi}} \int_{-x}^{x} e^{-\frac{\alpha^2}{2}} d\alpha$
5.950	0.00000 00081 91338	0.99999 99973 18575
51	00081 42741	99973 34909
52	00080 94423	99973 51146
53	00080 46384	99973 67287
54	00079 98622	99973 83332
5.955	0.00000 00079 51136	0.99999 99973 99282
56	00079 03924	99974 15137
57	00078 56984	99974 30898
58	00078 10315	99974 46565
59	00077 63916	99974 62139
5.960	0.00000 00077 17784	0.99999 99974 77621
61	00076 71919	99974 93010
62	00076 26319	99975 08309
63	00075 80982	99975 23516
64	00075 35908	99975 38633
5.965	0.00000 00074 91094	0.99999 99975 53660
66	00074 46539	99975 68597
67	00074 02241	99975 83446
68	00073 58200	99975 98206
69	00073 14413	99976 12879
5.970	0.00000 00072 70880	0.99999 99976 27464
71	00072 27598	99976 41963
72	00071 84567	99976 56375
73	00071 41785	99976 70701
74	00070 99251	99976 84942
5.975	0.00000 00070 56963	0.99999 99976 99098
76	00070 14920	99977 13170
77	00069 73120	99977 27158
78	00069 31563	99977 41063
79	00068 90246	99977 54884
5.980	0.00000 00068 49169	0.99999 99977 68624
81	00068 08330	99977 82281
82	00067 67727	99977 95857
83	00067 27360	99978 09352
84	00066 87227	99978 22767
5.985	0.00000 00066 47327	0.99999 99978 36101
86	00066 07658	99978 49356
87	00065 68220	99978 62532
88	00065 29010	99978 75629
89	00064 90028	99978 88648
5.990	0.00000 00064 51272	0.99999 99979 01590
91	00064 12741	99979 14454
92	00063 74434	99979 27241
93	00063 36349	99979 39951
94	00062 98486	99979 52586
5.995	0.00000 00062 60843	0.99999 99979 65146
96	00062 23418	99979 77630
97	00061 86211	99979 90039
98	00061 49220	99980 02375
99	00061 12445	99980 14636
6.000	0.00000 00060 75883	0.99999 99980 26825

x	$\frac{1}{\sqrt{2\pi}}\, e^{-\frac{x^2}{2}}$	$\frac{1}{\sqrt{2\pi}}\displaystyle\int_{-x}^{x} e^{-\frac{\alpha^2}{2}}\, d\alpha$
6.000	0.00000 00060 75883	0.99999 99980 26825
01	00060 39534	99980 38940
02	00060 03396	99980 50983
03	00059 67469	99980 62954
04	00059 31750	99980 74853
6.005	0.00000 00058 96240	0.99999 99980 86681
06	00058 60936	99980 98438
07	00058 25838	99981 10125
08	00057 90944	99981 21742
09	00057 56253	99981 33289
6.010	0.00000 00057 21765	0.99999 99981 44767
11	00056 87477	99981 56176
12	00056 53390	99981 67517
13	00056 19501	99981 78790
14	00055 85809	99981 89995
6.015	0.00000 00055 52314	0.99999 99982 01133
16	00055 19014	99982 12204
17	00054 85909	99982 23209
18	00054 52997	99982 34148
19	00054 20276	99982 45021
6.020	0.00000 00053 87747	0.99999 99982 55829
21	00053 55408	99982 66572
22	00053 23257	99982 77251
23	00052 91294	99982 87866
24	00052 59518	99982 98416
6.025	0.00000 00052 27927	0.99999 99983 08904
26	00051 96521	99983 19328
27	00051 65298	99983 29690
28	00051 34258	99983 39989
29	00051 03399	99983 50227
6.030	0.00000 00050 72721	0.99999 99983 60403
31	00050 42222	99983 70518
32	00050 11901	99983 80572
33	00049 81758	99983 90566
34	00049 51791	99984 00499
6.035	0.00000 00049 21999	0.99999 99984 10373
36	00048 92382	99984 20187
37	00048 62938	99984 29943
38	00048 33667	99984 39639
39	00048 04566	99984 49278
6.040	0.00000 00047 75637	0.99999 99984 58858
41	00047 46876	99984 68380
42	00047 18285	99984 77845
43	00046 89860	99984 87253
44	00046 61603	99984 96605
6.045	0.00000 00046 33511	0.99999 99985 05900
46	00046 05583	99985 15139
47	00045 77820	99985 24322
48	00045 50219	99985 33450
49	00045 22780	99985 42523
6.050	0.00000 00044 95502	0.99999 99985 51542

x	$\frac{1}{\sqrt{2\pi}} e^{-\frac{x^2}{2}}$	$\frac{1}{\sqrt{2\pi}} \int_{-x}^{x} e^{-\frac{\alpha^2}{2}} d\alpha$
6.050	0.00000 00044 95502	0.99999 99985 51542
51	00044 68384	99985 60506
52	00044 41425	99985 69415
53	00044 14625	99985 78271
54	00043 87981	99985 87074
6.055	0.00000 00043 61495	0.99999 99985 95823
56	00043 35163	99986 04520
57	00043 08987	99986 13164
58	00042 82964	99986 21756
59	00042 57094	99986 30296
6.060	0.00000 00042 31376	0.99999 99986 38785
61	00042 05810	99986 47222
62	00041 80393	99986 55608
63	00041 55126	99986 63943
64	00041 30008	99986 72228
6.065	0.00000 00041 05037	0.99999 99986 80463
66	00040 80213	99986 88649
67	00040 55536	99986 96784
68	00040 31003	99987 04871
69	00040 06615	99987 12909
6.070	0.00000 00039 82371	0.99999 99987 20897
71	00039 58269	99987 28838
72	00039 34309	99987 36731
73	00039 10490	99987 44575
74	00038 86812	99987 52373
6.075	0.00000 00038 63273	0.99999 99987 60123
76	00038 39873	99987 67826
77	00038 16611	99987 75482
78	00037 93486	99987 83092
79	00037 70497	99987 90656
6.080	0.00000 00037 47644	0.99999 99987 98175
81	00037 24925	99988 05647
82	00037 02341	99988 13074
83	00036 79890	99988 20457
84	00036 57571	99988 27794
6.085	0.00000 00036 35384	0.99999 99988 35087
86	00036 13328	99988 42336
87	00035 91403	99988 49540
88	00035 69606	99988 56701
89	00035 47939	99988 63819
6.090	0.00000 00035 26399	0.99999 99988 70893
91	00035 04987	99988 77924
92	00034 83701	99988 84913
93	00034 62541	99988 91859
94	00034 41506	99988 98763
6.095	0.00000 00034 20596	0.99999 99989 05625
96	00033 99809	99989 12446
97	00033 79145	99989 19225
98	00033 58604	99989 25963
99	00033 38184	99989 32659
6.100	0.00000 00033 17884	0.99999 99989 39315

x	$\dfrac{1}{\sqrt{2\pi}}e^{-\frac{x^2}{2}}$	$\dfrac{1}{\sqrt{2\pi}}\displaystyle\int_{-x}^{x}e^{-\frac{\alpha^2}{2}}\,d\alpha$
6.100	0.00000 00033 17884	0.99999 99989 39315
01	00032 97705	99989 45931
02	00032 77645	99989 52506
03	00032 57704	99989 59042
04	00032 37882	99989 65537
6.105	0.00000 00032 18176	0.99999 99989 71993
06	00031 98587	99989 78410
07	00031 79115	99989 84788
08	00031 59758	99989 91126
09	00031 40515	99989 97427
6.110	0.00000 00031 21387	0.99999 99990 03689
11	00031 02371	99990 09912
12	00030 83469	99990 16098
13	00030 64679	99990 22246
14	00030 46000	99990 28357
6.115	0.00000 00030 27432	0.99999 99990 34430
16	00030 08974	99990 40467
17	00029 90626	99990 46466
18	00029 72387	99990 52429
19	00029 54256	99990 58356
6.120	0.00000 00029 36233	0.99999 99990 64246
21	00029 18316	99990 70101
22	00029 00506	99990 75920
23	00028 82802	99990 81703
24	00028 65203	99990 87451
6.125	0.00000 00028 47709	0.99999 99990 93164
26	00028 30319	99990 98842
27	00028 13032	99991 04485
28	00027 95848	99991 10094
29	00027 78766	99991 15669
6.130	0.00000 00027 61785	0.99999 99991 21209
31	00027 44906	99991 26716
32	00027 28127	99991 32189
33	00027 11448	99991 37629
34	00026 94868	99991 43035
6.135	0.00000 00026 78387	0.99999 99991 48408
36	00026 62004	99991 53748
37	00026 45719	99991 59056
38	00026 29530	99991 64331
39	00026 13439	99991 69574
6.140	0.00000 00025 97442	0.99999 99991 74785
41	00025 81542	99991 79964
42	00025 65736	99991 85111
43	00025 50024	99991 90227
44	00025 34406	99991 95312
6.145	0.00000 00025 18881	0.99999 99992 00365
46	00025 03449	99992 05387
47	00024 88109	99992 10379
48	00024 72860	99992 15340
49	00024 57702	99992 20270
6.150	0.00000 00024 42635	0.99999 99992 25171

X	$\frac{1}{\sqrt{2\pi}}e^{-\frac{x^2}{2}}$	$\frac{1}{\sqrt{2\pi}}\int_{-x}^{x}e^{-\frac{\alpha^2}{2}}d\alpha$
6.150	0.00000 00024 42635	0.99999 99992 25171
51	00024 27658	99992 30041
52	00024 12770	99992 34881
53	00023 97971	99992 39692
54	00023 83260	99992 44473
6.155	0.00000 00023 68637	0.99999 99992 49225
56	00023 54102	99992 53948
57	00023 39653	99992 58642
58	00023 25291	99992 63306
59	00023 11015	99992 67943
6.160	0.00000 00022 96824	0.99999 99992 72551
61	00022 82718	99992 77130
62	00022 68696	99992 81681
63	00022 54758	99992 86205
64	00022 40904	99992 90701
6.165	0.00000 00022 27132	0.99999 99992 95169
66	00022 13443	99992 99609
67	00021 99836	99993 04022
68	00021 86310	99993 08409
69	00021 72866	99993 12768
6.170	0.00000 00021 59501	0.99999 99993 17100
71	00021 46217	99993 21406
72	00021 33013	99993 25685
73	00021 19887	99993 29938
74	00021 06840	99993 34165
6.175	0.00000 00020 93872	0.99999 99993 38365
76	00020 80981	99993 42540
77	00020 68167	99993 46689
78	00020 55430	99993 50813
79	00020 42770	99993 54911
6.180	0.00000 00020 30186	0.99999 99993 58984
81	00020 17677	99993 63032
82	00020 05243	99993 67055
83	00019 92884	99993 71053
84	00019 80599	99993 75026
6.185	0.00000 00019 68388	0.99999 99993 78975
86	00019 56250	99993 82900
87	00019 44185	99993 86800
88	00019 32192	99993 90677
89	00019 20272	99993 94529
6.190	0.00000 00019 08423	0.99999 99993 98358
91	00018 96646	99994 02163
92	00018 84939	99994 05944
93	00018 73302	99994 09703
94	00018 61736	99994 13438
6.195	0.00000 00018 50239	0.99999 99994 17150
96	00018 38811	99994 20839
97	00018 27452	99994 24505
98	00018 16162	99994 28149
99	00018 04939	99994 31770
6.200	0.00000 00017 93784	0.99999 99994 35368

306

x	$\frac{1}{\sqrt{2\pi}} e^{-\frac{x^2}{2}}$	$\frac{1}{\sqrt{2\pi}} \int_{-x}^{x} e^{-\frac{\alpha^2}{2}} d\alpha$
6.200	0.00000 00017 93784	0.99999 99994 35368
01	00017 82696	99994 38945
02	00017 71675	99994 42499
03	00017 60720	99994 46032
04	00017 49831	99994 49542
6.205	0.00000 00017 39008	0.99999 99994 53031
06	00017 28250	99994 56498
07	00017 17557	99994 59944
08	00017 06928	99994 63368
09	00016 96363	99994 66772
6.210	0.00000 00016 85863	0.99999 99994 70154
11	00016 75425	99994 73515
12	00016 65050	99994 76856
13	00016 54738	99994 80176
14	00016 44488	99994 83475
6.215	0.00000 00016 34300	0.99999 99994 86754
16	00016 24174	99994 90012
17	00016 14109	99994 93250
18	00016 04104	99994 96468
19	00015 94160	99994 99667
6.220	0.00000 00015 84276	0.99999 99995 02845
21	00015 74451	99995 06004
22	00015 64686	99995 09143
23	00015 54980	99995 12263
24	00015 45333	99995 15363
6.225	0.00000 00015 35744	0.99999 99995 18444
26	00015 26213	99995 21506
27	00015 16739	99995 24549
28	00015 07323	99995 27573
29	00014 97964	99995 30578
6.230	0.00000 00014 88661	0.99999 99995 33565
31	00014 79415	99995 36533
32	00014 70225	99995 39483
33	00014 61090	99995 42414
34	00014 52011	99995 45327
6.235	0.00000 00014 42986	0.99999 99995 48222
36	00014 34017	99995 51099
37	00014 25101	99995 53958
38	00014 16240	99995 56799
39	00014 07432	99995 59623
6.240	0.00000 00013 98678	0.99999 99995 62429
41	00013 89976	99995 65218
42	00013 81328	99995 67989
43	00013 72732	99995 70743
44	00013 64188	99995 73480
6.245	0.00000 00013 55696	0.99999 99995 76200
46	00013 47255	99995 78903
47	00013 38866	99995 81589
48	00013 30527	99995 84258
49	00013 22239	99995 86911
6.250	0.00000 00013 14002	0.99999 99995 89547

X	$\frac{1}{\sqrt{2\pi}} e^{-\frac{x^2}{2}}$	$\frac{1}{\sqrt{2\pi}} \int_{-x}^{x} e^{-\frac{\alpha^2}{2}} d\alpha$
6.250	0.00000 00013 14002	0.99999 99995 89547
51	00013 05814	99995 92167
52	00012 97676	99995 94771
53	00012 89588	99995 97358
54	00012 81549	99995 99929
6.255	0.00000 00012 73558	0.99999 99996 02484
56	00012 65616	99996 05023
57	00012 57723	99996 07547
58	00012 49877	99996 10054
59	00012 42079	99996 12546
6.260	0.00000 00012 34329	0.99999 99996 15023
61	00012 26625	99996 17483
62	00012 18969	99996 19929
63	00012 11359	99996 22359
64	00012 03795	99996 24775
6.265	0.00000 00011 96278	0.99999 99996 27175
66	00011 88806	99996 29560
67	00011 81379	99996 31930
68	00011 73998	99996 34285
69	00011 66662	99996 36626
6.270	0.00000 00011 59371	0.99999 99996 38952
71	00011 52124	99996 41263
72	00011 44921	99996 43560
73	00011 37762	99996 45843
74	00011 30646	99996 48111
6.275	0.00000 00011 23574	0.99999 99996 50366
76	00011 16545	99996 52606
77	00011 09559	99996 54832
78	00011 02616	99996 57044
79	00010 95715	99996 59242
6.280	0.00000 00010 88856	0.99999 99996 61427
81	00010 82039	99996 63598
82	00010 75263	99996 65755
83	00010 68529	99996 67899
84	00010 61836	99996 70029
6.285	0.00000 00010 55184	0.99999 99996 72146
86	00010 48572	99996 74250
87	00010 42001	99996 76341
88	00010 35470	99996 78418
89	00010 28979	99996 80483
6.290	0.00000 00010 22527	0.99999 99996 82534
91	00010 16115	99996 84573
92	00010 09742	99996 86599
93	00010 03409	99996 88612
94	00009 97113	99996 90612
6.295	0.00000 00009 90857	0.99999 99996 92600
96	00009 84639	99996 94576
97	00009 78458	99996 96539
98	00009 72316	99996 98489
99	00009 66211	99997 00428
6.300	0.00000 00009 60143	0.99999 99997 02354

X	$\dfrac{1}{\sqrt{2\pi}}\,e^{-\frac{x^2}{2}}$	$\dfrac{1}{\sqrt{2\pi}}\displaystyle\int_{-x}^{x} e^{-\frac{\alpha^2}{2}}\,d\alpha$
6.300	0.00000 00009 60143	0.99999 99997 02354
01	00009 54113	99997 04269
02	00009 48120	99997 06171
03	00009 42163	99997 08061
04	00009 36243	99997 09940
6.305	0.00000 00009 30359	0.99999 99997 11806
06	00009 24511	99997 13661
07	00009 18699	99997 15504
08	00009 12922	99997 17336
09	00009 07181	99997 19156
6.310	0.00000 00009 01475	0.99999 99997 20965
11	00008 95804	99997 22762
12	00008 90168	99997 24548
13	00008 84567	99997 26323
14	00008 79000	99997 28086
6.315	0.00000 00008 73467	0.99999 99997 29839
16	00008 67968	99997 31580
17	00008 62503	99997 33310
18	00008 57071	99997 35030
19	00008 51673	99997 36739
6.320	0.00000 00008 46307	0.99999 99997 38437
21	00008 40975	99997 40124
22	00008 35676	99997 41801
23	00008 30409	99997 43467
24	00008 25174	99997 45122
6.325	0.00000 00008 19972	0.99999 99997 46767
26	00008 14802	99997 48402
27	00008 09663	99997 50027
28	00008 04556	99997 51641
29	00007 99480	99997 53245
6.330	0.00000 00007 94436	0.99999 99997 54839
31	00007 89423	99997 56423
32	00007 84440	99997 57997
33	00007 79489	99997 59560
34	00007 74567	99997 61114
6.335	0.00000 00007 69676	0.99999 99997 62659
36	00007 64815	99997 64193
37	00007 59985	99997 65718
38	00007 55183	99997 67233
39	00007 50412	99997 68739
6.340	0.00000 00007 45670	0.99999 99997 70235
41	00007 40957	99997 71721
42	00007 36273	99997 73199
43	00007 31618	99997 74667
44	00007 26991	99997 76125
6.345	0.00000 00007 22394	0.99999 99997 77575
46	00007 17824	99997 79015
47	00007 13283	99997 80446
48	00007 08770	99997 81868
49	00007 04284	99997 83281
6.350	0.00000 00006 99827	0.99999 99997 84685

x	$\dfrac{1}{\sqrt{2\pi}} e^{-\frac{x^2}{2}}$	$\dfrac{1}{\sqrt{2\pi}} \displaystyle\int_{-x}^{x} e^{-\frac{\alpha^2}{2}}\, d\alpha$
6.350	0.00000 00006 99827	0.99999 99997 84685
51	00006 95396	99997 86080
52	00006 90994	99997 87467
53	00006 86618	99997 88844
54	00006 82269	99997 90213
6.355	0.00000 00006 77948	0.99999 99997 91573
56	00006 73653	99997 92925
57	00006 69384	99997 94268
58	00006 65142	99997 95603
59	00006 60926	99997 96929
6.360	0.00000 00006 56736	0.99999 99997 98246
61	00006 52572	99997 99556
62	00006 48434	99998 00857
63	00006 44322	99998 02149
64	00006 40235	99998 03434
6.365	0.00000 00006 36173	0.99999 99998 04710
66	00006 32136	99998 05979
67	00006 28124	99998 07239
68	00006 24137	99998 08491
69	00006 20175	99998 09735
6.370	0.00000 00006 16238	0.99999 99998 10972
71	00006 12324	99998 12200
72	00006 08435	99998 13421
73	00006 04570	99998 14634
74	00006 00729	99998 15839
6.375	0.00000 00005 96912	0.99999 99998 17037
76	00005 93119	99998 18227
77	00005 89349	99998 19410
78	00005 85602	99998 20584
79	00005 81879	99998 21752
6.380	0.00000 00005 78178	0.99999 99998 22912
81	00005 74501	99998 24065
82	00005 70847	99998 25210
83	00005 67215	99998 26348
84	00005 63606	99998 27479
6.385	0.00000 00005 60019	0.99999 99998 28603
86	00005 56454	99998 29719
87	00005 52912	99998 30828
88	00005 49391	99998 31931
89	00005 45893	99998 33026
6.390	0.00000 00005 42416	0.99999 99998 34114
91	00005 38960	99998 35196
92	00005 35527	99998 36270
93	00005 32114	99998 37338
94	00005 28723	99998 38399
6.395	0.00000 00005 25353	0.99999 99998 39453
96	00005 22004	99998 40500
97	00005 18675	99998 41541
98	00005 15368	99998 42575
99	00005 12081	99998 43602
6.400	0.00000 00005 08814	0.99999 99998 44623

x	$\dfrac{1}{\sqrt{2\pi}}\,e^{-\frac{x^2}{2}}$	$\dfrac{1}{\sqrt{2\pi}}\displaystyle\int_{-x}^{x} e^{-\frac{\alpha^2}{2}}\,d\alpha$
6.400	0.00000 00005 08814	0.99999 99998 44623
01	00005 05568	99998 45637
02	00005 02342	99998 46645
03	00004 99136	99998 47647
04	00004 95950	99998 48642
6.405	0.00000 00004 92784	0.99999 99998 49631
06	00004 89637	99998 50613
07	00004 86510	99998 51589
08	00004 83403	99998 52559
09	00004 80315	99998 53523
6.410	0.00000 00004 77246	0.99999 99998 54480
11	00004 74197	99998 55432
12	00004 71166	99998 56377
13	00004 68154	99998 57316
14	00004 65161	99998 58250
6.415	0.00000 00004 62187	0.99999 99998 59177
16	00004 59232	99998 60099
17	00004 56294	99998 61014
18	00004 53375	99998 61924
19	00004 50475	99998 62828
6.420	0.00000 00004 47592	0.99999 99998 63726
21	00004 44728	99998 64618
22	00004 41881	99998 65505
23	00004 39052	99998 66386
24	00004 36241	99998 67261
6.425	0.00000 00004 33447	0.99999 99998 68130
26	00004 30671	99998 68995
27	00004 27912	99998 69853
28	00004 25171	99998 70706
29	00004 22446	99998 71554
6.430	0.00000 00004 19739	0.99999 99998 72396
31	00004 17048	99998 73233
32	00004 14375	99998 74064
33	00004 11718	99998 74890
34	00004 09077	99998 75711
6.435	0.00000 00004 06454	0.99999 99998 76527
36	00004 03846	99998 77337
37	00004 01255	99998 78142
38	00003 98681	99998 78942
39	00003 96122	99998 79737
6.440	0.00000 00003 93579	0.99999 99998 80526
41	00003 91053	99998 81311
42	00003 88542	99998 82091
43	00003 86047	99998 82865
44	00003 83567	99998 83635
6.445	0.00000 00003 81103	0.99999 99998 84400
46	00003 78655	99998 85159
47	00003 76222	99998 85914
48	00003 73804	99998 86664
49	00003 71401	99998 87409
6.450	0.00000 00003 69013	0.99999 99998 88150

x	$\dfrac{1}{\sqrt{2\pi}}\,e^{-\frac{x^2}{2}}$	$\dfrac{1}{\sqrt{2\pi}}\displaystyle\int_{-x}^{x} e^{-\frac{\alpha^2}{2}}\,d\alpha$
6.450	0.00000 00003 69013	0.99999 99998 88150
51	00003 66641	99998 88885
52	00003 64283	99998 89616
53	00003 61940	99998 90343
54	00003 59612	99998 91064
6.455	0.00000 00003 57298	0.99999 99998 91781
56	00003 54999	99998 92493
57	00003 52714	99998 93201
58	00003 50444	99998 93904
59	00003 48188	99998 94603
6.460	0.00000 00003 45946	0.99999 99998 95297
61	00003 43718	99998 95987
62	00003 41504	99998 96672
63	00003 39305	99998 97353
64	00003 37119	99998 98029
6.465	0.00000 00003 34946	0.99999 99998 98701
66	00003 32788	99998 99369
67	00003 30643	99999 00032
68	00003 28511	99999 00692
69	00003 26393	99999 01346
6.470	0.00000 00003 24288	0.99999 99999 01997
71	00003 22197	99999 02644
72	00003 20118	99999 03286
73	00003 18053	99999 03924
74	00003 16001	99999 04558
6.475	0.00000 00003 13961	0.99999 99999 05188
76	00003 11935	99999 05814
77	00003 09921	99999 06436
78	00003 07920	99999 07054
79	00003 05932	99999 07667
6.480	0.00000 00003 03956	0.99999 99999 08277
81	00003 01992	99999 08883
82	00003 00041	99999 09485
83	00002 98103	99999 10084
84	00002 96176	99999 10678
6.485	0.00000 00002 94262	0.99999 99999 11268
86	00002 92360	99999 11855
87	00002 90469	99999 12438
88	00002 88591	99999 13017
89	00002 86725	99999 13592
6.490	0.00000 00002 84870	0.99999 99999 14164
91	00002 83027	99999 14732
92	00002 81196	99999 15296
93	00002 79376	99999 15856
94	00002 77568	99999 16413
6.495	0.00000 00002 75771	0.99999 99999 16967
96	00002 73985	99999 17516
97	00002 72211	99999 18063
98	00002 70448	99999 18605
99	00002 68696	99999 19144
6.500	0.00000 00002 66956	0.99999 99999 19680

x	$\dfrac{1}{\sqrt{2\pi}}e^{-\frac{x^2}{2}}$	$\dfrac{1}{\sqrt{2\pi}}\displaystyle\int_{-x}^{x}e^{-\frac{\alpha^2}{2}}\,d\alpha$
6.500	0.00000 00002 66956	0.99999 99999 19680
01	00002 65226	20212
02	00002 63507	20741
03	00002 61799	21266
04	00002 60102	21788
6.505	0.00000 00002 58416	0.99999 99999 22307
06	00002 56740	22822
07	00002 55075	23334
08	00002 53421	23842
09	00002 51777	24347
6.510	0.00000 00002 50143	0.99999 99999 24849
11	00002 48520	25348
12	00002 46907	25843
13	00002 45304	26335
14	00002 43711	26825
6.515	0.00000 00002 42129	0.99999 99999 27310
16	00002 40556	27793
17	00002 38994	28273
18	00002 37441	28749
19	00002 35899	29222
6.520	0.00000 00002 34366	0.99999 99999 29693
21	00002 32842	30160
22	00002 31329	30624
23	00002 29825	31085
24	00002 28331	31543
6.525	0.00000 00002 26846	0.99999 99999 31998
26	00002 25370	32451
27	00002 23904	32900
28	00002 22447	33346
29	00002 21000	33790
6.530	0.00000 00002 19562	0.99999 99999 34230
31	00002 18132	34668
32	00002 16712	35103
33	00002 15301	35535
34	00002 13899	35964
6.535	0.00000 00002 12506	0.99999 99999 36390
36	00002 11122	36814
37	00002 09746	37235
38	00002 08379	37653
39	00002 07021	38068
6.540	0.00000 00002 05672	0.99999 99999 38481
41	00002 04331	38891
42	00002 02999	39298
43	00002 01675	39703
44	00002 00360	40105
6.545	0.00000 00001 99053	0.99999 99999 40505
46	00001 97754	40901
47	00001 96464	41296
48	00001 95182	41687
49	00001 93908	42076
6.550	0.00000 00001 92642	0.99999 99999 42463

x	$\frac{1}{\sqrt{2\pi}}e^{-\frac{x^2}{2}}$	$\frac{1}{\sqrt{2\pi}}\int_{-x}^{x}e^{-\frac{\alpha^2}{2}}\,d\alpha$
6.550	0.00000 00001 92642	0.99999 99999 42463
51	00001 91384	42847
52	00001 90134	43228
53	00001 88893	43607
54	00001 87659	43984
6.555	0.00000 00001 86433	0.99999 99999 44358
56	00001 85214	44730
57	00001 84004	45099
58	00001 82801	45466
59	00001 81606	45830
6.560	0.00000 00001 80419	0.99999 99999 46192
61	00001 79239	46552
62	00001 78067	46909
63	00001 76902	47264
64	00001 75745	47617
6.565	0.00000 00001 74595	0.99999 99999 47967
66	00001 73453	48315
67	00001 72317	48661
68	00001 71189	49004
69	00001 70069	49346
6.570	0.00000 00001 68955	0.99999 99999 49685
71	00001 67849	50022
72	00001 66749	50356
73	00001 65657	50689
74	00001 64571	51019
6.575	0.00000 00001 63493	0.99999 99999 51347
76	00001 62421	51673
77	00001 61357	51997
78	00001 60299	52318
79	00001 59248	52638
6.580	0.00000 00001 58204	0.99999 99999 52955
81	00001 57166	53271
82	00001 56135	53584
83	00001 55111	53895
84	00001 54093	54204
6.585	0.00000 00001 53081	0.99999 99999 54511
86	00001 52077	54817
87	00001 51078	55120
88	00001 50086	55421
89	00001 49101	55720
6.590	0.00000 00001 48121	0.99999 99999 56017
91	00001 47148	56313
92	00001 46182	56606
93	00001 45221	56897
94	00001 44267	57187
6.595	0.00000 00001 43319	0.99999 99999 57474
96	00001 42376	57760
97	00001 41440	58044
98	00001 40510	58326
99	00001 39586	58606
6.600	0.00000 00001 38668	0.99999 99999 58884

x	$\dfrac{1}{\sqrt{2\pi}}\,e^{-\frac{x^2}{2}}$	$\dfrac{1}{\sqrt{2\pi}}\displaystyle\int_{-x}^{x}e^{-\frac{\alpha^2}{2}}\,d\alpha$
6.600	0.00000 00001 38668	0.99999 99999 58884
01	00001 37756	59161
02	00001 36849	59435
03	00001 35949	59708
04	00001 35054	59979
6.605	0.00000 00001 34165	0.99999 99999 60248
06	00001 33282	60516
07	00001 32404	60781
08	00001 31532	61045
09	00001 30666	61308
6.610	0.00000 00001 29805	0.99999 99999 61568
11	00001 28950	61827
12	00001 28100	62084
13	00001 27256	62339
14	00001 26417	62593
6.615	0.00000 00001 25583	0.99999 99999 62845
16	00001 24755	63095
17	00001 23933	63344
18	00001 23115	63591
19	00001 22303	63836
6.620	0.00000 00001 21496	0.99999 99999 64080
21	00001 20694	64322
22	00001 19898	64563
23	00001 19107	64802
24	00001 18320	65039
6.625	0.00000 00001 17539	0.99999 99999 65275
26	00001 16763	65509
27	00001 15992	65742
28	00001 15225	65973
29	00001 14464	66203
6.630	0.00000 00001 13708	0.99999 99999 66431
31	00001 12956	66658
32	00001 12210	66883
33	00001 11468	67107
34	00001 10731	67329
6.635	0.00000 00001 09999	0.99999 99999 67550
36	00001 09271	67769
37	00001 08549	67987
38	00001 07831	68203
39	00001 07117	68418
6.640	0.00000 00001 06408	0.99999 99999 68632
41	00001 05704	68844
42	00001 05004	69055
43	00001 04309	69264
44	00001 03618	69472
6.645	0.00000 00001 02932	0.99999 99999 69678
46	00001 02250	69883
47	00001 01573	70087
48	00001 00900	70290
49	00001 00231	70491
6.650	0.00000 00000 99567	0.99999 99999 70691

x	$\frac{1}{\sqrt{2\pi}} e^{-\frac{x^2}{2}}$	$\frac{1}{\sqrt{2\pi}} \int_{-x}^{x} e^{-\frac{\alpha^2}{2}} d\alpha$
6.650	0.00000 00000 99567	0.99999 99999 70691
51	98907	70889
52	98252	71086
53	97600	71282
54	96953	71477
6.655	0.00000 00000 96310	0.99999 99999 71670
56	95671	71862
57	95036	72053
58	94406	72242
59	93779	72430
6.660	0.00000 00000 93157	0.99999 99999 72617
61	92538	72803
62	91924	72987
63	91313	73171
64	90707	73353
6.665	0.00000 00000 90104	0.99999 99999 73533
66	89506	73713
67	88911	73891
68	88320	74069
69	87733	74245
6.670	0.00000 00000 87150	0.99999 99999 74420
71	86571	74593
72	85995	74766
73	85423	74937
74	84855	75108
6.675	0.00000 00000 84291	0.99999 99999 75277
76	83730	75445
77	83173	75612
78	82619	75777
79	82069	75942
6.680	0.00000 00000 81523	0.99999 99999 76106
81	80980	76268
82	80441	76430
83	79905	76590
84	79373	76749
6.685	0.00000 00000 78844	0.99999 99999 76908
86	78319	77065
87	77797	77221
88	77278	77376
89	76763	77530
6.690	0.00000 00000 76251	0.99999 99999 77683
91	75743	77835
92	75238	77986
93	74736	78136
94	74237	78285
6.695	0.00000 00000 73742	0.99999 99999 78433
96	73250	78580
97	72761	78726
98	72275	78871
99	71793	79015
6.700	0.00000 00000 71313	0.99999 99999 79158

x	$\dfrac{1}{\sqrt{2\pi}}\,e^{-\frac{x^2}{2}}$	$\dfrac{1}{\sqrt{2\pi}}\displaystyle\int_{-x}^{x} e^{-\frac{\alpha^2}{2}}\,d\alpha$
6.700	0.00000 00000 71313	0.99999 99999 79158
01	70837	79300
02	70364	79441
03	69894	79582
04	69427	79721
6.705	0.00000 00000 68963	0.99999 99999 79859
06	68502	79997
07	68044	80133
08	67589	80269
09	67137	80404
6.710	0.00000 00000 66689	0.99999 99999 80538
11	66242	80670
12	65799	80803
13	65359	80934
14	64922	81064
6.715	0.00000 00000 64487	0.99999 99999 81193
16	64056	81322
17	63627	81450
18	63201	81576
19	62778	81702
6.720	0.00000 00000 62357	0.99999 99999 81828
21	61940	81952
22	61525	82075
23	61113	82198
24	60703	82320
6.725	0.00000 00000 60296	0.99999 99999 82441
26	59892	82561
27	59491	82680
28	59092	82799
29	58695	82917
6.730	0.00000 00000 58302	0.99999 99999 83034
31	57911	83150
32	57522	83265
33	57136	83380
34	56753	83494
6.735	0.00000 00000 56372	0.99999 99999 83607
36	55993	83719
37	55618	83831
38	55244	83942
39	54873	84052
6.740	0.00000 00000 54504	0.99999 99999 84161
41	54138	84270
42	53775	84378
43	53413	84485
44	53054	84592
6.745	0.00000 00000 52698	0.99999 99999 84697
46	52343	84802
47	51991	84907
48	51642	85010
49	51294	85113
6.750	0.00000 00000 50949	0.99999 99999 85215

x	$\dfrac{1}{\sqrt{2\pi}}e^{-\frac{x^2}{2}}$	$\dfrac{1}{\sqrt{2\pi}}\displaystyle\int_{-x}^{x}e^{-\frac{\alpha^2}{2}}\,d\alpha$
6.750	0.00000 00000 50949	0.99999 99999 85215
51	50607	85317
52	50266	85418
53	49928	85518
54	49592	85618
6.755	0.00000 00000 49258	0.99999 99999 85716
56	48926	85815
57	48597	85912
58	48270	86009
59	47944	86105
6.760	0.00000 00000 47621	0.99999 99999 86201
61	47301	86296
62	46982	86390
63	46665	86484
64	46351	86577
6.765	0.00000 00000 46038	0.99999 99999 86669
66	45728	86761
67	45419	86852
68	45113	86943
69	44809	87032
6.770	0.00000 00000 44506	0.99999 99999 87122
71	44206	87210
72	43908	87299
73	43611	87386
74	43317	87473
6.775	0.00000 00000 43025	0.99999 99999 87559
76	42734	87645
77	42445	87730
78	42159	87815
79	41874	87899
6.780	0.00000 00000 41591	0.99999 99999 87982
81	41310	88065
82	41031	88148
83	40753	88229
84	40478	88311
6.785	0.00000 00000 40204	0.99999 99999 88391
86	39932	88471
87	39662	88551
88	39394	88630
89	39127	88709
6.790	0.00000 00000 38863	0.99999 99999 88787
91	38600	88864
92	38338	88941
93	38079	89017
94	37821	89093
6.795	0.00000 00000 37565	0.99999 99999 89169
96	37310	89244
97	37058	89318
98	36807	89392
99	36557	89465
6.800	0.00000 00000 36310	0.99999 99999 89538

x	$\dfrac{1}{\sqrt{2\pi}}\, e^{-\frac{x^2}{2}}$	$\dfrac{1}{\sqrt{2\pi}} \displaystyle\int_{-x}^{x} e^{-\frac{\alpha^2}{2}}\, d\alpha$
6.800	0.00000 00000 36310	0.99999 99999 89538
01	36064	89610
02	35819	89682
03	35576	89754
04	35335	89825
6.805	0.00000 00000 35095	0.99999 99999 89895
06	34857	89965
07	34621	90035
08	34386	90104
09	34153	90172
6.810	0.00000 00000 33921	0.99999 99999 90240
11	33691	90308
12	33462	90375
13	33235	90442
14	33009	90508
6.815	0.00000 00000 32785	0.99999 99999 90574
16	32562	90639
17	32341	90704
18	32121	90768
19	31903	90832
6.820	0.00000 00000 31686	0.99999 99999 90896
21	31471	90959
22	31257	91022
23	31044	91084
24	30833	91146
6.825	0.00000 00000 30624	0.99999 99999 91207
26	30415	91269
27	30208	91329
28	30003	91389
29	29799	91449
6.830	0.00000 00000 29596	0.99999 99999 91509
31	29394	91568
32	29194	91626
33	28995	91684
34	28798	91742
6.835	0.00000 00000 28602	0.99999 99999 91799
36	28407	91857
37	28213	91913
38	28021	91969
39	27830	92025
6.840	0.00000 00000 27641	0.99999 99999 92081
41	27452	92136
42	27265	92190
43	27079	92245
44	26894	92299
6.845	0.00000 00000 26711	0.99999 99999 92352
46	26529	92406
47	26348	92459
48	26168	92511
49	25989	92563
6.850	0.00000 00000 25812	0.99999 99999 92615

x	$\frac{1}{\sqrt{2\pi}}e^{-\frac{x^2}{2}}$	$\frac{1}{\sqrt{2\pi}}\int_{-x}^{x}e^{-\frac{\alpha^2}{2}}d\alpha$
6.850	0.00000 00000 25812	0.99999 99999 92615
51	25636	92666
52	25461	92718
53	25287	92768
54	25114	92819
6.855	0.00000 00000 24942	0.99999 99999 92869
56	24772	92918
57	24603	92968
58	24435	93017
59	24268	93066
6.860	0.00000 00000 24102	0.99999 99999 93114
61	23937	93162
62	23773	93210
63	23611	93257
64	23449	93304
6.865	0.00000 00000 23289	0.99999 99999 93351
66	23129	93397
67	22971	93443
68	22814	93489
69	22658	93535
6.870	0.00000 00000 22503	0.99999 99999 93580
71	22349	93625
72	22196	93669
73	22044	93713
74	21893	93757
6.875	0.00000 00000 21743	0.99999 99999 93801
76	21594	93844
77	21446	93887
78	21299	93930
79	21153	93973
6.880	0.00000 00000 21008	0.99999 99999 94015
81	20864	94057
82	20720	94098
83	20578	94139
84	20437	94181
6.885	0.00000 00000 20297	0.99999 99999 94221
86	20158	94262
87	20019	94302
88	19882	94342
89	19745	94381
6.890	0.00000 00000 19610	0.99999 99999 94421
91	19475	94460
92	19341	94499
93	19209	94537
94	19077	94575
6.895	0.00000 00000 18946	0.99999 99999 94614
96	18815	94651
97	18686	94689
98	18558	94726
99	18430	94763
6.900	0.00000 00000 18303	0.99999 99999 94800

X	$\dfrac{1}{\sqrt{2\pi}}\,e^{-\frac{x^2}{2}}$	$\dfrac{1}{\sqrt{2\pi}}\displaystyle\int_{-x}^{x} e^{-\frac{\alpha^2}{2}}\,d\alpha$
6.900	0.00000 00000 18303	0.99999 99999 94800
01	18177	94836
02	18052	94872
03	17928	94908
04	17805	94944
6.905	0.00000 00000 17682	0.99999 99999 94980
06	17561	95015
07	17440	95050
08	17320	95085
09	17201	95119
6.910	0.00000 00000 17082	0.99999 99999 95153
11	16964	95188
12	16848	95221
13	16732	95255
14	16616	95288
6.915	0.00000 00000 16502	0.99999 99999 95321
16	16388	95354
17	16275	95387
18	16163	95419
19	16051	95452
6.920	0.00000 00000 15941	0.99999 99999 95484
21	15831	95515
22	15722	95547
23	15613	95578
24	15505	95609
6.925	0.00000 00000 15398	0.99999 99999 95640
26	15292	95671
27	15187	95701
28	15082	95732
29	14978	95762
6.930	0.00000 00000 14874	0.99999 99999 95792
31	14772	95821
32	14670	95851
33	14568	95880
34	14467	95909
6.935	0.00000 00000 14368	0.99999 99999 95938
36	14268	95966
37	14170	95995
38	14072	96023
39	13974	96051
6.940	0.00000 00000 13878	0.99999 99999 96079
41	13782	96107
42	13686	96134
43	13592	96161
44	13498	96188
6.945	0.00000 00000 13404	0.99999 99999 96215
46	13311	96242
47	13219	96269
48	13128	96295
49	13037	96321
6.950	0.00000 00000 12947	0.99999 99999 96347

x	$\dfrac{1}{\sqrt{2\pi}}e^{-\frac{x^2}{2}}$	$\dfrac{1}{\sqrt{2\pi}}\displaystyle\int_{-x}^{x}e^{-\frac{\alpha^2}{2}}\,d\alpha$
6.950	0.00000 00000 12947	0.99999 99999 96347
51	12857	96373
52	12768	96399
53	12679	96424
54	12592	96449
6.955	0.00000 00000 12504	0.99999 99999 96474
56	12418	96499
57	12332	96524
58	12246	96549
59	12161	96573
6.960	0.00000 00000 12077	0.99999 99999 96597
61	11993	96621
62	11910	96645
63	11827	96669
64	11745	96693
6.965	0.00000 00000 11664	0.99999 99999 96716
66	11583	96739
67	11502	96762
68	11422	96785
69	11343	96808
6.970	0.00000 00000 11264	0.99999 99999 96831
71	11186	96853
72	11108	96875
73	11031	96897
74	10954	96919
6.975	0.00000 00000 10878	0.99999 99999 96941
76	10803	96963
77	10728	96985
78	10653	97006
79	10579	97027
6.980	0.00000 00000 10505	0.99999 99999 97048
81	10432	97069
82	10360	97090
83	10288	97111
84	10216	97131
6.985	0.00000 00000 10145	0.99999 99999 97151
86	10074	97172
87	10004	97192
88	09934	97212
89	09865	97231
6.990	0.00000 00000 09797	0.99999 99999 97251
91	09728	97271
92	09661	97290
93	09593	97309
94	09526	97328
6.995	0.00000 00000 09460	0.99999 99999 97347
96	09394	97366
97	09329	97385
98	09263	97404
99	09199	97422
7.000	0.00000 00000 09135	0.99999 99999 97440

x	$\dfrac{1}{\sqrt{2\pi}}\, e^{-\frac{x^2}{2}}$	$\dfrac{1}{\sqrt{2\pi}}\displaystyle\int_{-x}^{x} e^{-\frac{\alpha^2}{2}}\, d\alpha$
7.000	0.00000 00000 09135	0.99999 99999 97440
01	09071	97459
02	09008	97477
03	08945	97495
04	08882	97512
7.005	0.00000 00000 08820	0.99999 99999 97530
06	08759	97548
07	08698	97565
08	08637	97583
09	08577	97600
7.010	0.00000 00000 08517	0.99999 99999 97617
11	08457	97634
12	08398	97651
13	08339	97667
14	08281	97684
7.015	0.00000 00000 08223	0.99999 99999 97701
16	08166	97717
17	08109	97733
18	08052	97749
19	07996	97765
7.020	0.00000 00000 07940	0.99999 99999 97781
21	07884	97797
22	07829	97813
23	07774	97828
24	07720	97844
7.025	0.00000 00000 07666	0.99999 99999 97859
26	07612	97875
27	07559	97890
28	07506	97905
29	07453	97920
7.030	0.00000 00000 07401	0.99999 99999 97935
31	07349	97949
32	07298	97964
33	07247	97979
34	07196	97993
7.035	0.00000 00000 07145	0.99999 99999 98007
36	07095	98022
37	07046	98036
38	06996	98050
39	06947	98064
7.040	0.00000 00000 06898	0.99999 99999 98078
41	06850	98091
42	06802	98105
43	06754	98119
44	06707	98132
7.045	0.00000 00000 06660	0.99999 99999 98145
46	06613	98159
47	06566	98172
48	06520	98185
49	06475	98198
7.050	0.00000 00000 06429	0.99999 99999 98211

x	$\dfrac{1}{\sqrt{2\pi}}e^{-\frac{x^2}{2}}$	$\dfrac{1}{\sqrt{2\pi}}\displaystyle\int_{-x}^{x}e^{-\frac{\alpha^2}{2}}\,d\alpha$
7.050	0.00000 00000 06429	0.99999 99999 98211
51	06384	98224
52	06339	98236
53	06295	98249
54	06250	98262
7.055	0.00000 00000 06206	0.99999 99999 98274
56	06163	98286
57	06119	98299
58	06076	98311
59	06034	98323
7.060	0.00000 00000 05991	0.99999 99999 98335
61	05949	98347
62	05907	98359
63	05866	98371
64	05824	98382
7.065	0.00000 00000 05783	0.99999 99999 98394
66	05743	98405
67	05702	98417
68	05662	98428
69	05622	98439
7.070	0.00000 00000 05582	0.99999 99999 98451
71	05543	98462
72	05504	98473
73	05465	98484
74	05427	98495
7.075	0.00000 00000 05389	0.99999 99999 98506
76	05351	98516
77	05313	98527
78	05275	98538
79	05238	98548
7.080	0.00000 00000 05201	0.99999 99999 98558
81	05164	98569
82	05128	98579
83	05092	98589
84	05056	98599
7.085	0.00000 00000 05020	0.99999 99999 98610
86	04985	98620
87	04950	98629
88	04915	98639
89	04880	98649
7.090	0.00000 00000 04845	0.99999 99999 98659
91	04811	98669
92	04777	98678
93	04743	98688
94	04710	98697
7.095	0.00000 00000 04677	0.99999 99999 98706
96	04644	98716
97	04611	98725
98	04578	98734
99	04546	98743
7.100	0.00000 00000 04514	0.99999 99999 98752

X	$\frac{1}{\sqrt{2\pi}} e^{-\frac{x^2}{2}}$	$\frac{1}{\sqrt{2\pi}} \int_{-x}^{x} e^{-\frac{\alpha^2}{2}} d\alpha$
7.100	0.00000 00000 04514	0.99999 99999 98752
01	04482	98761
02	04450	98770
03	04418	98779
04	04387	98788
7.105	0.00000 00000 04356	0.99999 99999 98797
06	04325	98805
07	04295	98814
08	04264	98823
09	04234	98831
7.110	0.00000 00000 04204	0.99999 99999 98840
11	04174	98848
12	04145	98856
13	04115	98865
14	04086	98873
7.115	0.00000 00000 04057	0.99999 99999 98881
16	04028	98889
17	04000	98897
18	03971	98905
19	03943	98913
7.120	0.00000 00000 03915	0.99999 99999 98921
21	03887	98929
22	03860	98936
23	03833	98944
24	03805	98952
7.125	0.00000 00000 03778	0.99999 99999 98959
26	03751	98967
27	03725	98974
28	03698	98982
29	03672	98989
7.130	0.00000 00000 03646	0.99999 99999 98996
31	03620	99004
32	03594	99011
33	03569	99018
34	03543	99025
7.135	0.00000 00000 03518	0.99999 99999 99032
36	03493	99039
37	03468	99046
38	03444	99053
39	03419	99060
7.140	0.00000 00000 03395	0.99999 99999 99067
41	03371	99073
42	03347	99080
43	03323	99087
44	03299	99093
7.145	0.00000 00000 03276	0.99999 99999 99100
46	03253	99107
47	03229	99113
48	03206	99119
49	03184	99126
7.150	0.00000 00000 03161	0.99999 99999 99132

x	$\dfrac{1}{\sqrt{2\pi}}e^{-\frac{x^2}{2}}$	$\dfrac{1}{\sqrt{2\pi}}\displaystyle\int_{-x}^{x}e^{-\frac{\alpha^2}{2}}\,d\alpha$
7.150	0.00000 00000 03161	0.99999 99999 99132
51	03138	99139
52	03116	99145
53	03094	99151
54	03072	99157
7.155	0.00000 00000 03050	0.99999 99999 99163
56	03028	99169
57	03006	99175
58	02985	99181
59	02964	99187
7.160	0.00000 00000 02943	0.99999 99999 99193
61	02922	99199
62	02901	99205
63	02880	99211
64	02859	99216
7.165	0.00000 00000 02839	0.99999 99999 99222
66	02819	99228
67	02799	99233
68	02779	99239
69	02759	99245
7.170	0.00000 00000 02739	0.99999 99999 99250
71	02720	99255
72	02700	99261
73	02681	99266
74	02662	99272
7.175	0.00000 00000 02643	0.99999 99999 99277
76	02624	99282
77	02605	99287
78	02586	99293
79	02568	99298
7.180	0.00000 00000 02549	0.99999 99999 99303
81	02531	99308
82	02513	99313
83	02495	99318
84	02477	99323
7.185	0.00000 00000 02460	0.99999 99999 99328
86	02442	99333
87	02424	99338
88	02407	99343
89	02390	99347
7.190	0.00000 00000 02373	0.99999 99999 99352
91	02356	99357
92	02339	99362
93	02322	99366
94	02305	99371
7.195	0.00000 00000 02289	0.99999 99999 99375
96	02272	99380
97	02256	99384
98	02240	99389
99	02224	99393
7.200	0.00000 00000 02208	0.99999 99999 99398

X	$\dfrac{1}{\sqrt{2\pi}}\, e^{-\frac{x^2}{2}}$	$\dfrac{1}{\sqrt{2\pi}}\displaystyle\int_{-x}^{x} e^{-\frac{\alpha^2}{2}}\, d\alpha$
7.200	0.00000 00000 02208	0.99999 99999 99398
01	02192	99402
02	02176	99407
03	02161	99411
04	02145	99415
7.205	0.00000 00000 02130	0.99999 99999 99420
06	02115	99424
07	02099	99428
08	02084	99432
09	02069	99436
7.210	0.00000 00000 02055	0.99999 99999 99440
11	02040	99445
12	02025	99449
13	02011	99453
14	01996	99457
7.215	0.00000 00000 01982	0.99999 99999 99461
16	01967	99465
17	01953	99469
18	01939	99472
19	01925	99476
7.220	0.00000 00000 01911	0.99999 99999 99480
21	01898	99484
22	01884	99488
23	01871	99491
24	01857	99495
7.225	0.00000 00000 01844	0.99999 99999 99499
26	01830	99503
27	01817	99506
28	01804	99510
29	01791	99513
7.230	0.00000 00000 01778	0.99999 99999 99517
31	01765	99521
32	01753	99524
33	01740	99528
34	01728	99531
7.235	0.00000 00000 01715	0.99999 99999 99534
36	01703	99538
37	01690	99541
38	01678	99545
39	01666	99548
7.240	0.00000 00000 01654	0.99999 99999 99551
41	01642	99555
42	01630	99558
43	01619	99561
44	01607	99564
7.245	0.00000 00000 01595	0.99999 99999 99568
46	01584	99571
47	01572	99574
48	01561	99577
49	01550	99580
7.250	0.00000 00000 01539	0.99999 99999 99583

x	$\frac{1}{\sqrt{2\pi}} e^{-\frac{x^2}{2}}$	$\frac{1}{\sqrt{2\pi}} \int_{-x}^{x} e^{-\frac{\alpha^2}{2}} d\alpha$
7.250	0.00000 00000 01539	0.99999 99999 99583
51	01527	99586
52	01516	99589
53	01505	99592
54	01495	99595
7.255	0.00000 00000 01484	0.99999 99999 99598
56	01473	99601
57	01462	99604
58	01452	99607
59	01441	99610
7.260	0.00000 00000 01431	0.99999 99999 99613
61	01421	99616
62	01410	99619
63	01400	99621
64	01390	99624
7.265	0.00000 00000 01380	0.99999 99999 99627
66	01370	99630
67	01360	99632
68	01350	99635
69	01340	99638
7.270	0.00000 00000 01331	0.99999 99999 99641
71	01321	99643
72	01311	99646
73	01302	99648
74	01292	99651
7.275	0.00000 00000 01283	0.99999 99999 99654
76	01274	99656
77	01265	99659
78	01255	99661
79	01246	99664
7.280	0.00000 00000 01237	0.99999 99999 99666
81	01228	99669
82	01219	99671
83	01211	99674
84	01202	99676
7.285	0.00000 00000 01193	0.99999 99999 99678
86	01184	99681
87	01176	99683
88	01167	99685
89	01159	99688
7.290	0.00000 00000 01150	0.99999 99999 99690
91	01142	99692
92	01134	99695
93	01125	99697
94	01117	99699
7.295	0.00000 00000 01109	0.99999 99999 99701
96	01101	99704
97	01093	99706
98	01085	99708
99	01077	99710
7.300	0.00000 00000 01069	0.99999 99999 99712

328

x	$\dfrac{1}{\sqrt{2\pi}}e^{-\frac{x^2}{2}}$	$\dfrac{1}{\sqrt{2\pi}}\displaystyle\int_{-x}^{x}e^{-\frac{\alpha^2}{2}}\,d\alpha$
7.300	0.00000 00000 01069	0.99999 99999 99712
01	01062	99714
02	01054	99716
03	01046	99719
04	01039	99721
7.305	0.00000 00000 01031	0.99999 99999 99723
06	01024	99725
07	01016	99727
08	01009	99729
09	01001	99731
7.310	0.00000 00000 00994	0.99999 99999 99733
11	00987	99735
12	00980	99737
13	00972	99739
14	00965	99741
7.315	0.00000 00000 00958	0.99999 99999 99743
16	00951	99745
17	00944	99746
18	00938	99748
19	00931	99750
7.320	0.00000 00000 00924	0.99999 99999 99752
21	00917	99754
22	00911	99756
23	00904	99758
24	00897	99759
7.325	0.00000 00000 00891	0.99999 99999 99761
26	00884	99763
27	00878	99765
28	00871	99766
29	00865	99768
7.330	0.00000 00000 00859	0.99999 99999 99770
31	00852	99772
32	00846	99773
33	00840	99775
34	00834	99777
7.335	0.00000 00000 00828	0.99999 99999 99778
36	00822	99780
37	00816	99782
38	00810	99783
39	00804	99785
7.340	0.00000 00000 00798	0.99999 99999 99786
41	00792	99788
42	00786	99790
43	00781	99791
44	00775	99793
7.345	0.00000 00000 00769	0.99999 99999 99794
46	00764	99796
47	00758	99797
48	00752	99799
49	00747	99800
7.350	0.00000 00000 00741	0.99999 99999 99802

x	$\frac{1}{\sqrt{2\pi}} e^{-\frac{x^2}{2}}$	$\frac{1}{\sqrt{2\pi}} \int_{-x}^{x} e^{-\frac{\alpha^2}{2}} d\alpha$
7.350	0.00000 00000 00741	0.99999 99999 99802
51	00736	99803
52	00731	99805
53	00725	99806
54	00720	99808
7.355	0.00000 00000 00715	0.99999 99999 99809
56	00709	99810
57	00704	99812
58	00699	99813
59	00694	99815
7.360	0.00000 00000 00689	0.99999 99999 99816
61	00684	99817
62	00679	99819
63	00674	99820
64	00669	99822
7.365	0.00000 00000 00664	0.99999 99999 99823
66	00659	99824
67	00654	99825
68	00649	99827
69	00645	99828
7.370	0.00000 00000 00640	0.99999 99999 99829
71	00635	99831
72	00631	99832
73	00626	99833
74	00621	99834
7.375	0.00000 00000 00617	0.99999 99999 99836
76	00612	99837
77	00608	99838
78	00603	99839
79	00599	99841
7.380	0.00000 00000 00594	0.99999 99999 99842
81	00590	99843
82	00586	99844
83	00581	99845
84	00577	99846
7.385	0.00000 00000 00573	0.99999 99999 99848
86	00569	99849
87	00565	99850
88	00560	99851
89	00556	99852
7.390	0.00000 00000 00552	0.99999 99999 99853
91	00548	99854
92	00544	99855
93	00540	99856
94	00536	99858
7.395	0.00000 00000 00532	0.99999 99999 99859
96	00528	99860
97	00524	99861
98	00520	99862
99	00517	99863
7.400	0.00000 00000 00513	0.99999 99999 99864

x	$\frac{1}{\sqrt{2\pi}} e^{-\frac{x^2}{2}}$	$\frac{1}{\sqrt{2\pi}} \int_{-x}^{x} e^{-\frac{\alpha^2}{2}} d\alpha$
7.400	0.00000 00000 00513	0.99999 99999 99864
01	00509	99865
02	00505	99866
03	00502	99867
04	00498	99868
7.405	0.00000 00000 00494	0.99999 99999 99869
06	00490	99870
07	00487	99871
08	00483	99872
09	00480	99873
7.410	0.00000 00000 00476	0.99999 99999 99874
11	00473	99875
12	00469	99876
13	00466	99877
14	00462	99877
7.415	0.00000 00000 00459	0.99999 99999 99878
16	00455	99879
17	00452	99880
18	00449	99881
19	00445	99882
7.420	0.00000 00000 00442	0.99999 99999 99883
21	00439	99884
22	00436	99885
23	00432	99886
24	00429	99886
7.425	0.00000 00000 00426	0.99999 99999 99887
26	00423	99888
27	00420	99889
28	00417	99890
29	00414	99891
7.430	0.00000 00000 00411	0.99999 99999 99891
31	00407	99892
32	00404	99893
33	00401	99894
34	00398	99895
7.435	0.00000 00000 00396	0.99999 99999 99895
36	00393	99896
37	00390	99897
38	00387	99898
39	00384	99899
7.440	0.00000 00000 00381	0.99999 99999 99899
41	00378	99900
42	00375	99901
43	00373	99902
44	00370	99902
7.445	0.00000 00000 00367	0.99999 99999 99903
46	00364	99904
47	00362	99905
48	00359	99905
49	00356	99906
7.450	0.00000 00000 00354	0.99999 99999 99907

x	$\dfrac{1}{\sqrt{2\pi}}\, e^{-\frac{x^2}{2}}$	$\dfrac{1}{\sqrt{2\pi}} \displaystyle\int_{-x}^{x} e^{-\frac{\alpha^2}{2}}\, d\alpha$
7.450	0.00000 00000 00354	0.99999 99999 99907
51	00351	99907
52	00349	99908
53	00346	99909
54	00343	99909
7.455	0.00000 00000 00341	0.99999 99999 99910
56	00338	99911
57	00336	99911
58	00333	99912
59	00331	99913
7.460	0.00000 00000 00328	0.99999 99999 99913
61	00326	99914
62	00323	99915
63	00321	99915
64	00319	99916
7.465	0.00000 00000 00316	0.99999 99999 99917
66	00314	99917
67	00312	99918
68	00309	99919
69	00307	99919
7.470	0.00000 00000 00305	0.99999 99999 99920
71	00302	99920
72	00300	99921
73	00298	99922
74	00296	99922
7.475	0.00000 00000 00294	0.99999 99999 99923
76	00291	99923
77	00289	99924
78	00287	99925
79	00285	99925
7.480	0.00000 00000 00283	0.99999 99999 99926
81	00281	99926
82	00279	99927
83	00276	99927
84	00274	99928
7.485	0.00000 00000 00272	0.99999 99999 99928
86	00270	99929
87	00268	99930
88	00266	99930
89	00264	99931
7.490	0.00000 00000 00262	0.99999 99999 99931
91	00260	99932
92	00258	99932
93	00257	99933
94	00255	99933
7.495	0.00000 00000 00253	0.99999 99999 99934
96	00251	99934
97	00249	99935
98	00247	99935
99	00245	99936
7.500	0.00000 00000 00243	0.99999 99999 99936

x	$\dfrac{1}{\sqrt{2\pi}}\,e^{-\frac{x^2}{2}}$	$\dfrac{1}{\sqrt{2\pi}}\displaystyle\int_{-x}^{x} e^{-\frac{a^2}{2}}\,d\alpha$
7.500	0.00000 00000 00243	0.99999 99999 99936
01	00242	99937
02	00240	99937
03	00238	99938
04	00236	99938
7.505	0.00000 00000 00234	0.99999 99999 99939
06	00233	99939
07	00231	99940
08	00229	99940
09	00228	99940
7.510	0.00000 00000 00226	0.99999 99999 99941
11	00224	99941
12	00222	99942
13	00221	99942
14	00219	99943
7.515	0.00000 00000 00218	0.99999 99999 99943
16	00216	99944
17	00214	99944
18	00213	99944
19	00211	99945
7.520	0.00000 00000 00209	0.99999 99999 99945
21	00208	99946
22	00206	99946
23	00205	99946
24	00203	99947
7.525	0.00000 00000 00202	0.99999 99999 99947
26	00200	99948
27	00199	99948
28	00197	99948
29	00196	99949
7.530	0.00000 00000 00194	0.99999 99999 99949
31	00193	99950
32	00191	99950
33	00190	99950
34	00189	99951
7.535	0.00000 00000 00187	0.99999 99999 99951
36	00186	99952
37	00184	99952
38	00183	99952
39	00182	99953
7.540	0.00000 00000 00180	0.99999 99999 99953
41	00179	99953
42	00177	99954
43	00176	99954
44	00175	99954
7.545	0.00000 00000 00174	0.99999 99999 99955
46	00172	99955
47	00171	99955
48	00170	99956
49	00168	99956
7.550	0.00000 00000 00167	0.99999 99999 99956

x	$\frac{1}{\sqrt{2\pi}}e^{-\frac{x^2}{2}}$	$\frac{1}{\sqrt{2\pi}}\int_{-x}^{x}e^{-\frac{\alpha^2}{2}}\,d\alpha$
7.550	0.00000 00000 00167	0.99999 99999 99956
51	00166	99957
52	00165	99957
53	00163	99957
54	00162	99958
7.555	0.00000 00000 00161	0.99999 99999 99958
56	00160	99958
57	00158	99959
58	00157	99959
59	00156	99959
7.560	0.00000 00000 00155	0.99999 99999 99960
61	00154	99960
62	00153	99960
63	00151	99961
64	00150	99961
7.565	0.00000 00000 00149	0.99999 99999 99961
66	00148	99962
67	00147	99962
68	00146	99962
69	00145	99962
7.570	0.00000 00000 00144	0.99999 99999 99963
71	00143	99963
72	00141	99963
73	00140	99964
74	00139	99964
7.575	0.00000 00000 00138	0.99999 99999 99964
76	00137	99964
77	00136	99965
78	00135	99965
79	00134	99965
7.580	0.00000 00000 00133	0.99999 99999 99965
81	00132	99966
82	00131	99966
83	00130	99966
84	00129	99966
7.585	0.00000 00000 00128	0.99999 99999 99967
86	00127	99967
87	00126	99967
88	00125	99968
89	00124	99968
7.590	0.00000 00000 00123	0.99999 99999 99968
91	00123	99968
92	00122	99968
93	00121	99969
94	00120	99969
7.595	0.00000 00000 00119	0.99999 99999 99969
96	00118	99969
97	00117	99970
98	00116	99970
99	00115	99970
7.600	0.00000 00000 00114	0.99999 99999 99970

X	$\dfrac{1}{\sqrt{2\pi}}\,e^{-\frac{x^2}{2}}$	$\dfrac{1}{\sqrt{2\pi}}\displaystyle\int_{-x}^{x} e^{-\frac{\alpha^2}{2}}\,d\alpha$
7.600	0.00000 00000 00114	0.99999 99999 99970
01	00114	99971
02	00113	99971
03	00112	99971
04	00111	99971
7.605	0.00000 00000 00110	0.99999 99999 99972
06	00109	99972
07	00108	99972
08	00108	99972
09	00107	99972
7.610	0.00000 00000 00106	0.99999 99999 99973
11	00105	99973
12	00104	99973
13	00104	99973
14	00103	99973
7.615	0.00000 00000 00102	0.99999 99999 99974
16	00101	99974
17	00101	99974
18	00100	99974
19	00099	99974
7.620	0.00000 00000 00098	0.99999 99999 99975
21	00098	99975
22	00097	99975
23	00096	99975
24	00095	99975
7.625	0.00000 00000 00095	0.99999 99999 99976
26	00094	99976
27	00093	99976
28	00092	99976
29	00092	99976
7.630	0.00000 00000 00091	0.99999 99999 99977
31	00090	99977
32	00090	99977
33	00089	99977
34	00088	99977
7.635	0.00000 00000 00088	0.99999 99999 99977
36	00087	99978
37	00086	99978
38	00086	99978
39	00085	99978
7.640	0.00000 00000 00084	0.99999 99999 99978
41	00084	99978
42	00083	99979
43	00082	99979
44	00082	99979
7.645	0.00000 00000 00081	0.99999 99999 99979
46	00081	99979
47	00080	99979
48	00079	99980
49	00079	99980
7.650	0.00000 00000 00078	0.99999 99999 99980

x	$\frac{1}{\sqrt{2\pi}}e^{-\frac{x^2}{2}}$	$\frac{1}{\sqrt{2\pi}}\int_{-x}^{x}e^{-\frac{\alpha^2}{2}}d\alpha$
7.650	0.00000 00000 00078	0.99999 99999 99980
51	00078	99980
52	00077	99980
53	00076	99980
54	00076	99981
7.655	0.00000 00000 00075	0.99999 99999 99981
56	00075	99981
57	00074	99981
58	00074	99981
59	00073	99981
7.660	0.00000 00000 00072	0.99999 99999 99981
61	00072	99982
62	00071	99982
63	00071	99982
64	00070	99982
7.665	0.00000 00000 00070	0.99999 99999 99982
66	00069	99982
67	00069	99982
68	00068	99983
69	00068	99983
7.670	0.00000 00000 00067	0.99999 99999 99983
71	00067	99983
72	00066	99983
73	00066	99983
74	00065	99983
7.675	0.00000 00000 00065	0.99999 99999 99983
76	00064	99984
77	00064	99984
78	00063	99984
79	00063	99984
7.680	0.00000 00000 00062	0.99999 99999 99984
81	00062	99984
82	00061	99984
83	00061	99984
84	00060	99985
7.685	0.00000 00000 00060	0.99999 99999 99985
86	00059	99985
87	00059	99985
88	00058	99985
89	00058	99985
7.690	0.00000 00000 00058	0.99999 99999 99985
91	00057	99985
92	00057	99986
93	00056	99986
94	00056	99986
7.695	0.00000 00000 00055	0.99999 99999 99986
96	00055	99986
97	00054	99986
98	00054	99986
99	00054	99986
7.700	0.00000 00000 00053	0.99999 99999 99986

x	$\frac{1}{\sqrt{2\pi}} e^{-\frac{x^2}{2}}$	$\frac{1}{\sqrt{2\pi}} \int_{-x}^{x} e^{-\frac{\alpha^2}{2}} d\alpha$
7.700	0.00000 00000 00053	0.99999 99999 99986
01	00053	99986
02	00052	99987
03	00052	99987
04	00052	99987
7.705	0.00000 00000 00051	0.99999 99999 99987
06	00051	99987
07	00050	99987
08	00050	99987
09	00050	99987
7.710	0.00000 00000 00049	0.99999 99999 99987
11	00049	99988
12	00049	99988
13	00048	99988
14	00048	99988
7.715	0.00000 00000 00047	0.99999 99999 99988
16	00047	99988
17	00047	99988
18	00046	99988
19	00046	99988
7.720	0.00000 00000 00046	0.99999 99999 99988
21	00045	99988
22	00045	99989
23	00045	99989
24	00044	99989
7.725	0.00000 00000 00044	0.99999 99999 99989
26	00044	99989
27	00043	99989
28	00043	99989
29	00043	99989
7.730	0.00000 00000 00042	0.99999 99999 99989
31	00042	99989
32	00042	99989
33	00041	99989
34	00041	99990
7.735	0.00000 00000 00041	0.99999 99999 99990
36	00040	99990
37	00040	99990
38	00040	99990
39	00039	99990
7.740	0.00000 00000 00039	0.99999 99999 99990
41	00039	99990
42	00038	99990
43	00038	99990
44	00038	99990
7.745	0.00000 00000 00038	0.99999 99999 99990
46	00037	99991
47	00037	99991
48	00037	99991
49	00036	99991
7.750	0.00000 00000 00036	0.99999 99999 99991

x	$\dfrac{1}{\sqrt{2\pi}}e^{-\frac{x^2}{2}}$	$\dfrac{1}{\sqrt{2\pi}}\displaystyle\int_{-x}^{x}e^{-\frac{\alpha^2}{2}}\,d\alpha$
7.750	0.00000 00000 00036	0.99999 99999 99991
51	00036	99991
52	00036	99991
53	00035	99991
54	00035	99991
7.755	0.00000 00000 00035	0.99999 99999 99991
56	00035	99991
57	00034	99991
58	00034	99991
59	00034	99991
7.760	0.00000 00000 00033	0.99999 99999 99992
61	00033	99992
62	00033	99992
63	00033	99992
64	00032	99992
7.765	0.00000 00000 00032	0.99999 99999 99992
66	00032	99992
67	00032	99992
68	00031	99992
69	00031	99992
7.770	0.00000 00000 00031	0.99999 99999 99992
71	00031	99992
72	00031	99992
73	00030	99992
74	00030	99992
7.775	0.00000 00000 00030	0.99999 99999 99992
76	00030	99993
77	00029	99993
78	00029	99993
79	00029	99993
7.780	0.00000 00000 00029	0.99999 99999 99993
81	00028	99993
82	00028	99993
83	00028	99993
84	00028	99993
7.785	0.00000 00000 00028	0.99999 99999 99993
86	00027	99993
87	00027	99993
88	00027	99993
89	00027	99993
7.790	0.00000 00000 00027	0.99999 99999 99993
91	00026	99993
92	00026	99993
93	00026	99993
94	00026	99994
7.795	0.00000 00000 00026	0.99999 99999 99994
96	00025	99994
97	00025	99994
98	00025	99994
99	00025	99994
7.800	0.00000 00000 00025	0.99999 99999 99994

X	$\dfrac{1}{\sqrt{2\pi}}\,e^{-\frac{x^2}{2}}$
7.801 to 7.805	0.00000 00000 00024
7.806 to 7.811	00023
7.812 to 7.816	00022
7.817 to 7.822	00021
7.823 to 7.829	00020
7.830 to 7.836	0.00000 00000 00019
7.837 to 7.843	00018
7.844 to 7.850	00017
7.851 to 7.858	00016
7.859 to 7.867	00015
7.868 to 7.876	0.00000 00000 00014
7.877 to 7.885	00013
7.886 to 7.896	00012
7.897 to 7.908	00011
7.909 to 7.920	00010
7.921 to 7.934	0.00000 00000 00009
7.935 to 7.950	00008
7.951 to 7.968	00007
7.969 to 7.989	00006
7.990 to 8.014	00005
8.015 to 8.045	0.00000 00000 00004
8.046 to 8.087	00003
8.088 to 8.150	00002
8.151 to 8.284	00001
8.285 and over	00000

X	$\dfrac{1}{\sqrt{2\pi}}\displaystyle\int_{-x}^{x} e^{-\frac{\alpha^2}{2}}\,d\alpha$
7.800 to 7.814	0.99999 99999 99994
7.815 to 7.840	99995
7.841 to 7.871	99996
7.872 to 7.913	99997
7.914 to 7.976	99998
7.977 to 8.111	0.99999 99999 99999
8.112 and over	1.00000 00000 00000

TABLE II

$$\frac{1}{\sqrt{2\pi}} e^{-\frac{x^2}{2}} \text{ and } \left[1 - \frac{1}{\sqrt{2\pi}} \int_{-x}^{x} e^{-\frac{\alpha^2}{2}} d\alpha \right] = \frac{2}{\sqrt{2\pi}} \int_{x}^{\infty} e^{-\frac{\alpha^2}{2}} d\alpha$$

x	$\frac{1}{\sqrt{2\pi}}e^{-\frac{x^2}{2}}$	$\frac{2}{\sqrt{2\pi}}\int_x^\infty e^{-\frac{\alpha^2}{2}}\,d\alpha$	x	$\frac{1}{\sqrt{2\pi}}e^{-\frac{x^2}{2}}$	$\frac{2}{\sqrt{2\pi}}\int_x^\infty e^{-\frac{\alpha^2}{2}}\,d\alpha$
6.00	6.075883 (− 9)	1.973175 (− 9)	6.50	2.669557 (−10)	8.032001 (−11)
6.01	5.721765	1.855233	6.51	2.501430	7.515081
6.02	5.387747	1.744171	6.52	2.343657	7.030739
6.03	5.072721	1.639597	6.53	2.195615	6.576969
6.04	4.775637	1.541142	6.54	2.056720	6.151883
6.05	4.495502	1.448458	6.55	1.926418	5.753708
6.06	4.231376	1.361215	6.56	1.804191	5.380778
6.07	3.982371	1.279103	6.57	1.689550	5.031526
6.08	3.747644	1.201825	6.58	1.582036	4.704483
6.09	3.526399	1.129107	6.59	1.481215	4.398266
6.10	3.317884	1.060685	6.60	1.386680	4.111578
6.11	3.121387	9.963114 (−10)	6.61	1.298049	3.843200
6.12	2.936233	9.357536	6.62	1.214962	3.591989
6.13	2.761785	8.787907	6.63	1.137079	3.356869
6.14	2.597442	8.252148	6.64	1.064082	3.136832
6.15	2.442635	7.748295	6.65	9.956718 (−11)	2.930930
6.16	2.296824	7.274494	6.66	9.315666	2.738276
6.17	2.159501	6.828999	6.67	8.715016	2.558034
6.18	2.030186	6.410160	6.68	8.152279	2.389422
6.19	1.908423	6.016422	6.69	7.625116	2.231706
6.20	1.793784	5.646316	6.70	7.131328	2.084195
6.21	1.685863	5.298460	6.71	6.668850	1.946244
6.22	1.584276	4.971549	6.72	6.235741	1.817246
6.23	1.488661	4.664352	6.73	5.830178	1.696631
6.24	1.398678	4.375709	6.74	5.450446	1.583866
6.25	1.314002	4.104527	6.75	5.094938	1.478452
6.26	1.234329	3.849775	6.76	4.762142	1.379917
6.27	1.159371	3.610481	6.77	4.450638	1.287824
6.28	1.088856	3.385730	6.78	4.159095	1.201759
6.29	1.022527	3.174660	6.79	3.886261	1.121335
6.30	9.601433 (−10)	2.976456	6.80	3.630962	1.046192
6.31	9.014752	2.790355	6.81	3.392094	9.759875 (−12)
6.32	8.463073	2.615633	6.82	3.168624	9.104051
6.33	7.944361	2.451612	6.83	2.959580	8.491463
6.34	7.456696	2.297652	6.84	2.764051	7.919318
6.35	6.998266	2.153149	6.85	2.581182	7.384999
6.36	6.567363	2.017537	6.86	2.410170	6.886055
6.37	6.162376	1.890282	6.87	2.250264	6.420190
6.38	5.781785	1.770880	6.88	2.100756	5.985256
6.39	5.424156	1.658858	6.89	1.960986	5.579239
6.40	5.088140	1.553770	6.90	1.830332	5.200254
6.41	4.772462	1.455196	6.91	1.708212	4.846537
6.42	4.475922	1.362743	6.92	1.594081	4.516436
6.43	4.197388	1.276039	6.93	1.487427	4.208406
6.44	3.935793	1.194735	6.94	1.387769	3.920999
6.45	3.690133	1.118502	6.95	1.294659	3.652862
6.46	3.459460	1.047030	6.96	1.207676	3.402727
6.47	3.242882	9.800292 (−11)	6.97	1.126423	3.169410
6.48	3.039559	9.172262	6.98	1.050533	2.951801
6.49	2.848699	8.583637	6.99	9.796573 (−12)	2.748862
6.50	2.669557	8.032001	7.00	9.134720	2.559625

TABLE II 341

X	$\frac{1}{\sqrt{2\pi}}e^{-\frac{x^2}{2}}$	$\frac{2}{\sqrt{2\pi}}\int_x^\infty e^{-\frac{\alpha^2}{2}}\,d\alpha$	X	$\frac{1}{\sqrt{2\pi}}e^{-\frac{x^2}{2}}$	$\frac{2}{\sqrt{2\pi}}\int_x^\infty e^{-\frac{\alpha^2}{2}}\,d\alpha$
7.00	9.134720 (-12)	2.559625 (-12)	7.50	2.434321 (-13)	6.381783 (-14)
7.01	8.516731	2.383181	7.51	2.258312	5.912736
7.02	7.939756	2.218682	7.52	2.094820	5.477624
7.03	7.401129	2.065335	7.53	1.942970	5.074032
7.04	6.898352	1.922398	7.54	1.801947	4.699715
7.05	6.429087	1.789178	7.55	1.670992	4.352582
7.06	5.991145	1.665026	7.56	1.549400	4.030694
7.07	5.582477	1.549337	7.57	1.436512	3.732242
7.08	5.201165	1.441545	7.58	1.331715	3.455550
7.09	4.845413	1.341120	7.59	1.234440	3.199055
7.10	4.513544	1.247569	7.60	1.144156	2.961307
7.11	4.203984	1.150430	7.61	1.060370	2.740959
7.12	3.915263	1.079271	7.62	9.826205 (-14)	2.536757
7.13	3.646007	1.003689	7.63	9.104809	2.347537
7.14	3.394928	9.333092 (-13)	7.64	8.435532	2.172217
7.15	3.160823	8.677790	7.65	7.814670	2.009793
7.16	2.942568	8.067706	7.66	7.238781	1.859331
7.17	2.739109	7.499777	7.67	6.704660	1.719963
7.18	2.549463	6.971142	7.68	6.209329	1.590886
7.19	2.372710	6.479132	7.69	5.750017	1.471350
7.20	2.207990	6.021256	7.70	5.324148	1.360662
7.21	2.054500	5.595188	7.71	4.929328	1.258177
7.22	1.911489	5.198757	7.72	4.563331	1.163297
7.23	1.778255	4.829940	7.73	4.224085	1.075466
7.24	1.654142	4.486847	7.74	3.909669	9.941681 (-15)
7.25	1.538538	4.167716	7.75	3.618294	9.189255
7.26	1.430870	3.870903	7.76	3.348300	8.492939
7.27	1.330603	3.594875	7.77	3.098143	7.848613
7.28	1.237239	3.338202	7.78	2.866388	7.252455
7.29	1.150311	3.099550	7.79	2.651705	6.700919
7.30	1.069384	2.877677	7.80	2.452855	6.190718
7.31	9.940504 (-13)	2.671424	7.81	2.268690	5.718799
7.32	9.239314	2.479710	7.82	2.098143	5.282334
7.33	8.586727	2.301527	7.83	1.940223	4.878700
7.34	7.979436	2.135939	7.84	1.794009	4.505464
7.35	7.414353	1.982069	7.85	1.658648	4.160373
7.36	6.888599	1.839102	7.86	1.533347	3.841335
7.37	6.399486	1.706280	7.87	1.417370	3.546413
7.38	5.944507	1.582895	7.88	1.310034	3.273811
7.39	5.521324	1.468288	7.89	1.210705	3.021865
7.40	5.127754	1.361845	7.90	1.118796	2.789034
7.41	4.761762	1.262994	7.91	1.033760	2.573889
7.42	4.421450	1.171203	7.92	9.550924 (-15)	2.375106
7.43	4.105049	1.085977	7.93	8.823229	2.191459
7.44	3.810909	1.006853	7.94	8.150162	2.021813
7.45	3.537491	9.334023 (-14)	7.95	7.527687	1.865115
7.46	3.283361	8.652248	7.96	6.952059	1.720393
7.47	3.047183	8.019482	7.97	6.419806	1.586744
7.48	2.827711	7.432261	7.98	5.927709	1.463333
7.49	2.623784	6.887361	7.99	5.472786	1.349388
7.50	2.434321	6.381783	8.00	5.052271	1.244192

TABLE II

X	$\frac{1}{\sqrt{2\pi}}e^{-\frac{x^2}{2}}$	$\frac{2}{\sqrt{2\pi}}\int_x^\infty e^{-\frac{\alpha^2}{2}}d\alpha$	X	$\frac{1}{\sqrt{2\pi}}e^{-\frac{x^2}{2}}$	$\frac{2}{\sqrt{2\pi}}\int_x^\infty e^{-\frac{\alpha^2}{2}}d\alpha$
8.00	5.052271 (−15)	1.244192 (−15)	8.50	8.166236 (−17)	1.895907 (−17)
8.01	4.663601	1.147084	8.51	7.500413	1.739334
8.02	4.304400	1.057452	8.52	6.888188	1.595533
8.03	3.972469	9.747267 (−16)	8.53	6.325304	1.463477
8.04	3.665768	8.983847	8.54	5.807836	1.342218
8.05	3.382408	8.279404	8.55	5.332169	1.230885
8.06	3.120639	7.629445	8.56	4.894970	1.128675
8.07	2.878841	7.029817	8.57	4.493168	1.034850
8.08	2.655513	6.476677	8.58	4.123936	9.487314 (−18)
8.09	2.449265	5.966473	8.59	3.784668	8.696933
8.10	2.258809	5.495919	8.60	3.472963	7.971610
8.11	2.082956	5.061976	8.61	3.186611	7.306058
8.12	1.920600	4.661837	8.62	2.923578	6.695411
8.13	1.770723	4.292904	8.63	2.681987	6.135197
8.14	1.632378	3.952779	8.64	2.460115	5.621302
8.15	1.504691	3.639243	8.65	2.256372	5.149943
8.16	1.386854	3.350246	8.66	2.069295	4.717643
8.17	1.278117	3.083895	8.67	1.897540	4.321204
8.18	1.177788	2.838439	8.68	1.739866	3.957688
8.19	1.085226	2.612262	8.69	1.595134	3.624395
8.20	9.998379 (−16)	2.403870	8.70	1.462296	3.318842
8.21	9.210765	2.211885	8.71	1.340387	3.038748
8.22	8.484347	2.035032	8.72	1.228517	2.782018
8.23	7.814437	1.872134	8.73	1.125872	2.546726
8.24	7.196703	1.722107	8.74	1.031700	2.331104
8.25	6.627137	1.583945	8.75	9.453104 (−18)	2.133527
8.26	6.102039	1.456725	8.76	8.660679	1.952504
8.27	5.617984	1.339590	8.77	7.933887	1.786663
8.28	5.171811	1.231753	8.78	7.267360	1.634747
8.29	4.760596	1.132485	8.79	6.656163	1.495600
8.30	4.381639	1.041114	8.80	6.095758	1.368162
8.31	4.032445	9.570207 (−17)	8.81	5.581978	1.251459
8.32	3.710709	8.796331	8.82	5.110990	1.144597
8.33	3.414302	8.084235	8.83	4.679275	1.046757
8.34	3.141257	7.429053	8.84	4.283597	9.571860 (−19)
8.35	2.889759	6.826297	8.85	3.920986	8.751930
8.36	2.658130	6.271826	8.86	3.588711	8.001444
8.37	2.444824	5.761823	8.87	3.284266	7.314590
8.38	2.248409	5.292770	8.88	3.005347	6.686036
8.39	2.067568	4.861422	8.89	2.749841	6.110891
8.40	1.901082	4.464786	8.90	2.515806	5.584669
8.41	1.747826	4.100107	8.91	2.301459	5.103256
8.42	1.606765	3.764843	8.92	2.105164	4.662882
8.43	1.476941	3.456652	8.93	1.925418	4.260088
8.44	1.357470	3.173377	8.94	1.760844	3.891704
8.45	1.247539	2.913028	8.95	1.610175	3.554824
8.46	1.146396	2.673775	8.96	1.472252	3.246784
8.47	1.053347	2.453930	8.97	1.346008	2.965144
8.48	9.677543 (−17)	2.251939	8.98	1.230466	2.707668
8.49	8.890276	2.066371	8.99	1.124730	2.472304
8.50	8.166236	1.895907	9.00	1.027977	2.257177

TABLE II   343

X	$\frac{1}{\sqrt{2\pi}}e^{-\frac{x^2}{2}}$	$\frac{2}{\sqrt{2\pi}}\int_x^\infty e^{-\frac{\alpha^2}{2}}d\alpha$	X	$\frac{1}{\sqrt{2\pi}}e^{-\frac{x^2}{2}}$	$\frac{2}{\sqrt{2\pi}}\int_x^\infty e^{-\frac{\alpha^2}{2}}d\alpha$
9.00	1.027977 (-18)	2.257177 (-19)	9.50	1.007794 (-20)	2.098903 (-21)
9.01	9.394536 (-19)	2.060565	9.51	9.164143 (-21)	1.906625
9.02	8.584672	1.880893	9.52	8.332374	1.731791
9.03	7.843838	1.716718	9.53	7.575341	1.572832
9.04	7.166219	1.566718	9.54	6.886400	1.428323
9.05	6.546485	1.429683	9.55	6.259488	1.296963
9.06	5.979747	1.304506	9.56	5.689079	1.177567
9.07	5.461526	1.190170	9.57	5.170133	1.069057
9.08	4.987717	1.085749	9.58	4.698054	9.704494 (-22)
9.09	4.554557	9.903906 (-20)	9.59	4.268653	8.808501
9.10	4.158599	9.033183	9.60	3.878112	7.994442
9.11	3.796685	8.238197	9.61	3.522949	7.254899
9.12	3.465920	7.512433	9.62	3.199992	6.583116
9.13	3.163656	6.849929	9.63	2.906351	5.972948
9.14	2.887463	6.245233	9.64	2.639392	5.418798
9.15	2.635119	5.693355	9.65	2.396713	4.915573
9.16	2.404587	5.189732	9.66	2.176131	4.458640
9.17	2.194004	4.730190	9.67	1.975652	4.043781
9.18	2.001663	4.310914	9.68	1.793463	3.667160
9.19	1.826001	3.928414	9.69	1.627912	3.325287
9.20	1.665588	3.579498	9.70	1.477495	3.014986
9.21	1.519115	3.261249	9.71	1.340843	2.733371
9.22	1.385385	2.971002	9.72	1.216707	2.477815
9.23	1.263301	2.706319	9.73	1.103954	2.245930
9.24	1.151860	2.464972	9.74	1.001550	2.035544
9.25	1.050145	2.244927	9.75	9.085534 (-22)	1.844683
9.26	9.573160 (-20)	2.044322	9.76	8.241097	1.671552
9.27	8.726055	1.861459	9.77	7.474397	1.514521
9.28	7.953112	1.694786	9.78	6.778349	1.372105
9.29	7.247911	1.542883	9.79	6.146504	1.242959
9.30	6.604580	1.404457	9.80	5.573000	1.125856
9.31	6.017749	1.278324	9.81	5.052502	1.019686
9.32	5.482512	1.163403	9.82	4.580158	9.234355 (-23)
9.33	4.994380	1.058709	9.83	4.151557	8.361878
9.34	4.549254	9.633412 (-21)	9.84	3.762688	7.571084
9.35	4.143386	8.764773	9.85	3.409902	6.854398
9.36	3.773350	7.973669	9.86	3.089884	6.204939
9.37	3.436018	7.253253	9.87	2.799619	5.616461
9.38	3.128530	6.597273	9.88	2.536369	5.083291
9.39	2.848274	6.000026	9.89	2.297642	4.600279
9.40	2.592865	5.456307	9.90	2.081177	4.162750
9.41	2.360122	4.961369	9.91	1.884916	3.766462
9.42	2.148056	4.510880	9.92	1.706993	3.407562
9.43	1.954850	4.100890	9.93	1.545710	3.082555
9.44	1.778843	3.727794	9.94	1.399526	2.788271
9.45	1.618522	3.388307	9.95	1.267040	2.521832
9.46	1.472502	3.079432	9.96	1.143981	2.280627
9.47	1.339523	2.798437	9.97	1.038195	2.062288
9.48	1.218430	2.542831	9.98	9.396325 (-23)	1.864668
9.49	1.108174	2.310343	9.99	8.503421	1.685817
9.50	1.007794	2.098903	10.00	7.694599	1.523971

CONSTANTS

π	= 3.14159	26535	89793	2
$1/\pi$	= 0.31830	98861	83790	7
$\sqrt{\pi}$	= 1.77245	38509	05516	0
$1/\sqrt{\pi}$	= 0.56418	95835	47756	3
$\sqrt{2\pi}$	= 2.50662	82746	31000	5
$1/\sqrt{2\pi}$	= 0.39894	22804	01432	7
$2/\sqrt{\pi}$	= 1.12837	91670	95512	6
$\log_{10}\pi$	= 0.49714	98726	94133	9
$\log_{10}\sqrt{2\pi}$	= 0.39908	99341	79057	5
e	= 2.71828	18284	59045	2
$\log_{10}e$	= 0.43429	44819	03251	8
$\log_{10}2$	= 0.30102	99956	63981	2

OTHER TABLES
BY
THE PROJECT FOR THE COMPUTATION OF MATHEMATICAL TABLES

(1) Table of Powers, (1939).

Contains first 10 powers of integers from 1 to 1,000.

(2) Tables of the Exponential Function e^x, (1939).

The ranges and intervals of the argument and the number of decimal places in the entries are given below:

Range of x	Interval of x	No. of Decimals Given
−2.5000 to 1.0000	0.0001	18
1.0000 to 2.5000	0.0001	15
2.500 to 5.000	0.001	15
5.00 to 10.00	0.01	12

(3) Tables of Circular and Hyperbolic Sines and Cosines, (1939).

Contains 9 decimal place values of sin x, cos x, sinh x and cosh x for x (in radians) ranging from 0 to 2 at intervals of 0.0001.

(4) Tables of Sines and Cosines, (1940).

Contains 8 decimal place values of sines and cosines for radian arguments ranging from 0 to 25 at intervals of 0.001.

(5) Tables of Planck's Radiation and Photon Functions. (published in Jour. Opt. Soc. Amer., Feb. 1940).

Contains various tables pertaining to emission of energy and photons over a wide range of wave lengths.

OTHER TABLES

BY

THE PROJECT FOR THE COMPUTATION OF MATHEMATICAL TABLES

(6) Tables of Sine, Cosine, and Exponential Integrals (1940).

Vol. I: 9 decimal place values of $Si(x)$, $Ci(x)$, $Ei(x)$, and $Ei(-x)$ for x ranging between 0 and 1 at intervals of 0.0001.

Vol. II: The same functions tabulated from 0 to 10 at intervals of 0.001 to 9 and 10 significant figures.

(7) Table of Natural Logarithms of Integers from 1 to 100,000 to 16 Decimal Places (1941).

(8) Table of Natural Logarithms of Decimal Numbers from 0 to 10 at Intervals of 0.0001 to 16 Decimal Places (1941).

TABLES IN PROCESS OF REPRODUCTION OR COMPUTATION

(1) Table of the Probability Functions:

$$\frac{1}{\sqrt{2\pi}} e^{-x^2/2}, \qquad \frac{1}{\sqrt{2\pi}} \int_{-x}^{x} e^{-t^2/2} dt$$

for x ranging from 0 to 1 at intervals of 0.0001 and from 1 to 8.4 at intervals of 0.001 to 15 decimal places.

(2) Tables of the definite integrals:

$$A(k,n) = \int_0^1 x^k \sin n\pi x \, dx \quad \text{and} \quad B(k,n) = \int_0^1 x^k \cos n\pi x \, dx$$

for k = 0, 1, 2, ..., 10 and n = 1, 2, ... 100, to 15 decimals.

(3) Table of the Fractional Powers x^y for both x and y ranging from 0 to 1 at intervals of 0.01 to 15 decimal places.

TABLES IN PROCESS OF REPRODUCTION OR COMPUTATION

(4) *Table of* arctan x *in* radians to 12 decimal places for $x = [0(.001)7(.01)50(.1)300(1)2,000'10)10,000]$.

(5) *Table of Bessel Functions* $J_0(z)$, $J_1(z)$, $Y_0(z)$, and $Y_1(z)$.

A 10 decimal place table for the complex arguments, $z = \rho e^{i\varphi}$ where ρ ranges from 0 to 10 at intervals of 0.01 and φ ranges from 0° to 90° at intervals of 5°.

(6) *Table of Bessel Functions of Order* $\pm 1/3$, $\pm 2/3$, $\pm 1/4$, $\pm 3/4$.

A 10 decimal place table for real and pure imaginary arguments, x and xi, where x ranges from 0 to 10 at intervals of 0.01.

(7) *Table of* $Q_n(x) = \sqrt{\frac{\pi}{2x}} J_{n+\frac{1}{2}}(x)$.

A 10 decimal place table for arguments ranging from $x = 0$ to $x = 10$ at intervals of 0.01, and for integral n ranging from −21 to +20.

(8) *Table of Grid Coordinates (American Polyconic Projection)*.

Coordinates to one decimal place in yards for 5 minute intervals of latitude and longitude, the range of latitude being from 7° to 28°.

(9) *Table of Lagrangian Interpolants*.

Five-point Lagrangian interpolation coefficients at intervals of 0.001.

(10) *Tables of Stellar Functions for "Point-Source" Models*.

TABLES IN PROCESS OF REPRODUCTION OR COMPUTATION

(11) Hydraulic Tables.

Extension of existing tables, based on the formulae of Manning and Kutter for the solution of hydraulic problems.

(12) Tables of the Section Modulus and Moment of Inertia of Ordinary Angles, Bulb Angles, and Channels with Various Plate Combinations.

(13) Table of Electronic Functions.

(a) $G = \dfrac{1}{\sqrt{1-\beta^2}}$, for β ranging from 0 to 0.99999 99990 at various intervals. This table also includes the functions

$$V = \frac{m_0 c^2}{e} (G-1) \text{ and } H\rho = \frac{m_0 c^2}{e} \beta G.$$